Mike Holt's Illustrated Guide to

Electrical NEC Exam Preparation

Based on the 2005 *NEC*

D1546942

www.*NEC*code.com
1.888.NEC®CODE

Mike Holt Enterprises, Inc.
1.888.NEC.CODE • NECcode.com • Info@NECcode.com

NOTICE TO THE READER

Mike Holt's Illustrated Guide to
Electrical NEC Exam Preparation
4th Edition

Technical Illustrator: Mike Culbreath
Cover Design: Tracy Jette
Layout Design and Typesetting: Cathleen Kwas

COPYRIGHT © 2005 Charles Michael Holt Sr.
ISBN: 1-932685-15-4

For more information, call 1.888.NEC®CODE, or E-mail Info@MikeHolt.com.

www.NECcode.com
1.888.NEC®code

This logo is a registered trademark of Mike Holt Enterprises, Inc.

To request examination copies of this or other Mike Holt Publications, call:
Phone: 1.888.NEC®CODE • Fax: 1.954.720.7944
or E-mail: **Info@MikeHolt.com**
or visit Mike Holt Online: **www.NECcode.com**

You can download a sample PDF of all our publications by visiting www.NECcode.com

I dedicate this book to the
Lord Jesus Christ,
my mentor and teacher.

Exam Preparation

You'll learn everything you need to know to pass your exam the first time!

Comprehensive Library

The Journeyman Comprehensive Library includes the Electrical Exam Preparation textbook/workbook, three 4.5 hour Theory videos or DVDs, the Basic Electrical Theory textbook/workbook, ten 4 to 4.5 hour *NEC* videos or DVDs, Understanding the *NEC* Volumes 1 and 2 textbooks, the *NEC* Exam Practice Questions textbook, and five 2 to 4 hour Calculations videos or DVDs. The Master/Contractor Comprehensive Library includes everything in the Journeyman Library, plus three additional Calculations videos or DVDs.

TOP SELLER!

Journeyman and Master/Contractor Simulated Exams

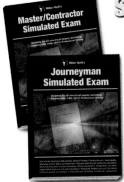

These books were designed to give you experience in taking exams under conditions similar to the actual competency exam and to help you determine the subject areas on which to really focus your study time.

Intermediate Library

The Journeyman Intermediate Library includes the Electrical Exam Preparation textbook/workbook, Illustrated Changes to the *NEC* textbook, two 4.5 hour *NEC* videos or DVDs, and five 2 to 4 hour Calculations videos or DVDs. The Master/Contractor Intermediate Library includes everything in the Journeyman Library, plus three additional Calculations videos or DVDs. This is our most popular library!

Call us today at 1.888.NEC®CODE, or visit us online at www.NECcode.com for the latest information and pricing.

ONE TEAM

To Our Instructors and Students:

We are committed to providing you the finest product with the fewest errors, but we are realistic and know that there might be errors found and reported after the printing of this book. The last thing we want is for you to have problems finding, communicating, or accessing this information. It is unacceptable to us for there to be even one error in our textbooks or answer keys. For this reason, we are asking you to work together with us as **One Team**.

Students: Please report any errors that you might find to your instructor.
Instructors: Please communicate these errors to us.

Our Commitment:

We will continue to list all of the corrections that come through for all of our textbooks and answer keys on our Website. We will always have the most up-to-date answer keys available to instructors to download from our instructor Website. We realize your time is very valuable and shouldn't have to be spent searching for this updated information, so we're outlining where to go for all of this below:

To view textbook and answer key corrections: Students and instructors go to our Website, www.MikeHolt.com, click on "Books" in the sidebar of links, and then click on "Corrections."

To download the most up-to-date answer keys: Instructors go to our Website, www.MikeHolt.com, click on "Instructors" in the sidebar of links and then click on "Answer Keys." On this page you will find instructions for how to access and download these answer keys.

If you are not registered as an instructor you will need to register. Your registration will be sent to our educational director who in turn reviews and approves your registration. In your approval E-mail will be the login and password so you can have access to all of the answer keys. If you have a situation that needs immediate attention, please contact the office directly at 1-888-NEC-CODE.

1.888.NEC®CODE or visit us online at www.NECcode.com

Table of Contents

Introduction

Passing an important electrical exam is the dream of all those who care about improving themselves and their families. Unfortunately, many don't pass the exam at all, and few pass it the first time. The primary reasons that people fail their exam is because they are not prepared on the technical material and/or they don't know how to take the exam.

Most electrical exams contain questions on electrical theory, basic electrical calculations, the *Code*, and important and difficult *National Electrical Code* Calculations. This book contains hundreds of illustrations, examples, almost 3,200 practice questions covering all of these subjects and 36 practice quizzes. This book is intended to be used with the *2005 National Electrical Code*.

How to Use This Book

Each unit of this book contains objectives, explanations with graphics, examples, steps for calculations, formulas and practice calculations, and 2005 *NEC* questions and quizzes. As you read this book, review the author's comments, graphics, and examples with your 2005 *Code* book.

The writing style of this book is intended to be informal and relaxed. Graphics in color are included to make the learning easy and fun.

After you've read each unit, you need to take about ten hours to complete the unit questions. Each of the 12 units include the following:

- Unit Calculation Practice Questions
- Unit Calculation Challenge Questions

Once you have answered these unit questions, then take the three *NEC* quizzes for each unit. These quizzes are:

- Review Quiz. Each of these contain 100 questions that are in *Code* order and take you step by step through each of the nine chapters and Annex C of the *National Electrical Code*.

- Practice Quiz. Each of these contain 50 questions that are presented in random *NEC* order and contain questions different than those in the Review Quizzes.

- Challenge Quiz. Each of these contain 50 questions that cover all nine chapters and Annex C of the *NEC*. The questions in the challenge quizzes do not follow the chapters of the *Code* book (as the other quizzes do); they are organized in a random manner, and you might find them harder to answer. Scores for the first few challenge quizzes might be somewhat lower than you would like to see. But, as you go through this book and take the review and practice quizzes, you'll learn a great deal and gain a better understanding of the material. This improved knowledge and understanding will help you improve on the challenge quizzes as you proceed.

   If you have difficulty with a question or section in the book, skip it for now and get back to it later. Don't frustrate yourself! The answer key is intended to be very clear, so be sure to review those questions that you miss.

Journeyman or Master/Contractor Units

If you are using this book to pass a Journeyman Exam, complete Units 1–9 in its entirety (including the unit calculation practice and challenge questions, and the *NEC* quizzes), as well as the *NEC* quizzes in Units 10–12.

If you are using this book to pass a Master/Contractor's Exam, complete Units 1–12 in its entirety (including the unit calculation practice and challenge questions, and the *NEC* quizzes).

Helpful Tips

This book contains many cross references to other related *Code* rules. Please, take the time to review the cross references.

As you progress through this book, you will find some formulas, rules, or some comments that you don't understand. Don't get frustrated. Highlight the section in the book that you are having a problem with. Discuss it with your boss, inspector, co-worker, etc., and maybe they'll have some additional feedback. If necessary, just skip the difficult points and get back to them later. Once you've completed the book, review those highlighted sections again and see if you understand.

Some words are italicized to bring them to your attention. Be sure that you understand the terms before you continue with each unit.

Workbook Errors and Corrections

Humans develop the text and layout of this workbook, and since currently none of us is perfect, there may be a few errors. This could occur because the *NEC* is dramatically changed each *Code* cycle; new Articles are added, some deleted, some relocated, and many renumbered. In addition, this workbook must be written within a very narrow window of opportunity; after the *NEC* has been published (September), yet before it's enforceable (January).

You can be sure we work a tremendous number of hours and use all of our available resources to produce the finest product with the fewest errors. We take great care in researching the *Code* requirements to ensure this workbook is correct. If you feel there's an error of any type in this workbook (typo, grammar, or technical), no matter how insignificant, please let us know.

Any errors found after printing are listed on our Website, so if you find an error, first check to see if it has already been corrected. Go to www.MikeHolt.com, click on the "Books" link, and then the "Corrections" link (www.MikeHolt.com/bookcorrections.htm).

If you do not find the error listed on the Website, contact us by E-mailing corrections@MikeHolt.com, calling 1.888.NEC.CODE (1.888.632.2633), or faxing 954.720.7944. Be sure to include the book title, page number, and any other pertinent information.

Internet

Today as never before, you can get your technical questions answered by posting them to Mike Holt's Code Forum. Just visit www.MikeHolt.com and click on the "Code Forum" link.

Different Interpretations

Some electricians, contractors, instructors, inspectors, engineers, and others enjoy the challenge of discussing the *Code* requirements, hopefully in a positive and a productive manner. This action of challenging each other is important to the process of better understanding the *NEC*'s requirements and its intended application. However, if you're going to get into an *NEC* discussion, please do not spout out what you think without having the actual *Code* in your hand. The professional way of discussing an *NEC* requirement is by referring to a specific section, rather than by talking in vague generalities.

Passing Your Exam

This textbook was designed to help you prepare for your *National Electrical Code* exam.

Understanding the Emotional Aspects of Learning

To learn effectively, you must develop an attitude that learning is a process that will help you grow both personally and professionally. The learning process has an emotional as well as an intellectual component that we must recognize. To understand what affects our learning, consider the following:

Positive Image. Many feel disturbed by the expectations of being treated like children and we often feel threatened with the learning experience.

Uniqueness. Each of us will understand the subject matter from different perspectives and we all have some unique learning problems and needs.

Resistance to Change. People tend to resist change and resist information that appears to threaten their comfort level of knowledge. However, we often support new ideas that support our existing beliefs.

Dependence and Independence. The dependent person is afraid of disapproval and often will not participate in class discussion and will tend to wrestle alone. The independent person spends too much time asserting differences and too little time trying to understand others' views.

Fearful. Most of us feel insecure and afraid of learning, until we understand the process. We fear that our performance will not match the standard set by us or by others.

Egocentric. Our ego tendency is to prove someone is wrong, with a victorious surge of pride. Learning together without a win/lose attitude can be an exhilarating learning experience.

Emotional. It is difficult to discard our cherished ideas in the face of contrary facts when overpowered by the logic of others.

Getting the Best Grade

Studies have concluded that for students to get their best grades, they must learn to get the most from their natural abilities. It's not how long you study or how high your IQ is, it's what you do and how you study that counts the most. To get your best grade, you must make a decision to do your best and follow as many of the following techniques as possible.

Reality. These instructions are a basic guide to help you get the maximum grade. It is unreasonable to think that all of the instructions can be followed to the letter all of the time. Day-to-day events and unexpected situations must be taken into consideration.

Support. You need encouragement in your studies and you need support from your loved ones and employer. To properly prepare for your exam, you need to study 10 to 15 hours per week for about 3 to 6 months.

Communication with Your Family. Good communication with your family is very important because studying every night and on weekends can cause much tension and stress. Try to get their support, cooperation, and encouragement during this difficult time. Let them know the benefits to the family and what passing the exam means. Be sure to plan some special time with them during this preparation period; don't go overboard and leave them alone too long.

Stress. Stress can really take the wind out of you. It takes practice, but get into the habit of relaxing before you begin your studies. Stretch, do a few sit-ups and push-ups, take a 20-

minute walk, or a few slow, deep breaths. Close your eyes for a couple of minutes, and deliberately relax the muscle groups that are associated with tension, such as the shoulders, back, neck, and jaw.

Attitude. Maintaining a positive attitude is important. It helps keep you going and helps keep you from getting discouraged.

Training. Preparing for the exam is the same as training for any event. Get plenty of rest and avoid intoxicating drugs, including alcohol. Stretching or exercising each day for at least 10 minutes helps you get in a better mood. Eat light meals such as pasta, chicken, fish, vegetables, fruit, etc. Try to avoid red meat, butter, sugar, salt, and high-fat content foods. They slow you down and make you tired and sleepy.

Eye Care. It is very important to have your eyes checked! Human eyes were not designed to constantly focus on something less than arm's length away. Our eyes were designed for survival, spotting food and enemies at a distance. Your eyes will be under tremendous stress because of prolonged, near-vision reading, which can result in headaches, fatigue, nausea, squinting, or eyes that burn, ache, water, or tire easily. Be sure to tell your eye doctor that you are studying to pass an exam (bring this book and the *Code* book with you) and that you expect to do a tremendous amount of  reading and writing. Reading glasses can reduce eye discomfort.

Reducing Eye Strain. Be sure to look up occasionally, away from near tasks to distant objects. Your work area should be three times brighter than the rest of the room. Don't read under a single lamp in a dark room. Try to eliminate glare. Mixing of fluorescent and incandescent lighting can be helpful.

Posture. Sit up straight, chest up, shoulders back, so both eyes are an equal distance from what you are viewing.

Getting Organized. Our lives are so busy that simply making time for homework and exam preparation is almost impossible. You can't waste time looking for a pencil or missing paper. Keep everything you need together. Maintain folders, one for notes, one for exams and answer keys, and one for miscellaneous items.

Study Location. It is very important that you have a private study area available at all times. Keep your materials there. The dining room table is not a good spot.

Time Management. Time management and planning are very important. There simply are not enough hours in the day to get everything done. Make a schedule that allows time for work, rest, study, meals, family, and recreation. Establish a schedule that is consistent from day-to-day. Have a calendar and immediately plan your exam preparation schedule. Try to follow the same routine

each week and try not to become overtired. Learn to pace yourself to accomplish as much as you can without the need for cramming.

Clean Up Your Act. Keep all of your papers neat, clean, and organized. Now is not the time to be sloppy. If you are not neat, now is an excellent time to begin.

Speak Up in Class. If you are in a class-  room setting, the most important part of the learning process is class participation. If you don't understand the instructor's point, ask for clarification. Don't try to get attention by asking questions you already know the answer to.

Study With a Friend. Studying with a friend can make learning more enjoyable. You can push and encourage each other. You are more likely to study if someone else is depending on you. Students who study together perform above average because they try different approaches and explain their solutions to each other. Those who study alone spend most of their time reading and rereading the text and trying the same approach time after time even though it is unsuccessful.

Study Anywhere/Anytime. To make the most of your limited time, always keep a copy of the book(s) with you. Any time you get a minute free, study! Continue to study any chance you get. You can study at the supply house when waiting for your material; you can study during your coffee break, or even while you're at the doctor's office. Become creative!

You need to find your best study time. For some, it could be late at night when the house is quiet. For others, it's the first thing in the morning before things get going.

Set Priorities. Once you begin your study, stop all phone calls, TV shows, radio, snacks, and other interruptions. You can always take care of it later.

Preparing to Take the Exam

Have the Proper Supplies. First of all, make sure you have everything needed several days before the exam. The night before the exam is not the time to be out buying pencils, calculators, and batteries. The night before the exam, you should have a checklist (prepared in advance) of everything you could possibly need. The following is a sample checklist to get you started:

- Six sharpened #2H pencils or two mechanical pencils with extra #2H leads. The type with the larger lead is better for filling in the answer key.

- Two calculators. Most examining boards require quiet, paperless calculators. Solar calculators are great, but there may not be enough light to operate them.

- Spare batteries. Two sets of extra batteries should be taken. It's very unlikely you'll need them, but...

- Extra glasses if you use them.

- A wrist watch to ensure that you stay on track.

- All your reference materials, even the ones not on the list. Let the proctors tell you which ones are not permitted.

- Bring something to drink. Coffee is excellent.

- Some fruit, nuts, aspirin, etc.

- Know where the exam is going to take place and how long it takes to get there. Arrive at least 30 minutes early.

Meals. It is also a good idea to pack a lunch rather than going out. It can give you a little extra time to review the material for the afternoon portion of the exam, and it reduces the chance of coming back late.

Taking the Exam

Being prepared for an exam means more than just knowing electrical concepts, the *Code*, and the calculations. Have you felt prepared for an exam, then choked when actually taking it? Many good and knowledgeable people didn't pass their exam because they did not know "how to take an exam."

Taking exams is a learned process that takes practice and involves strategies. The following suggestions are designed to help you learn these methods:

Relax. This is easier said than done, but it is one of the most important factors in passing your exam. Stress and tension cause us to choke or forget. Everyone has had experiences where they became tense and couldn't think straight. The first step is becoming aware of the tension, and the second step is to make a deliberate effort to relax. Make sure you're comfortable; remove clothes if you are hot, or put on a jacket if you are cold.

There are many ways to relax and you have to find a method that works for you. Two of the easiest methods that work very well for many people follow:

Breathing Technique: Take a few slow deep breaths every few minutes. Do not confuse this with hyperventilation, which is abnormally fast breathing.

Single-Muscle Relaxation: When we are tense or stressful, many of us do things like clench our jaw, squint our eyes, or tense our shoulders without even being aware of it. If you find a muscle

group that does this, deliberately relax that one group. The rest of the muscles will automatically relax also. Try to repeat this every few minutes, and it will help you stay more relaxed during the exam.

Understand the Question. To answer a question correctly, you must first understand the question. One word in a question can totally change the meaning of it. Carefully read every word of every question. Underlining key words in the question will help you focus.

Skip the Difficult Questions. Contrary to popular belief, you do not have to answer one question before going on to the next one. The irony is that the question you get stuck on is one that you'll probably get wrong. This will result in not having enough time to answer the easy questions. You will get all stressed-out worrying that you will not complete the exam on time, and a chain reaction is started. More people fail their exams this way than for any other reason.

The following strategy should be used to avoid getting into this situation:

- **First Pass:** Answer the questions you know. Give yourself about 30 seconds for each question. If you can't find the answer in your reference book within the 30 seconds, go on to the next question. Chances are that you'll come across the answers while looking up another question. The total time for the first pass should be 25 percent of the exam time.

- **Second Pass:** This pass is done the same as the first pass except that you allow a little more time for each question, about 60 seconds. If you still can't find the answer, go on to the next one. Don't get stuck. Total time for the second pass should be about 30 percent of the exam time.

- **Third Pass:** See how much time is left and subtract 30 minutes. Spend the remaining time equally on each question. If you still haven't answered the question, it's time to make an educated guess. Never leave a question unanswered.

- **Fourth Pass:** Use the last 30 minutes of the exam to transfer your answers from the exam booklet to the answer key. Read each question and verify that you selected the correct answer on the test book. Transfer the answers carefully to the answer key. With the remaining time, see if you can find the answer to those questions you guessed at.

Guessing. When time is running out and you still have unanswered questions, GUESS! Never leave a question unanswered.

You can improve your chances of getting a question correct by the process of elimination. When one of the choices is "none of these," or "none of the above," it is usually not the correct answer. This improves your chances from one-out-of-four (25 percent), to one-out-of-three (33 percent). Guess "all of these" or "all of the above," and don't select the high or low number.

How do you pick one of the remaining answers? Some people toss a coin, others will count up how many of the answers were As, Bs, Cs, and Ds and use the one with the most as the basis for their guess.

Checking Your Work. The first thing to check (and you should be watching out for this during the whole exam) is to make sure you mark the answer in the correct spot. People have failed the exam by one-half of a point. When they reviewed their exam, they found they correctly answered several questions on the test booklet, but marked the wrong spot on the exam answer sheet. They knew the answer was "(b) False" but marked in "(d)" in error. Another thing to be very careful of, is marking the answer for, let's say question 7, in the spot reserved for question 8.

Changing Answers. When re-reading the question and checking the answers during the fourth pass, resist the urge to change an answer. In most cases, your first choice is best and if you aren't sure, stick with the first choice. Only change answers if you are sure you made a mistake. Multiple choice exams are graded electronically so be sure to thoroughly erase any answer that you changed. Also erase any stray pencil marks from the answer sheet.

Rounding Off. You should always round your answers to the same number of places as the exam's answers.

Example: If an exam has multiple choice of:

(a) 2.2   (b) 2.1
(c) 2.3   (d) none of these

And your calculation comes out to 2.16, do not choose the answer (d) none of these. The correct answer is (a) 2.2, because the answers in this case are rounded off to the tenth.

Example: It could be rounded to tens, such as:

(a) 50   (b) 60
(c) 70   (d) none of these.

For this group, an answer such as 67 would be (c) 70, while an answer of 63 would be (b) 60. The general rule is to check the question's choice of answers and then round off your answer to match it.

Things To Be Careful of Checklist

- Don't get stuck on any one question.

- Read each question carefully.

- Be sure you mark the answer in the correct spot on the answer sheet.

- Don't get flustered or extremely tense.

Summary Checklist

- Make sure everything is ready and packed the night before the exam.

- Don't try to cram the night before the exam—if you don't know it by then, it's too late!

- Have a good breakfast. Get the thermos and energy snacks ready.

- Take all your reference books. Let the proctors tell you what you can't use.

- Know where the exam is to be held and arrive early.

- Bring identification and your confirmation papers from the license board if this is required.

- Review your *NEC* while you wait for your exam to begin.

- Try to stay relaxed.

- Determine the time per question for each pass and don't forget to save 30 minutes for transferring your answers to the answer key.

- Remember—in the first pass answer only the easy questions. In the second pass, spend a little more time per question, but don't get stuck. In the third pass, use the remainder of the time minus 30 minutes. In the fourth pass, check your work and transfer the answers to the answer key.

The National Electrical Code

The *National Electrical Code (NEC)* is written for persons who understand electrical terms, theory, safety procedures, and electrical trade practices. These individuals include electricians, electrical contractors, electrical inspectors, electrical engineers, designers, and other qualified persons. The *Code* was not written to serve as an instructive or teaching manual for untrained individuals [90.1(C)].

Learning to use the *NEC* is somewhat like learning to play the game of chess; it's a great game if you enjoy mental warfare. You must first learn the names of the game pieces, how the pieces are placed on the board, and how each piece moves.

In the electrical world, this is equivalent to completing a comprehensive course on basic electrical theory, such as:

- What electricity is and how is it produced
- Dangers of electrical potential: fire, arc blast, arc fault, and electric shock
- Direct current
- Series and parallel circuits
- Electrical formulas
- Alternating current
- Induction, motors, generators, and transformers

Once you understand the fundamentals of the game of chess, you're ready to start playing the game. Unfortunately, at this point all you can do is make crude moves, because you really do not understand how all the information works together. To play chess well, you will need to learn how to use your knowledge by working on subtle strategies before you can work your way up to the more intriguing and complicated moves.

Again, back to the electrical world, this is equivalent to completing a course on the basics of electrical theory. You have the foundation upon which to build, but now you need to take it to the next level, which you can do by reading the Understanding the National Electrical Code, Volume 1 textbook, watching its companion video or DVD, and answering the *NEC* practice questions in this workbook.

Not a Game

Electrical work isn't a game, and it must be taken very seriously. Learning the basics of electricity, important terms and concepts, as well as the basic layout of the *NEC* gives you just enough knowledge to be dangerous. There are thousands of specific and unique applications of electrical installations, and the *Code* doesn't cover every one of them. To safely apply the *NEC*, you must understand the purpose of a rule and how it affects the safety aspects of the installation.

NEC Terms and Concepts

The *NEC* contains many technical terms, so it's crucial that *Code* users understand their meanings and their applications. If you do not understand a term used in a *Code* rule, it will be impossible to properly apply the *NEC* requirement. Be sure you understand that Article 100 defines the terms that apply to *two or more* Articles. For example, the term "Dwelling Unit" applies to many Articles. If you do not know what a Dwelling Unit is, how can you possibly apply the *Code* requirements for it?

In addition, many Articles have terms that are unique for that specific Article. This means that the definition of those terms is only applicable for that given Article. For example, Article 250 Grounding and Bonding has the definitions of a few terms that are only to be used within Article 250.

Small Words, Grammar, and Punctuation

It's not only the technical words that require close attention, because even the simplest of words can make a big difference to the intent of a rule. The word "or" can imply alternate choices for equipment wiring methods, while "and" can mean an additional requirement. Let's not forget about grammar and punctuation. The location of a comma "," can dramatically change the requirement of a rule.

Slang Terms or Technical Jargon

Electricians, engineers, and other trade-related professionals use slang terms or technical jargon that isn't shared by all. This makes it very difficult to communicate because not everybody understands the intent or application of those slang terms. So where possible, be sure you use the proper word, and do not use a word if you do not understand its definition and application. For example, lots of electricians use the term "pigtail" when describing the short conductor for the connection of a receptacle, switch, luminaire, or equipment. Although they may understand it, not everyone does. **Figure 1**

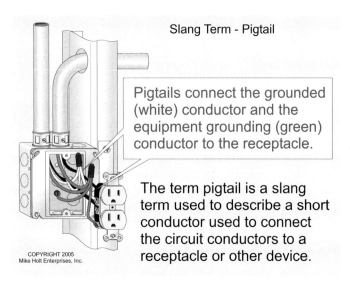

Slang Term - Pigtail

Pigtails connect the grounded (white) conductor and the equipment grounding (green) conductor to the receptacle.

The term pigtail is a slang term used to describe a short conductor used to connect the circuit conductors to a receptacle or other device.

COPYRIGHT 2005
Mike Holt Enterprises, Inc.

Figure 1

NEC Style and Layout

Before we get into the details of the *NEC*, we need to take a few moments to understand its style and layout. Understanding the structure and writing style of the *Code* is very important before it can be used effectively. If you think about it, how can you use something if you don't know how it works? Okay, let's get started. The *National Electrical Code* is organized into nine components.

- Table of Contents
- Chapters 1 through 9 (major categories)
- Articles 90 through 830 (individual subjects)
- Parts (divisions of an Article)
- Sections and Tables (*Code* requirements)
- Exceptions (*Code* permissions)
- Fine Print Notes (explanatory material)
- Index
- Annexes (information)

1. Table of Contents. The Table of Contents displays the layout of the Chapters, Articles, and Parts as well as the page numbers. It's an excellent resource and should be referred to periodically to observe the interrelationship of the various *NEC* components.

When attempting to locate the rules for a particular situation, knowledgeable *Code* users often go first to the Table of Contents to quickly find the specific *NEC* section that applies.

2. Chapters. There are nine Chapters, each of which is divided into Articles. The Articles fall into one of four groupings: General Requirements (Chapters 1 through 4), Specific Requirements (Chapters 5 through 7), Communications Systems (Chapter 8), and Tables (Chapter 9).

- Chapter 1 General
- Chapter 2 Wiring and Protection
- Chapter 3 Wiring Methods and Materials
- Chapter 4 Equipment for General Use
- Chapter 5 Special Occupancies
- Chapter 6 Special Equipment
- Chapter 7 Special Conditions
- Chapter 8 Communications Systems (Telephone, Data, Satellite, and Cable TV)
- Chapter 9 Tables—Conductor and Raceway Specifications

3. Articles. The *NEC* contains approximately 140 Articles, each of which covers a specific subject. For example:

- Article 110 General Requirements
- Article 250 Grounding and Bonding
- Article 300 Wiring Methods
- Article 430 Motors
- Article 500 Hazardous (Classified) Locations
- Article 680 Swimming Pools, Spas, Hot Tubs, and Fountains
- Article 725 Remote-Control, Signaling, and Power-Limited Circuits
- Article 800 Communications Systems

4. Parts. Larger Articles are subdivided into Parts. For example, Article 110 has been divided into multiple parts:

- Part I. General (Sections 110.1—110.23)
- Part II. 600 Volts, Nominal, or Less (110.26—110.27)
- Part III. Over 600 Volts, Nominal (110.30—110.59)

Note: Because the Parts of a *Code* Article aren't included in the Section numbers, we have a tendency to forget what "Part" the *NEC* rule is relating to. For example, Table 110.34(A) contains the working space clearances for electrical equipment. If we aren't careful, we might think this table applies to all electrical installations, but Table 110.34(A) is located in Part III, which contains the requirements for Over 600 Volts, Nominal installations. The rules for working clearances for electrical equipment for systems 600V or less are contained in Table 110.26(A)(1), which is located in Part II. 600 Volts, Nominal, or Less.

5. Sections and Tables.

Sections: Each *NEC* rule is called a *Code* Section. A *Code* Section may be broken down into subsections by letters in parentheses (A), (B), etc. Numbers in parentheses (1), (2), etc., may further break down a subsection, and lowercase letters (a), (b), etc., further break the rule down to the third level. For example, the rule requiring all receptacles in a dwelling unit bathroom to be GFCI protected is contained in Section 210.8(A)(1). Section 210.8(A)(1) is located in Chapter 2, Article 210, Section 8, sub-section (A), sub-subsection (1).

Many in the industry incorrectly use the term "Article" when referring to a *Code* Section. For example, they say "Article 210.8," when they should say "Section 210.8."

Tables: Many *Code* requirements are contained within Tables, which are lists of *NEC* requirements placed in a systematic arrangement. The titles of the Tables are extremely important; they must be carefully read in order to understand the contents, applications, limitations, etc., of each Table in the *Code*. Many times notes are provided in a table; be sure to read them as well, since they are also part of the requirement. For example, Note 1 for Table 300.5 explains how to measure the cover when burying cables and raceways, and Note 5 explains what to do if solid rock is encountered.

6. Exceptions.

Exceptions are *Code* requirements that provide an alternative method to a specific requirement. There are two types of exceptions—mandatory and permissive. When a rule has several exceptions, those exceptions with mandatory requirements are listed before the permissive exceptions.

Mandatory Exception: A mandatory exception uses the words "shall" or "shall not." The word "shall" in an exception means that if you're using the exception, you're required to do it in a particular way. The term "shall not" means it isn't permitted.

Permissive Exception: A permissive exception uses words such as "is permitted," which means that it's acceptable to do it in this way.

7. Fine Print Note (FPN).

A Fine Print Note contains explanatory material intended to clarify a rule or give assistance, but it isn't a *Code* requirement.

8. Index.

The Index contained in the *NEC* is excellent and is helpful in locating a specific rule.

9. Annexes.

Annexes aren't a part of the *NEC* requirements, and are included in the *Code* for informational purposes only.

- Annex A. Product Safety Standards
- Annex B. Application Information for Ampacity Calculation
- Annex C. Conduit and Tubing Fill Tables for Conductors and Fixture Wires of the Same Size
- Annex D. Examples
- Annex E. Types of Construction
- Annex F. Cross-Reference Tables (1999, 2002, and 2005 *NEC*)
- Annex G. Administration and Enforcement

Note: Changes to the *NEC* since the previous edition(s) are identified in the margins by a vertical line (|), but rules that have been relocated aren't identified as a change. In addition, the location from which the *Code* rule was removed has no identifier.

How to Locate a Specific Requirement

How to go about finding what you're looking for in the *Code* depends, to some degree, on your experience with the *NEC*. *Code* experts typically know the requirements so well that they just go to the *NEC* rule without any outside assistance. The Table of Contents might be the only thing very experienced *Code* users need to locate their requirement. On the other hand, average *Code* users should use all of the tools at their disposal, and that includes the Table of Contents and the Index.

Table of Contents: Let's work out a simple example: What *NEC* rule specifies the maximum number of disconnects permitted for a service? If you're an experienced *Code* user, you'll know that Article 230 applies to "Services," and because this Article is so large, it's divided up into multiple parts (actually 8 parts). With this knowledge, you can quickly go to the Table of Contents (page 70-2) and see that it lists the Service Equipment Disconnecting Means requirements in Part VI, starting at page 70-77.

Note: The number 70 precedes all page numbers because the *NEC* is standard number 70 within the collection of *NFPA* standards.

Index: If you used the Index, which lists subjects in alphabetical order, to look up the term "service disconnect," you would see that there's no listing. If you tried "disconnecting means," then "services," you would find the Index specifies that the rule is located at 230, Part VI. Because the *NEC* doesn't give a page number in the Index, you'll need to use the Table of Contents to get the page number, or flip through the *Code* to Article 230, then continue to flip until you find Part VI.

As you can see, although the index is very comprehensive, it's not that easy to use if you do not understand how the index works. But if you answer the almost 3,200 calculation and *NEC* questions in this textbook, you'll become a master at finding things in the *Code* quickly.

Many people complain that the *NEC* only confuses them by taking them in circles. As you gain experience in using the *Code*

and deepen your understanding of words, terms, principles, and practices, you will find the *NEC* much easier to understand and use than you originally thought.

Customizing Your *Code* Book

One way to increase your comfort level with the *Code* is to customize it to meet your needs. You can do this by highlighting and underlining important *NEC* requirements, and by attaching tabs to important pages.

Highlighting: As you answer the questions in this workbook, and read through the Understanding the National Electrical Code, Volume 1 textbook, be sure you highlight those requirements in the *Code* that are most important to you. Use yellow for general interest and orange for important requirements you want to find quickly. Be sure to highlight terms in the Index and Table of Contents as you use them.

Because of the size of the 2005 *NEC*, I recommend you highlight in green the Parts of Articles that are important for your applications, particularly:

> Article 230 Services
> Article 250 Grounding and Bonding
> Article 430 Motors, Motor Circuits, and Controllers

Underlining: Underline or circle key words and phrases in the *NEC* with a red pen (not a lead pencil) and use a 6 in. ruler to keep lines straight and neat. This is a very handy way to make important requirements stand out. A small 6 in. ruler also comes in handy for locating specific information in the many *Code* tables.

Tabbing the *NEC*: Placing tabs on important *Code* Articles, Sections, and Tables will make it very easy to access important *NEC* requirements. However, too many tabs will defeat the purpose. You can order a custom set of *Code* tabs, designed by Mike Holt, online at www.MikeHolt.com, or by calling us at 1.888.*NEC*.Code (1.888.632.2633).

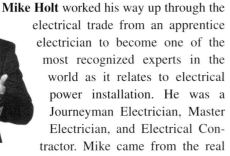

Mike Holt Enterprises Team

About the Author

Mike Holt worked his way up through the electrical trade from an apprentice electrician to become one of the most recognized experts in the world as it relates to electrical power installation. He was a Journeyman Electrician, Master Electrician, and Electrical Contractor. Mike came from the real world, and he has a unique understanding of how the *NEC* relates to electrical installations from a practical standpoint. You will find his writing style to be simple, nontechnical, and practical.

Did you know that Mike didn't finish high school? So if you struggled in high school or if you didn't finish it at all, don't let this get you down, you're in good company. As a matter of fact, Mike Culbreath, Master Electrician, who produces the finest electrical graphics in the history of the electrical industry, didn't finish high school either! So two high school dropouts produced the text and graphics in this textbook! However, realizing that success depends on one's continuing pursuit of education, Mike immediately attained his GED (as did Mike Culbreath) and ultimately attended the University of Miami's Graduate School for a Master's degree in Business Administration (MBA).

Mike Holt resides in Central Florida, is the father of seven children, and has many outside interests and activities. He is a former National Barefoot Waterskiing Champion (1988 and 1999), who set five barefoot water-ski records, and he continues to train year-round at a national competition level [www.barefootcentral.com].

Mike enjoys motocross racing, but at the age of 52 decided to retire from that activity (way too many broken bones, concussions, collapsed lung, etc., but what a rush). He has taken up 1/2 scale NASCAR racing instead, drives the No. 24 car, and is actually doing quite well. Mike also enjoys snow skiing and spending time with his family. What sets Mike apart from some is his commitment to living a balanced lifestyle; he places God first, then family, career, and self.

Educational Director

Sarina Snow was born and raised in "The Bronx" (Yankee Stadium Area), then moved to New Jersey with her husband Freddy where they raised their three children. They moved to Florida in 1979 and have totally loved the move to a warmer climate. Sarina has worked with Mike Holt for over twenty years and has literally learned the business from the ground up. She remembers typing Mike's books using carbon paper BC (Before Computers). She has developed a strong relationship with the industry by attending Mike's classes and seminars, and by accompanying Mike to many trade shows in various states to get a deeper understanding of the trade firsthand. Her love and devotion to Mike and Company (actually the original name of Mike Holt Enterprises) has given her the ability to be the "Mom" in the industry. "She Cares," sums it up.

Graphic Illustrator

Mike Culbreath devoted his career to the electrical industry and worked his way up from an apprentice electrician to master electrician. While working as a journeyman electrician, he suffered a serious on-the-job knee injury. With a keen interest in continuing education for electricians, and as part of his rehabilitation program, he completed courses at Mike Holt Enterprises, Inc. and then passed the exam to receive his Master Electrician's license.

In 1986, after attending classes at Mike Holt Enterprises, he joined the staff to update material and later studied computer graphics and began illustrating Mike Holt's textbooks and magazine articles. He's worked with Mike Holt Enterprises for over 15 years and, as Mike Holt has proudly acknowledged, has helped to transform his words and visions into lifelike graphics.

Mike Culbreath resides in northern Michigan with his wife Toni, and two children: Dawn and Mac. He is helping Toni fulfill her dream by helping her develop and build a quality horse boarding, training, and teaching facility. Mike enjoys working with children by volunteering as a leader for a 4-H archery club and assisting with the local 4-H horse club. He also enjoys fishing, gardening, and cooking.

Editorial

Toni Culbreath completed high school graduation requirements by the end of the first semester of her senior year. She went on to complete courses for computer programming at a trade school by March of that year, and then returned to participate in graduation ceremonies with her high school class.

Toni became associated with Mike Holt Enterprises in 1994 in the area of software support and training and now enjoys the challenges of editing Mike Holt's superb material. She is certified as a therapeutic riding instructor and is extensively involved in Michigan's 4-H horse programs at both the county and state level.

Barbara Parks has been working for Mike Holt Enterprises for the last several years as a Writer's Assistant. She has edited most of Mike Holt's books and various projects over this period of time. She is a retired lady, working part time at home and thoroughly enjoys "keeping busy."

Technical Editorial Director

Steve Arne has been involved in the electrical industry since 1974 working in various positions from electrician to full-time instructor and department chair in technical post secondary education. Steve has developed curriculum for many electrical training courses and has developed university business and leadership courses. Currently, Steve offers occasional exam prep and Continuing Education *Code* classes.

Steve believes that as a teacher he understands the joy of helping others as they learn and experience new insights. His goal is to help others understand more of the technological marvels that surround us. Steve thanks God for the wonders of His creation and for the opportunity to share it with others.

Steve and his lovely wife Deb live in Rapid City, South Dakota where they are both active in their church and community. They have two grown children and five grandchildren.

Cover Design

Tracy Jette has enjoyed working in the field of Graphic Design for over 10 years. She loves all aspects of design, and finds that spending time outdoors camping and hiking with her family and friends is a great inspiration. Tracy is very happy to have recently joined Mike Holt Enterprises and has found that working from home brings a harmony to her life with her 3 boys (10-year-old twins and a 7-year-old), her husband of 16 years, Mario, and her work life.

Layout Design and Production

Cathleen Kwas has been in the publishing industry for over 26 years. She's worn many hats–copy editor, desktop publisher, prepress manager, project coordinator, communications director, book designer, and graphic artist.

Cathleen is very happily married to Michael and lives in beautiful Lake Mary, Florida with their adorable Maltese-ShihTzu puppies, Bosco and Gracie.

Special Acknowledgments

First I want to thank God for my life. I want to thank Him for even the most difficult of times, because this has helped me become a man that I hope honors Him in my actions. My loving Godly wife is always by my side, and there's no question that I could not have achieved any of my success without her continued support. She is a selfless mother and wife. She made the difficult decision to stay at home and support her family; the successes of her husband and her children are God's reward for her sacrifice. To my wonderful children, Belynda, Melissa, Autumn, Steven, Michael, Meghan, and Brittney—I love every moment we shared together (well, most moments). Thank you for loving me and knowing God.

I would like to thank all the people in my life that believed in me, and those who spurred me on. Thanks to the Electrical Construction & Maintenance *(EC&M)* magazine for my first "big break" in 1980, and Joe McPartland who helped and encouraged me from 1980 to 1992. Joe, I'll never forget to help others as you've helped me. I would also like to thank Joe Salimando, the former publisher of the Electrical Contractor magazine produced by the National Electrical Contractors Association (*NECA*) for my second "big break" in 1995.

A special thank you must be sent to the staff at the National Fire Protection Association (NFPA), publishers of the *NEC*—in particular Jeff Sargent for his assistance in answering my many *NEC* questions. Jeff, you're a "first class" guy, and I admire your dedication and commitment to helping others, including me, to understand the *Code*. Other former NFPA staff members I would like to thank include John Caloggero, Joe Ross, and Dick Murray for their help in the past.

Phil Simmons, former Executive Director of the International Association of Electrical Inspectors (IAEI)—you're truly a Godly man whom I admire, and I do want to thank you for your help, especially in grounding. Other people who have been important in my personal and technical development include James Stallcup, Dick Loyd, Mark Ode, DJ Clements, Morris Trimmer, Tony Silvestri, and the infamous Marvin Weiss.

A personal thank you goes to Sarina, my long-time friend and office manager. Thank you for covering the office for me while I spend so much time writing textbooks, conducting seminars, and producing videos and DVDs. Your love and concern for the customer has contributed significantly to the success of Mike Holt Enterprises, Inc., and it has been wonderful working side-by-side and nurturing this company's growth from its small beginnings. Also thank you for loving my family and me and for being there during those many difficult times.

Mike Holt Enterprises Team Acknowledgments

There are many people who played a role in the development and production of this textbook. I would like to start with Mike Culbreath, Master Electrician, who has been with me for over 15 years, helping me transform my words and thoughts into lifelike graphics.

Also, a thank you goes to Cathleen Kwas for the outstanding electronic layout of this textbook, and Tracy Jette for the amazing front and back cover.

Finally, I would like to thank Toni Culbreath and Barbara Parks who worked tirelessly to proofread and edit the final stages of this publication. Their attention to detail and dedication to this project is greatly appreciated.

Special Thank You

I would like to thank my assistant, Tara Martin, for her outstanding work in coordinating this book. In addition to her excellent organizational skills, she has displayed a great team attitude and demonstrated calm patience when juggling many projects at the same time—especially when we're on deadline!

Advisory Committee

Thanks are also in order for the following individuals who reviewed the manuscript and offered invaluable suggestions and feedback.

Victor M. Ammons, P.E.
Director of Electrical Engineering,
The Prisco Group,
Hopewell, New Jersey

Steve Arne

Technical Director, Mike Holt Enterprises, Inc.,
Rapid City, South Dakota

Mike Culbreath

Graphic Designer, Mike Holt Enterprises, Inc.
Alden, Michigan

Leo W. Moritz, P.E.

Senior Electrical Engineer,
Chicago, Illinois

Jerry Peck

Inspector and Instructor,
Inspection Services Associates, Inc.,
Pembroke Pines, Florida

Terry Schneider

Electrical Field Inspection Supervisor,
Colorado Springs, Colorado

Brooke Stauffer

Executive Director of Standards and Safety,
National Electrical Contractors Association,
Bethesda, Maryland

James Thomas

Electrical/Electronics Instructor,
James Sprunt Community College,
Kenansville, North Carolina

J. Kevin Vogel, P.E.

Design and Quotations, Crescent Electric Supply,
Coeur d'Alene, Idaho

Joseph Wages Jr.

Instructor
Siloam Springs, Arkansas

A Very Special Thank You

To my beautiful wife, Linda, and my seven children:
Belynda, Melissa, Autumn, Steven, Michael,
Meghan, and Brittney—
thank you for loving me so much.

Video Team Members

Steve Arne

Technical Editorial Director, Mike Holt
Enterprises, Inc.
Electrical Instructor, Arne Electro Tech,
Rapid City, South Dakota
http://electricalmaster.com

Steve Arne has been involved in the electrical industry since 1974, working in various positions from electrician to full-time instructor and department chair in technical post secondary education. He has a Bachelor's Degree in Technical Education and a Master's Degree in Administrative Studies with a human resources emphasis. Licenses held by Steve include Electrical Master, Electrical Inspector, Electrical Contractor, and Real Estate Home Inspector. He is a board member of the Black Hills Chapter of the SD Electrical Council and a member of the SD Real Estate Task Force on Home Inspection. He also enjoys developing his own Websites.

Steve and his lovely wife Deb have celebrated over 32 years of marriage in Rapid City, South Dakota where they are both active in their church and community. They have two grown children and five grandchildren.

Dennis Carlson

Master Electrician/Electrical Instructor
The Industrial Company (T.I.C.)
Steamboat Springs, Colorado

Dennis Carlson started in the electrical trade in 1980 with Simmons Electric based in Greeley, Colorado and did residential and commercial work with them until 1985. He then went to work for Atkinson Electric based out of Ft. Collins, Colorado until 1987, also doing residential and commercial work.

Dennis has since worked on various industrial projects for TIC (The Industrial Company) as a journeyman, electrical foreman, and project coordinator. He is presently the Manager of the Electrical Craft Training Program for TIC.

Dennis instructs levels 1, 2, 3, and 4th year trainees. With the use of Mike Holt's Electrician Exam Preparation book, he has had a success rate of 90% with his 4th year trainees on the Colorado State electrical exam.

Dennis lives in Steamboat Springs, with his wife Cindy and their son Josh. Their daughter is enrolled at CSU in Ft. Collins, studying for a degree in biology.

Mike Culbreath

Graphic Illustrator,
Mike Holt Enterprises, Inc.
Alden, Michigan

Mike Culbreath devoted his career to the electrical industry and worked his way up from an apprentice electrician to master electrician. While working as a journeyman electrician, he suffered a serious on-the-job knee injury. With a keen interest in continuing education for electricians, and as part of his rehabilitation program, he completed courses at Mike Holt Enterprises, Inc. and then passed the exam to receive his Master Electrician's license.

In 1986, after attending classes at Mike Holt Enterprises, he joined the staff to update material and later studied computer graphics and began illustrating Mike Holt's textbooks and magazine articles. He's worked with Mike Holt Enterprises for over 15 years and, as Mike Holt has proudly acknowledged, has helped to transform his words and visions into lifelike graphics.

Mike resides in northern Michigan with his wife Toni, and two children: Dawn and Mac. Mike enjoys working with children by volunteering as a leader for a 4-H archery club, assisting with the local 4-H horse club, fishing, gardening, and cooking.

James E. Jones, Jr.

Electrical Instructor
Oklahoma State University
Okmulgee, Oklahoma

James E. Jones, Jr. is an Electrical Instructor at Oklahoma State University, Okmulgee Campus, specializing in the High-Voltage Lineman Program and Electrical Construction Program. He has over 25 years in the electrical field, working as a lineman, electrical superintendent, maintenance electrician, commercial electrician, electrical instructor, and Director of Education & Training.

He currently holds a Texas Master Electrician's license and is registered in several cities and towns in the Dallas/Ft. Worth area.

James grew up in a rural area of Arkansas and joined the U.S. Air Force after graduating from high school. He retired from the military after 21 years of service as an electrician/lineman. He currently holds a Baccalaureate Degree in Occupational Education with a specialization in Corporate Training Development and Electrical Power Systems.

John Mills

Master Electrician/Electrical Instructor
Premier Electrical Company/Dade County School Board
Miami Springs, Florida

John Mills is an instructor for Mike Holt Enterprises and is a certified electrical contractor, certified inspector, plan reviewer, and CBO. John started in the electrical trade in 1980 as a helper and attended an ABC Apprenticeship Program, then worked his way up to master electrician. John has been an instructor for 20 years, teaching master and journeyman exam preparation courses and Florida State certification courses.

John resides in Miami, Florida with his wife Corina and their four sons. John's hobbies are working with wood and metal. He makes wooden bowls and furniture from trees that have been cut down. He enjoys making things for his children as well as fishing, family picnics, and vacations with his family.

Merle D. Rogers

Electrical Instructor
Los Angeles Trade Technical College
Los Angeles, California

Merle D. Rogers was an Organizer for Local 11 for three years and Local 47 for one year. He earned a California Electrical Inspection certificate through the International Conference of Building Officials (ICBO) and worked for Kaiser Svervdrup Engineering as a Motor Control and Instrumentation Inspector.

Merle began teaching with the Los Angeles IBEW/NECA Training Trust and taught Process Instrumentation and Control for three years, and apprenticeship for one year. He helped begin an Instrumentation Program at the San Bernardino Training Trust. He became a full-time teacher at Los Angeles Trade Technical College three years ago and was recently certified by the U.S. Department of Labor as an OSHA Construction Outreach Trainer. He has created the curriculum for several new courses now taught at LATTC.

"Professor Rogers" appeared on the Discovery Channel's, the Monster House television program, and was an expert witness on hand tools in one of the largest lawsuits involving hand tools in many years (In Re: Leatherman Tool Company).

Eric Stromberg
Electrical Engineer/Instructor
Dow Chemical
Lake Jackson, Texas

Eric Stromberg enrolled in the University of Houston in 1976, with Electrical Engineering as his major. During the first part of his college years, Eric worked for a company that specialized in installing professional sound systems. Later, he worked for a small electrical company and eventually became a journeyman electrician.

After graduation from college in 1982, Eric went to work for an electronics company that specialized in fire alarm systems for high-rise buildings. He became a state licensed fire alarm installation superintendent and was also a member of IBEW local union 716. In 1989, Eric began a career with The Dow Chemical Company as an Electrical Engineer designing power distribution systems for large industrial facilities. In 1997 Eric began teaching National Electric Code classes.

Eric currently resides in Lake Jackson, Texas, with his wife Jane and three children: Ainsley, Austin, and Brieanna.

James Thomas
Master Electrician/Electrical Instructor
James Sprunt Community College
Kenansville, NC

James Thomas has been working in the Electrical Field since 1985 and is licensed in the state of North Carolina. He has worked in textile mills, poultry plants, and industrial installations as well as residential and commercial electrical jobs. He has been an instructor for electrical and electronics courses (including the National Electrical Code) full-time at James Sprunt Community College in Kenansville NC for over 13 years, and has taught thousands of individuals. He previously taught at Pitt Community College in Greenville NC and Cape Fear Community College in Wilmington NC.

James earned a diploma in electrical installation and maintenance, and holds a BS in business management from Mount Olive College in Mount Olive, NC. He is currently working on his MS in Digital Communications from East Carolina University in Greenville, NC. James also served in the Air Force Reserve in Goldsboro NC for 16 years.

Kevin Vogel
Electrical Engineer/Instructor
Crescent Electric
Cour d'Alene, Idaho

Kevin graduated from Santa Clara University in 1964 with a Bachelor of Science Degree in Mechanical Engineering. A licensed professional engineer since 1968, he formerly worked as chief engineer for a manufacturer of electric heating products and (the first) thermoplastic outlet boxes. He has also worked as an electrician and holds a Master Electrician's license.

In 1978, Kevin was co-founder of an electrical wholesale distribution company that was sold to Crescent Electric Supply Co. in 1991. Kevin continues to work in that part of the industry. He also provides expert witness testimony in civil and criminal cases, and serves as a certified instructor for National Electrical Code-related courses at North Idaho College.

Kevin married his lovely wife, Linda, in 1966 and they have been blessed with thirteen wonderful children and, so far, twelve grandchildren. He is extremely grateful to God for all the gifts that He has bestowed on him and his loved ones.

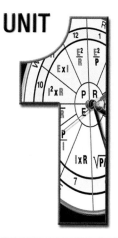

UNIT 1

Electrician's Math and Basic Electrical Formulas

Introduction

In order to construct a building that will last into the future, a strong foundation is a prerequisite. Footings must be dug that extend to a depth sufficient to endure frost or other soil conditions and meet local requirements. Concrete with reinforcing material such as rebar is incorporated for the footings and the foundation walls. The foundation is a part of the building that is not visible in the finished structure, but is extremely essential in erecting a building that will have the necessary strength to endure.

The math and basic electrical concepts of this unit are very similar to the foundation of a building. The concepts in this unit are the essential basics that you must understand, because you will build upon them as you study electrical circuits and systems. As your studies continue, you'll find that a good foundation in electrical theory and math will help you understand why the *NEC* contains certain provisions.

This unit includes math, electrical fundamentals, and an explanation of the operation of electrical meters to help you visualize some practical applications. You'll be amazed at how often your electrical studies return to the basics of this unit. Ohm's law and the electrical formulas related to it, are the foundation of all electrical circuits.

Every student begins at a different level of understanding, and you may find this unit an easy review, or you may find it requires a high level of concentration. In any case, be certain that you fully understand the concepts of this unit and are able to successfully complete the questions at the end of the unit before going on. A solid foundation will help in your successful study of the rest of this book.

PART A—ELECTRICIAN'S MATH

Introduction

Numbers can take different forms:

Whole numbers: 1, 20, 300, 4,000, 5,000

Decimals: 0.80, 1.25, 0.75, 1.15

Fractions: 1/2, 1/4, 5/8, 4/3

Percentages: 80%, 125%, 250%, 500%

You'll need to be able to convert these numbers from one form to another and back again, because all of these number forms are part of electrical work and electrical calculations.

You'll also need to be able to do some basic algebra. Many people have a fear of algebra, but as you work through the material here you will see there is nothing to fear but fear itself.

1.1 Whole Numbers

Whole numbers are exactly what the term implies. These are numbers that do not contain any fractions, decimals, or a percentage.

1.2 Decimal

The decimal method is used to display numbers other than whole numbers, fractions or percentages; such as, 0.80, 1.25, 1.732, etc.

1.3 Fractions

A fraction represents part of a whole number. If you use a calculator for adding, dividing, subtracting, or multiplying, you need to convert the fraction to a decimal or whole number. To change a fraction to a decimal or whole number, divide the numerator (top number) by the denominator (bottom number).

► Examples:

1/6= one divided by six = 0.166
2/5= two divided by five = 0.40
3/6= three divided by six = 0.50
5/4= five divided by four = 1.25
7/2= seven divided by two = 3.5

1.4 Percentages

Use of a percentage is another method used to display a value. One hundred percent (100%) means all of the value; fifty percent (50%) means one-half of a value, and twenty-five percent (25%) means one-fourth of a value.

For convenience in multiplying or dividing by a percentage, convert the percentage value to a whole number or decimal, and then use this value for the calculation. When changing a percent value to a decimal or whole number, move the decimal point two places to the left. **Figure 1–1**

► Examples

Percentage	Number
32.5%	0.325
80%	0.80
125%	1.25
250%	2.50

1.5 Multiplier

When a number needs to be changed by multiplying it by a percentage, this number is called a multiplier. The first step is to convert the percentage to a decimal, then multiply the original number by the decimal value.

Converting Percentages to Decimals

Percentage   Drop "%"   Decimal

32.5%   .32.5%   0.325

Move the decimal point two places to the left.

Copyright 2003 Mike Holt Enterprises, Inc.

Figure 1–1

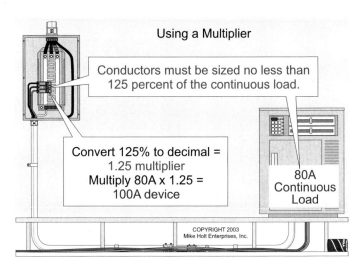

Using a Multiplier

Conductors must be sized no less than 125 percent of the continuous load.

Convert 125% to decimal = 1.25 multiplier
Multiply 80A x 1.25 = 100A device

80A Continuous Load

COPYRIGHT 2003
Mike Holt Enterprises, Inc.

Figure 1–2

► **Example A**

An overcurrent protection device (breaker or fuse) must be sized no less than 125 percent of the continuous load. If the load is 80A, the overcurrent protection device will have to be sized no smaller than _____. **Figure 1–2**

(a) 80A   (b) 100A
(c) 125A   (d) none of these

• Answer: (b) 100A

Step 1   Convert 125 percent to a decimal: 1.25

Step 2   Multiply the value 80 by 1.25 = 100A

► **Example B**

The maximum continuous load on an overcurrent protection device is limited to 80 percent of the device rating. If the protective device is rated 50A, what is the maximum continuous load permitted on the protective device? **Figure 1–3**

(a) 80A   (b) 125A
(c) 50A   (d) none of these

• Answer: (d) none of these

Step 1   Convert 80 percent to a decimal: 0.80

Step 2   Multiply the value 50A by 0.80 = 40A

1.6 Percent Increase

The following steps accomplish increasing a number by a specific percentage:

Step 1   Convert the percent to a decimal value.

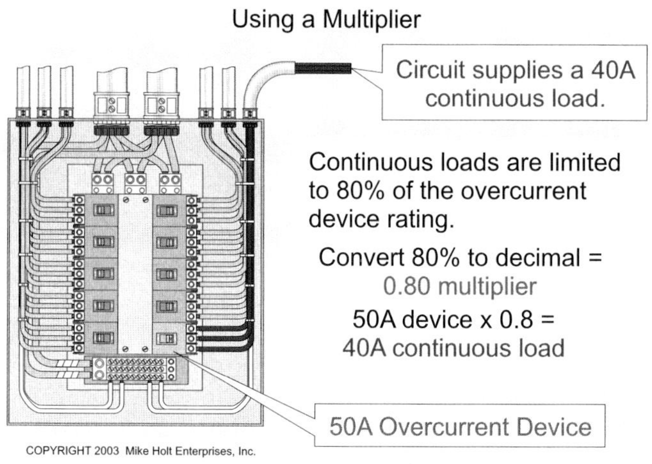

Using a Multiplier

Circuit supplies a 40A continuous load.

Continuous loads are limited to 80% of the overcurrent device rating.

Convert 80% to decimal = 0.80 multiplier

50A device x 0.8 = 40A continuous load

50A Overcurrent Device

COPYRIGHT 2003 Mike Holt Enterprises, Inc.

Figure 1–3

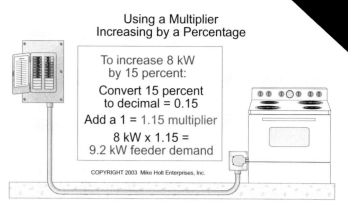

Using a Multiplier
Increasing by a Percentage

To increase 8 kW by 15 percent:
Convert 15 percent to decimal = 0.15
Add a 1 = 1.15 multiplier
8 kW x 1.15 = 9.2 kW feeder demand

COPYRIGHT 2003 Mike Holt Enterprises, Inc.

Figure 1–4

Step 2   Add one to the decimal value to create the multiplier.

Step 3   Multiply the original number by the multiplier (Step 2).

▶ **Example A**

Increase the whole number 45 by 35 percent.

Step 1   Convert 35 percent to decimal form: 0.35

Step 2   Add one to the decimal value:
1 + 0.35 = 1.35

Step 3   Multiply 45 by the multiplier 1.35:
45 x 1.35 = 60.75

▶ **Example B**

If the feeder demand load for a range is 8 kW and it is required to be increased by 15 percent, the total demand load will be _____. Figure 1–4

(a) 8 kW   (b) 15 kW
(c) 6.80 kW   (d) 9.20 kW

• Answer: (d) 9.20 kW

Step 1   Convert to decimal form: 15 percent = 0.15

Step 2   Add one to the decimal: 1 + 0.15 = 1.15

Step 3   Multiply 8 by the multiplier 1.15:
8 kW x 1.15 = 9.20 kW

1.7 Reciprocals

The reciprocal of a number is obtained when a number is converted into a fraction with the number one as the numerator (top

number). The reciprocal of a number can be determined by following these steps:

Step 1   Convert the number to a decimal value.

Step 2   Divide the value into the number one.

▶ **Example A**

What is the reciprocal of 80 percent?

(a) 0.80   (b) 100%
(c) 125%   (d) none of these

• Answer: (c) 125%

Step 1   Convert the 80 percent into a decimal (move the decimal two places to the left): 80 percent = 0.80

Step 2   Divide 0.80 into the number one:
1/0.80 = 1.25 or 125 percent

▶ **Example B**

What is the reciprocal of 125 percent?

(a) 0.80   (b) 100%
(c) 125%   (d) none of these

• Answer: (a) 0.80

Step 1   Convert the 125 percent into a decimal:
125 percent = 1.25

Step 2   Divide 1.25 into the number one:
1/1.25 = 0.80 or 80 percent

1.8 Squaring a Number

Squaring a number is accomplished by multiplying the number by itself.

$$10^2 = 10 \times 10 = 100$$
$$23^2 = 23 \times 23 = 529$$

onsumed in watts by a 12 AWG conductor
id has a total resistance of 0.40 ohms, if the
uit conductors is 16A?

Formula: $P = I^2 \times R$

(Answers are rounded to the nearest 50).

(a) 50   (b) 150
(c) 100   (d) none of these

- Answer: (c) 100
  $P = I^2 \times R$
  $I = 16A$
  $R = 0.40$ ohms
  $P = 16A^2 \times 0.40$ ohms
  $P = 16A \times 16A \times 0.40$ ohms
  $P = 102.40$ W

► **Example B**

What is the area in square inches (sq in.) of a trade size 1 raceway with a diameter of 1.049 in.?

Formula: Area $= \pi \times r^2$
$\pi = 3.14$
r = radius (is equal to 0.50 of the diameter).

(a) 1   (b) 0.86
(c) 0.34   (d) 0.50

- Answer: (b) 0.86
  Area $= \pi \times r^2$
  Area $= 3.14 \times (0.50 \times 1.049)^2$
  Area $= 3.14 \times 0.5245^2$
  Area $= 3.14 \times (0.5245 \times 0.5245)$
  Area $= 3.14 \times 0.2751$
  Area $= 0.86$ sq in.

► **Example C**

What is the sq in. area of an 8 in. pizza? **Figure 1–5A**

(a) 50   (b) 75
(c) 25   (d) none of these

- Answer: (a) 50
  Area $= \pi \times r^2$
  Area $= 3.14 \times (0.50 \times 8)^2$
  Area $= 3.14 \times 4^2$
  Area $= 3.14 \times 4 \times 4$
  Area $= 3.14 \times 16$
  Area $= 50$ sq in.

Squaring

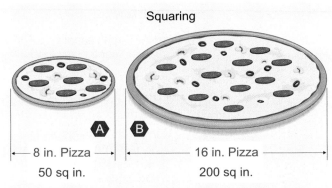

8 in. Pizza   16 in. Pizza
50 sq in.   200 sq in.

If you double the diameter of a circle,
the area increases by a factor of four.

COPYRIGHT 2003 Mike Holt Enterprises, Inc.

Figure 1–5

► **Example D**

What is the sq in. area of a 16 in. pizza? **Figure 1–5B**

(a) 100   (b) 200
(c) 150   (d) none of these

- Answer: (b) 200
  Area $= \pi \times r^2$
  Area $= 3.14 \times (0.50 \times 16)^2$
  Area $= 3.14 \times 8^2$
  Area $= 3.14 \times 8 \times 8$
  Area $= 3.14 \times 64$
  Area $= 200$ sq in.

AUTHOR'S COMMENT: As you see in examples C and D, if you double the diameter of the circle, the area contained in the circle is increased by a factor of four! By the way, a large pizza is always cheaper per sq in. than a small pizza.

1.9 Square Root

Deriving the square root ($\sqrt{n}$) of a number is the opposite of squaring a number. The square root of 36 is a number that, when multiplied by itself, gives the product 36. The $\sqrt{36}$ is equal to six (6), because six, multiplied by itself (6^2) equals the number 36.

Because it's difficult to do this manually, we'll just use the square root key of the calculator.

► **Example**

$\sqrt{3}$: Depending on your calculator's instructions, enter the number 3 in the calculator, then press the square root key = 1.732.

$\sqrt{1,000}$: enter the number 1,000, then press the square root key = 31.62.

If your calculator does not have a square root key, don't worry about it. For all practical purposes of this textbook, the only number you need to know the square root of is the $\sqrt{3}$, which equals approximately 1.732.

To multiply, divide, add, or subtract a number by a square root value, determine the decimal value, then perform the math function.

▶ **Example A**

36,000W/(208V x $\sqrt{3}$) is equal to _____.

(a) 120A   (b) 208A
(c) 360A   (d) 100A

• Answer: (d) 100A

Step 1   Determine the decimal value for the $\sqrt{3} = 1.732$

Step 2   Divide 36,000W by (208V x 1.732) = 100A

▶ **Example B**

The phase voltage, 208V/$\sqrt{3}$ is equal to _____.

(a) 120V   (b) 208V
(c) 360V   (d) none of these

• Answer: (a) 120V

Step 1   Determine the decimal value for the $\sqrt{3} = 1.732$

Step 2   Divide 208V by 1.732 = 120V

1.10 Volume

The volume of an enclosure is expressed in cubic inches (cu in.), which is determined by multiplying the length, by the width, by the depth of the enclosure.

▶ **Example**

What is the volume of a conduit body that has the dimensions 2 x 2 x 6 in.? **Figure 1–6**

(a) 20 cu in.   (b) 24 cu in.
(c) 30 cu in.   (d) none of these

• Answer: (b) 24 cu in.
  2 x 2 x 6 = 24 cu in.

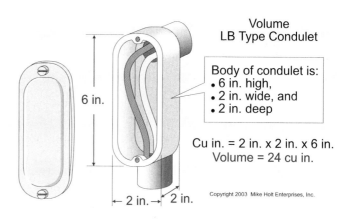

Volume
LB Type Condulet

Body of condulet is:
• 6 in. high,
• 2 in. wide, and
• 2 in. deep

Cu in. = 2 in. x 2 in. x 6 in.
Volume = 24 cu in.

Copyright 2003 Mike Holt Enterprises, Inc.

Figure 1–6

1.11 Kilo

The letter "k" in the electrical trade is used for the abbreviation of the metric prefix "kilo," which represents a value of 1,000.

▶ **Example A**

What is the wattage of an 8 kW rated range?

(a) 8W   (b) 8,000W
(c) 4,000W   (d) none of these

• Answer: (b) 8,000W
  Wattage equals kW x 1,000. In this case:
  8 kW x 1,000 = 8,000W

▶ **Example B**

A 300W load will have a _____ kW rating. **Figure 1–7**

(a) 300 kW   (b) 3,000 kW
(c) 30 kW   (d) 0.30 kW

• Answer: (d) 0.30 kW
  kW = Watts/1,000
  kW = 300W/1,000 = 0.30 kW

AUTHOR'S COMMENT: The use of the letter "k" is not limited to "kW." It is often used for kVA (1,000 volt-amps), and kcmil (1,000 circular mils).

1.12 Rounding Off

There is no specific rule for rounding off, but rounding to two or three "significant figures" should be sufficient for most electrical calculations. Numbers below five are rounded down, while numbers five and above are rounded up.

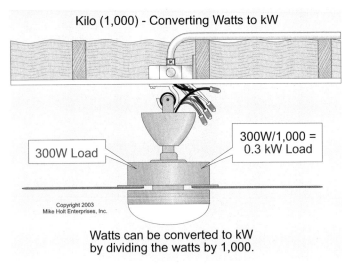

Kilo (1,000) - Converting Watts to kW

300W Load

300W/1,000 = 0.3 kW Load

Copyright 2003
Mike Holt Enterprises, Inc.

Watts can be converted to kW
by dividing the watts by 1,000.

Figure 1–7

► **Examples**

0.1245—fourth number is five or above =
0.125 rounded up

1.674—fourth number is below five =
1.67 rounded down

21.99—fourth number is five or above =
22 rounded up

367.2—fourth number is below five =
367 rounded down

Rounding Answers for Multiple Choice Questions

You should round your answers in the same manner as the multiple choice selections given in the question.

► **Example**

The sum* of 12, 17, 28, and 40 is equal to _____.

    (a) 70   (b) 80
    (c) 90   (d) 100

    • Answer: (d) 100
      *A sum is the result of adding numbers.

The sum of these values equals 97, but this is not listed as one of the choices. The multiple choice selections in this case are rounded off to the closest "tens."

1.13 Parentheses

Whenever numbers are in parentheses, complete the mathematical function within the parentheses before proceeding with the rest of the problem.

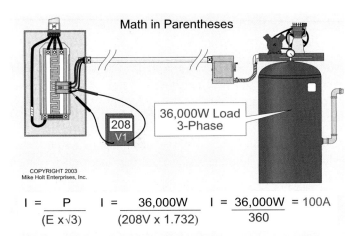

Math in Parentheses

36,000W Load
3-Phase

208
V1

COPYRIGHT 2003
Mike Holt Enterprises, Inc.

$$I = \frac{P}{(E \times \sqrt{3})} \quad I = \frac{36,000W}{(208V \times 1.732)} \quad I = \frac{36,000W}{360} = 100A$$

Whenever numbers are in parentheses, we must complete the mathematical function within the parentheses before proceeding with the rest of the problem.

Figure 1–8

What is the current of a 36,000W, 208V, three-phase load?
Figure 1–8

    Formula: Ampere (I) = Watts/(E x $\sqrt{3}$)

        (a) 50A   (b) 100A
        (c) 150A   (d) none of these

       • Answer: (b) 100A

Step 1   Perform the operation inside the parentheses first—determine the product of: 208V x 1.732 = 360

Step 2   Divide 36,000W by 360 = 100A

1.14 Testing Your Answer for Reasonableness

When working with any mathematical calculation, don't just blindly do a calculation. When you perform the mathematical calculation, you need to know if the answer is greater than or less than the values given in the problem. Always do a "reality check" to be certain that your answer is not nonsense. Even the best of us make mistakes at times, so always examine your answer to make sure it makes sense!

► **Example**

The input of a transformer is 300W; the transformer efficiency is 90 percent. Since output is always less than input because of efficiency, what is the transformer output? Figure 1–9

        (a) 300W   (b) 270W
        (c) 333W   (d) 500W

       • Answer: (b) 270W

Testing Your Answer for Reasonableness

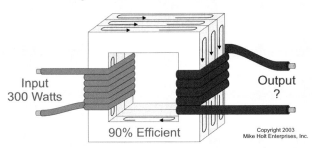

If you know the output must be less than the input where efficiency is involved, you will know the answer must be less than 300. The only multiple choice selection less than 300 is (b) 270. No calculation is necessary.

Figure 1–9

Since the output has to be less than the input (300W), you would not have to perform any mathematical calculation; the only multiple choice selection that is less than 300W is (b) 270W.

▶ **Example A**

The math to get the answer was:
    300W x 0.90 = 270W

To check your answer:
    270W/0.90 = 300W

▶ **Example B**

If the math was:
    36,000W/360= 100A

To check your answer:
    100A x 360 = 36,000W

> **AUTHOR'S COMMENT:** One of the nice things about mathematical equations is that you can usually test to see if your answer is correct. To do this test, substitute the answer you arrived at back into the equation you are working with, and verify that it is indeed an equality. This method of checking your math will become easier once you know more of the formulas and how they relate to each other.

PART B—BASIC ELECTRICAL FORMULAS
Introduction

Now that you've mastered the math and understand some basics about electrical circuits, you are ready to take your knowledge of electrical formulas to the next level. One of the things we are going to do here is strengthen your proficiency with Ohm's Law. Many false notions about the application of *NEC* Article 250 and *NEC* Chapter 3 wiring methods arise when people can use Ohm's Law only when solving practice problems on paper but lack a real understanding of how it works and how to apply it. You will have that understanding, and you will not be subject to those false notions—or the unsafe conditions they lead to. But, we won't stop with Ohm's Law. You are also going to have a high level of proficiency with the power equation. One of the tools for handling the power equation—and Ohm's Law—with ease is the power wheel. You will be able to use that to solve all kinds of problems.

1.15 Electrical Circuit

An electrical circuit consists of the power source, the conductors, and the load. A switch can be placed in series with the circuit conductors to control the operation of the load (on or off). Figure 1–10

> **AUTHOR'S COMMENT:** According to the "electron current flow theory," current always flows from the negative terminal of the source, through the circuit and load, to the positive terminal of the source.

1.16 Power Source

Electrical pressure necessary to move electrons out of their orbit around the nucleus of an atom can be produced by chemical, magnetic, photovoltaic, and other means. The two categories of power sources are direct current (dc) and alternating current (ac).

Electrical Circuit

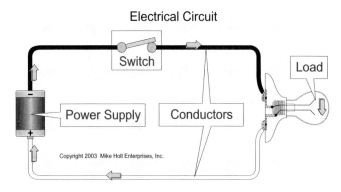

There must be a complete path from the power source through the load, and back to the power source in order for electrons to flow.

Figure 1–10

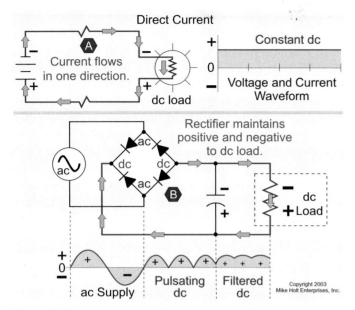

Figure 1–11

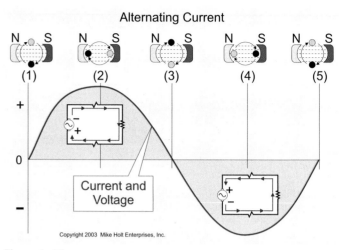

Figure 1–12

Direct Current

The polarity and the output voltage from a dc power source never change direction. One terminal will be negative and the other will be positive, relative to each other. Direct-current power is often produced by batteries, dc generators, and electronic power supplies. Figure 1–11

Direct current is used for electroplating, street trolley and railway systems, or where a smooth and wide range of speed control is required for a motor-driven application. Direct current is also used for control circuits and electronic instruments.

Alternating Current

Alternating-current power sources produce a voltage that changes polarity and magnitude. Alternating current is produced by an ac power source such as an ac generator. The major advantage of ac over dc is the ease at which voltage can be changed through the use of a transformer. Figure 1–12

> **AUTHOR'S COMMENT:** Alternating current accounts for more than 90 percent of all electric power used throughout the world.

1.17 Conductance

Conductance or conductivity is the property of a metal that permits current to flow. The best conductors in order of their conductivity are: silver, copper, gold, and aluminum. Many people think that gold is the best conductor, but that is not the case. Figure 1–13

1.18 Circuit Resistance

The total resistance of a circuit includes the resistance of the power supply, the circuit wiring, and the load. Appliances such as heaters and toasters use high-resistance conductors to produce the heat needed for the application. Because the resistance of the power source and conductor is so much smaller than that of the load, they are generally ignored in circuit calculations. Figure 1–14

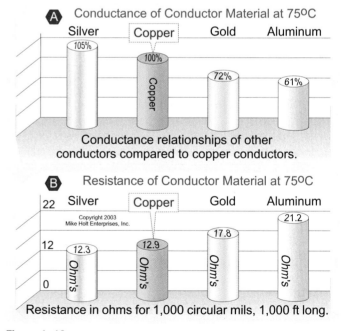

Figure 1–13

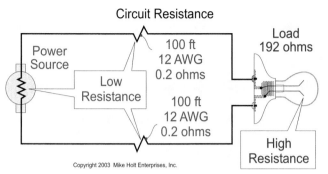

The resistance of the circuit conductors and the power source are usually very low and are often ignored when calculating resistance in a circuit.

Figure 1–14

1.19 Ohm's Law

Ohm's Law is used to demonstrate the relationship between the dc circuit's current intensity (I), its electromotive force (E), and the resistance (R). It is expressed by the formula, I = E/R.

The German physicist Georg Simon Ohm (1787-1854) stated that current is directly proportional to voltage, and inversely proportional to resistance. **Figure 1–15**

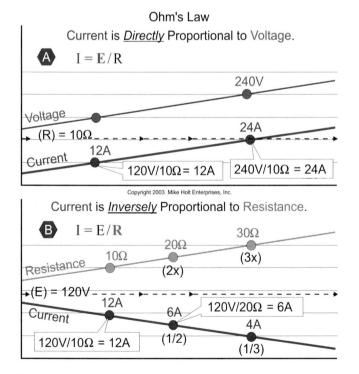

Figure 1–15

Direct proportion means that changing one factor results in a direct change to another factor in the same direction and by the same magnitude. **Figure 1–15A**

If the voltage increases 25 percent, the current will increase 25 percent—in direct proportion (for a given resistance). If the voltage decreases 25 percent, the current will decrease 25 percent—in direct proportion (for a given resistance).

Inverse proportion means that increasing one factor will result in a decrease in another factor by the same magnitude, or a decrease in one factor will result in an increase of the same magnitude in another factor. **Figure 1–15B**

If the resistance increases by 25 percent, the current will decrease by 25 percent—in inverse proportion (for a given voltage), or if the resistance decreases by 25 percent, the current will increase by 25 percent—in inverse proportion (for a given voltage).

1.20 Ohm's Law and Alternating Current

Direct Current

In a dc circuit, the only opposition to current flow is the physical resistance of the material that the current flows through. This opposition is measured in ohms and is called resistance.

Alternating Current

In an ac circuit, there are three factors that oppose current flow: the resistance of the material, the inductive reactance of the circuit, and the capacitive reactance of the circuit.

> **AUTHOR'S COMMENT:** For now, we will assume that the effects of inductance and capacitance on the circuit are insignificant and they will be ignored.

1.21 Ohm's Law Formula Circle

Ohm's Law, the relationship between current, voltage, and resistance expressed in the formula, I = E/R, can be transposed to E = I x R or R = E/I. In order to use these formulas, two of the values must be known.

> **AUTHOR'S COMMENT:** Place your thumb on the unknown value in **Figure 1–16**, and the two remaining variables will "show" you the correct formula.

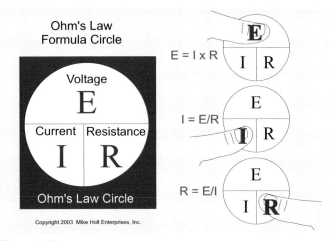

Figure 1–16

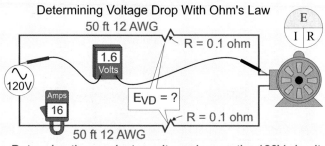

Determine the conductor voltage drop on the 120V circuit.

Formula: $E_{VD} = I \times R$

Copyright 2003 Mike Holt Enterprises, Inc.

To determine the voltage drop of conductors, use the resistance of conductors.

Known: I = 16A (given), R of each conductor = 0.1 ohm

$$E_{VD} = I \times R$$
$$E_{VD} = 16A \times 0.1 \text{ ohm} = 1.6V$$
$$E_{VD} = 1.6V \text{ per conductor}$$

Voltage drop of both conductors = 16A x 0.2 ohms = 3.2V

Note: Load operates at 120V - 3.2 VD = 116.8V

Figure 1–18

▶ **Current Example**

120V supplies a lamp that has a resistance of 192 ohms. What is the current flow in the circuit? **Figure 1–17**

    (a) 0.60A   (b) 0.50A
    (c) 2.5A   (d) 1.3A

    • Answer: (a) 0.60A

Step 1   What is the question? What is "I?"

Step 2   What do you know?
        E = 120V, R = 192 ohms

Step 3   The formula is I = E/R

Step 4   The answer is I = 120V/192 ohms

Step 5   The answer is I = 0.625A

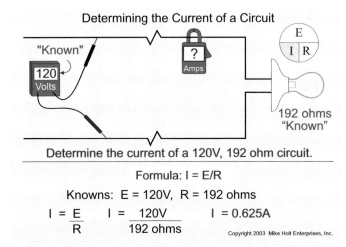

Determine the current of a 120V, 192 ohm circuit.

Formula: I = E/R

Knowns: E = 120V, R = 192 ohms

$$I = \frac{E}{R} \qquad I = \frac{120V}{192 \text{ ohms}} \qquad I = 0.625A$$

Copyright 2003 Mike Holt Enterprises, Inc.

Figure 1–17

▶ **Voltage Drop Example**

What is the voltage drop over two 12 AWG conductors (resistance of 0.20 ohms for 100 ft) supplying a 16A load located 50 ft from the power supply? **Figure 1–18**

    (a) 16V   (b) 32V
    (c) 1.6V   (d) 3.2V

    • Answer: (d) 3.2V

Step 1   What is the question? What is "E?"

Step 2   What do you know about the conductors?

        I = 16A, R = 0.20 ohms. The *NEC* lists the ac resistance of 1,000 ft of 12 AWG as 2 ohms. The resistance of 100 ft is equal to 0.20 ohms. **Figure 1–19**

Step 3   The formula is E = I x R

Step 4   The answer is E = 16A x 0.20 ohms

Step 5   The answer is E = 3.2V

▶ **Resistance Example**

What is the resistance of the circuit conductors when the conductor voltage drop is 3V and the current flowing in the circuit is 100A? **Figure 1–20**

    (a) 0.03 ohms   (b) 2 ohms
    (c) 30 ohms   (d) 300 ohms

    • Answer: (a) 0.03 ohms

Conductor Resistance
Resistance is 2 ohms per 1000 ft
12 AWG
Resistance is 0.2 ohms for 100 ft
COPYRIGHT 2003
Mike Holt Enterprises, Inc.
Each 12 AWG is 50 ft x 2 wires = 100 ft in circuit
To determine the resistance of 100 ft of 12 AWG
NEC Chapter 9, Table 9, 1,000 ft of 12 AWG = 2 ohms.
2 ohms/1,000 ft = 0.002 ohms per ft
0.002 ohms per ft x 100 ft = 0.2 ohms for 100 ft

Figure 1–19

Step 1 What is the question? What is "R?"

Step 2 What do you know about the conductors?
E = 3V dropped, I = 100A

Step 3 The formula is R = E/I

Step 4 The answer is R = 3V/100A

Step 5 The answer is R = 0.03 ohms

1.22 PIE Formula Circle

The PIE formula circle demonstrates the relationship between power, current, and voltage, and it is expressed in the formula P = I x E. This formula can be transposed to I = P/E or E = P/I. In order to use these formulas, two of the values must be known.

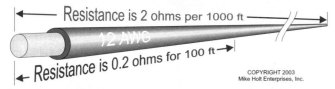

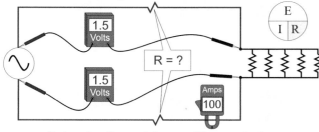

Determining Resistance of Conductors
1.5 Volts
1.5 Volts
R = ?
Amps 100
E
I R
Determine the resistance of the conductors.
Formula: R = E/I
Known: E_{VD} = 1.5 VD per conductor, I = 100A
R = E/I   R = 1.5 VD/100A   R = 0.015 ohms per conductor
R = 0.015 ohm x 2 conductors = 0.03 ohm, both conductors
OR... R = 3 VD/100A = 0.03 ohms for both conductors
Copyright 2003 Mike Holt Enterprises, Inc.

Figure 1–20

Power - "PIE" Formula Circle
Power
P
Current I
Voltage E
PIE Circle
P = I x E
I = P/E
E = P/I
Copyright 2003
Mike Holt Enterprises, Inc.

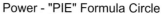

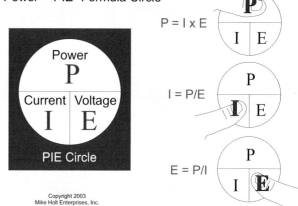

Figure 1–21

AUTHOR'S COMMENT: Place your thumb on the unknown value in **Figure 1–21** and the two remaining variables will "show" you the correct formula.

▶ Power Loss Example

What is the power loss in watts for two conductors that carry 12A and have a voltage drop of 3.6V? **Figure 1–22**

(a) 4.3W (b) 43.2W
(c) 432W (d) none of these

- Answer: (b) 43.2W

Determining Conductor Power Loss
1.8 Volts
1.8 Volts
Represents conductor from source to load.
P = ?
Amps 12
P
I E
Determine the power loss on the conductors.
Formula: P = I x E
Copyright 2003
Mike Holt Enterprises, Inc.
Known: I = 12A
Known: E of conductors = 1.8 VD per conductor
P = I x E_{VD} P = 12A x 1.8 VD
P = 21.6W per conductor
Power is additive:
21.6W x 2 conductors = 43.2W lost
OR... P = 12A x (1.8 VD + 1.8 VD) =
P = 12A x 3.6 VD = 43.2W lost

Figure 1–22

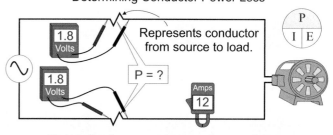

Step 1   What is the question? What is "P?"

Step 2   What do you know?
I = 12A, E = 3.60 VD

Step 3   The formula is P = I x E

Step 4   The answer is P = 12A x 3.6V

Step 5   The answer is 43.2W

▶ **Current Example**

What is the current flow in amperes through a 7.50 kW heat strip rated 230V when connected to a 230V power supply? **Figure 1–23**

    (a) 25A   (b) 33A

    (c) 39A   (d) none of these

    • Answer: (b) 33A

Step 1   What is the question? What is "I?"

Step 2   What do you know?
P = 7,500W, E = 230V

Step 3   The formula is I = P/E

Step 4   The answer is I = 7,500/230V

Step 5   The answer is 32.6A

1.23 Formula Wheel

The formula wheel is a combination of the Ohm's Law and the PIE formula wheels. The formulas in the formula wheel can be used for dc circuits or ac circuits with unity power factor. **Figure 1–24**

Circuit Current Flow

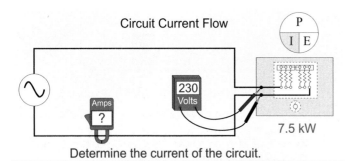

Determine the current of the circuit.

Formula: I = P/E
Known: P = 7.5 kW x 1,000 = 7,500W
Known: E = 230V

$$I = \frac{P}{E} \quad I = \frac{7,500W}{230V} \quad I = 32.6A$$

Copyright 2003 Mike Holt Enterprises, Inc.

Figure 1–23

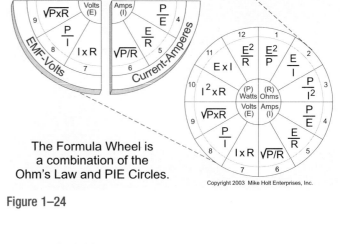

The Formula Wheel

The Formula Wheel is a combination of the Ohm's Law and PIE Circles.

Copyright 2003 Mike Holt Enterprises, Inc.

Figure 1–24

AUTHOR'S COMMENT: Unity power factor is explained in Unit 3. For the purpose of this Unit, we will assume a unity power factor for all ac circuits.

1.24 Using the Formula Wheel

The formula wheel is divided into four sections with three formulas in each section. **Figure 1–25.** When working the formula wheel, the key to getting the correct answer is to follow these steps:

Step 1   Know what the question is asking for: I, E, R, or P.

Step 2   Determine the knowns: I, E, R, or P.

Step 3   Determine which section of the formula wheel applies: I, E, R, or P.

Step 4   Select the formula from that section, based on what you know.

Step 5   Work out the calculation.

▶ **Example**

The total resistance of two 12 AWG conductors, 75 ft long is 0.30 ohms, and the current through the circuit is 16A. What is the power loss of the conductors? **Figure 1–26**

    (a) 20W   (b) 75W

    (c) 150W   (d) 300W

    • Answer: (b) 75W

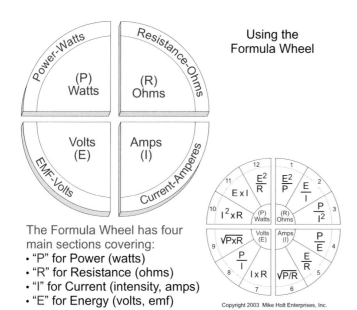

Using the
Formula Wheel

The Formula Wheel has four
main sections covering:
• "P" for Power (watts)
• "R" for Resistance (ohms)
• "I" for Current (intensity, amps)
• "E" for Energy (volts, emf)

Copyright 2003 Mike Holt Enterprises, Inc.

Figure 1–25

Step 1 What is the question? What is the power loss of the conductors? "P."

Step 2 What do you know about the conductors?
I = 16A, R = 0.30 ohms

Step 3 What is the formula? $P = I^2 \times R$

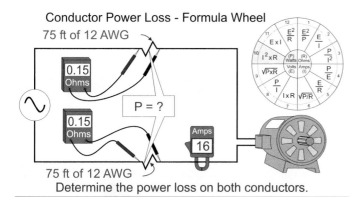

Conductor Power Loss - Formula Wheel
75 ft of 12 AWG
0.15 Ohms
P = ?
0.15 Ohms
Amps 16
75 ft of 12 AWG
Determine the power loss on both conductors.

Formula 10: $P = I^2 \times R$
Known: I = 16A
Known: R of one conductor = *0.15 ohms
*0.15 ohms determined by *NEC* Ch 9, Tbl 9 (per ft method)

$P = I^2 \times R$
$P = (16A \times 16A) \times 0.15$ ohms
$P = 256A \times 0.15$ ohms
$P = 38.4W$ on one conductor
$P = 38.4W \times 2$ conductors
$P = 76.8W$ on both conductors

Or
$P = I^2 \times R$
$P = (16A \times 16A) \times 0.3$ ohms
$P = 256A \times 0.3$ ohms
$P = 76.8W$ on both conductors

Copyright 2003 Mike Holt Enterprises, Inc.

Figure 1–26

Step 4 Calculate the answer:
$P = 16A^2 \times 0.30$ ohms $= 76.8W$

Step 5 The answer is 76.8W

1.25 Power Losses of Conductors

Power in a circuit can be either "useful" or "wasted." Most of the power used by loads such as fluorescent lighting, motors, or stove elements is consumed in useful work. However, the heating of conductors, transformers, and motor windings is wasted work. Wasted work is still energy used; therefore it must be paid for, so we call these power losses.

▶ **Example**

What is the conductor power loss in watts for a 10 AWG conductor that has a voltage drop of 7.2V and carries a current flow of 24A? Figure 1–27

(a) 17W   (b) 173W
(c) 350W   (d) none of these

• Answer: (b) 173W

Step 1 What is the problem asking you to find? What is wasted? "P."

Step 2 What do you know about the conductors?
I = 24A
E = 7.20 VD

Step 3 The formula is $P = I \times E$

Step 4 Calculate the answer: $P = 24A \times 7.20$ VD

Step 5 The answer is 172.8W

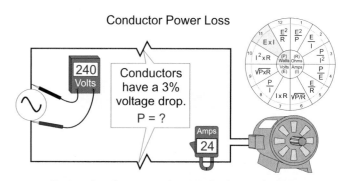

Conductor Power Loss

240 Volts
Conductors have a 3% voltage drop.
P = ?
Amps 24

Determine the power loss on both conductors.

Formula 11: $P = E_{VD} \times I$
Known: I = 24A, E_{VD} = 240V $\times$ 3% = 7.2 VD
$P = E_{VD} \times I$
$P = 7.2$ VD $\times 24A = 172.8W$

Copyright 2003
Mike Holt Enterprises, Inc.

Figure 1–27

1.26 Cost of Power

Since we pay our electric bills on the basis of power consumed in watts, we should understand how to determine the cost of power.

▶ **Example**

What does it cost per year (at 8.60 cents per kWh) for the power loss of two 10 AWG circuit conductors that have a total resistance of 0.30 ohms with a current flow of 24A? Figure 1–28

    (a) $1.30   (b) $13.00
    (c) $130   (d) $1,300

    • Answer: (c) $130

Step 1   Determine the power consumed:
         $P = I^2 \times R$
         $P = 24A^2 \times 0.30$ ohms
         $P = 172.8W$

Step 2   Convert answer in Step 1 to kW:
         $P = 172.8W/1,000W$
         $P = 0.1728$ kW

Step 3   Determine cost per hour:
         (0.086 dollars per kWh) x 0.172.80 kW
         = 0.01486 dollars per hr

Step 4   Determine dollars per day:
         0.01486 dollars per hr x (24 hrs per day)
         = 0.3567 dollars per day

Step 5   Determine dollars per year.
         0.3567 dollars per day x (365 days per year) =
         $130.20 per year

AUTHOR'S COMMENT: That's a lot of money just to heat up two 10 AWG conductors for one circuit. Imagine how much it costs to heat up the conductors for an entire building!

1.27 Power Changes with the Square of the Voltage

The voltage applied to the resistor dramatically affects the power consumed by a resistor. This is because power is determined by the square of the voltage. This means that if the voltage is doubled, the power will increase four times. If the voltage is decreased 50 percent, the power will decrease to 25 percent of its original value. Figure 1–29

▶ **Power Example at 230V**

What is the power consumed by a 9.60 kW heat strip rated 230V connected to a 230V circuit? Figure 1–30

    (a) 7.85 kW   (b) 9.60 kW
    (c) 11.57 kW   (d) none of these

    • Answer: (b) 9.60 kW

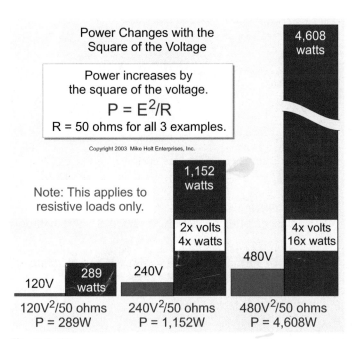

Figure 1–28

Figure 1–29

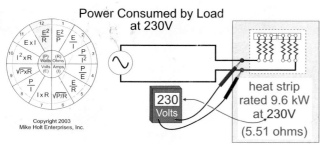

Power Consumed by Load at 230V

heat strip rated 9.6 kW at 230V (5.51 ohms)

230 Volts

Copyright 2003
Mike Holt Enterprises, Inc.

Determine the power consumed by the load at 230V.

Formula 12: $P = E^2/R$

Knowns: E = 230V, R = 5.51 ohms

$P = E^2/R$
$P = (230V \times 230V)/5.51 \text{ ohms} = 9,600W$

5.51 ohm resistor consumes 9.6 kW at 230V.

Figure 1–30

Step 1 What is the problem asking you to find?
Power consumed by the resistance.

Step 2 What do you know about the heat strip?
You were given P = 9.60 kW in the statement of the problem.

▶ **Power Example at 208V**

What is the power consumed by a 9.60 kW heat strip rated 230V connected to a 208V circuit? **Figure 1–31**

(a) 7.85 kW   (b) 9.60 kW
(c) 11.57 kW   (d) none of these

• Answer: (a) 7.85 kW

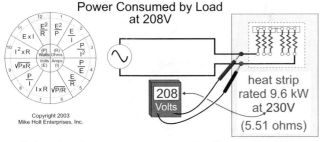

Power Consumed by Load at 208V

heat strip rated 9.6 kW at 230V (5.51 ohms)

208 Volts

Copyright 2003
Mike Holt Enterprises, Inc.

Determine the power consumed by the load at 208V.

Formula 12: $P = E^2/R$

Knowns: E = 208V, R = 5.51 ohms

$P = E^2/R$
$P = (208V \times 208V)/5.51 \text{ ohms} = 7,852W$

5.51 ohm resistor consumes 7.85 kW at 208V.

Figure 1–31

Step 1 What is the problem asking you to find?
Power consumed by the resistance.

Step 2 What do you know about the heat strip?
E = 208V, R = 5.51 ohms

Step 3 The formula to determine power is:
$P = E^2/R$

Step 4 The answer is:
$P = 208V^2/5.51 \text{ ohms}$
$P = 7,851W$ or 7.85 kW

AUTHOR'S COMMENT: It is important to realize that the resistance of the heater unit does not change—it is a property of the material that the current flows through and is not dependent on the voltage applied.

Thus, for a small change in voltage, there is a considerable change in power consumption by this heater.

AUTHOR'S COMMENT: The current flow for this heat strip is $I = P/E$.

$P = 7,851W$
$E = 208V$
$I = 7,851W/208V$
$I = 38A$

▶ **Power Example at 240V**

What is the power consumed by a 9.60 kW heat strip rated 230V connected to a 240V circuit? **Figure 1–32**

(a) 7.85 kW   (b) 9.60 kW
(c) 10.45 kW   (d) 11.57 kW

• Answer: (c) 10.45 kW

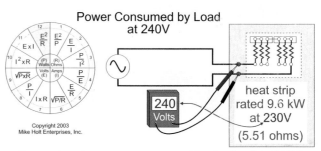

Power Consumed by Load at 240V

heat strip rated 9.6 kW at 230V (5.51 ohms)

240 Volts

Copyright 2003
Mike Holt Enterprises, Inc.

Determine the power consumed by the load at 240V.

Formula 12: $P = E^2/R$

Knowns: E = 230V, R = 5.51 ohms

$P = E^2/R$
$P = (240V \times 240V)/5.51 \text{ ohms} = 10,454W$

5.51 ohm resistor consumes 10.45 kW at 240V.

Figure 1–32

Step 1 What is the problem asking you to find?
Power consumed by the resistance.

Step 2 What do you know about the resistance?
R = 5.51 ohms*

*The resistance of the heat strip is determined by the formula $R = E^2/P$.

E = Nameplate voltage rating of the resistance, 230V
P = Nameplate power rating of the resistance, 9,600W

$R = E^2/P$
$R = 230V^2/9,600W$
R = 5.51 ohms

Step 3 The formula to determine power is:
$P = E^2/R$

Step 4 The answer is:
P = 240V x 240V/5.51 ohms
P = 10,454W
P = 10.45 kW

> **AUTHOR'S COMMENT:** The current flow for this heat strip is I = P/E.
>
> P = 10,454W
> E = 240V
> I = 10,454W/240V
> I = 44A

As you can see, when the voltage changes, the power changes by the square of the change in the voltage, but the current changes in direct proportion.

PART C—BASIC ELECTRIC METERS

Introduction

Electromechanical meters use a coil of wire around a soft iron core. This arrangement is immersed in a magnetic field that is provided by two permanent magnets. As current flows through the coil, the magnetic field created around this coil interacts with the permanent magnets along with the needle that is connected to the coil. This mechanism is referred to as a Galvanometer.

Some meters use a solenoid coil and a movable core to measure voltage, current, and resistance. A solenoid coil is a multiple-turn coil of wire that produces a strong magnetic field inside the coil when current flows through it.

Digital meters are commonly in use today. It is beyond the scope of this textbook to describe how they function. (Besides, they don't have any cool mechanical devices that you can look at and see move around like the old meters so they're not as much fun to talk about). Digital meters are used to measure ac voltage and current, dc voltage and current, and resistance.

1.28 Voltmeter

Voltmeters are used to measure both dc and ac voltage. An analog voltmeter has a resistor connected in series with a coil that allows a very small amount of current, produced by the voltage being measured across the resistance, to flow through the solenoid coil.

The purpose of the resistor in the meter is to limit the current flow through the meter to a very small amount. As current flows through the meter coil, the electromagnetic field of the coil exerts force on a soft iron bar that is in the center of the coil, causing it to move against spring tension and, in turn, causing the pointer attached to the bar to move.

The greater the voltage, the greater the current flow through the meter; the greater the magnetic field produced, the farther the iron bar is drawn into the coil and the greater the movement of the pointer. In the case of the Galvanometer, the current through the coil interacts with the permanent magnetic field and causes the loop of wire to pivot, thereby causing the meter needle to move with it.

1.29 DC Voltmeter

Voltmeters are connected in parallel with the circuit and measure the difference of potential between the two test leads, Figure 1-33. Place the red lead on the spot where you expect to measure positive dc voltage, and place the black lead on the location that you expect to show a negative potential, relative to where the red lead is placed.

If it is unknown which is more positive or negative, momentarily touch the leads to the circuit in the locations to measure the dc voltage; if the meter pegs to the left, simply reverse the leads so that deflection is in the correct direction.

> **AUTHOR'S COMMENT:** "Pegging" the meter means that the pointer on the meter is driven against the stop, (moving opposite of the intended direction). Pegging of the meter only occurs when the leads are incorrectly placed on a dc current with an electromechanical voltmeter.

Basic Voltmeter - Simplified

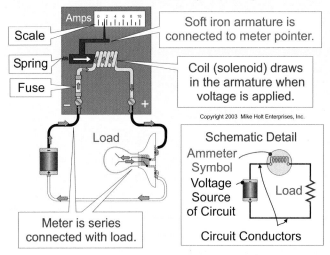

Figure 1–33

1.30 DC Ammeter

DC ammeters are used to measure dc current (current that flows in one direction only). DC ammeters can be either for direct connection to the circuit, or they can be of the clamp-on variety. In meters that are built for direct connection, actual circuit current (or a portion of the actual circuit current) is connected in series with the meter coil.

As the full current of the circuit flows through the meter coil, the magnetic field causes the meter needle to deflect. The greater the current flow through the coil, the greater the magnetic field produced by the coil, and the greater the deflection of the needle.

There are also dc clamp-on ammeters. Whereas ac clamp-on meters operate on the principle that a fluctuating magnetic field will induce an alternating current in a conductive loop that is immersed in the field, dc clamp-on meters use a semiconductor effect called the "Hall Effect." A magnetic field will cause particle displacement within the semiconductor that is detectable and measurable.

Measuring currents larger than 10 milliamperes (mA) with a directly connected meter often requires the use of a resistor, called a shunt, in parallel with the meter movement's coil. The resistance of the shunt is a known value, in relation to the internal resistance of the meter, and so the current that travels through the shunt is a known multiple of the current that travels through the meter.

> **AUTHOR'S COMMENT:** To shunt means to bypass. A dc ammeter is sometimes called a shunt meter.

Basic DC Ammeter - (Simplified)

Figure 1–34

DC ammeters of the direct connection type must be connected in series with the power source and the load, **Figure 1–34**. If a dc ammeter is accidentally connected in parallel with the load, the meter will operate at the source voltage and the current flowing through the meter will be extremely high. This will blow the internal fuse protecting the meter. However, if the meter does not have any internal fuse protection (inexpensive meter), it will likely destroy the meter.

When dc ammeters are connected in series with the circuit, dc current polarity (+ or –) must be observed. If the meter is connected in reverse polarity, the meter coil will move in the opposite direction, pegging the meter in the negative direction and possibly damaging its delicate movement. Connect the red lead to the positive terminal of the voltage source, and the black lead should be connected to the negative terminal of the voltage source.

> **CAUTION:** *To prevent damaging the meter from excessive current, do not connect a dc current meter of the direct connection type to a circuit unless you know the approximate maximum current flowing in the circuit. If you are unsure of the maximum current flow of the circuit, start with the highest possible ampere setting.*

1.31 Clamp-on AC Ammeter

Clamp-on ac ammeters are used to measure ac currents. A clamp-on ammeter has a coil that is clamped around the conductor and detects the rising and falling magnetic field being produced due to the alternating-current flow through the conductor. Clamp-on ac ammeters are used for measuring the circuit current without breaking the circuit.

AUTHOR'S COMMENT: The expanding and collapsing magnetic field around the conductor being tested induces a voltage in the sensing coil, which causes current to flow through the meter's coil.

To operate a clamp-on ammeter, the sensing coil of the meter is placed around the ac circuit conductor that carries current. The expanding and collapsing magnetic field around the conductor being measured induces a force in the soft iron movable core, causing electrons to flow in the meter circuit.

As current flows through the meter coil, the magnetic field draws in the soft iron bar against spring pressure. The greater the circuit current flow through the coil, the greater the electromagnetic field produced within the coil. This will result in greater induced current in the meter circuit. **Figure 1–35**

1.32 Ohmmeters

Ohmmeters are used to measure the resistance or opposition to current flow of a circuit or component. An ohmmeter has a moving coil and a dc power supply (battery) and it is connected in series with the resistor being measured.

As current flows through the coil of the ohmmeter, the magnetic field around the coil draws in the soft iron bar. The greater the current flow through the circuit, the greater the magnetic field produced inside the coil, and the farther the iron bar is drawn into the coil, moving the pointer further. **Figure 1–36**

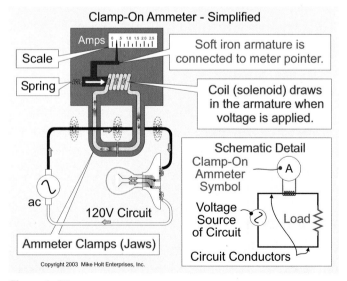

Figure 1–35

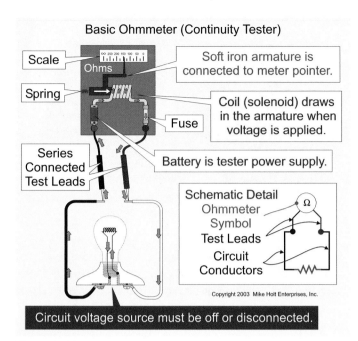

Figure 1–36

1.33 Wheatstone Bridge

The Wheatstone Bridge meter is used for extremely accurate resistance measurements. It consists of two known-value precision resistors, a precision variable resistor, a galvanometer (an ammeter that has its pointer in the center with no current flow through it), and an unknown resistor. When the bridge is "balanced," the galvanometer pointer is aimed straight up, indicating no current flow. To determine the value of the unknown resistor, the variable resistor is adjusted until the bridge is balanced. The unknown resistance is determined by the formula:

$$R = (S \times P)/Q$$

where S is the variable resistor's value, and P and Q are the precision resistors of known value.

1.34 Megohmmeter

The Megohmmeter, or Megger, is used to measure very high-resistance values, such as those found in cable insulation or between motor or transformer windings. Meggers use a relatively high voltage (500 to 1,000V) in order to determine the resistance in megohms (one million ohms).

A battery can power a Megger, or it may be hand-cranked to produce the desired voltage.

Unit 1 Conclusion

The foundation has been laid in this unit for further study of the exciting world of electricity. These basic mathematical concepts and electrical fundamentals will serve you well as you build on this foundation.

You've gained skill in working with Ohm's Law and the power equation, and can use the power wheel to solve a wide variety of electrical problems. You also know how to calculate voltage drop and power loss, and can relate the costs in real dollars. Some examples of the practical applications of electricity were shown in the working principles of electrical meters.

As you work through the practice questions, you'll see how well you have mastered the mathematical concepts and how ready you are to put them to use in electrical formulas. Always remember to check your answer when you are done—then you'll know you have a right answer every time. As useful as these skills are, there is still more to learn. But, your mastery of the basic electrical formulas means you are well prepared. Work through the questions that follow, and go back over the instructional material if you have any difficulty. When you believe you know the material in Unit 1, you are ready to tackle the electrical circuits of Unit 2.

Unit 1 Calculation Practice Questions

(• Indicates that 75% or fewer of those who took this exam answered the question correctly.)

PART A—ELECTRICIAN'S MATH

1.3 Fractions

1. The decimal equivalent for the fraction "1/2" is _____.

   (a) 0.5   (b) 5   (c) 2   (d) 0.2

2. The approximate decimal equivalent for the fraction "4/18" is _____.

   (a) 4.5   (b) 3.5   (c) 2.5   (d) 0.2

1.4 Percentages

3. To change a percent value to a decimal or whole number, move the decimal point two places to the _____.

   (a) right   (b) left   (c) depends   (d) none of these

4. The decimal equivalent for "75 percent" is _____.

   (a) 0.075   (b) 0.75   (c) 7.5   (d) 75

5. The decimal equivalent for "225 percent" is _____.

   (a) 225   (b) 22.5   (c) 2.25   (d) 0.225

6. The decimal equivalent for "300 percent" is _____.

   (a) 0.03   (b) 0.30   (c) 3   (d) 30.0

1.5 Multiplier

7. The method of increasing a number by another number is done by using a _____.

   (a) percentage   (b) decimal   (c) fraction   (d) multiplier

8. An overcurrent protection device (breaker or fuse) must be sized no less than 125 percent of the continuous load. If the load is 16A, the overcurrent protection device will have to be sized at no less than _____.

   (a) 20A   (b) 23A   (c) 17A   (d) 30A

9. The maximum continuous load on an overcurrent protection device is limited to 80 percent of the device rating. If the overcurrent device is rated 100A, the maximum continuous load is _____.

   (a) 72A   (b) 80A   (c) 90A   (d) 125A

1.6 Percent Increase

10. The feeder calculated load for an 8 kW load, increased by 20 percent is _____.

    (a) 8 kW   (b) 9.60 kW   (c) 6.40 kW   (d) 10 kW

1.7 Reciprocals

11. What is the reciprocal of 1.25?

    (a) 0.80   (b) 1.10   (c) 1.25   (d) 1.5

12. A continuous load requires an overcurrent protection device sized no smaller than 125 percent of the load. What is the maximum continuous load permitted on a 100A overcurrent protection device?

    (a) 100A   (b) 125A   (c) 80A   (d) none of these

1.8 Squaring a Number

13. Squaring a number is accomplished by multiplying the number by itself.

    (a) True   (b) False

14. What is the power consumed in watts by a 12 AWG conductor that is 100 ft long and has a resistance (R) of 0.20 ohms, when the current (I) in the circuit is 16A? Formula: Power = I^2 x R.

    (a) 75W   (b) 50W   (c) 100W   (d) 200W

15. What is the area in sq in. of a trade size 2 raceway? Formula: Area = Pi x r^2, Pi = 3.14, r = radius (1/2 of the diameter)

    (a) 1 sq in.   (b) 2 sq in.   (c) 3 sq in.   (d) 4 sq in.

16. The numeric equivalent of 42 is _____.

    (a) 2   (b) 8   (c) 16   (d) 32

17. The numeric equivalent of 12^2 is _____.

    (a) 3.46   (b) 24   (c) 144   (d) 1,728

1.9 Square Root

18. Deriving the square root of a number is almost the same as squaring a number.

    (a) True   (b) False

19. What is the approximate square root of 1,000 ($\sqrt{1,000}$)?

    (a) 3   (b) 32   (c) 100   (d) 500

20. The square root of 3 ($\sqrt{3}$) is _____.

    (a) 1.732   (b) 9   (c) 729   (d) 1.5

1.10 Volume

21. The volume of an enclosure is expressed in _____, and it is calculated by multiplying the length, by the width, by the depth of the enclosure.

    (a) cubic inches   (b) weight   (c) inch-pounds   (d) none of these

22. What is the volume (in cubic inches) of a 4 x 4 x 1.50 in. box?

    (a) 20 cu in.   (b) 24 cu in.   (c) 30 cu in.   (d) 33 cu in.

1.11 Kilo

23. What is the kW of a 75W load?

    (a) 75 kW   (b) 7.50 kW   (c) 0.75 kW   (d) 0.075 kW

1.12 Rounding Off

24. The approximate sum of 2, 7, 8, and 9 is equal to _____.

    (a) 20   (b) 25   (c) 30   (d) 35

1.13 Parentheses

25. What is the maximum distance that two 14 AWG conductors can be run if they carry 16A and the maximum allowable voltage drop is 10V?

    D = (Cmil x VD)/(2 x K x I)
    D = (4,110 cmil x 10V)/(2 x 12.90 ohms x 16A)

    (a) 50 ft   (b) 75 ft   (c) 100 ft   (d) 150 ft

26. What is the current in amperes of an 18 kW, 208V, three-phase load?

    Current: I = VA/(E x √3)
    Current: I = 18,000W/(208V x 1.732)

    (a) 25A   (b) 50A   (c) 100A   (d) 150A

1.14 Testing Your Answer for Reasonableness

27. The output power of a transformer is 100W and the transformer efficiency is 90 percent. What is the transformer input if the output is lower than the input? Formula: Input = Output/Efficiency

    (a) 90W   (b) 110W   (c) 100W   (d) 125W

PART B—BASIC ELECTRICAL FORMULAS

1.15 Electrical Circuit

28. An electrical circuit consists of the _____.

    (a) power source   (b) conductors   (c) load   (d) all of these

29. According to the electron flow theory, electrons leave the _____ terminal of the source, flow through the conductors and load(s), and return to the _____ terminal of the source.

    (a) positive, negative   (b) negative, positive   (c) negative, negative   (d) positive, positive

1.16 Power Source

30. The polarity and the output voltage from a dc power source changes direction. One terminal will be negative and the other will be positive.

    (a) True   (b) False

31. Direct current is used for electroplating, street trolley and railway systems, or where a smooth and wide range of speed control is required for a motor-driven application.

    (a) True   (b) False

32. The polarity and the output voltage from an ac power source never change direction.

   (a) True   (b) False

33. The major advantage of ac over dc is the ease of voltage regulation by the use of a transformer.

   (a) True   (b) False

1.17 Conductance

34. Conductance is the property that permits current to flow.

   (a) True   (b) False

35. The best conductors, in order of their conductivity, are: gold, silver, copper, and aluminum.

   (a) True   (b) False

36. Conductance or conductivity is the property of metal that permits current to flow. The best conductors in order of their conductivity are: _____.
   (a) gold, silver, copper, aluminum   (b) gold, copper, silver, aluminum
   (c) silver, gold, copper, aluminum   (d) silver, copper, gold, aluminum

1.18 Circuit Resistance

37. The circuit resistance includes the resistance of the _____.

   (a) power source   (b) conductors   (c) load   (d) all of these

38. Often the resistance of the power source and conductor are ignored in circuit calculations.

   (a) True   (b) False

1.19 Ohm's Law

39. The Ohm's Law formula, I = E/R, states that current is _____ proportional to the voltage, and _____ proportional to the resistance.

   (a) indirectly, inversely   (b) inversely, directly   (c) inversely, indirectly   (d) directly, inversely

40. Ohm's Law demonstrates the relationship between circuit _____.

   (a) intensity   (b) EMF   (c) resistance   (d) all of these

1.20 Ohm's Law and Alternating Current

41. In a dc circuit, the only opposition to current flow is the physical resistance of the material. This opposition is called reactance and it is measured in ohms.

   (a) True   (b) False

42. In an ac circuit, the factors that oppose current flow are _____.

   (a) resistance   (b) inductive reactance   (c) capacitive reactance   (d) all of these

1.21 Ohm's Law Formula Circle

43.   What is the voltage drop of two 12 AWG conductors (0.40 ohms) supplying a 16A load, located 100 ft from the power supply? Formula: EVD = I x R

(a) 6.4 ohms   (b) 12.8 ohms   (c) 1.6 ohms   (d) 3.2 ohms

44.   What is the resistance of the circuit conductors when the conductor voltage drop is 7.2V and the current flow is 50A? Formula: R = E/I

(a) 0.14 ohms   (b) 0.30 ohms   (c) 3 ohms   (d) 14 ohms

1.22 PIE Formula Circle

45.   What is the power loss in watts of a conductor that carries 24A and has a voltage drop of 7.2V? Formula: P = I x E

(a) 175W   (b) 350W   (c) 700W   (d) 2,400W

46.   What is the approximate power consumed by a 10 kW heat strip rated 230V, when connected to a 208V circuit? Formula: P = E^2/R

(a) 8.20 kW   (b) 9.3 kW   (c) 10.90 kW   (d) 11.20 kW

1.23 Formula Wheel

47.   The formulas in the power wheel apply to _____.

(a) dc   (b) ac with unity power factor
(c) dc or ac circuits   (d) a and b

1.24 Using the Formula Wheel

48.   When working any formula, the key to getting the correct answer is following these four steps:

Step 1:   Know what the question is asking you to find.
Step 2:   Determine the knowns of the circuit.
Step 3:   Select the formula.
Step 4:   Work out the formula calculation.

(a) True   (b) False

1.25 Power Losses of Conductors

49.   Power in a circuit can be either "useful" or "wasted." Wasted work is still energy used; therefore it must be paid for, so we call this _____.

(a) resistance   (b) inductive reactance   (c) capacitive reactance   (d) power loss

50.   The total circuit resistance of two 12 AWG conductors (each 100 ft long) is 0.40 ohms. If the current of the circuit is 16A, what is the power loss of both conductors? Formula: P = I^2 x R

(a) 75W   (b) 100W   (c) 300W   (d) 600W

51.   What is the conductor power loss for a 120V circuit that has a 3 percent voltage drop and carries a current flow of 12A? Formula: P = I x E

(a) 43W   (b) 86W   (c) 172W   (d) 1,440W

1.26 Cost of Power

52.   What does it cost per year (at 8 cents per kWh) for the power loss of a 12 AWG conductor (100 ft long) that has a total resistance of 0.40 ohms and a current flow of 16A? Formula: Cost per Year = Power for the Year in kWh x $0.08

      (a) $33   (b) $54   (c) $72   (d) $89

1.27 Power Changes with the Square of the Voltage

53.   The voltage applied to the resistor dramatically affects the power consumed by a resistor because power is affected in direct proportion to the voltage.

      (a) True   (b) False

54.   What is the power consumed by a 10 kW heat strip that's rated 230V, if it's connected to a 115V circuit? Formula: $P = E^2/R$

      (a) 2.50 kW   (b) 5 kW   (c) 7.50 kW   (d) 15 kW

PART C—BASIC ELECTRIC METERS

1.29 DC Voltmeter

55.   Voltmeters are connected in _____ with the circuit or component and measure the difference of potential between the two test leads.

      (a) series   (b) parallel   (c) series-parallel   (d) none of these

1.30 DC Ammeter

56.   DC ammeters of the direct connection type must be connected in _____ with the power source and the load. If connected in reverse polarity, the coil will move in the opposite direction.

      (a) series   (b) parallel   (c) series-parallel   (d) none of these

1.31 Clamp-on AC Ammeter

57.   A clamp-on ac ammeter has a coil that is clamped around the conductor and detects the rising and falling _____ field being produced due to the ac flow through the conductor.

      (a) static   (b) current   (c) power   (d) magnetic

1.32 Ohmmeters

58.   Ohmmeters measure the _____ or opposition to current flow of a circuit or component.

      (a) voltage   (b) current   (c) power   (d) resistance

1.33 Wheatstone Bridge

59.   The Wheatstone Bridge meter is used for extremely accurate _____ measurements.

      (a) voltage   (b) current   (c) power   (d) resistance

1.34 Megohmmeter

60.   The megohmmeter (megger) is used to measure very high-_____ values, such as those found in cable insulation, or motor and transformer windings.

      (a) voltage   (b) current   (c) power   (d) resistance

Unit 1 Calculation Challenge Questions

PART A—ELECTRICIAN'S MATH

1.11 Kilo

1.   •One kVA is equal to _____.

     (a) 100 VA   (b) 1,000V   (c) 1,000W   (d) 1,000 VA

PART B—BASIC ELECTRICAL FORMULAS

1.17 Conductance

2.   •_____ is not an insulator.

     (a) Bakelite   (b) Oil   (c) Air   (d) Salt water

1.19 Ohm's Law

3.   •If the contact resistance of a connection increases and the current of the circuit (load) remains the same, the voltage dropped across the connection will _____.

     (a) increase   (b) decrease   (c) remain the same (d) cannot be determined

4.   •To double the current of a circuit when the voltage remains constant, the R (resistance) must be _____.

     (a) doubled   (b) reduced by half (c) increased   (d) none of these

5.   •An ohmmeter is being used to test a relay coil. The equipment instructions indicate that the resistance of the coil should be between 30 and 33 ohms. The ohmmeter indicates that the actual resistance is less than 22 ohms. This reading would most likely indicate _____.

     (a) the coil is okay (b) an open coil   (c) a shorted coil   (d) a meter problem

1.23 Formula Wheel

6.   •To calculate the energy consumed in watts by a resistive appliance, you need to know _____ of the circuit.

     (a) the voltage and current   (b) the current and resistance
     (c) the voltage and resistance (d) any of these pairs of variables

7.   •The power consumed of a resistor can be expressed by the formula I^2 x R. If 120V is applied to a 10 ohm resistor, the power consumed will be _____.

     (a) 510W   (b) 1050W   (c) 1230W   (d) 1440W

8.   •Power loss in a circuit because of heat can be determined by the formula _____.

     (a) P = R x I   (b) P = I x R   (c) P = I^2 x R   (d) none of these

9. •The energy consumed by a 5 ohm resistor will be _____ than the energy consumed by a 10 ohm resistor, assuming the current in both cases remains the same.

(a) more   (b) less

10. When a lamp that is rated 500W at 115V is connected to a 120V power supply, the current of the circuit will be _____. Tip: The power does not remain the same when voltage is changed and you need to determine the resistance of the load first.

(a) 3.8A   (b) 4.5A   (c) 2.7A   (d) 5.5A

1.27 Power Changes with the Square of the Voltage

11. A 120V-rated toaster will produce _____ heat when supplied by 115V.

(a) more   (b) less   (c) the same   (d) none of these

12. •When a 100W, 115V lamp operates at 126.5V (10 percent above its nameplate rating), the lamp will consume approximately _____.

(a) 50W   (b) 75W   (c) 121W   (d) 150W

13. •A 1,500W resistive heater is rated 230V and it is connected to a 208V supply. The power consumed for this load at 208V will be approximately _____.

(a) 1,625W   (b) 1,750W   (c) 1,850W   (d) 1,225W

14. •The total resistance of a circuit is 12 ohms. The load has a resistance of 10 ohms and the wire has a resistance of 0.20 ohms. If the current of the circuit is 12A, then the power consumed by the 0.20 ohm circuit conductors is approximately _____.

(a) 8W   (b) 29W   (c) 39W   (d) 45W

PART C—BASIC ELECTRIC METERS

15. •The best instrument for detecting an electric current is a(n) _____.

(a) ohmmeter   (b) voltmeter   (c) ammeter   (d) wattmeter

16. When measuring the resistance of a circuit with an ohmmeter, polarity (+ or -) must be observed.

(a) True   (b) False

17. •When the test leads of an ohmmeter are shorted together, the meter will read _____ on the scale.

(a) zero or near zero ohms   (b) 1,000   (c) infinity   (d) any of these

18. •A short circuit is indicated by a reading of _____ when tested with an ohmmeter.

(a) zero or near zero ohms   (b) megohms   (c) infinity   (d) R

19. Voltmeters can be used to measure _____.

(a) grounded circuits only   (b) voltage potential   (c) ac voltages only   (d) dc voltages only

20. Voltmeters must be connected in _____ with the circuit component being tested.

(a) series   (b) parallel   (c) series-parallel   (d) multiwire

21. To measure the voltage across a load, you need to connect a(n) _____.

    (a) voltmeter across the load
    (b) ammeter across the load
    (c) voltmeter in series with the load
    (d) ammeter in series with the load

22. A voltmeter is connected in _____ to the load when measuring voltage at the load.

    (a) series   (b) parallel   (c) series-parallel   (d) none of these

23. •In the course of normal operation, the least effective instrument for determining that a generator may overheat because it is over-loaded is a(n) _____.

    (a) ammeter   (b) voltmeter   (c) wattmeter   (d) none of these

24. •An analog direct-current voltmeter (not a digital meter) can be used to measure _____.

    (a) power   (b) frequency   (c) polarity   (d) power factor

25. •Polarity must be observed when connecting an analog voltmeter to _____ current circuit.

    (a) an alternating   (b) a direct   (c) any   (d) polarity doesn't matter

(• Indicates that 75% or fewer of those who took this exam answered the question correctly.)

Article 90 Introduction to the *National Electrical Code*

Article 90 opens by saying the *NEC* isn't intended as a design specification or instruction manual. The *National Electrical Code* has one purpose only. That is "the practical safeguarding of persons and property from hazards arising from the use of electricity."

Article 90 then describes the scope and arrangement of the *Code*.

1.   The *NEC* is _____.

   (a) intended to be a design manual
   (b) meant to be used as an instruction guide for untrained persons
   (c) for the practical safeguarding of persons and property
   (d) published by the Bureau of Standards

2.   •The *Code* contains provisions considered necessary for safety, which will not necessarily result in ___.

   (a) efficient use   (b) convenience
   (c) good service or future expansion of electrical use   (d) all of these

3.   The following systems must be installed in accordance with the *NEC*:

   (a) signaling   (b) communications   (c) power and lighting   (d) all of these

4.   The *Code* does not cover installations in ships, watercraft, railway rolling stock, aircraft, or automotive vehicles.

   (a) True   (b) False

5.   Installations of communications equipment that are under the exclusive control of communications utilities, and located outdoors or in building spaces used exclusively for such installations _____ covered by the *Code*.

   (a) are   (b) are sometimes   (c) are not   (d) might be

6.   Service laterals installed by an electrical contractor must be installed in accordance with the *NEC*.

   (a) True   (b) False

7.   Utilities may be subject to compliance with codes and standards covering their regulated activities as adopted under governmental law or regulation.

   (a) True   (b) False

8.   Chapters 1 through 4 of the *NEC* apply _____.

   (a) generally to all electrical installations   (b) to special occupancies and conditions
   (c) to special equipment and material   (d) all of these

9.   The requirements in "Annexes" must be complied with.

   (a) True   (b) False

10. The authority having jurisdiction is not required to enforce any requirements of Chapter 7 (Signaling Circuits) or Chapter 8 (Communications Circuits), because this is not within the scope of enforcement.

    (a) True   (b) False

11. A *Code* rule may be waived or alternative methods of installation approved that may be contrary to the *NEC*, if the authority having jurisdiction gives verbal or written consent.

    (a) True   (b) False

12. Explanatory material, such as references to other standards, references to related sections of the *NEC*, or information related to a *Code* rule, is included in the form of Fine Print Notes (FPNs).

    (a) True   (b) False

13. Compliance with either the metric or the inch-pound unit of measurement system is permitted.

    (a) True   (b) False

CHAPTER 1 GENERAL

Article 100 Definitions

Article 100—Definitions. Part I of Article 100 contains the definitions of terms used throughout the *Code* for systems that operate at 600V or less. The definitions of terms in Part II apply to systems that operate at over 600V.

14. Capable of being reached quickly for operation, renewal, or inspections without resorting to portable ladders and such is known as _____.

    (a) accessible (equipment)   (b) accessible (wiring methods)
    (c) accessible, readily   (d) all of these

15. A junction box located above a suspended ceiling having removable panels is considered to be _____.

    (a) concealed   (b) accessible   (c) readily accessible   (d) recessed

16. •A generic term for a group of nonflammable synthetic chlorinated hydrocarbons used as electrical insulating media is _____.

    (a) oil   (b) girasol   (c) askarel   (d) phenol

17. Where no statutory requirement exists, the authority having jurisdiction could be a property owner or his/her agent, such as an architect or engineer.

    (a) True   (b) False

18. The connection between the grounded conductor and the equipment grounding conductor at the service is accomplished by installing a(n) _____ jumper.

    (a) main bonding   (b) bonding   (c) equipment bonding   (d) circuit bonding

19. The conductors between the final overcurrent protection device and the outlet(s) are known as the _____ conductors.

    (a) feeder   (b) branch-circuit   (c) home run   (d) none of these

20. A branch circuit that supplies only one utilization equipment is a(n) _____ branch circuit.

    (a) individual   (b) general-purpose   (c) isolated   (d) special-purpose

21. The *Code* defines a(n) _____ as a structure that stands alone or that is cut off from adjoining structures by firewalls, with all openings therein protected by approved fire doors.

    (a) unit   (b) apartment   (c) building   (d) utility

22. _____ is a qualifying term indicating that there is a purposely-introduced delay in the tripping action of the circuit breaker, which decreases as the magnitude of the current increases.

    (a) Adverse-time   (b) Inverse-time   (c) Time delay   (d) Timed unit

23. NM cable is considered _____ if rendered inaccessible by the structure or finish of the building.

    (a) inaccessible   (b) concealed   (c) hidden   (d) enclosed

24. A separate portion of a conduit or tubing system that provides access through a removable cover(s) to the interior of the system at a junction of two or more sections of the system, or at a terminal point of the system, is defined as a(n) _____.

    (a) junction box   (b) accessible raceway   (c) conduit body   (d) pressure connector

25. A load is considered to be continuous if the maximum current is expected to continue for _____ or more.

    (a) 1/2 hour   (b) 1 hour   (c) 2 hours   (d) 3 hours

26. •The _____ of any system is the ratio of the maximum demand of a system, or part of a system, to the total connected load of a system under consideration.

    (a) load   (b) demand factor   (c) minimum load   (d) computed factor

27. Which of the following does the *Code* recognize as a device?

    (a) Switch   (b) Light bulb   (c) Transformer   (d) Motor

28. Constructed so that dust will not enter the enclosing case under specified test conditions is known as _____.

    (a) dusttight   (b) dustproof   (c) dust rated   (d) all of these

29. Varying duty is defined as _____.

    (a) intermittent operation in which the load conditions are regularly recurrent
    (b) operation at a substantially constant load for an indefinite length of time
    (c) operation for alternate intervals of load and rest, or load, no load, and rest
    (d) operation at loads and for intervals of time, both of which may be subject to wide variations

30. Surrounded by a case, housing, fence, or wall(s) that prevents persons from accidentally contacting energized parts is called _____.

    (a) guarded   (b) covered   (c) protection   (d) enclosed

31. When the term exposed, as it relates to live parts, is used by the *Code*, it refers to _____.

    (a) capable of being inadvertently touched or approached nearer than a safe distance by a person
    (b) parts that are not suitably guarded, isolated, or insulated
    (c) wiring on, or attached to, the surface or behind panels designed to allow access
    (d) a and b

32. The *Code* defines a _____ as: "all circuit conductors between the service equipment, the source of a separately derived system, or other power-supply source and the final branch-circuit overcurrent device."

    (a) feeder   (b) branch circuit   (c) service   (d) all of these

33. Connected to earth or to some conducting body that serves in place of the earth is called _____.

    (a) grounding   (b) bonded   (c) grounded   (d) all of these

34. _____ is defined as intentionally connected to earth through a ground connection or connections of sufficiently low impedance and having sufficient current-carrying capacity to prevent the buildup of voltages that may result in undue hazards to connected equipment or to persons.

    (a) Effectively grounded   (b) A proper wiring system   (c) A lighting rod   (d) A grounded conductor

35. A "Class A" GFCI protection device is designed to de-energize the circuit when the ground-fault current is approximately _____.

    (a) 4 mA   (b) 5 mA   (c) 6 mA   (d) any of these

36. A system intended to provide protection of equipment from damaging line-to-ground fault currents by operating to cause a disconnecting means to open all ungrounded conductors of the faulted circuit at levels less than the supply circuit overcurrent device is defined as _____.

    (a) ground-fault protection of equipment   (b) guarded
    (c) personal protection   (d) automatic protection

37. The grounding electrode conductor is the conductor used to connect the grounding electrode to the equipment grounding conductor and the grounded conductor at _____.

    (a) the service   (b) each building or structure supplied by feeder(s)
    (c) the source of a separately derived system   (d) all of these

38. A _____ is an accommodation that combines living, sleeping, sanitary, and storage facilities.

    (a) guest room   (b) guest suite   (c) dwelling unit   (d) single family dwelling

39. A handhole enclosure is an enclosure identified for use in underground systems, provided with an open or closed bottom, and sized to allow personnel to _____, for the purpose of installing, operating, or maintaining equipment or wiring or both.

    (a) enter and exit freely   (b) reach into but not enter   (c) have full working space   (d) examine visually

40. Recognized as suitable for the specific purpose, function, use, environment, and application is the definition of _____.

    (a) labeled   (b) identified (as applied to equipment)
    (c) listed   (d) approved

41. _____ means that an object is not readily accessible to persons unless special means for access are used.

    (a) Isolated   (b) Secluded   (c) Protected   (d) Locked

42. An outlet intended for the direct connection of a lampholder, a luminaire, or a pendant cord terminating in a lampholder is a(n) _____.

    (a) outlet   (b) receptacle outlet   (c) lighting outlet   (d) general-purpose outlet

43. A _____ location may be temporarily subject to dampness and wetness.

    (a) dry   (b) damp   (c) moist   (d) wet

44. The term "luminaire" includes "fixture(s)" and "lighting fixture(s)."

    (a) True   (b) False

45. A(n) _____ is a point on the wiring system at which current is taken to supply utilization equipment.

    (a) box   (b) receptacle   (c) outlet   (d) device

46. Outline lighting may not include light sources such as light emitting diodes (LEDs).

    (a) True   (b) False

47. An overload is the same thing as a short circuit or ground fault.

    (a) True   (b) False

48. The *Code* defines a(n) _____ as one familiar with the construction and operation of the electrical equipment and installations, and who has received safety training on the hazards involved.

    (a) inspector   (b) master electrician   (c) journeyman electrician   (d) qualified person

49. Something constructed, protected, or treated so as to prevent rain from interfering with the successful operation of the apparatus under specified test conditions is defined as _____.

    (a) raintight   (b) waterproof   (c) weathertight   (d) rainproof

50. A contact device installed at an outlet for the connection of an attachment plug is known as a(n) _____.

    (a) attachment point   (b) tap   (c) receptacle   (d) wall plug

51. When one electrical circuit controls another circuit through a relay, the first circuit is called a _____.

    (a) control circuit   (b) remote-control circuit   (c) signal circuit   (d) controller

52. A(n) _____ system is a premises wiring system whose power is derived from a source of electric energy or equipment other than a service, and that has no direct electrical connection, including a solidly connected grounded circuit conductor, to supply conductors originating in another system.

    (a) separately derived   (b) classified   (c) direct   (d) emergency

53. Overhead-service conductors from the last pole or other aerial support to and including the splices, if any, are called _____ conductors.

    (a) service-entrance   (b) service-drop   (c) service   (d) overhead service

54. The _____ is the necessary equipment, usually consisting of a circuit breaker(s) or switch(es) and fuse(s) and their accessories, connected to the load end of service conductors to a building or other structure, or an otherwise designated area, and intended to constitute the main control and cutoff of the supply.

    (a) service equipment   (b) service
    (c) service disconnect   (d) service overcurrent protection device

55. The _____ is the point of connection between the facilities of the serving utility and the premises wiring.

    (a) service entrance   (b) service point
    (c) overcurrent protection   (d) beginning of the wiring system

56. The combination of all components and subsystems that convert solar energy into electrical energy is called a _____ system.

    (a) solar   (b) solar voltaic   (c) separately derived source   (d) solar photovoltaic

57. A _____ switch is a manually operated device used in conjunction with a transfer switch to provide a means of directly connecting load conductors to a power source, and of disconnecting the transfer switch.

(a) transfer   (b) motor-circuit   (c) general-use snap   (d) bypass isolation

58. An isolating switch is one that is _____.

(a) not readily accessible to persons unless special means for access is used
(b) capable of interrupting the maximum operating overload current of a motor
(c) intended for use in general distribution and branch circuits
(d) intended for isolating an electrical circuit from the source of power

59. A thermal protector may consist of one or more heat-sensing elements integral with the motor or motor-compressor and an external control device.

(a) True   (b) False

60. The voltage of a circuit is defined by the *Code* as the _____ root-mean-square (effective) difference of potential between any two conductors of the circuit.

(a) lowest   (b) greatest   (c) average   (d) nominal

61. An enclosure or device constructed so that moisture will not enter the enclosure or device under specific test conditions is called _____.

(a) watertight   (b) moistureproof   (c) waterproof   (d) rainproof

Article 110 Requirements for Electrical Installations

This article contains the general requirements for electrical installations.

62. In determining equipment to be installed, considerations such as the following should be evaluated:

(a) Mechanical strength   (b) Cost   (c) Arcing effects   (d) a and c

63. To be *Code*-compliant, listed or labeled equipment must be installed and used in accordance with any instructions included in the _____.

(a) catalog   (b) product   (c) listing or labeling   (d) all of these

64. Conductor sizes are expressed in American Wire Gage (AWG) or in _____.

(a) inches   (b) circular mils   (c) square inches   (d) AWG

65. A wiring method included in the *Code* is recognized as being a(n) _____ wiring method.

(a) expensive   (b) efficient   (c) suitable   (d) cost-effective

66. Circuit-protective devices are used to clear a fault without the occurrence of extensive damage to the electrical components of the circuit. Faults can occur between two or more of the _____ or between any circuit conductor and the grounding conductor or enclosing metal raceway.

(a) bonding jumpers   (b) grounding jumpers   (c) wiring harnesses   (d) circuit conductors

67. Unless identified for use in the operating environment, no conductors or equipment can be _____ having a deteriorating effect on the conductors or equipment.

    (a) located in damp or wet locations
    (b) exposed to fumes, vapors, or gases
    (c) exposed to liquids or excessive temperatures
    (d) all of these

68. Some cleaning and lubricating compounds contain chemicals that cause severe deteriorating reactions with plastics.

    (a) True
    (b) False

69. Accepted industry workmanship practices are described in ANSI/NECA 1-2000, Standard Practices for Good Workmanship in Electrical Contracting, and other ANSI approved installation standards.

    (a) True
    (b) False

70. Conductors must be _____ to provide ready and safe access in underground and subsurface enclosures into which persons enter for installation and maintenance.

    (a) bundled
    (b) tied together
    (c) color-coded
    (d) racked

71. For mounting electrical equipment on a masonry wall, it is acceptable to drill a hole in the masonry and drive a wooden plug into the hole, then use sheet rock screws drilled into the wooden plug

    (a) True
    (b) False

72. Many terminations and equipment are marked with _____.

    (a) an etching tool
    (b) a removable label
    (c) a tightening torque
    (d) the manufacturer's initials

73. Connection by means of wire-binding screws, studs, or nuts having upturned lugs or the equivalent are permitted for _____ or smaller conductors.

    (a) 10 AWG
    (b) 8 AWG
    (c) 6 AWG
    (d) none of these

74. The temperature rating associated with the ampacity of a _____ must be so selected and coordinated so as not to exceed the lowest temperature rating of any connected termination, conductor, or device.

    (a) terminal
    (b) conductor
    (c) device
    (d) all of these

75. For circuits rated 100A or less, when the equipment terminals are listed for use with 75°C conductors, the _____ column of Table 310.16 must be used to determine the ampacity of THHN conductors installed.

    (a) 60°C
    (b) 75°C
    (c) 30°C
    (d) 90°C

76. Conductors must have their ampacity determined using the _____ column of Table 310.16 for circuits rated over 100A, or marked for conductors larger than 1 AWG, unless the equipment terminals are listed for use with higher temperature rated conductors.

    (a) 60°C
    (b) 75°C
    (c) 30°C
    (d) 90°C

77. On a _____ secondary where the midpoint of one phase winding is grounded, the phase conductor having the higher voltage-to-ground must be identified by an outer finish that is orange in color, or by tagging or other effective means. Such identification must be placed at each point where a connection is made if the grounded conductor is also present.

    (a) single-phase, 3-wire
    (b) three-phase, 4-wire delta-connected
    (c) three-phase, 4-wire wye-connected
    (d) three-phase, 3-wire delta-connected

78. Identification of the high leg of a three-phase, 4-wire delta connected system is required _____.

    (a) at the service disconnect only
    (b) at each point on the system where a connection is made if the equipment grounding conductor is also present
    (c) at each point on the system where a connection is made if the grounding electrode conductor is also present
    (d) at each point on the system where a connection is made if the grounded conductor is also present

79. Switchboards, panelboards, industrial control panels, meter socket enclosures, and motor control centers in commercial and industrial occupancies that are likely to require _____ while energized must be field marked to warn qualified persons of the danger associated with an arc flash from line-to-line or ground faults.

    (a) examination   (b) adjustment   (c) servicing or maintenance   (d) a, b, or c

80. Each disconnecting means must be legibly marked to indicate its purpose unless located and arranged so _____.

    (a) that they can be locked out and tagged   (b) they are not readily accessible
    (c) the purpose is evident   (d) that they operate at less than 300 volts-to-ground

81. Sufficient access and _____ must be provided and maintained about all electrical equipment to permit ready and safe operation and maintenance of such equipment.

    (a) ventilation   (b) cleanliness   (c) circulation   (d) working space

82. Working-space distances for enclosed live parts must be measured from the _____ of equipment or apparatus, if such are enclosed.

    (a) enclosure   (b) opening   (c) a or b   (d) none of these

83. The minimum working clearance on a circuit that is 120V to ground, with exposed live parts on one side and no live or grounded parts on the other side of the working space, is _____.

    (a) 1 ft   (b) 3 ft   (c) 4 ft   (d) 6 ft

84. Concrete, brick, or tile walls are considered as _____, as it applies to working-space requirements.

    (a) inconsequential   (b) in the way   (c) grounded   (d) none of these

85. The working space in front of the electric equipment must not be less than _____ wide, or the width of the equipment, whichever is greater.

    (a) 15 in.   (b) 30 in.   (c) 40 in.   (d) 60 in.

86. When normally-enclosed live parts are exposed for inspection or servicing, the working space, if in a passageway or general open space, must be suitably _____.

    (a) accessible   (b) guarded   (c) open   (d) enclosed

87. For equipment rated 1,200A or more that contains overcurrent devices, switching devices, or control devices, at least one entrance, measuring not less than 24 in. wide and 6 1/2 ft high, must be provided at each end of the working space. Where the entrance to the working space has a personnel door, the door _____.

    (a) must open either in or out with simple pressure and must not have any lock
    (b) must open in the direction of egress and be equipped with panic hardware or other devices so the door can open under simple pressure
    (c) must be removed
    (d) must be equipped with an electronic opener

88. Illumination must be provided for all working spaces about service equipment, switchboards, panelboards, and motor control centers _____.

    (a) over 600V   (b) located indoors
    (c) rated 1,200 amperes or more   (d) using automatic means of control

89. The minimum headroom for working spaces about service equipment, switchboards, panelboards, or motor control centers must be 6 1/2 ft, except for service equipment or panelboards in existing dwelling units that do not exceed 200A.

    (a) True   (b) False

90. •Heating, cooling, or ventilating equipment (including ducts) that service the electrical room or space cannot be installed in the dedicated space above a panelboard or switchboard.

    (a) True   (b) False

91. Unless specified otherwise, live parts of electrical equipment operating at _____ or more must be guarded.

    (a) 12V   (b) 15V   (c) 50V   (d) 24V

92. Live parts of electrical equipment operating at _____ or more must be guarded against accidental contact by approved enclosures or by suitable permanent, substantial partitions, or screens arranged so that only qualified persons have access to the space within reach of the live parts.

    (a) 20V   (b) 30V   (c) 50V   (d) 100V

93. Entrances to rooms and other guarded locations containing exposed live parts must be marked with conspicuous _____ forbidding unqualified persons to enter.

    (a) warning signs   (b) alarms   (c) a and b   (d) neither a nor b

94. Openings in ventilated dry-type _____, or similar openings in other equipment over 600V, must be designed so that foreign objects inserted through these openings will be deflected from energized parts.

    (a) lampholders   (b) motors   (c) fuseholders   (d) transformers

95. •For switchboards and control panels, operating at over 600V, nominal, and exceeding 6 ft in width, there must be one entrance at each end of the equipment. _____ entrance(s) is (are) required for the working space if the depth of the working space is twice that required by 110.34(A).

    (a) One   (b) Two   (c) Three   (d) Four

96. _____ must be provided to give safe access to the working space around equipment over 600V installed on platforms, balconies, mezzanine floors, or in attic or roof rooms or spaces.

    (a) Ladders   (b) Platforms or ladders
    (c) Permanent ladders or stairways (d) Openings

97. When switches, cutouts, or other equipment operating at 600V, nominal, or less are installed in a vault, room, or enclosure where there are exposed live parts or exposed wiring operating at over 600V, nominal, the high-voltage equipment must be effectively separated from the space occupied by _____ by a suitable partition, fence, or screen.

    (a) the access area   (b) the low-voltage equipment
    (c) unauthorized persons   (d) motor-control equipment

98.   Switches or other equipment operating at 600V, nominal, or less and serving only equipment within a high-voltage vault, room, or enclosure is permitted to be installed in the _____ enclosure, room, or vault without a partition, fence, or screen if accessible to qualified persons only.

(a) restricted   (b) medium-voltage   (c) sealed   (d) high-voltage

99.   Illumination must be provided for all working spaces about electrical equipment operating at over 600V. The lighting outlets must be arranged so that persons changing lamps or making repairs on the lighting system are not endangered by _____ or other equipment.

(a) live parts   (b) rotating parts   (c) bright lamps   (d) panelboards

CHAPTER 2 WIRING AND PROTECTION

Article 200 Use and Identification of Grounded Conductors

This article contains the requirements for the use and identification of the grounded conductor and its terminals.

100.   Article 200 contains the requirements for _____.

(a) identification of terminals   (b) grounded conductors in premises wiring systems
(c) identification of grounded conductors   (d) all of these

(• Indicates that 75% or fewer of those who took this exam answered the question correctly.)

1. Compliance with the provisions of the *Code* will result in _____.

    (a) good electrical service
    (b) an efficient electrical system
    (c) an electrical system essentially free from hazard
    (d) all of these

2. •A conductor encased within material of composition or thickness that is not recognized by this *Code* as electrical insulation is considered _____.

    (a) noninsulating   (b) bare   (c) covered   (d) protected

3. •Equipment approved for use in dry locations only must be protected against permanent damage from the weather during _____.

    (a) design   (b) building construction   (c) inspection   (d) none of these

4. •In a grounded system, the conductor that connects the grounded conductor of a service, a feeder supplying a separate building or structure, or the source of a separately derived system to the grounding electrode is called the _____ conductor.

    (a) main grounding   (b) common main   (c) equipment grounding   (d) grounding electrode

5. •The *Code* applies to the installation of _____.

    (a) electrical conductors and equipment within or on public and private buildings
    (b) outside conductors and equipment on the premises
    (c) optical fiber cable
    (d) all of these

6. •The required working clearance for access to live parts operating at 300V to ground, where there are exposed live parts on one side and grounded parts on the other side, is _____ according to Table 110.26(A).

    (a) 3 ft   (b) 3 1/2 ft   (c) 4 ft   (d) 4 1/2 ft

7. •What size THHN conductor is required for a 50A circuit if the equipment is listed and identified for use with a 75°C conductor? Tip: Table 310.16 lists conductor ampacities.

    (a) 10 AWG   (b) 8 AWG   (c) 6 AWG   (d) all of these

8. A _____ is a device or group of devices that serves to govern in some predetermined manner the electric power delivered to the apparatus to which it is connected.

    (a) relay   (b) breaker   (c) transformer   (d) controller

9. A _____ is a single unit that provides independent living facilities for persons, including permanent provisions for living, sleeping, cooking, and sanitation.

    (a) two-family dwelling   (b) one-family dwelling   (c) dwelling unit   (d) multifamily dwelling

10. A circuit breaker is a device designed to _____ a circuit by nonautomatic means and to open the circuit automatically on a pre-determined overcurrent without damage to itself when properly applied within its rating.

    (a) blow   (b) disconnect   (c) connect   (d) open and close

11. A device intended for the protection of personnel, that functions to de-energize a circuit or portion thereof within an established period of time when a current-to-ground exceeds the values established for a "Class A Device," is a(n) _____.

    (a) dual-element fuse
    (b) inverse-time breaker
    (c) ground-fault circuit interrupter
    (d) safety switch

12. A form of general-use switch constructed so that it can be installed in device boxes or on box covers, or otherwise used in conjunction with wiring systems recognized by the *Code* is called a _____ switch.

    (a) transfer
    (b) motor-circuit
    (c) general-use snap
    (d) bypass isolation

13. A hoistway is any _____ in which an elevator or dumbwaiter is designed to operate.

    (a) hatchway or well hole
    (b) vertical opening or space
    (c) shaftway
    (d) all of these

14. A raintight enclosure is constructed or protected so that exposure to a beating rain will not result in the entrance of water under specified test conditions.

    (a) True
    (b) False

15. A signaling circuit is any electric circuit that energizes signaling equipment.

    (a) True
    (b) False

16. A single panel or group of panel units designed for assembly in the form of a single panel is called a _____.

    (a) switchboard
    (b) disconnect
    (c) panelboard
    (d) switch

17. A system or circuit conductor that is intentionally grounded is a(n) _____.

    (a) grounding conductor
    (b) unidentified conductor
    (c) grounded conductor
    (d) none of these

18. A(n) _____ branch circuit supplies energy to one or more outlets to which appliances are to be connected and has no permanently connected luminaires (lighting fixtures) that are not a part of an appliance.

    (a) general purpose
    (b) multiwire
    (c) individual
    (d) appliance

19. A(n) _____ enclosure is so constructed or protected that exposure to the weather will not interfere with successful operation.

    (a) weatherproof
    (b) weathertight
    (c) weather-resistant
    (d) all weather

20. A(n) _____ is a device, group of devices, or other means by which the conductors of a circuit can be disconnected from their source of supply.

    (a) feeder
    (b) enclosure
    (c) disconnecting means
    (d) conductor interrupter

21. Acceptable to the authority having jurisdiction means _____.

    (a) identified
    (b) listed
    (c) approved
    (d) labeled

22. According to the *Code*, automatic is self-acting, operating by its own mechanism when actuated by some impersonal influence, such as _____.

    (a) change in current strength
    (b) temperature
    (c) mechanical configuration
    (d) all of these

23. Admitting close approach, not guarded by locked doors, elevation, or other effective means, is commonly referred to as _____.

   (a) accessible (equipment)   (b) accessible (wiring methods)
   (c) accessible, readily   (d) all of these

24. At least one entrance, not less than 24 in. wide and 6 ft 6 in. high, must be provided to give access to the working space about electrical equipment that operates at over 600V, nominal. For switchboards and control panels that exceed 6 ft in width, there must be one entrance at each end of such equipment, except where the working space is twice that required in 110.34(A).

   (a) True   (b) False

25. Conduit installed underground or encased in concrete slabs that are in direct contact with the earth is considered a _____ location.

   (a) dry   (b) damp   (c) wet   (d) moist

26. Electrical equipment that depends on _____ for cooling of exposed surfaces must be installed so that airflow over such surfaces is not prevented by walls or by adjacent installed equipment.

   (a) outdoor air   (b) natural circulation of air and convection
   (c) artificial cooling and circulation   (d) magnetic induction

27. Electrical installations over 600V located in _____, where locks or other approved means control access, are considered to be accessible to qualified persons only.

   (a) a room or closet   (b) a vault
   (c) an area surrounded by a wall, screen, or fence (d) any of these

28. Enclosures housing electrical apparatus that are controlled by a lock are considered _____ to qualified persons.

   (a) readily accessible   (b) accessible   (c) available   (d) none of these

29. Equipment enclosed in a case or cabinet that is provided with a means of sealing or locking so that live parts cannot be made accessible without opening the enclosure is said to be _____.

   (a) guarded   (b) protected   (c) sealable   (d) lockable

30. Equipment intended to break current at other than fault levels must have an interrupting rating at nominal circuit voltage sufficient for the current that must be interrupted.

   (a) True   (b) False

31. Equipment or materials to which a symbol or other identifying mark of a product evaluation organization that is acceptable to the authority having jurisdiction has been attached is known as _____.

   (a) listed   (b) labeled   (c) approved   (d) rated

32. Equipment such as raceways, cables, wireways, cabinets, panels, etc. can be located above or below other electrical equipment when the associated equipment does not extend more than _____ from the front of the electrical equipment.

   (a) 3 in.   (b) 6 in.   (c) 12 in.   (d) 30 in.

33. For equipment rated 1,200A or more that contains overcurrent devices, switching devices, or control devices, there must be one entrance to the required working space not less than 24 in. wide and 6 ft 6 in. high at each end of the working space. Where the depth of the working space is twice that required by 110.26(A)(1), _____ entrance(s) are permitted.

   (a) one   (b) two   (c) three   (d) none of these

34. In the event the *Code* requires new products, constructions, or materials that are not yet available at the time a new edition is adopted, the _____ may permit the use of the products, constructions, or materials that comply with the most recent previous edition of this *Code* adopted by the jurisdiction.

   (a) architect
   (c) authority having jurisdiction

   (b) master electrician
   (d) supply house

35. In the *NEC*, conductors must be _____ unless otherwise provided.

   (a) bare   (b) stranded   (c) copper   (d) aluminum

36. Outline lighting may include an arrangement of _____ to outline or call attention to certain features such as the shape of a building or the decoration of a window.

   (a) incandescent lamps
   (c) electrically powered light sources

   (b) electric-discharge lighting
   (d) a, b, or c

37. Soldered splices must first be spliced or joined so as to be mechanically and electrically secure without solder and then be soldered.

   (a) True   (b) False

38. The authority having jurisdiction (AHJ) has the responsibility _____.

   (a) for making interpretations of the rules of the *Code*
   (b) for deciding upon the approval of equipment and materials
   (c) for waiving specific requirements in the *Code* and allowing alternate methods and material if safety is maintained
   (d) all of these

39. The *Code* covers all of the following electrical installations except _____.

   (a) floating buildings
   (b) in or on private and public buildings
   (c) industrial substations
   (d) electrical generation installations on property owned or leased by the electric utility company

40. The dedicated equipment space for electrical equipment that is required for panelboards is measured from the floor to a height of _____ above the equipment, or to the structural ceiling, whichever is lower.

   (a) 3 ft   (b) 6 ft   (c) 12 ft   (d) 30 ft

41. The high leg (wild leg) of a three-phase, 4-wire delta-connected system must be identified by using _____.

   (a) an outer finish that is red in color or by other effective means
   (b) an outer finish that is orange in color or by other effective means
   (c) permanent lettering on the conductor installed by the manufacturer of the wire
   (d) this is no longer required

42. The manufacturer's name, trademark, or other descriptive marking must be placed on all electric equipment. Where required by the *Code*, markings such as voltage, current, wattage, or other ratings must be provided with sufficient durability to withstand _____.

   (a) the voltages encountered   (b) painting and other finishes applied
   (c) the environment involved   (d) lack of planning by the installer

43. The *NEC* term to define wiring methods that are not concealed is _____.

   (a) open   (b) uncovered   (c) exposed   (d) bare

44. The service conductors between the terminals of the service equipment and a point usually outside the building, clear of building walls, where they are joined by tap or splice to the service drop are called _____ service entrance conductors.

   (a) underground   (b) complete   (c) overhead   (d) grounded

45. To guard live parts over 50V but less than 600V, the equipment can be _____.

   (a) located in a room accessible to qualified persons only   (b) located on a balcony
   (c) elevated 8 ft or more above the floor   (d) any of these

46. Unguarded live parts operating at 30,000V located above a working space must be elevated at least _____ above the working space.

   (a) 24 ft   (b) 18 ft   (c) 12 ft   (d) 9 1/2 ft

47. Unused cable or raceway openings in electrical equipment must be _____

   (a) filled with cable clamps or connectors only
   (b) taped over with electrical tape
   (c) repaired only by welding or brazing in a metal slug
   (d) effectively closed by fittings that provide protection substantially equivalent to the wall of the equipment

48. Utilities include entities that are designated or recognized by governmental law or regulation by public service/utility commissions.

   (a) True   (b) False

49. Utilization equipment is equipment that utilizes electricity for _____ purposes.

   (a) electromechanical   (b) heating   (c) lighting   (d) any of these

50. Where switches, cutouts, or similar equipment operating at 600V, nominal, or less are installed in a vault, room, or enclosure where they are exposed to energized parts at over 600V, nominal, the high-voltage equipment must be effectively separated from the space occupied by the low-voltage equipment by a suitable _____.

   (a) partition   (b) fence   (c) screen   (d) any of these

(• Indicates that 75% or fewer of those who took this exam answered the question correctly.)

1. Branch-circuit conductors supplying a single continuous-duty motor must have an ampacity not less than _____ rating.

   (a) 125 percent of the motor's nameplate current rating
   (b) 125 percent of the motor's full-load current as determined by 430.6(A)(1)
   (c) 125 percent of the motor's full locked-rotor
   (d) 80 percent of the motor's full-load current

2. When HDPE enters a box, fitting, or other enclosure, a(n) _____ must be provided to protect the wire from abrasion where the box design does not provide such protection.

   (a) bushing   (b) adapter   (c) a or b   (d) reducing bushing

3. _____ conductor cables 4 AWG and larger marked for use in cable trays, or for CT use, are permitted within a raised floor of an information technology equipment room.

   (a) Green   (b) Insulated   (c) Single   (d) all of these

4. _____ connectors must not be used for concealed installations of liquidtight flexible metal conduit.

   (a) Straight   (b) Angle   (c) Grounding-type   (d) none of these

5. _____ must not be used for switching emergency lighting circuits.

   (a) Single-pole switches   (b) Switches connected in series
   (c) 3- and 4-way switches   (d) b and c

6. _____ protection for fixture wires must be as specified in 240.5.

   (a) Arc-fault   (b) Overcurrent   (c) Ground-fault   (d) Lightning

7. _____ rated in amperes is permitted as a controller for all motors.

   (a) A branch-circuit inverse-time circuit breaker   (b) A molded-case switch
   (c) both a and b   (d) none of these

8. •A _____ receptacle without GFCI protection can be located in a dwelling unit garage to supply one appliance, which is not easily moved, if the receptacle is located within the dedicated space for the appliance.

   (a) multioutlet   (b) duplex   (c) single   (d) none of these

9. •A Class III, Division_____ location is where easily ignitible fibers or combustible flying material are stored or handled but not manufactured.

   (a) 1   (b) 2   (c) 3   (d) all of these

10. •A device that, by insertion in a receptacle, establishes a connection between the conductors of the attached flexible cord and the conductors connected permanently to the receptacle is called a(n) _____.

    (a) attachment plug   (b) plug cap   (c) plug   (d) any of these

11. •A single receptacle installed on an individual branch circuit must be rated at least _____ percent of the rating of the branch circuit.

(a) 50   (b) 60   (c) 90   (d) 100

12. •EMT must be supported within 3 ft of each coupling.

(a) True   (b) False

13. •For a circuit to be considered a multiwire branch circuit, it must have _____.

(a) two or more ungrounded conductors with a voltage potential between them
(b) a grounded conductor having equal voltage potential between it and each ungrounded conductor of the circuit
(c) a grounded conductor connected to the grounded neutral terminal of the system
(d) all of these

14. •For box fill calculations, a reduction of _____ conductor(s) can be made for one hickey and two internal clamps.

(a) 1   (b) 2   (c) 3   (d) zero

15. •Metal enclosures for grounding electrode conductors must be electrically continuous, from the point of attachment to cabinets or equipment, to the grounding electrode.

(a) True   (b) False

16. •Metal raceways, cable trays, cable armor, cable sheath, enclosures, frames, fittings, and other metal noncurrent-carrying parts that serve as the grounding conductor must be _____ where necessary to ensure electrical continuity and to have the capacity to conduct safely any fault current likely to be imposed.

(a) grounded   (b) effectively bonded   (c) soldered or welded   (d) any of these

17. •Multiwire branch circuits must _____.

(a) supply only line-to-neutral loads
(b) not be allowed in dwelling units
(c) have their conductors originate from different panelboards
(d) none of these

18. •Overhead service-drop conductors must have a horizontal clearance of _____ from a pool.

(a) 6 ft   (b) 10 ft   (c) 8 ft   (d) 4 ft

19. •Service-entrance conductors must not be spliced or tapped.

(a) True   (b) False

20. •The demand factors of Table 220.42 must apply to the computed load of feeders to areas in hospitals, hotels, and motels where the entire lighting is likely to be used at one time, as in operating rooms, ballrooms, or dining rooms.

(a) True   (b) False

21. •The maximum unbalanced feeder load for household electric ranges, wall-mounted ovens, counter-mounted cooking units, and electric dryers must be considered as _____ percent of the load on the ungrounded conductors as determined in accordance with Table 220.55 for ranges and Table 220.54 for dryers.

(a) 50   (b) 70   (c) 85   (d) 115

22.   •Underground service conductors between the street main and the first point of connection to the service entrance are known as the _____.

(a) utility service   (b) service lateral   (c) service drop   (d) main service conductors

23.   •What size copper grounding electrode conductor is required for a service that has three sets of 500 kcmil copper conductors per phase?

(a) 1 AWG   (b) 1/0 AWG   (c) 2/0 AWG   (d) 3/0 AWG

24.   •When installing direct-buried cables, a _____ must be used at the end of a conduit that terminates underground.

(a) splice kit   (b) terminal fitting   (c) bushing   (d) b or c

25.   •When the service contains two to six service disconnecting means, they must be _____.

(a) the same size   (b) grouped at one location   (c) in the same enclosure   (d) none of these

26.   15 and 20A, single-phase, 125V receptacles located within _____ of the inside walls of a pool or fountain must be protected by a ground-fault circuit interrupter.

(a) 8 ft   (b) 10 ft   (c) 15 ft   (d) 20 ft

27.   A _____ is a building or portion of a building in which one or more self-propelled vehicles can be kept for use, sale, storage, rental, repair, exhibition, or demonstration purposes.

(a) garage   (b) residential garage   (c) service garage   (d) commercial garage

28.   A _____ is a structure transportable in one or more sections that is built on a chassis and designed to be used as a dwelling, with or without a permanent foundation.

(a) manufactured home   (b) mobile home   (c) dwelling unit   (d) all of these

29.   A _____ is an accommodation with two or more contiguous rooms comprising a compartment, with or without doors between such rooms, that provides living, sleeping, sanitary, and storage facilities.

(a) guest room   (b) guest suite   (c) dwelling unit   (d) single family dwelling

30.   A _____ is permitted in lieu of a box or terminal fitting at the end of a conduit where the raceway terminates behind an unenclosed switchboard or similar equipment.

(a) bushing   (b) bonding bushing   (c) coupling   (d) connector

31.   A 15 or 20A, 125V, single-phase receptacle outlet must be located within 25 ft of heating, air-conditioning, and refrigeration equipment for _____ occupancies.

(a) dwelling   (b) commercial   (c) industrial   (d) all of these

32.   A box or conduit body is not required for splices and taps in direct-buried conductors and cables as long as the splice is made with a splicing device that is identified for the purpose.

(a) True   (b) False

33.   A cable tray is a unit or assembly of units or sections and associated fittings forming a _____ system used to securely fasten or support cables and raceways.

(a) structural   (b) flexible   (c) movable   (d) secure

34. A Class I, Division 1 location is one in which _____.

    (a) ignitible concentrations of flammable gases or vapors can exist under normal operating conditions
    (b) ignitible concentrations of such gases or vapors may exist frequently because of repair or maintenance operations or because of leakage
    (c) breakdown or faulty operation of equipment or processes might release ignitible concentrations of flammable gases or vapors, and might also cause simultaneous failure of electrical equipment
    (d) all of these

35. A component of an electrical system that is intended to carry or control but not utilize electric energy is a(n) _____.

    (a) raceway   (b) fitting   (c) device   (d) enclosure

36. A conduit seal fitting must be installed in each conduit that passes from a Class I, Division 2 location into an unclassified location. Conduit boundary seals are not required to be _____, but must be identified for the purpose of minimizing the passage of gases under normal operating conditions.

    (a) listed   (b) installed   (c) explosionproof   (d) accessible

37. A cord connector on a permanently installed cord pendant is considered a receptacle outlet.

    (a) True   (b) False

38. A device that establishes an electrical connection to the earth is the _____.

    (a) grounding electrode conductor   (b) grounding conductor
    (c) grounding electrode   (d) grounded conductor

39. A disconnect must be provided in each ungrounded conductor for each capacitor bank, and must _____.

    (a) open all ungrounded conductors simultaneously
    (b) be permitted to disconnect the capacitor from the line as a regular operating procedure
    (c) be rated no less than 135 percent of the rated current of the capacitor
    (d) all of these

40. A fuel cell system typically consists of a reformer, stack, power inverter, and auxiliary equipment.

    (a) True   (b) False

41. A grounding electrode is required if a building or structure is supplied by a feeder or by more than one branch circuit.

    (a) True   (b) False

42. A horsepower-rated inverse-time circuit breaker can serve as both a motor controller and disconnecting means if _____.

    (a) it opens all ungrounded conductors
    (b) it is protected by an overcurrent device in each ungrounded conductor
    (c) it is manually operable, or both power and manually operable
    (d) all of these

43. A lighting and appliance branch-circuit panelboard contains six 3-pole breakers and eight 2-pole breakers. The maximum allowable number of single-pole breakers that can be added to this panelboard is _____.

    (a) 8   (b) 16   (c) 28   (d) 42

44. A limited care facility is an area used on a(n) _____ basis for the housing of four or more persons who are incapable of self-preservation because of age, physical limitation due to accident or illness, or mental limitations, mental illness, or chemical dependency.

    (a) occasional   (b) 10 hour or less per day   (c) 24 hour   (d) temporary

45. A listed luminaire or a listed assembly is permitted to be cord-connected if located _____ the outlet box, the cord is continuously visible for its entire length outside the luminaire, and the cord is not subject to strain or physical damage.

    (a) within   (b) directly below   (c) directly above   (d) adjacent to

46. A minimum of _____ of working clearance is required to live parts operating at 300 volts-to-ground, where there are exposed live parts on one side and no live or grounded parts on the other side.

    (a) 2 ft   (b) 3 ft   (c) 4 ft   (d) 6 ft

47. A minimum of 70 percent of all recreational vehicle sites with electrical supply must each be equipped with a _____,125V receptacle.

    (a) 15A   (b) 20A   (c) 30A   (d) 50A

48. A motor control conductor that is tapped from the load side of a motor branch-circuit short-circuit and ground-fault protective device is not considered to be a branch-circuit conductor, and must be protected in accordance with 430.72.

    (a) True   (b) False

49. A multiwire branch circuit is not permitted in a Class I, Zone 1, location unless all conductors of the circuit can be opened simultaneously.

    (a) True   (b) False

50. A one-family or two-family dwelling unit requires a minimum of _____ GFCI receptacle(s) to be installed outdoors.

    (a) zero   (b) one   (c) two   (d) three

UNIT

Electrical Circuits

Introduction

In Unit 1, a foundation was laid for your continuing study of the topic of electricity. The math, basic electrical concepts, and electrical formulas you learned are essential to understanding the topics covered in Unit 2.

The basic requirements of a practical electrical circuit are the presence of an electrical source, an electrical load, and a complete path of current flow from the source to the load and returning again to the source. The path of current flow can be configured in many ways, and the way this path is designed is one factor that determines the amount of current flow at any specific point of the circuit, and how many volts are measured across any particular component. The configuration of the current-flow path can be expressed as a series path, a parallel path, or a combination series-parallel path.

In this unit, you will learn about series circuits, parallel circuits, combinations of series and parallel circuits, and a special application called a multiwire branch circuit. Multiwire branch circuits have unique safety requirements, and the *Code* makes special provisions for their use. Be sure to understand the roles of current and voltage in each of these different types of circuits and how to find the total resistance of a given circuit. The questions at the end of the unit will help solidify your understanding of these circuits.

This Unit makes use of some direct-current (dc) circuits and some alternating-current (ac) circuits, and their similarities in series and parallel resistive circuits will be explained. In Unit 3, more about the differences between direct-current and alternating-current circuits will be explained as you continue to learn about how electricity works.

PART A—SERIES CIRCUITS

Introduction

A series circuit is a circuit in which a specific amount of current leaves the voltage source and flows through every electrical device in a single path before it returns to the voltage source. Figure 2–1

It is important to understand that in a series circuit, current is identical through ALL circuit elements of the circuit.

2.1 Practical Uses of the Series Circuit

In a series circuit, if any part of the circuit is open, the current in the circuit will stop.

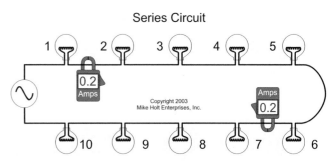

Current is the same magnitude in every part of a series circuit.

Figure 2–1

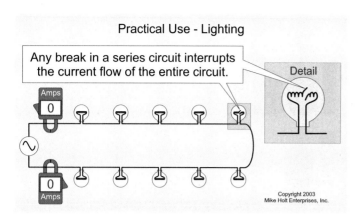

Figure 2–2

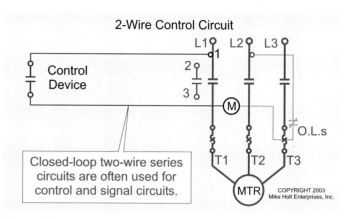

Figure 2–3

Lighting

A series circuit is not useful for lighting because if one lamp burns out, all the other lamps on the circuit will go out. Figure 2-2

Many strings of Christmas lights are made in series circuits—if one bulb burns out, it requires examining EVERY bulb in order to find the bad one because the entire string stops burning when this occurs! Most of the newer Christmas light lamps used in series string lighting have a shorting bar. When one lamp burns out, the lamp leads are shorted together (shorting bar) and the rest of the string stays lit.

> **AUTHOR'S COMMENT:** If, however, there are ten lamps in the string, and one burns out, the rest of the lamps will operate at 10% higher voltage, causing the other nine lamps to burn out even quicker.

For most practical purposes, series circuits, also called closed-loop systems, are not used for building wiring; however, they are often used for control and signal circuits.

Control Circuit

Closed-loop (series) circuits are often used for the purpose of controlling (starting and stopping) electrical equipment. Figure 2-3

Signaling Circuit

Two-wire closed-loop (series) circuits are often used to give a signal that something has occurred. It could indicate that a door is open, a process is operating, or there is fire or smoke. For example, the discontinuation of current flow when part of the circuit is opened is important for the operation of burglar alarm circuits. Figure 2-4

Internal Equipment Wiring

The internal wiring of many types of equipment, such as motor windings, will be connected in series. For example, a 115/230V rated motor connected to a 230V circuit must have the windings connected in series so that each winding will receive at least 115V. Figure 2-5

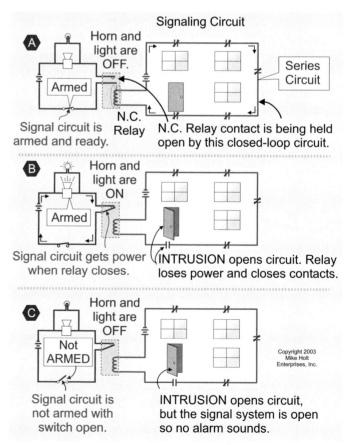

Figure 2–4

Internal Equipment Wiring - Series

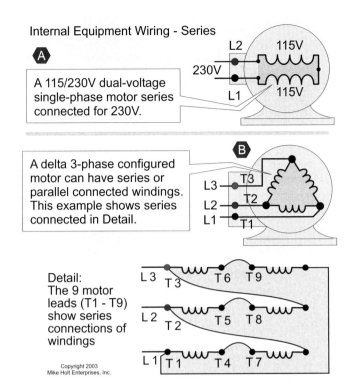

A A 115/230V dual-voltage single-phase motor series connected for 230V.

B A delta 3-phase configured motor can have series or parallel connected windings. This example shows series connected in Detail.

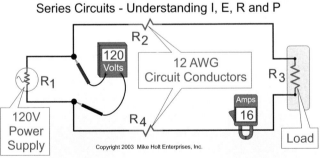

Detail: The 9 motor leads (T1 - T9) show series connections of windings

Copyright 2003
Mike Holt Enterprises, Inc.

Figure 2–5

2.2 Understanding Series Calculations

It is important to understand the relationship between current, voltage, resistance, and power in series circuits. Figure 2-6

Resistance

Resistance opposes the flow of electrons. In a series circuit, the total circuit resistance is equal to the sum of all the series resistances. Resistance is additive: $R_T = R_1 + R_2 + R_3 + R_4$. Figure 2-7

Series Circuits - Understanding I, E, R and P

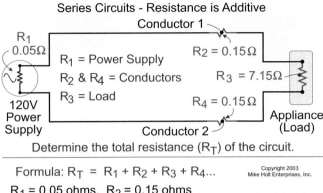

Series Circuits - Resistance is Additive

R_1 = Power Supply
R_2 & R_4 = Conductors
R_3 = Load

Determine the total resistance (R_T) of the circuit.

Formula: $R_T = R_1 + R_2 + R_3 + R_4...$
Copyright 2003 Mike Holt Enterprises, Inc.

R_1 = 0.05 ohms, R_2 = 0.15 ohms
R_3 = 7.15 ohms, R_4 = 0.15 ohms

R_T = 0.05 ohms + 0.15 ohms + 7.15 ohms + 0.15 ohms
R_T = 7.5 ohms

Figure 2–7

▶ **Example**

R_1 Power Supply	0.05 ohms
R_2 Conductor No. 1	0.15 ohms
R_3 Appliance	7.15 ohms
R_4 Conductor No. 2	0.15 ohms
R_T Total Resistance	7.50 ohms

Voltage

The voltage, also called electromotive force (EMF), provides the pressure necessary to move electrons through the circuit. However, the power supply, the conductors, and the appliance all have resistance (although the power supply's resistance is usually ignored) that opposes the current flow. The opposition (resistance) to current flow (amperes) results in a voltage drop of the circuit voltage, and can be calculated by the formula $E_{VD} = I \times R$.

Kirchoff's Voltage Law

Kirchoff's Voltage Law states that in a series circuit, the sum of the voltages (or "voltage drops") across all of the resistors in the series circuit is equal to the applied voltage.

The voltage drop across each resistor can be determined by the formula $E_{VD} = I \times R$. Figure 2-8

I = Current of circuit
R = Resistance of resistor

Power Supply	16A x 0.05 ohms	=	0.80V
Conductor 1	16A x 0.15 ohms	=	2.40V
Appliance	16A x 7.15 ohms	=	114.40V
Conductor 2	16A x 0.15 ohms	=	2.40V
Total	16A x 7.50 ohms	=	120.00V

R₁ - Power Supply   R₃ - Load Resistance
R₂ - Conductor Resistance   R₄ - Conductor Resistance

R_{Total} = Power Supply (R_1) + Conductors ($R_{2,4}$) + Load (R_3)

Figure 2–6

51

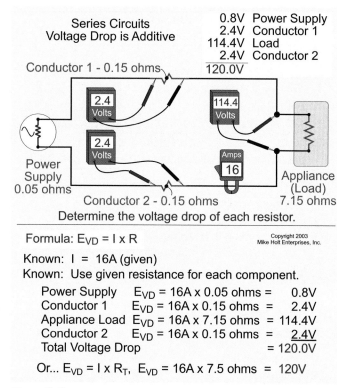

Series Circuits
Voltage Drop is Additive

0.8V	Power Supply
2.4V	Conductor 1
114.4V	Load
2.4V	Conductor 2
120.0V	

Determine the voltage drop of each resistor.

Formula: $E_{VD} = I \times R$

Copyright 2003
Mike Holt Enterprises, Inc.

Known: I = 16A (given)
Known: Use given resistance for each component.

Power Supply E_{VD} = 16A x 0.05 ohms =   0.8V
Conductor 1 E_{VD} = 16A x 0.15 ohms =   2.4V
Appliance Load E_{VD} = 16A x 7.15 ohms = 114.4V
Conductor 2 E_{VD} = 16A x 0.15 ohms =   2.4V
Total Voltage Drop   = 120.0V

Or... $E_{VD} = I \times R_T$, E_{VD} = 16A x 7.5 ohms = 120V

Figure 2–8

In addition, the voltage of the power supply is distributed or divided among the circuit resistances according to the Law of Proportion. The Law of Proportion means that the supply voltage is distributed among all the resistances, according to the proportion of resistance each resistance has relative to the total resistance. Figure 2-9

	Resistance	Percentage	Voltage
Power Source	0.05 ohms	0.67%	0.80V
Conductor No. 1	0.15 ohms	2.00%	2.40V
Appliance	7.15 ohms	95.33%	114.40V
Conductor No. 2	0.15 ohms	2.00%	2.40V
Total	7.50 ohms	100%	120.00V

Kirchoff's Current Law

Kirchoff's Current Law states that the sum of currents flowing into a junction equals the sum of currents flowing away from the junction. Another way to say it is, current flowing through each resistor of the series circuit will be the same. Figure 2-10

To calculate the current in a series circuit, you need to know the power-supply voltage (E_S) and the total circuit resistance (R_T). The current of the circuit can be determined by the formula $I_T = E_S/R_T$. In the following example, the current of the circuit is equal to 120V/7.5 ohms = 16A. Since this is a series circuit, every component of the circuit has 16A flowing through it.

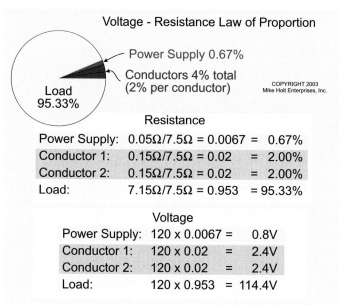

Voltage - Resistance Law of Proportion

Power Supply 0.67%
Conductors 4% total
(2% per conductor)
Load 95.33%

COPYRIGHT 2003
Mike Holt Enterprises, Inc.

Resistance

Power Supply: 0.05Ω/7.5Ω = 0.0067 = 0.67%
Conductor 1:   0.15Ω/7.5Ω = 0.02 = 2.00%
Conductor 2:   0.15Ω/7.5Ω = 0.02 = 2.00%
Load: 7.15Ω/7.5Ω = 0.953 = 95.33%

Voltage

Power Supply: 120 x 0.0067 =   0.8V
Conductor 1:   120 x 0.02 =   2.4V
Conductor 2:   120 x 0.02 =   2.4V
Load: 120 x 0.953 = 114.4V

Figure 2–9

AUTHOR'S COMMENT: The current flowing through each resistance can be calculated by I = E/R, where E (voltage) represents the voltage drop across the individual resistances, not the voltage source!

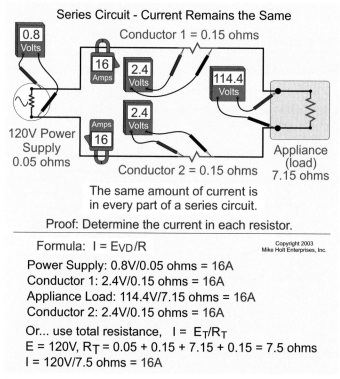

Series Circuit - Current Remains the Same

Conductor 1 = 0.15 ohms

120V Power Supply 0.05 ohms

Conductor 2 = 0.15 ohms

Appliance (load) 7.15 ohms

The same amount of current is in every part of a series circuit.

Proof: Determine the current in each resistor.

Formula: $I = E_{VD}/R$

Copyright 2003
Mike Holt Enterprises, Inc.

Power Supply: 0.8V/0.05 ohms = 16A
Conductor 1: 2.4V/0.15 ohms = 16A
Appliance Load: 114.4V/7.15 ohms = 16A
Conductor 2: 2.4V/0.15 ohms = 16A

Or... use total resistance, I = E_T/R_T
E = 120V, R_T = 0.05 + 0.15 + 7.15 + 0.15 = 7.5 ohms
I = 120V/7.5 ohms = 16A

Figure 2–10

Power Source	I	=	0.80V/0.05 ohms	=	16A
Conductor No. 1	I	=	2.4V/0.15 ohms	=	16A
Appliance	I	=	114.4V/7.15 ohms	=	16A
Conductor No. 2	I	=	2.4V/0.15 ohms	=	16A
Total Resistance	I	=	120.0V/7.5	=	16A

Power

The power consumed in a series circuit will equal the sum of the power consumed by all of the resistances in the series circuit. The Law of Conservation of Energy states that the power supply (battery, etc.) will only produce as much power as that consumed by the circuit elements. Power is a result of current flowing through a resistance and is calculated by the formula $P = I^2 \times R$.

▶ **Example**

Power Source	P	=	$16A^2 \times 0.05$ ohms	=	12.8W
Conductor No. 1	P	=	$16A^2 \times 0.15$ ohms	=	38.4W
Appliance	P	=	$16A^2 \times 7.15$ ohms	=	1,830.4W
Conductor No. 2	P	=	$16A^2 \times 0.15$ ohms	=	38.4W

Power can also be calculated according to the law of proportion.

	Resistance	Percentage	Power
Power Source	0.05 ohms	0.67%	12.8W
Conductor No. 1	0.15 ohms	2.00%	38.4W
Appliance	7.15 ohms	95.33%	1,830.0W
Conductor No. 2	0.15 ohms	2.00%	38.4W
Total Resistance	7.50 ohms	100%	1,920.0W

2.3 Series Circuit Calculations

When performing series circuit calculations, the following steps should be helpful: Figure 2-11

Step 1 Determine the resistance of each resistive element in the circuit. Often, the resistance of each element is given in the problem. If you know the nameplate voltage and power (wattage) rating of the appliance or equipment, you can determine its resistance by the formula $R = E^2/P$.

E = Nameplate voltage rating (squared)
P = Nameplate power rating

Step 2 Calculate the total resistance (R_T) of the circuit,
$R_T = R_1 + R_2 + R_3 + R_4$.

Step 3 The current of the circuit can be determined by the formula $I = E_S/R_T$.

E_S = Voltage Source
R_T = Total circuit resistance (Step 2)

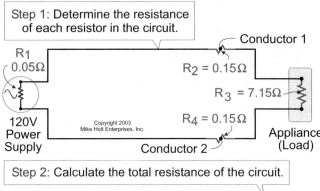

Series Circuit Calculations

Step 1: Determine the resistance of each resistor in the circuit.

R₁ 0.05Ω
R₂ = 0.15Ω
R₃ = 7.15Ω
R₄ = 0.15Ω
Conductor 1
Conductor 2
120V Power Supply
Appliance (Load)
Copyright 2003 Mike Holt Enterprises, Inc.

Step 2: Calculate the total resistance of the circuit.

R_T = 0.05 + 0.15 + 7.15 + 0.15 ohms = 7.5 ohms

Step 3: Determine the current of the circuit.

$I = E_S/R_T = 120V/7.5$ ohms = 16A

Figure 2–11

2.4 Power Calculations

If you know the current of the circuit and the resistance of each resistor, the power of each resistor can be determined by the formula $P = I^2 \times R$. Figure 2-12

I^2 = Current of circuit (squared) (Step 3)
R = Resistance of the resistor (Step 1)

The power of the circuit can be determined by adding up the power of all of the resistors or by the formula $P = I^2 \times R_T$.

I^2 = Current of the circuit (squared)
R_T = Resistance total of the circuit

2.5 Variations

There are often many different ways to solve an electrical circuit problem involving voltage, current, resistance and power. It is also often possible to verify or check one's work by solving the problem different ways.

2.6 Series Circuit Notes

Note 1: The total resistance of a series circuit is equal to the sum of all of the resistances of the circuit.

Note 2: Current is the same value through all of the resistances.

Note 3: The sum of the voltage drops across all resistances equals the voltage of the source.

Note 4: The sum of the power consumed by all resistors equals the total power consumed by the circuit.

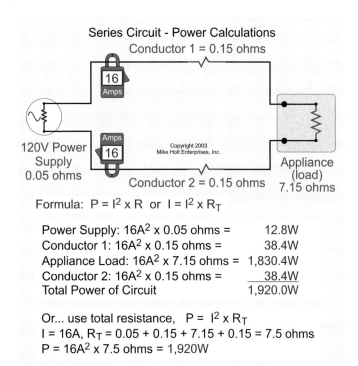

Series Circuit - Power Calculations

Conductor 1 = 0.15 ohms

16 Amps

120V Power Supply 0.05 ohms

Amps 16

Copyright 2003 Mike Holt Enterprises, Inc.

Conductor 2 = 0.15 ohms

Appliance (load) 7.15 ohms

Formula: $P = I^2 \times R$ or $I = I^2 \times R_T$

Power Supply: $16A^2 \times 0.05$ ohms =	12.8W
Conductor 1: $16A^2 \times 0.15$ ohms =	38.4W
Appliance Load: $16A^2 \times 7.15$ ohms =	1,830.4W
Conductor 2: $16A^2 \times 0.15$ ohms =	38.4W
Total Power of Circuit	1,920.0W

Or... use total resistance, $P = I^2 \times R_T$
$I = 16A$, $R_T = 0.05 + 0.15 + 7.15 + 0.15 = 7.5$ ohms
$P = 16A^2 \times 7.5$ ohms = 1,920W

Figure 2–12

2.7 Series-Connected Power Supplies

When power supplies are connected in series, the voltage of the power supply will be additive (provided the polarities are connected properly). Figure 2-13 and Figure 2-14

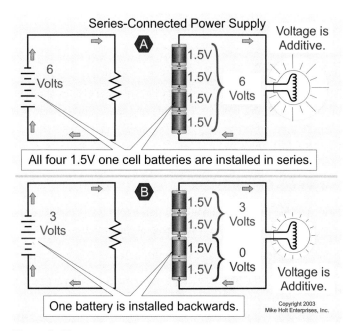

Series-Connected Power Supply

Voltage is Additive.

A

6 Volts

1.5V
1.5V
1.5V
1.5V

6 Volts

All four 1.5V one cell batteries are installed in series.

B

3 Volts

1.5V
1.5V
1.5V
1.5V

3 Volts

0 Volts

Voltage is Additive.

One battery is installed backwards.

Copyright 2003 Mike Holt Enterprises, Inc.

Figure 2–13

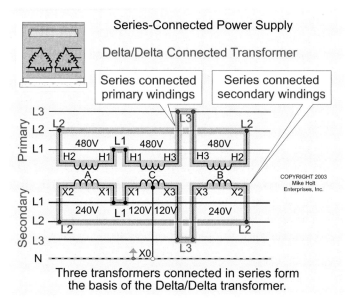

Series-Connected Power Supply

Delta/Delta Connected Transformer

Series connected primary windings

Series connected secondary windings

Primary

L3
L2
L1

480V L1 480V   480V
H2 H1   H1 H3   H3 H2
A   C   B

COPYRIGHT 2003 Mike Holt Enterprises, Inc.

Secondary

L1
L2
L3

X2 X1   X1 X3   X3 X2
240V   L1 120V 120V   240V

L2 L1   L2

N   X0   L3

Three transformers connected in series form the basis of the Delta/Delta transformer.

Figure 2–14

PART B—PARALLEL CIRCUITS

Introduction

"Parallel" is a term used to describe a method of connecting electrical components so that there are two or more paths on which current may flow. Figure 2-15

A parallel circuit is one with several different paths for the electricity to travel. It's like a river that has been divided up into smaller streams and all the streams come back to form the river once again.

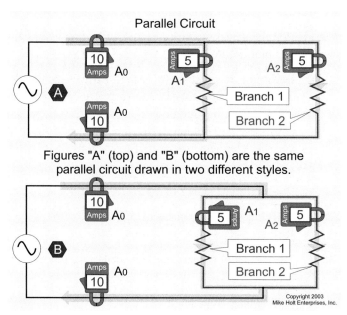

Parallel Circuit

10 Amps A0

5 A1

5 A2

Branch 1

Branch 2

10 Amps A0

Figures "A" (top) and "B" (bottom) are the same parallel circuit drawn in two different styles.

10 Amps A0

5 A1

5 A2

Branch 1

Branch 2

10 Amps A0

Copyright 2003 Mike Holt Enterprises, Inc.

Figure 2–15

A parallel circuit has extremely different characteristics than a series circuit. For one, the total resistance of a parallel circuit is not equal to the sum of the resistors. The total resistance in a parallel circuit is always less than any of the branch resistances. Adding more parallel resistances to the paths cause the total resistance in the circuit to decrease.

2.8 Practical Uses of the Parallel Circuit

For most purposes, parallel circuits are used for building wiring.

Receptacle

When wiring receptacles on a circuit, they are connected in parallel to each other. Figure 2–16

Lighting

Another example is lights connected in parallel to each other. Figure 2–17A

The major advantage of a parallel circuit is that if any branch of the circuit is opened or turned off, the power supply continues to provide voltage to the remaining parts of the circuit. Figure 2–17B

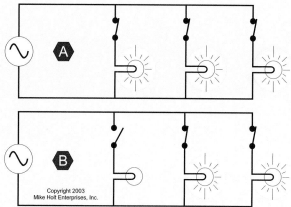
Practical Use - Lights in Parallel

An advantage of parallel circuits is that if any part of the circuit is opened, the remaining portion of the circuit is still operable.

Figure 2–17

Other Uses

Parallel circuits, also called open-loop systems, are used for fire alarm pull stations and smoke detectors. If any initiating device (pull station or smoke detector) closes, the signal circuit is complete and the alarm will sound. Figure 2–18

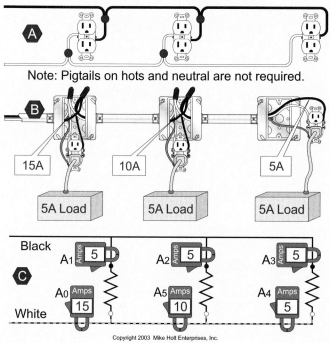
Practical Use - Receptacles in Parallel
All three parts of this diagram represent three receptacles wired in parallel.

Figure 2–16

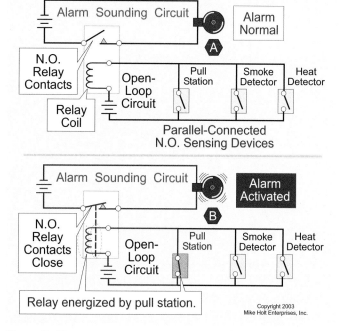
Practical Use of Parallel Connection

Figure 2–18

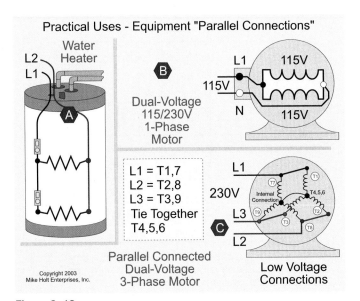

Figure 2–19

Often electrical components within appliances, such as water heaters and motors, have their components connected in parallel. Figure 2–19

2.9 Understanding Parallel Calculations

It is important to understand the relationship between voltage, current, power, and resistance of a parallel circuit.

Voltage

In a pure parallel circuit (one with no resistors in series with the parallel resistors), the voltage drop across each resistance is equal to the voltage supplied by the power source (ignoring any voltage drop in the source and conductors). Figure 2–20

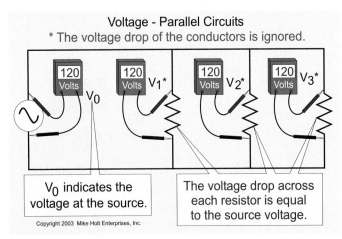

Voltage - Parallel Circuits
* The voltage drop of the conductors is ignored.

V_0 indicates the voltage at the source.

The voltage drop across each resistor is equal to the source voltage.

Copyright 2003 Mike Holt Enterprises, Inc.

Figure 2–20

For the moment, we will ignore the voltage drop and power loss effects of the conductor and power supply as it is usually much, much smaller than the drop across the resistive elements.

Kirchoff's Current Law

In a parallel circuit, current from the power source will branch in different directions and magnitudes. The current in each branch is dependent on the resistance of each branch. Kirchoff's Current Law states that the total current provided by the source to a parallel circuit will be equal to the sum of the currents of all of the branches.

The current in each branch can be calculated by the formula $I = E/R$. Figure 2–21

E = Voltage of each branch.
R = Resistance of each branch (appliance).

The current of each branch is as follows: $I = E/R$

Coffee Pot (R_1)	P = 120V/16 ohms	=	7.50A
Skillet (R_2)	P = 120V/13 ohms	=	9.17A
Blender (R_3)	P = 120V/36 ohms	=	3.33A
	Total Current		= 20.00A

AUTHOR'S COMMENT: The resistance and currents have been rounded off.

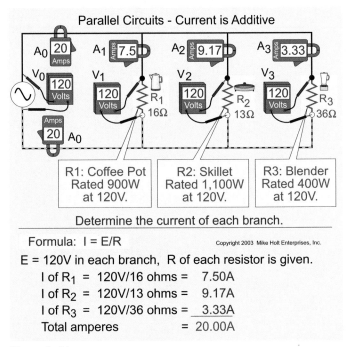

Parallel Circuits - Current is Additive

R1: Coffee Pot Rated 900W at 120V.
R2: Skillet Rated 1,100W at 120V.
R3: Blender Rated 400W at 120V.

Determine the current of each branch.

Formula: I = E/R   Copyright 2003 Mike Holt Enterprises, Inc.
E = 120V in each branch, R of each resistor is given.
I of R_1 = 120V/16 ohms =   7.50A
I of R_2 = 120V/13 ohms =   9.17A
I of R_3 = 120V/36 ohms =   3.33A
Total amperes   = 20.00A

Figure 2–21

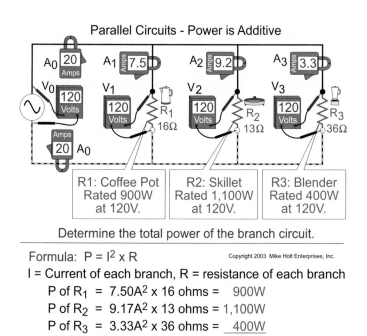

Figure 2–22

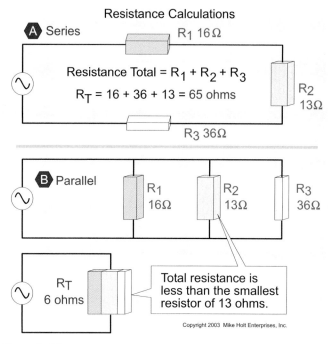

Figure 2–23

Power

When current flows through a resistor, power is consumed. The power consumed by each branch of the parallel circuit can be determined by the formulas: $P = I^2 \times R$, $P = E \times I$, or $P = E^2/R$.

The total power consumed in a parallel circuit will equal the sum of the branches' powers. Figure 2–22

Using the formula $P = I^2 \times R$, determine the power of each resistor:

Coffee Pot	P =	$7.50A^2$ x 16 ohms	=	900W
Skillet	P =	$9.17A^2$ x 13 ohms	=	1,100W
Blender	P =	$3.33A^2$ x 36 ohms	=	400W
		Total Circuit Power	=	2,400W

2.10 Circuit Resistance

Calculating total circuit resistance is different in parallel and series circuits. In a series circuit, resistance total is equal to the sum of resistances, Figure 2–23A. In a parallel circuit, the total circuit resistance is always less than the smallest resistance. Figure 2–23B

There are three basic methods of calculating the total resistance of a parallel circuit; the Equal Resistance method, the Product-Over-Sum method, and the Reciprocal method.

Equal Resistance Method

When all of the resistances of the parallel circuit have the same resistance, the total resistance is found by dividing the resistance of one resistive element by the total number of resistors in parallel.

▶ **Example A**

The total resistance of three 10 ohm resistors in parallel is _____. Figure 2–24

    (a) 10 ohms   (b) 20 ohms
    (c) 30 ohms   (d) none of these

    • Answer: (d) none of these
      R_T = Resistance of One Resistor/Number of Resistors
      R_T = 10 ohms/3
      R_T = 3.33 ohms

▶ **Example B**

The total resistance of ten 10 ohm resistors in parallel is _____.

    (a) 10 ohms   (b) 100 ohms
    (c) 50 ohms   (d) none of these

    • Answer: (d) none of these
      R_T = Resistance of One Resistor/Number of Resistors
      R_T = 10 ohms/10
      R_T = 1 ohm

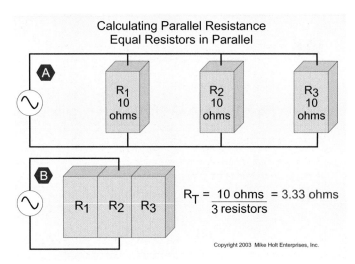

Calculating Parallel Resistance
Equal Resistors in Parallel

$$R_T = \frac{10 \text{ ohms}}{3 \text{ resistors}} = 3.33 \text{ ohms}$$

Copyright 2003 Mike Holt Enterprises, Inc.

Figure 2–24

Product-Over-Sum Method

This method is used to calculate the resistance of two resistances at a time:

$$R_T = R_1 \times R_2 \text{ (product)}/R_1 + R_2 \text{ (sum)}$$

AUTHOR'S COMMENT: The term "product" means the answer obtained when numbers are multiplied. The term "sum" means the answer obtained by adding a group of numbers.

▶ **Example**

The resistance of a 900W coffee pot is 16 ohms and the resistance of a 1,100W skillet is approximately 13 ohms; the appliances are connected in parallel. What is the total resistance of the two appliances? **Figure 2–25A** and **Figure 2–25B**

(a) 16 ohms   (b) 13 ohms
(c) 29 ohms   (d) 7.2 ohms

• Answer: (d) 7.2 ohms
$$R_T = (R_1 \times R_2)/(R_1 + R_2)$$
$$R_T = (16 \times 13)/(16 + 13)$$
$$R_T = 7.20 \text{ ohms}$$

The total resistance of a parallel circuit is always less than the smallest resistance.

The "product-over-sum" method can be used to determine the resistance total for more than two resistors in a parallel circuit, but only two resistors can be dealt with at a time. If more than two resistances are in parallel, the "product-over-sum" method must be applied several times, each time considering the equivalent resistance of the last two resistances looked at as a "new" resistance for the equation.

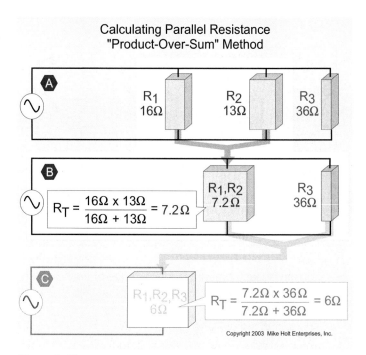

Calculating Parallel Resistance
"Product-Over-Sum" Method

$$R_T = \frac{16\Omega \times 13\Omega}{16\Omega + 13\Omega} = 7.2\Omega$$

$$R_T = \frac{7.2\Omega \times 36\Omega}{7.2\Omega + 36\Omega} = 6\Omega$$

Copyright 2003 Mike Holt Enterprises, Inc.

Figure 2–25

▶ **Example**

What is the total resistance of a 16 ohm, 13 ohm, and 36 ohm resistor connected in parallel? **Figure 2–26A**

(a) 43 ohms   (b) 65 ohms
(c) 6 ohms   (d) 26 ohms

• Answer: (c) 6 ohms
The 16 and 13 ohm resistors are treated as an "equivalent" single resistor of 7.2 ohms (previous example). The resistance of the circuit will be calculated as follows: **Figure 2–26B** and **Figure 2–26C**

$$R_T = (R_{1,2} \times R_3)/(R_{1,2} + R_3)$$
$$R_T = 7.2 \times 36/7.2 + 36$$
$$R_T = 6 \text{ ohms}$$

AUTHOR'S COMMENT: The answer must be less than the smallest resistor of the circuit (13V).

Reciprocal Method

The advantage of the "reciprocal" method in determining the total resistance of a parallel circuit is that this formula can be used for as many resistances as the parallel circuit contains.

$$R_T = 1/(^1/R_1 + {}^1R_2 + {}^1/R_3 \dots)$$

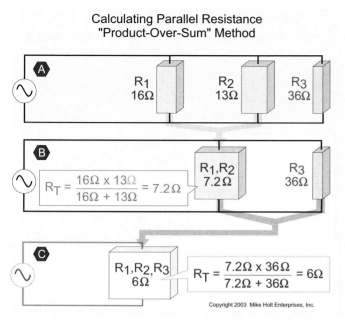

Figure 2–26

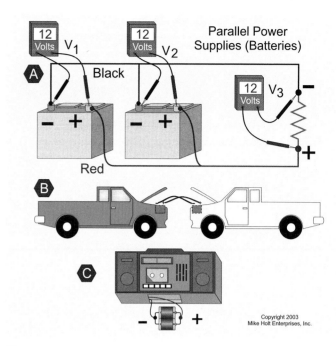

Figure 2–27

▶ **Example**

What is the resistance total of a 16 ohm, 13 ohm, and 36 ohm resistor connected in parallel?

  (a) 13 ohms   (b) 16 ohms

  (c) 36 ohms   (d) 6 ohms

  • Answer: (d) 6 ohms

    $R_T = 1/(1/16 \text{ ohms} + 1/13 \text{ ohms} + 1/36 \text{ ohms})$

    $R_T = 1/(0.0625 \text{ ohms} + 0.0769 \text{ ohms} + 0.0278 \text{ ohms})$

    $R_T = 1/(0.1672 \text{ ohms})$

    $R_T = 6 \text{ ohms}$

2.11 Parallel Circuit Notes

A parallel circuit has the following characteristics:

Note 1: Resistance total is less than the smallest resistance and you can find total resistance in a parallel circuit with the following formula:

$$R_T = 1/(^1/R_1 + {}^1/R_2 + {}^1/R_3 \ldots)$$

Note 2: The sum of the currents through each path is equal to the total current that flows from the source.

Note 3: Power total is equal to the sum of the branches' powers.

Note 4: Voltage is the same across each component of the parallel circuit.

Note 5: A parallel circuit has two or more paths for current to flow through.

2.12 Parallel-Connected Power Supplies

When power supplies are connected in parallel, the voltage remains the same, but the current, or in the case of batteries the amp-hour capacity, will be increased. To place batteries in parallel to each other, connect them with the proper polarity, which is (+) to (+) and (–) to (–). **Figure 2–27A**

> **AUTHOR'S COMMENT:** When jumping a car battery, place the red cables on the positive (+) terminals and the black cables on the negative (–) terminals. **Figure 2–27B**

Batteries are often connected in parallel in radios, toys, and other appliances that operate on dc power. **Figure 2–27C**

PART C—SERIES-PARALLEL CIRCUITS

Introduction

A series-parallel circuit is a circuit that contains some resistances in series and some in parallel to each other. That portion of the series-parallel circuit that contains resistances in series must comply with the rules for series circuits. That portion of the

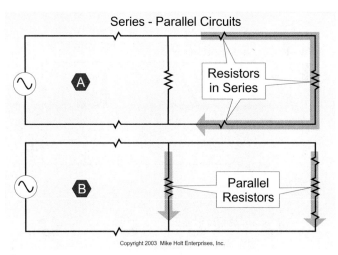

Figure 2–28

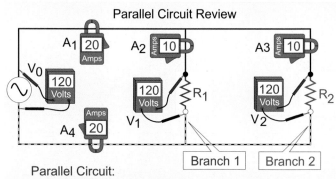

Parallel Circuit:
- Resistance is less than the smallest resistor.
- Current is additive.
- Power is additive.
- Voltage is constant.
- Multiple paths for current to flow.

Figure 2–30

series-parallel circuit that contains resistances in parallel must comply with the rules for parallel circuits. In all cases, however, it's good to remember that Ohm's Law always prevails. Figure 2–28

2.13 Review of Series and Parallel Circuits

To understand series-parallel circuits, we must review the rules for series and parallel circuits.

Series Circuit Review, Figure2–29

Note 1: The total resistance of the series circuit is equal to the sum of all of the resistances of the circuit.

Note 2: Current is constant.

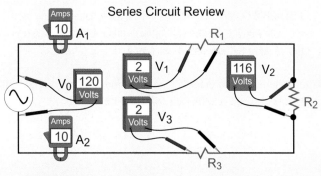

Series Circuit:
- Resistance is additive, $R_1 + R_2 + R_3$...
- Current remains the same
- Voltage is additive
  Voltage Source (V_0) = $V_1 + V_2 + V_3$...
- Power is additive, $P_1 + P_2 + P_3$...

Figure 2–29

Note 3: The sum of the voltage drop of all resistances must equal the voltage of the source.

Note 4: The sum of the power consumed by all resistances equals the total power of the circuit.

Parallel Circuit Review, Figure2–30

Note 1: Resistance total is less than the smallest resistance and you can find total resistance in a parallel circuit with the following formula:

$$R_T = 1/(^1/R_1 + {}^1/R_2 + {}^1/R_3 \ldots)$$

Note 2: The sum of the currents through each path is equal to the total current that flows from the source.

Note 3: Power total is equal to the sum of the branches' powers.

Note 4: Voltage is the same across each component of the parallel circuit.

Note 5: A parallel circuit has two or more paths for current to flow through.

2.14 Working Series-Parallel Circuits

When working with series-parallel circuits, it is best to redraw the circuit so you can see the series components and the parallel branches. Each circuit should be examined to determine the best plan of attack—some turn out to be easier to analyze if you tackle the parallel elements first and then combine them with the series elements. Figure 2–31

Other circuits are best worked by combining series elements first and then combining the result with the parallel resistances. In

Working Series-Parallel Circuits

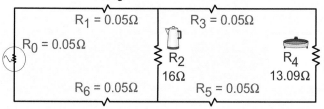

R1, R3, R5, and R6 are each 25 ft of 12 AWG, 0.05 ohms NEC Chapter 9, Table 9 per ft resistance:
2 ohms/1,000 ft x 25 ft = 0.05 ohms per 25 ft.

R_2 is a coffee pot rated 900W at 120V

$R_2 = E^2/P = 120V^2/900W = 16$ ohms

R_4 is a skillet rated 1,100W at 120V

$R_4 = E^2/P = 120V^2/1,100W = 13.09$ ohms

Figure 2–31

Figure 2–31, the series combination of R_3, R_4, and R_5 is the first step.

Step 1 Series: Determine the resistance total of each series branch using the formula:

$R_T = R_3 + R_4 + R_5$. Figure 2–32A

R_3 Conductor (25 ft of 12 AWG)	=	0.05 ohms
R_4 Skillet (1,100W)	=	13.09 ohms
R_5 Conductor (25 ft of 12 AWG)	=	0.05 ohms
		13.19 ohms

Calculating Series - Parallel Circuit Resistance

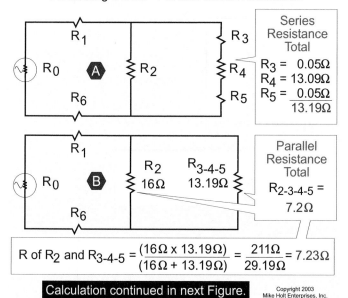

R of R_2 and R_{3-4-5} = $\dfrac{(16\Omega \times 13.19\Omega)}{(16\Omega + 13.19\Omega)}$ = $\dfrac{211\Omega}{29.19\Omega}$ = 7.23Ω

Calculation continued in next Figure. Copyright 2003 Mike Holt Enterprises, Inc.

Figure 2–32

The circuit can now be redrawn showing the relationship between the two conductors and the two parallel branches. **Figure 2–32B**

Step 2 Parallel: Determine the resistance total of the two parallel branches. **Figure 2–32B**

AUTHOR'S COMMENT: The resistance total of the two branches will be less than that of the smallest branch (13.19 ohms). Since we are only trying to determine the total resistance of two parallel branches, the Product-Over-Sum method can be used to determine the resistance.

R Total = $(R_2 \times R_{3,4,5})/(R_2 + R_{3,4,5})$
R Total = (16 ohms x 13.19 ohms)/
        (16 ohms + 13.19 ohms)
R Total = 7.23 ohms

AUTHOR'S COMMENT: When working series-parallel circuits, keep breaking the circuit down from series to parallel to series to parallel, etc., until you have only one resistance. **Figure 2–33**

2.15 Voltage

Even though the current is different in the different resistors, remember that Ohm's Law always works. Every complicated problem is really just a series of easy problems that are waiting to be worked out. To calculate the voltage of each resistor, simply consider each one on a case by case basis and multiply its value by the current flowing through it.

Calculating Series - Parallel Circuit Resistance

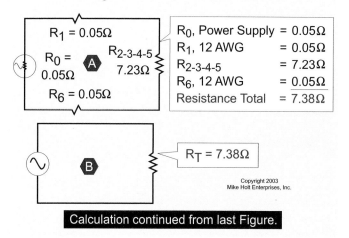

Calculation continued from last Figure.

Figure 2–33

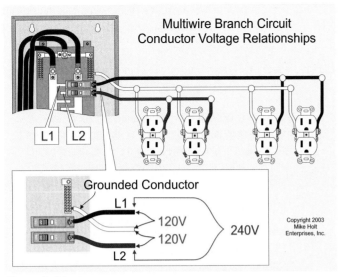

Figure 2–34

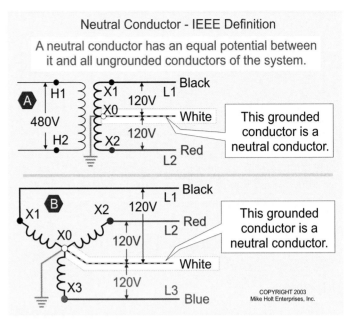

Figure 2–35

AUTHOR'S COMMENT: Determining the current flowing through each resistor is very complicated and beyond the scope of this textbook.

PART D—MULTIWIRE BRANCH CIRCUITS

Introduction

Understanding series, parallel, and series-parallel circuits is the foundation for understanding multiwire circuits. A multiwire circuit is a circuit consisting of two or more ungrounded conductors (hot wires) that have a voltage between them, and an equal voltage between each ungrounded conductor and the grounded neutral conductor. A typical 3-wire, 120/240V, single-phase circuit is an example. **Figure 2–34**

2.16 Neutral Conductor

According to the IEEE Dictionary, a neutral conductor is the conductor that has an equal potential difference between it and the other output conductors of a 3- or 4-wire system. Therefore, a neutral conductor will be the white/gray wire from a 3-wire, 120/240V, single-phase, or a 4-wire, 120/208V, three-phase system. **Figure 2–35**

AUTHOR'S COMMENT: Since a neutral conductor can only be from a 3- or 4-wire system, the white wire of a 2-wire, 120V, single-phase or 4-wire, 120/240V, three-phase high-leg delta system is not a neutral conductor—it's a grounded conductor. **Figure 2–36**

2.17 Grounded Conductor

The grounded conductor, according to the *NEC*, is a conductor that is intentionally grounded. In the case of home wiring (3-wire, 120/240V, single-phase), the grounded conductor is often called the neutral conductor, and it will be either white or gray in color in accordance with the *National Electrical Code*.

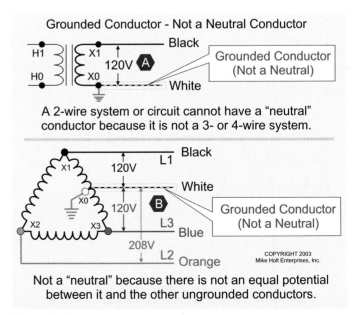

Figure 2–36

2-Wire Circuit
Current on Grounded Conductor

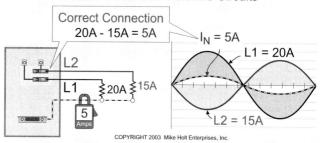

The current flowing in the grounded (neutral) conductor will be the same as the current in the ungrounded (hot) conductor.

COPYRIGHT 2003 Mike Holt Enterprises, Inc.

Figure 2–37

AUTHOR'S COMMENT: For convenience, I will refer to the neutral and the grounded conductor as the grounded neutral conductor.

2.18 Current Flow on the Grounded Neutral Conductor

To understand the current flow on the grounded neutral conductor, review the following circuits.

2-Wire Circuit

The current flowing in the grounded neutral conductor of a 2-wire circuit will be the same as the current flowing in the ungrounded (hot) conductor. Figure 2–37

Neutral Current on Multiwire Circuits

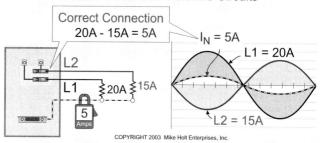

Currents on the grounded (neutral) conductor cancel because the current flowing through the grounded (neutral) conductor at any instant from the two phase conductors oppose each other.

Figure 2–39

3-Wire, 120/240V, Single-Phase Circuit

The current flowing in the grounded neutral conductor of a 3-wire, 120/240V, single-phase circuit will equal the difference in current flowing in the ungrounded conductors $(I_N = I_{Line1} - I_{Line2})$. Figure 2–38

The current on the grounded neutral conductor is equal to the difference in ungrounded conductor current because at any instant the currents on the two ungrounded conductors oppose each other. Figure 2–39

CAUTION: *If the ungrounded conductors of a multiwire circuit are not terminated to different phases, the currents on the ungrounded conductors will not cancel, but will add on the grounded neutral conductor. This can cause the neutral current*

3-Wire 1-Phase Circuit
Current on Grounded Conductor

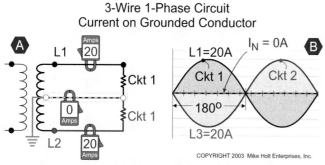

The current flowing in the grounded (neutral) conductor will be the difference between the current flowing in Line 1 and Line 2.

COPYRIGHT 2003 Mike Holt Enterprises, Inc.

Figure 2–38

Caution - Connection of Ungrounded Conductors of Multiwire Circuit

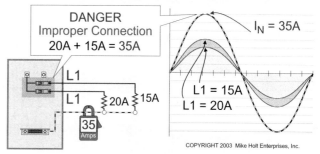

If the ungrounded conductors of a multiwire circuit are not terminated to different phases, the current on the grounded (neutral) conductor will add instead of cancel, which can overload the grounded (neutral) conductor.

Figure 2–40

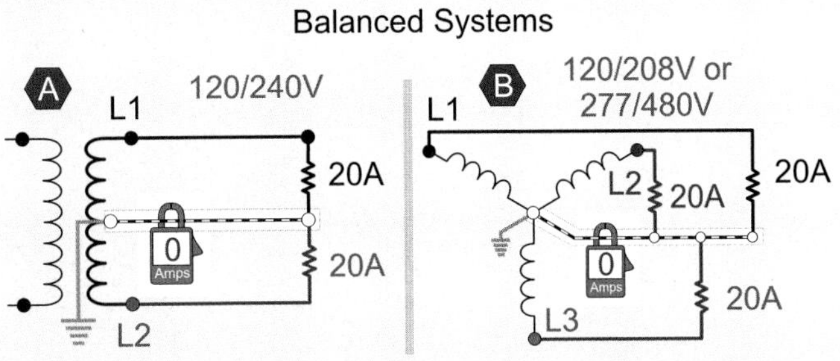

Balanced Systems

If the current flow in each line of a multiwire circuit is the same, the grounded (neutral) conductor will carry zero amperes.

COPYRIGHT 2003 Mike Holt Enterprises, Inc.

Figure 2–41

to be in excess of the grounded neutral conductor rating.
Figure 2–40

AUTHOR'S COMMENT: This is one reason white neutral conductors sometimes turn brown or black.

2.19 Balanced Systems

If the current in each ungrounded conductor of a multiwire circuit is the same, the grounded neutral conductor will carry 0A. This applies to 3-wire, 120/240V, single-phase and all three-phase circuits, regardless of configuration or voltage. Figure 2–41

2.20 Unbalanced Current

The current flowing on the grounded neutral conductor of a multiwire circuit is called "unbalanced current."

Unbalanced 120/240V 3-Wire Circuit

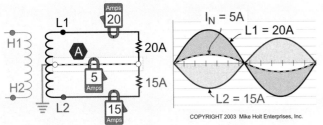

COPYRIGHT 2003 Mike Holt Enterprises, Inc.

The grounded (neutral) conductor of a 3-wire 120/240V circuit will carry current only when the ungrounded conductors do not have identical current flow. The unbalanced current is the difference between line 1 and line 2.

Figure 2–42

3-Wire, 120/240V, Single-Phase Circuit

The neutral conductor of a 3-wire, 120/240V, single-phase circuit will only carry current when the current on the ungrounded conductors is not identical. The unbalanced current is equal to: $I_{Line1} - I_{Line2}$. Figure 2–42

3-Wire Circuit from a 4-wire, Three-Phase System

The grounded neutral conductor of a 3-wire, 120/208V or 277/480V, three-phase circuit from a 4-wire, three-phase system will always carry neutral current. The current on the grounded neutral conductor of a 3-wire circuit supplied from a 4-wire, three-phase system is determined by the following formula:

$$I_N = \sqrt{[(L1^2 + L2^2 + L3^2) - [(L1 \times L2) + (L2 \times L3) + (L1 \times L3)]]}$$

▶ **Example**

What is the neutral current for a 3-wire, 120/208V, single-phase circuit, if each ungrounded conductor carries 20A, and the circuit is supplied from a 4-wire, 120/208V, three-phase system? Figure 2–43

(a) 80A   (b) 100A
(c) 20A   (d) 0A

• Answer: (c) 20A
$$I_N = \sqrt{[(20^2 + 20^2 + 0) - (20^2 + 0 + 0)]}$$
$$I_N = \sqrt{400}$$
$$I_N = 20A$$

Unbalanced Current - 3-Wire Circuit on 4-Wire System

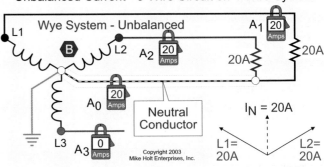

Copyright 2003
Mike Holt Enterprises, Inc.

The neutral of a 3-wire circuit from a 4-wire wye system carries about the same current as the phase conductors.

$$I_N = \sqrt{(L1^2 + L2^2 + L3^2) - [(L1 \times L2) + (L2 \times L3) + (L1 \times L3)]}$$
$$I_N = \sqrt{(20^2 + 20^2 + 0^2) - [(20 \times 20) + (20 \times 0) + (20 \times 0)]}$$
$$I_N = \sqrt{(400 + 400 + 0) - (400 + 0 + 0)}$$
$$I_N = \sqrt{800 - 400} \qquad I_N = \sqrt{400} \qquad I_N = 20A$$

Figure 2–43

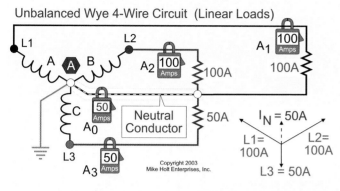

Neutral Current - 4-Wire Wye Circuit

Unbalanced Wye 4-Wire Circuit (Linear Loads)

$$I_N = \sqrt{(L1^2 + L2^2 + L3^2) - [(L1 \times L2) + (L2 \times L3) + (L1 \times L3)]}$$

$$I_N = \sqrt{22,500 - 20,000} \quad I_N = \sqrt{2,500} \quad I_N = 50A$$

Figure 2–44

4-Wire, Three-Phase Circuit

The neutral conductor of a 4-wire, 120/208V or 277/480V, three-phase system will have neutral current when the ungrounded conductors are not identically loaded. The current on the grounded neutral conductor of a 4-wire circuit supplied from a 4-wire system is determined by the following formula:

$$I_N = \sqrt{[(L1^2 + L2^2 + L3^2) - [(L1 \times L2) + (L2 \times L3) + (L1 \times L3)]]}$$

▶ **Example**

What is the neutral current for a 4-wire, 120/208V, three-phase circuit, if Line 1 = 100A, Line 2 = 100A and Line 3 = 50A? Figure 2–44

(a) 50A   (b) 100A
(c) 125A   (d) 0A

• Answer: (a) 50A
$$I_N = \sqrt{[(100^2 + 100^2 + 50^2) - [(100 \times 100) + (100 \times 50) + (100 \times 50)]]}$$
$$I_N = \sqrt{2,500}A$$
$$I_N = 50A$$

2.21 Multiwire Branch Circuit

Multiwire branch circuits are more cost-effective than 2-wire circuits in that they have fewer conductors for a given number of circuits, which enables the use of a smaller raceway. In addition, multiwire branch circuits result in lower circuit voltage drop.

Reduced Number of Conductors. Instead of four conductors for two 2-wire circuits, three conductors can be used with single-phase wiring, and instead of six conductors for three 2-wire circuits, four conductors can be used with three-phase wiring.

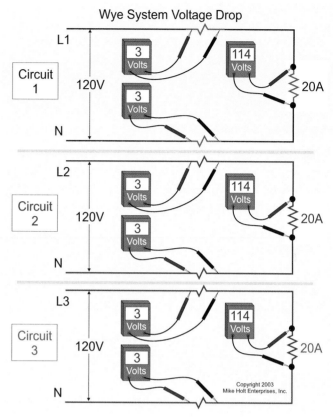

Wye System Voltage Drop

Figure 2–45

Reduced Raceway Size. If the number of circuit conductors is reduced, the size of the raceway can often be reduced. Reducing the number of conductors and installing a smaller raceway is very cost-effective. The cost savings include the material and labor, as well as overhead.

Reduced Circuit Voltage Drop. The voltage drop of the circuit conductors is dependent upon the magnitude of current and conductor resistance: $E_{VD} = I \times R$.

2-Wire Circuit Voltage Drop

A typical 2-wire circuit will have current flow over both the ungrounded and grounded neutral conductors. Therefore, the circuit voltage drop includes the voltage drop of both conductors.

▶ **Example**

What is the voltage drop of two 12 AWG conductors, each 75 ft long, supplying a 2-wire, 20A load? Figure 2–45

(a) 2V   (b) 4V
(c) 3V   (d) 6V

• Answer: (d) 6V

$E_{VD} = I \times R$
$I = 20A$
$R = (2 \text{ ohms per } 1{,}000 \text{ ft}/1{,}000) \times 75 \text{ ft} \times 2 \text{ wires}$
$R = 0.30 \text{ ohms}$
$E_{VD} = 20A \times 0.30 \text{ ohms}$
$E_{VD} = 6V$

Multiwire Circuit Voltage Drop

A balanced 3-wire, single-phase or 4-wire, three-phase multiwire branch circuit will have current flow only on the ungrounded circuit conductors. Therefore, the circuit voltage drop only includes the voltage drop of one conductor.

▶ **Example**

What is the circuit voltage drop over each line conductor of a balanced 4-wire multiwire circuit? Each conductor is 12 AWG, 75 ft long, supplying a 20A load. **Figure 2–46**

(a) 2V   (b) 4V
(c) 3V   (d) 6V

• Answer: (c) 3V

The grounded neutral conductor in a balanced 4-wire system effectively has 0A of current flow (the three return currents cancel each other out because of their phase relationship). Thus, by Ohm's Law, the voltage drop over this conductor is 0V. The remaining phase conductor voltage drop can be calculated as follows:

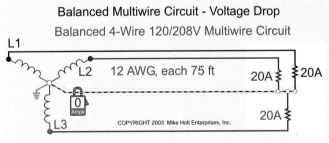

Balanced Multiwire Circuit - Voltage Drop
Balanced 4-Wire 120/208V Multiwire Circuit

L1
L2   12 AWG, each 75 ft   20A   20A
0 Amps
20A
L3
COPYRIGHT 2003 Mike Holt Enterprises, Inc.

The grounded (neutral) conductor in a balanced 4-wire system effectively has no current flow. Thus, the voltage drop on the grounded (neutral) conductor is 0V. The remaining phase conductor voltage drop can be calculated as follows:

$E_{VD} = IR, I = 20A,$
$R = 2 \text{ ohms per } 1{,}000 \text{ ft} = 0.15 \text{ ohms for } 75 \text{ ft}$
$E_{VD} = 20A \times 0.15 \text{ ohms} = 3 \text{ volts dropped}$

Figure 2–46

$E_{VD} = I \times R$
$I = 20A$
$R = (2 \text{ ohms per } 1{,}000 \text{ ft}/1{,}000) \times 75 \text{ ft} \times 1 \text{ wire}$
$R = 0.15 \text{ ohms}$
$E_{VD} = 20A \times 0.15 \text{ ohms}$
$E_{VD} = 3V$

2.22 Dangers of Multiwire Circuits

As in life, there are no benefits without risk. Yes, multiwire circuits offer fewer conductors, reduced raceway size and voltage drop; however, improper wiring or mishandling of multiwire circuits can cause a fire hazard because of conductor overloading and/or the destruction of equipment connected because of over, as well as under, operating voltage.

Fire Hazard

Failure to terminate the ungrounded conductors to separate phases can cause the grounded neutral conductor to become overloaded from excessive neutral current, and the insulation can be damaged or destroyed. Conductor overheating is known to decrease insulating material service life, potentially resulting in a fire from arcing faults in hidden locations. We don't know just how long conductor insulation will last, but heat does decrease its life span. **Figure 2–47**

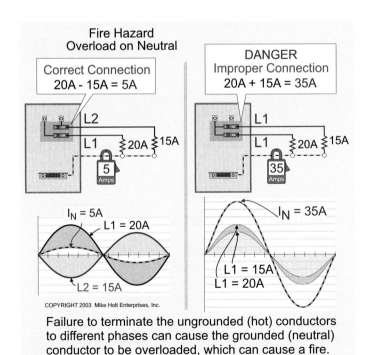

Fire Hazard
Overload on Neutral

Correct Connection
20A - 15A = 5A

DANGER
Improper Connection
20A + 15A = 35A

L2
L1   20A   15A
5 Amps

L1
L1   20A   15A
35 Amps

$I_N = 5A$
L1 = 20A

$I_N = 35A$

L2 = 15A

L1 = 15A
L1 = 20A

COPYRIGHT 2003 Mike Holt Enterprises, Inc.

Failure to terminate the ungrounded (hot) conductors to different phases can cause the grounded (neutral) conductor to be overloaded, which can cause a fire.

Figure 2–47

Destruction of Equipment as Well as Fire Hazard

The opening of the ungrounded or grounded neutral conductor of a 2-wire circuit during the replacement of a device does not cause a safety hazard, so pigtailing of these conductors is not required.

If the continuity of the grounded neutral conductor of a multi-wire circuit is interrupted (open), there could be a fire and/or destruction of electrical equipment resulting from overvoltage or undervoltage.

▶ **Example**

A 3-wire, 120/240V circuit supplies a 1,200W, 120V hair dryer and a 600W, 120V television. If the grounded neutral conductor is interrupted, it will cause the 120V television to operate at 160V and consume 1,067W of power (instead of 600W) for only a few seconds before it burns up. **Figure 2–48**

Step 1 Determine the resistance of each appliance, $R = E^2/P$.

Hair Dryer
$R = 120V^2/1,200W$
$R = 12$ ohms

Television
$R = 120V^2/600W$
$R = 24$ ohms

Step 2 Determine the current of the circuit.
$I = E/R$
$I = 240V/(12 \text{ ohms} + 24 \text{ ohms})$
$I = 6.7A$

Step 3 Determine the operating voltage for each appliance, $E = I \times R$.

Hair Dryer Operates at $= 6.7A \times 12$ ohms
Hair Dryer Operates at $= 80V$
Television Operates at $= 6.7A \times 24$ ohms
Television Operates at $= 160V$

2.23 NEC Requirements

Because of the dangers associated with an open grounded neutral conductor, the *NEC* specifies that the continuity of the grounded neutral conductor cannot be dependent upon any wiring device. In other words, the grounded neutral conductors of a multiwire circuit should be spliced together, and a wire brought out to the device. This way, if the receptacle is removed, it will not result in an open grounded neutral conductor. Figure 2–49

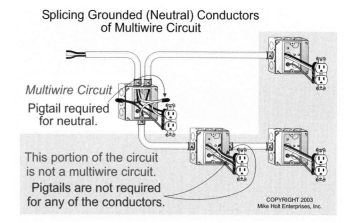

Splicing Grounded (Neutral) Conductors
of Multiwire Circuit

Multiwire Circuit
Pigtail required for neutral.

This portion of the circuit is not a multiwire circuit.
Pigtails are not required for any of the conductors.

COPYRIGHT 2003
Mike Holt Enterprises, Inc.

Because of the dangers associated with an open grounded (neutral) conductor, the NEC specifies that the grounded (neutral) conductors of a multiwire circuit be spliced together.

Figure 2–49

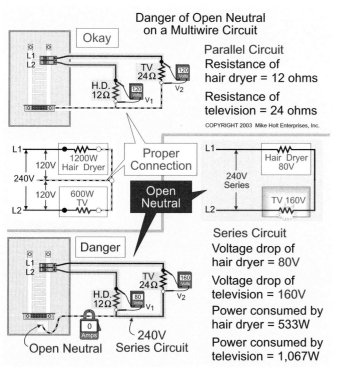

Danger of Open Neutral
on a Multiwire Circuit

Okay

TV 24Ω
H.D. 12Ω

Parallel Circuit
Resistance of hair dryer = 12 ohms

Resistance of television = 24 ohms

COPYRIGHT 2003 Mike Holt Enterprises, Inc.

Proper Connection

1200W Hair Dryer 120V
600W TV 120V
240V

Open Neutral

Hair Dryer 80V
240V Series
TV 160V

Series Circuit
Voltage drop of hair dryer = 80V

Voltage drop of television = 160V

Power consumed by hair dryer = 533W

Power consumed by television = 1,067W

Danger

TV 24Ω
H.D. 12Ω
0 Amps
240V

Open Neutral   Series Circuit

Figure 2–48

Unit 2 Conclusion

In completing this unit, you have laid another block in the foundation of your understanding. You have learned about series circuits, parallel circuits, and combinations of series and parallel circuits. It is important to be able to look at a circuit and visualize the relationship between the components and be able to predict what the voltage or current should be in various locations of the circuit. This ability will greatly enhance your troubleshooting success on real branch circuits.

In this unit, you learned about a special circuit called the multiwire branch circuit. There are special *Code* considerations for multiwire branch circuits. You now know how important it is to correctly install multiwire circuits with neutral connections that are very securely made. A neutral must never be opened on an energized multiwire branch circuit, as this can result in placing both undervoltages and over-voltages on circuit components, which can result in damage.

You learned about Kirchoff's Law in this unit. If you understand the application of Kirchoff's law, you are less likely to be misled by some of the incorrect "myths" that are commonly accepted in the electrical industry concerning fault current flow, particularly as it relates to the practices of grounding versus bonding. For instance, does current always take only the path of least resistance? Is current always seeking a path to the earth? Ponder these questions as you continue your study in the intriguing field of electricity.

Unit 2 Calculation Practice Questions

(• Indicates that 75% or fewer of those who took this exam answered the question correctly.)

PART A—SERIES CIRCUITS

Introduction

1. A series circuit is a circuit in which a specific amount of current leaves the voltage source and flows through every electrical device in a single path before it returns to the voltage source.

    (a) True   (b) False

2.1 Practical Uses of the Series Circuit

2. For most practical purposes, series circuits are used for _____ circuits.

    (a) signal   (b) control   (c) a and b   (d) none of these

3. A 115/230V rated motor connected to a 230V circuit must have the windings connected in series so that each winding will receive at least 230V.

    (a) True   (b) False

2.2 Understanding Series Calculations

4. Resistance opposes the flow of electrons. In a series circuit, the total circuit resistance is equal to the sum of all of the resistances in series.

    (a) True   (b) False

5. The opposition to current flow results in a voltage drop of the circuit voltage.

    (a) True   (b) False

6. Kirchoff's Voltage Law states that in a series circuit, the sum of the voltage drops across all of the resistors will equal the applied voltage.

    (a) True   (b) False

7. No matter how many resistances there are in a series circuit, the sum of the voltages across all of the resistances will equal the voltage of the source according to the Law of Proportion.

    (a) True   (b) False

8. Kirchoff's Current Law states that in a series circuit, the current is _____ through the transformer, the conductors, and the appliance.

    (a) proportional   (b) distributed   (c) additive   (d) the same

9. The power consumed in a series circuit is equal to the power consumed by the largest resistance in the series circuit.

    (a) True   (b) False

2.3 Series Circuit Calculations

10. To determine the resistance of each resistive element in the circuit, use the formula $R = E^2/P$. E is the rated voltage of the resistor, and P is the rated power of the resistor.

    (a) True   (b) False

11. To calculate the total resistance of the circuit: $R_T = R_1 + R_2 + R_3 + ...$

    (a) True   (b) False

12. The current of the circuit can be determined by the formula $I = E_S/R_T$.

    (a) True   (b) False

2.4 Power Calculations

13. If you know the current of the circuit and the resistance of each resistor, the power of each resistor can be determined by the formula $P = I^2 \times R$.

    (a) True   (b) False

2.5 Variations

14. There can never be variations in the formulas used or the order in which they are used for series circuits.

    (a) True   (b) False

2.7 Series-Connected Power Supplies

15. When power supplies are connected in series, the circuit voltage remains the same as when only one power supply is connected to it, provided that all the polarities are connected properly.

    (a) True   (b) False

PART B—PARALLEL CIRCUITS

Introduction

16. A parallel circuit is a circuit where there are two or more paths in which current may flow.

    (a) True   (b) False

2.9 Understanding Parallel Calculations

17. In a parallel circuit, the voltage drop across each resistance is equal to the sum of the voltage drops of each of the resistors in parallel.

    (a) True   (b) False

18. According to Kirchoff's Current Law, the total current provided by the source to a parallel circuit equals the sum of the currents of all of the branches.

    (a) True   (b) False

19. The total power consumed in a parallel circuit equals the sum of the branches' powers.

    (a) True   (b) False

2.10 Circuit Resistance

20. In a parallel circuit, the total circuit resistance is always greater than the smallest resistance.

(a) True   (b) False

21. The total resistance of a parallel circuit can be calculated by the _____ method.

(a) equal resistance   (b) product-over-sum   (c) reciprocal   (d) any of these

22. According to the equal resistance method, when all the resistances of the parallel circuit have the same resistance, divide the resistance of one element by the largest resistor in parallel.

(a) True   (b) False

23. The product-over-sum method is used to calculate the resistance of _____ resistance(s) at a time.

(a) one   (b) two   (c) three   (d) four

24. The advantage of the reciprocal method is that the formula can be used for as many resistances as the parallel circuit contains.

(a) True   (b) False

2.12 Parallel-Connected Power Supplies

25. When power supplies are connected in parallel, the voltage remains the same, but the current or amp-hour capacity will be increased.

(a) True   (b) False

PART C—SERIES-PARALLEL CIRCUITS
Introduction

26. A _____ is a circuit that contains some resistances in series and some resistances in parallel with each other.

(a) parallel circuit   (b) series circuit   (c) series-parallel circuit   (d) none of these

27. That portion of the series-parallel circuit that contains resistances in series must comply with the rules for series circuits.

(a) True   (b) False

28. That portion of the series-parallel circuit that contains resistances in parallel must comply with the rules for parallel circuits.

(a) True   (b) False

2.14 Working Series-Parallel Circuits

29. When working with series-parallel circuits, it is best to redraw the circuit so you can see the series components and the parallel branches.

(a) True   (b) False

PART D—MULTIWIRE BRANCH CIRCUITS
Introduction

30. A multiwire circuit has two or more ungrounded conductors having a potential difference between them, and having an equal difference of potential between each ungrounded conductor and the grounded conductor.

(a) True   (b) False

31. According to the *IEEE Dictionary*, a neutral conductor has the same equal potential between it and all ungrounded conductors of a _____ system.

    (a) 2-wire   (b) 3-wire   (c) 4-wire   (d) b or c

2.16 Neutral Conductor

32. A 2-wire, 120V circuit contains _____.

    (a) a neutral conductor   (b) a grounded conductor
    (c) two ungrounded conductors   (d) b and c

33. A 3-wire, 120/240V circuit from a three-phase delta transformer contains a(n) _____.

    (a) neutral conductor   (b) grounded conductor
    (c) ungrounded conductor   (d) b and c

2.17 Grounded Conductor

34. The grounded conductor is a conductor that is intentionally grounded to the earth.

    (a) True   (b) False

2.18 Current Flow on the Grounded Neutral Conductor

35. The current on the grounded conductor of a 2-wire circuit is _____ of the current on the ungrounded conductor.

    (a) 0%   (b) 70%   (c) 80%   (d) 100%

36. A balanced 3-wire, 120/240V, single-phase circuit is connected so that the ungrounded conductors are from different transformer phases (Line 1 and Line 2). The current on the grounded conductor is _____ of the ungrounded conductor current.

    (a) 0%   (b) 70%   (c) 80%   (d) 100%

37. The grounded conductor of a 3-wire, 120/240V, single-phase circuit will only carry the unbalanced current when the circuit is not balanced.

    (a) True   (b) False

38. If the ungrounded conductors of a multiwire circuit are not terminated to different phases, this can cause the neutral current to be in excess of the grounded conductor rating.

    (a) True   (b) False

2.19 Balanced Systems

39. If the current in each ungrounded conductor of a multiwire circuit is the same, the grounded conductor carries 0A.

    (a) True   (b) False

40. What is the neutral current for a 4-wire, 120/208V circuit, where L_1 = 20A, L_2 = 20A, and L_3 = 20A?

    (a) 0A   (b) 10A   (c) 20A   (d) none of these

2.20 Unbalanced Current

41. The current flowing on the grounded conductor of a multiwire circuit is called unbalanced current.

    (a) True   (b) False

42. The neutral conductor of a 3-wire, 120/240V, single-phase circuit only carries current when the current on the ungrounded conductors is not identical.

    (a) True   (b) False

43. The neutral conductor of a 3-wire, 120/208V or 277/480V circuit supplied from a 4-wire, three-phase system never carries neutral current.

    (a) True   (b) False

44. The neutral conductor of a 4-wire, 120/208V or 277/480V, three-phase system has neutral current flow when the ungrounded conductors are equally loaded.

    (a) True   (b) False

2.21 Multiwire Branch Circuit

45. Multiwire branch circuits have more conductors for a given number of circuits, which requires the use of a larger raceway.

    (a) True   (b) False

46. A balanced multiwire branch circuit has current flow only on the ungrounded conductors.

    (a) True   (b) False

47. What is the voltage drop of two 12 AWG conductors, each 100 ft in length, supplying a 2-wire, 16A load? The resistance of 12 AWG conductors is 2 ohms per 1,000 ft.

    (a) 3.2V   (b) 6.4V   (c) 7.2V   (d) 9.6V

48. What is the voltage drop of each ungrounded conductor of a 4-wire multiwire circuit? Each conductor is 12 AWG, 100 ft in length, supplying a 16A load. The resistance of 12 AWG conductors is 2 ohms per 1,000 ft.

    (a) 3.2V   (b) 6.4V   (c) 7.2V   (d) 9.6V

2.22 Dangers of Multiwire Circuits

49. Improper wiring or mishandling of multiwire branch circuits can cause _____ connected to the circuit.

    (a) overloading of the ungrounded conductors   (b) overloading of the grounded conductors
    (c) destruction of equipment because of overvoltage   (d) b and c

50. The opening of the ungrounded or grounded conductor of a _____ circuit during the replacement of a device does not cause a safety hazard, so pigtailing of these conductors is not required.

    (a) 2-wire   (b) 3-wire   (c) 4-wire   (d) all of these

2.23 *NEC* Requirements

51. Because of the dangers associated with an open grounded conductor, the continuity of the _____ conductor in a multiwire branch circuit cannot be dependent upon the receptacle.

    (a) ungrounded   (b) grounded   (c) a and b   (d) none of these

(• Indicates that 75% or fewer of those who took this exam answered the question correctly.)

PART A—SERIES CIRCUITS

2.2 Understanding Series Calculations

1. •A series circuit contains two resistors, one rated 4 ohms and the other rated 8 ohms. If the total voltage drop across both resistors equals 12V, then the current that passes through either resistor will be _____.

    (a) 1A   (b) 2A   (c) 4A   (d) 8A

2. •A series circuit has four 40 ohm resistors and the power supply is 120V. The voltage drop of each resistor will be _____.

    (a) one-quarter of the source voltage   (b) 30V
    (c) the same across each resistor   (d) all of these

3. •The power consumed in a series circuit is _____.

    (a) the sum of the power consumed of each load   (b) determined by the formula $PT = I^2 \times R_T$
    (c) determined by the formula $P_T = E \times I$ (d) all of these

4. •The reading on voltmeter 2 (V2) is _____ (see **Figure 2-50**).

    (a) 5V   (b) 7V   (c) 10V   (d) 6V

5. The voltmeter connected across the switch reads _____ (see **Figure 2-51**).

    (a) 3V   (b) 12V   (c) 6V   (d) 18V

PART B—PARALLEL CIRCUITS

2.9 Understanding Parallel Calculations

6. •In general, when multiple light bulbs are wired in a single luminaire, they are connected in _____ to each other.

    (a) series   (b) series-parallel   (c) parallel   (d) order of wattage

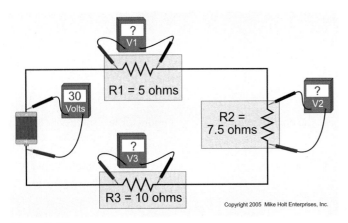

Figure 2–50

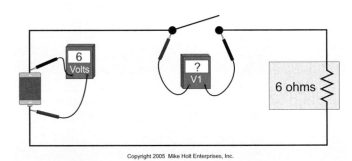

Figure 2–51

7.   •A single-phase, dual-rated, 120/240V motor will have its winding connected in _____ when supplied by 120V.

(a) series   (b) parallel   (c) series-parallel   (d) parallel-series

8.   •The voltmeters shown in Figure 2-52 are connected _____ each of the loads.

(a) in series to   (b) across   (c) in parallel to   (d) b and c

9.   •If the supply voltage is 120V, the total energy consumed for four 10 ohm resistors will be more if all resistors are connected _____.

(a) in series   (b) in series-parallel   (c) in parallel   (d) any of these

2.10 Circuit Resistance

10.   •A parallel circuit has three resistors. One resistor is rated 2 ohms, one is rated 3 ohms, and the other is rated 4 ohms. The total resistance of the parallel circuit is _____. Remember, the total resistance of any parallel circuit is always less than the smallest resistor.

(a) 0.50 ohms   (b) 1 ohm   (c) 2 ohms   (d) 3 ohms

Figure 2-53 applies to the next three questions:

11.   •The total current of the circuit can be measured by ammeter _____ (see Figure 2-53).

(a) A1   (b) A2   (c) A3   (d) none of these

12.   If Bell 2 consumes 12W of power when supplied by two 12V batteries (connected in series), the resistance of this bell is _____ (see Figure 2-53).

(a) 12 ohms   (b) 24 ohms   (c) 36 ohms   (d) 48 ohms

13.   Determine the total circuit resistance of the parallel circuit based on the following facts (see Figure 2-53):

1. The current on ammeter 1 reads 0.75A.
2. The voltage of the circuit is 30V.
3. Bell 2 has a resistance of 48 ohms.
Tip: The total resistance of a parallel circuit is always less than the smallest resistor.

(a) 22 ohms   (b) 32 ohms   (c) 42 ohms   (d) 60 ohms

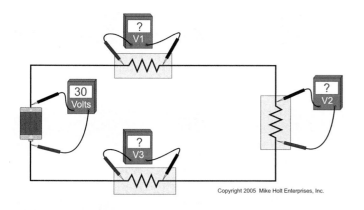

Figure 2–52

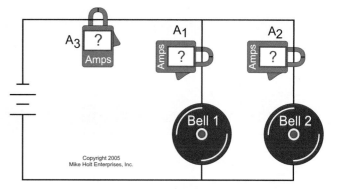

Figure 2–53

PART C—SERIES-PARALLEL CIRCUITS

2.14 Working Series-Parallel Circuits

Figure 2-54 applies to the next three questions:

14. •The total current of this circuit can be read on _____ (see Figure 2-54).

    (a) Ammeter 1   (b) Ammeter 2
    (c) Ammeter 3   (d) all of these

15. •The reading of Voltmeter 2 (V2) is _____ (see Figure 2-54).

    (a) 1.5V   (b) 4V
    (c) 5V   (d) 8V

16. •The reading of V4 is _____ (see Figure 2-54).

    (a) 1.5V   (b) 3V
    (c) 5V   (d) 8V

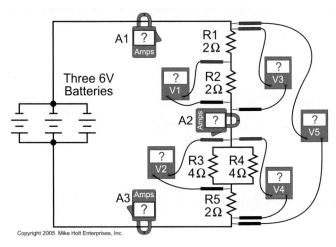

Figure 2–54

Figure 2-55 applies to the next two questions:

17. Resistor R1 has a resistance of 5 ohms and resistors R2, R3, and R4 have a resistance of 15 ohms each. The total resistance of this series-parallel circuit is _____ (see Figure 2-55).

    (a) 50 ohms   (b) 35 ohms
    (c) 25 ohms   (d) 10 ohms

18. •What is the voltage drop across R_1, if R_1 is equal to 5 ohms and the total resistance of R_2, R_3, and R_4 is 5 ohms (see Figure 2-55)?

    (a) 60V   (b) 33V
    (c) 40V   (d) 120V

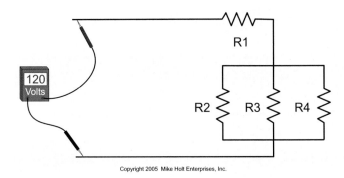

Figure 2–55

PART D—MULTIWIRE BRANCH CIRCUITS

2.22 Dangers of Multiwire Circuits

19. •If the neutral of the circuit in the diagram is opened, the circuit becomes one series circuit of 240V. Under this condition, the current of the circuit is _____. Tip: Determine the total resistance (see Figure 2-56).

    (a) 0.67A   (b) 0.58A
    (c) 2.25A   (d) 0.25A

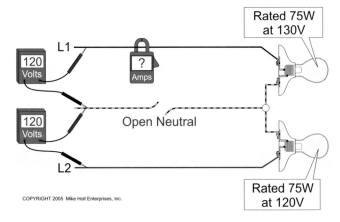

Figure 2–56

(• Indicates that 75% or fewer of those who took this exam answered the question correctly.)

Article 200 Use and Identification of Grounded Conductors

This article contains the requirements for identification of the grounded conductor and its terminals.

1. Premises wiring must not be electrically connected to a supply system unless the supply system contains, for any grounded conductor of the interior system, a corresponding conductor that is ungrounded.

    (a) True   (b) False

2. The application of distinctive marking at the terminals during the process of installation must identify the grounded conductor of _____ metal-sheathed cable.

    (a) armored   (b) mineral-insulated   (c) copper   (d) aluminum

3. Grounded conductors larger than 6 AWG must be identified by _____.

    (a) a continuous white or gray outer finish along their entire length
    (b) three continuous white stripes along their entire length
    (c) distinctive white or gray tape or paint at terminations
    (d) a, b, or c

4. Where grounded conductors of different wiring systems are installed in the same raceway, cable, or enclosure, each grounded conductor must be identified in a manner that makes it possible to distinguish the grounded conductors for each system. This means of identification must be_____.

    (a) permanently posted at each branch-circuit panelboard
    (b) posted inside each junction box where both system neutrals are present
    (c) done using a listed labeling technique
    (d) all of these

5. A cable containing an insulated conductor with a white outer finish can be used for single pole, 3-way or 4-way switch loops, if it is permanently reidentified by painting or other effective means at its termination, and at each location where the conductor is visible and accessible.

    (a) True   (b) False

6. Receptacles, polarized attachment plugs, and cord connectors for plugs and polarized plugs must have the terminal intended for connection to the grounded conductor identified. Identification must be by a metal or metal coating that is substantially _____ in color, or by the word white or the letter W located adjacent to the identified terminal.

    (a) green   (b) white   (c) gray   (d) b or c

7. No _____ can be attached to any terminal or lead so as to reverse designated polarity.

    (a) grounded conductor   (b) grounding conductor   (c) ungrounded conductor   (d) grounding connector

Article 210 Branch Circuits

This article contains the requirements for branch circuits, such as conductor sizing, identification, GFCI protection of receptacles, and receptacle and lighting outlet requirements.

8. 120/208V or 480Y/227V, three-phase, 4-wire, wye systems used to supply nonlinear loads such as personal computers, energy-efficient electronic ballasts, electronic dimming, etc., cause distortion of the phase and neutral currents producing high, unwanted, and potentially hazardous harmonic neutral currents. The *Code* cautions us that the system design for multiwire branch circuits should allow for the possibility of high harmonic neutral currents.

    (a) True   (b) False

9. When more than one nominal voltage system exists in a building, each ungrounded system conductor must be identified by system. The means of identification must be permanently posted at each branch-circuit panelboard.

    (a) True   (b) False

10. Where more than one nominal voltage system exists in a building, each _____ conductor of a branch circuit, where accessible, must be identified by system.

    (a) grounded   (b) ungrounded   (c) grounding   (d) all of these

11. A branch-circuit voltage that exceeds 277 volts-to-ground and does not exceed 600V between conductors is used to wire the auxiliary equipment of electrical discharge lamps mounted on poles. The minimum height of these luminaires must not be less than _____.

    (a) 31 ft   (b) 15 ft   (c) 18 ft   (d) 22 ft

12. Where two or more branch circuits supply devices or equipment on the same yoke, a means to disconnect simultaneously all ungrounded (hot) conductors that supply those devices or equipment must be provided _____.

    (a) at the point where the branch circuit originates   (b) at the location of the device or equipment
    (c) at the point where the feeder originates   (d) none of these

13. All 15 and 20A, 125V single-phase receptacles installed in bathrooms of _____ must have ground-fault circuit-interrupter (GFCI) protection for personnel.

    (a) guest rooms in hotels/motels   (b) dwelling units
    (c) office buildings   (d) all of these

14. GFCI protection is required for all 15 and 20A, 125V single-phase receptacles in accessory buildings that have a floor located at or below grade level not intended as _____ and limited to storage areas, work areas, or similar use.

    (a) habitable   (b) finished   (c) a or b   (d) none of these

15. GFCI protection for personnel is required for fixed electric snow melting or deicing equipment receptacles that are not readily accessible and are supplied by a dedicated branch circuit.

    (a) True   (b) False

16. GFCI protection for personnel is required for all 15 and 20A, 125V single-phase receptacles installed to serve the countertop surfaces in dwelling unit kitchens.

    (a) True   (b) False

17. All 15 and 20A, 125V single-phase receptacles installed in dwelling unit boathouses must have GFCI protection for personnel.

    (a) True   (b) False

18. GFCI protection for personnel is required for all 15 and 20A, 125V single-phase receptacles installed on rooftops in other than dwelling units, including those for fixed electric snow melting or deicing equipment.

    (a) True   (b) False

19. In locations other than dwelling units, a kitchen _____.

    (a) is required to have GFCI protection on all 15 and 20A, 125V single-phase receptacles
    (b) includes a sink
    (c) includes permanent facilities for food preparation and cooking
    (d) all of these

20. Ground-fault circuit-interrupter protection for personnel must be provided for outlets that supply boat hoists installed in dwelling unit locations and supplied by a 15 or 20A, 120V branch circuit.

    (a) True   (b) False

21. Two or more _____, 120V small-appliance branch circuits must be provided to supply power for the receptacle outlets in the dwelling unit kitchen, dining room, breakfast room, pantry, or similar dining areas.

    (a) 15A   (b) 20A   (c) 30A   (d) either 20A or 30A

22. An individual 20A circuit is permitted to supply power to a single dwelling unit bathroom for receptacle outlet(s) and other equipment within the same bathroom.

    (a) True   (b) False

23. All 15 or 20A, 120V branch circuits that supply outlets in dwelling unit bedrooms must be AFCI protected by a listed arc-fault circuit interrupter of the combination type after January 1, 2008.

    (a) True   (b) False

24. _____ provided with permanent provisions for cooking must have branch circuits and outlets installed to meet the rules for dwelling units.

    (a) Guest rooms   (b) Guest suites   (c) Commercial kitchens   (d) a and b

25. The recommended maximum total voltage drop on both the feeder and branch-circuit conductors combined is _____ percent.

    (a) 3   (b) 2   (c) 5   (d) 4.6

26. Where a branch circuit supplies continuous loads, or any combination of continuous and noncontinuous loads, the rating of the overcurrent device must not be less than the noncontinuous load plus 125 percent of the continuous load.

    (a) True   (b) False

27. When connected to a branch circuit supplying _____ or more receptacles or outlets, a receptacle must not supply a total cord-and-plug connected load in excess of the maximum specified in Table 210.21(B)(2).

    (a) two   (b) three   (c) four   (d) five

28. •If a 20A branch circuit supplies multiple 125V receptacles, the receptacles must have an ampere rating of no less than _____.

    (a) 10A   (b) 15A   (c) 20A   (d) 30A

29. The total rating of utilization equipment fastened in place, other than luminaires, must not exceed _____ percent of the branch-circuit ampere rating where the circuit also supplies receptacles for cord-and-plug connected equipment not fastened in place and/or lighting units.

    (a) 50   (b) 75   (c) 100   (d) 125

30. _____ in dwelling units must supply only loads within that dwelling unit or loads associated only with that dwelling unit.

    (a) Service-entrance conductors   (b) Ground-fault protection
    (c) Branch circuits   (d) none of these

31. Receptacle outlets installed for a specific appliance in a dwelling unit, such as a clothes washer, dryer, range, or refrigerator, must be within _____ of the intended location of the appliance.

    (a) sight   (b) 6 ft
    (c) 3 ft   (d) readily accessible, no maximum distance

32. When applying the general provisions for receptacle spacing to the rooms of a dwelling unit, which require receptacles in the wall space, no point along the floor line in any wall space of a dwelling unit may be more than _____ from an outlet.

    (a) 12 ft   (b) 10 ft   (c) 8 ft   (d) 6 ft

33. In a dwelling unit, each wall space of _____ or wider requires a receptacle.

    (a) 2 ft   (b) 3 ft   (c) 4 ft   (d) 5 ft

34. In dwelling units, outdoor receptacles can be connected to one of the 20A small-appliance branch circuits.

    (a) True   (b) False

35. A receptacle connected to one of the small-appliance branch circuits can be used to supply an electric clock.

    (a) True   (b) False

36. Receptacles installed in a kitchen to serve countertop surfaces must be supplied by not fewer than _____small-appliance branch circuits.

    (a) one   (b) two   (c) three   (d) no minimum

37. A receptacle outlet must be installed at each wall counter space that is 12 in. or wider so that no point along the wall line is more than _____, measured horizontally, from a receptacle outlet in that space.

    (a) 10 in.   (b) 12 in.   (c) 16 in.   (d) 24 in.

38. At least one receptacle outlet must be installed at each peninsular countertop or island not containing a sink or range top, having a long dimension of _____ in. or greater, and a short dimension of _____ in. or greater.

    (a) 12, 24   (b) 24, 12   (c) 24, 48   (d) 48, 24

39. For the purpose of determining the placement of receptacles in a dwelling unit kitchen, a(n) _____ countertop is measured from the connecting edge.

    (a) island   (b) usable   (c) peninsular   (d) cooking

40. Kitchen and dining room countertop receptacle outlets in dwelling units must be installed above the countertop surface, and not more than ___ above the countertop.

    (a) 12 in.   (b) 20 in.   (c) 24 in.   (d) none of these

41. The required receptacle for a dwelling unit countertop surface can be mounted a maximum height of _____ above a dwelling unit kitchen counter surface.

    (a) 10 in.   (b) 12 in.   (c) 18 in.   (d) 20 in.

42. In dwelling units, the required wall receptacle outlet is allowed to be installed on the side or front of the basin cabinet if no lower than _____ below the countertop.

    (a) 12 in.   (b) 18 in.   (c) 24 in.   (d) 36 in.

43. At least one receptacle outlet accessible from grade level and not more than _____ above grade must be installed at each dwelling unit of a multifamily dwelling located at grade level and provided with individual exterior entrance/egress.

    (a) 3 ft   (b) 6 1/2 ft   (c) 8 ft   (d) 24 in.

44. For a one-family dwelling, at least one receptacle outlet is required in each _____.

    (a) basement   (b) attached garage
    (c) detached garage with electric power   (d) all of these

45. Hallways in dwelling units that are _____ long or longer require a receptacle outlet.

    (a) 12 ft   (b) 10 ft   (c) 8 ft   (d) 15 ft

46. Guest rooms or guest suites provided with permanent provisions for _____ must have receptacle outlets installed in accordance with all of the applicable requirements for a dwelling unit in accordance with 210.52.

    (a) whirlpool tubs   (b) bathing   (c) cooking   (d) internet access

47. The number of receptacle outlets for guest rooms in hotels and motels must not be less than that required for a dwelling unit, in accordance with 210.52(A). These receptacles can be located to be convenient for permanent furniture layout, but no fewer than _____ receptacle outlets must be readily accessible

    (a) 4   (b) 2   (c) 6   (d) 1

48. A 15 or 20A, 125V, single-phase receptacle outlet must be installed at an accessible location for the servicing of heating, air-conditioning, and refrigeration equipment. The receptacle must be located on the same level and within _____ of the heating, air-conditioning, and refrigeration equipment.

    (a) 10 ft   (b) 15 ft   (c) 20 ft   (d) 25 ft

49. In a dwelling unit, at least _____ wall switch-controlled lighting outlet(s) must be installed in every dwelling unit habitable room and bathroom.

    (a) one   (b) three   (c) six   (d) none of these

50. In _____ rooms other than kitchens and bathrooms of dwelling units, one or more receptacles controlled by a wall switch are permitted in lieu of lighting outlets.

    (a) habitable   (b) finished   (c) all   (d) a and b

51. In a dwelling unit, illumination from a lighting outlet must be provided at the exterior side of each outdoor entrance or exit that has grade-level access.

    (a) True   (b) False

52. Where a lighting outlet(s) is installed for interior stairways, there must be a wall switch at each floor landing that includes an entryway where the stairway between floor levels has four risers or more.

    (a) True   (b) False

53. In a dwelling unit, at least one lighting outlet _____ located at the point of entry to the attic, underfloor space, utility room, and basement must be installed where these spaces are used for storage or contain equipment requiring servicing.

    (a) that is unswitched and   (b) containing a switch
    (c) controlled by a wall switch   (d) b or c

54. For other than dwelling units, a lighting outlet containing a switch or controlled by a wall switch is required near equipment requiring servicing in attics or underfloor spaces, and at least one point of control must be located at the point of entrance to the attic or underfloor space.

    (a) True   (b) False

Article 215 Feeders

This article covers the requirements for installation, minimum size, and ampacity of feeders.

55. The feeder conductor ampacity must not be less than that of the service-entrance conductors where the feeder conductors carry the total load supplied by service-entrance conductors with an ampacity of _____ or less.

    (a) 100A   (b) 60A   (c) 55A   (d) 30A

56. Where installed in a metal raceway, all feeder conductors using a common grounded conductor must be _____.

    (a) insulated for 600V   (b) enclosed within the same raceway
    (c) shielded   (d) none of these

57. When a feeder supplies _____ in which equipment grounding conductors are required, the feeder must include or provide a grounding means to which the equipment grounding conductors of the branch circuits must be connected.

    (a) equipment disconnecting means   (b) electrical systems
    (c) branch circuits   (d) electric-discharge lighting equipment

58. Ground-fault protection of equipment is not required at the feeder disconnect if ground-fault protection of equipment is provided on the _____ side of the feeder.

    (a) load   (b) supply   (c) service   (d) none of these

Article 220 Branch-Circuit, Feeder, and Service Calculations

This article provides the requirements for sizing branch circuits, feeders, and services, and for determining the number of receptacles on a circuit and the number of branch circuits required.

59. When computations in Article 220 result in a fraction of an ampere that is less than _____, such fractions can be dropped.

    (a) 0.49   (b) 0.50   (c) 0.51   (d) none of these

60. •When determining the load for luminaires for branch circuits, the load must be based on the _____.

(a) wattage rating of the luminaire socket   (b) maximum VA rating of the equipment and lamps
(c) wattage rating of the lamps   (d) none of these

61. For other than dwelling occupancies, banks, or office buildings, each receptacle outlet must be computed at not less than _____ VA for each single or each multiple receptacle on one yoke.

(a) 1,500   (b) 180   (c) 20   (d) 3

62. The 3 VA per square foot general lighting load for dwelling units includes general-use receptacles and lighting outlets and no additional load calculations are required for these.

(a) True   (b) False

63. The minimum feeder load for show-window lighting is _____ per-linear-foot.

(a) 400 VA   (b) 200 VA   (c) 300 VA   (d) 180 VA

64. •Receptacle loads for nondwelling units, computed in accordance with 220.14(H) and (I), are permitted to be _____.

(a) added to the lighting loads and made subject to the demand factors of Table 220.42
(b) made subject to the demand factors of Table 220.44
(c) made subject to the lighting demand loads of Table 220.12
(d) a or b

65. The feeder and service load for fixed electric space heating must be computed at _____ percent of the total connected load.

(a) 125   (b) 100   (c) 80   (d) 200

66. When sizing a feeder for the fixed appliance loads in dwelling units, a demand factor of 75 percent of the total nameplate ratings can be applied if there are _____ or more appliances fastened in place on the same feeder (not including washer, dryer, heating, or air conditioning).

(a) two   (b) three   (c) four   (d) five

67. The load for electric clothes dryers in a dwelling unit must be _____ watts or the nameplate rating, whichever is larger, per dryer.

(a) 1,500   (b) 4,500   (c) 5,000   (d) 8,000

68. The feeder demand load for four 6 kW cooktops is _____ kW.

(a) 17   (b) 4   (c) 12   (d) 24

69. For identically sized ranges rated more than 12 kW but not more than 27 kW, the maximum demand in column C must be increased by _____ percent of the column C value for each additional kilowatt of rating, or major fraction thereof, by which the rating of individual ranges exceeds 12 kW.

(a) 125   (b) 10   (c) 5   (d) 80

70. The feeder demand load for ranges individually rated more than 8 3/4 kW and of different ratings, but none exceeding 27 kW, is calculated by adding all of the ranges together and dividing by the total number of ranges to find an average value. The column C value for the number of ranges is then increased by _____ percent for each kW or major fraction that the average value exceeds 12 kW.

(a) 125   (b) 10   (c) 5   (d) 80

71. Table 220.56 may be applied to compute the load for thermostatically controlled or intermittently used _____ and other kitchen equipment in a commercial kitchen.

    (a) commercial electric cooking equipment
    (b) dishwasher booster heaters
    (c) water heaters
    (d) all of these

72. Where it is unlikely that two or more noncoincident loads will be in use simultaneously, it is permissible to use only the _____ loads on at any given time in computing the total load to a feeder.

    (a) smaller of the
    (b) largest of the
    (c) difference between the
    (d) none of these

73. There must be no reduction in the size of the grounded conductor on _____ type loads.

    (a) dwelling unit
    (b) hospital
    (c) nonlinear
    (d) motel

74. Feeder and service-entrance conductors with demand loads determined by the use of 220.82 are permitted to have the _____ load determined by 220.61.

    (a) feeder
    (b) circuit
    (c) neutral
    (d) none of these

75. A demand factor of _____ percent applies to a multifamily dwelling with ten units if the optional calculation method is used.

    (a) 75
    (b) 60
    (c) 50
    (d) 43

76. The calculated load to which the demand factors of Table 220.84 apply must include the _____ rating of all appliances that are fastened in place, permanently connected, or located to be on a specific circuit. These include ranges, wall-mounted ovens, counter-mounted cooking units, clothes dryers, water heaters, and space heaters.

    (a) calculated
    (b) nameplate
    (c) circuit
    (d) overcurrent protection

77. Feeder conductors for new restaurants are not required to be of _____ ampacity than the service-entrance conductors.

    (a) greater
    (b) lesser
    (c) equal
    (d) none of these

78. When a farm dwelling has electric heat and the farm operation has electric grain-drying systems, Part _____ of Article 220 cannot be used to compute the dwelling load where the dwelling and farm load are supplied by a common service.

    (a) I
    (b) II
    (c) III
    (d) IV

Article 225 Outside Wiring

This article covers installation requirements for equipment, including conductors located outside, on, or between buildings, poles, and other structures on the premises.

79. Open individual conductors must not be smaller than _____ AWG copper for spans up to 50 ft in length and _____ AWG copper for a longer span, unless supported by a messenger wire.

    (a) 10, 8
    (b) 6, 8
    (c) 6, 6
    (d) 8, 8

80. Where a mast is used for overhead conductor support of outside branch circuits and feeders, it must have adequate mechanical strength, or braces or guy wires to support it, to withstand the strain caused by the conductors. Only _____ conductors can be attached to the mast.

    (a) communications
    (b) fiber optic
    (c) feeder or branch circuit
    (d) all of these

81. The minimum clearance for overhead conductors not exceeding 600V that pass over commercial areas subject to truck traffic is _____.

    (a) 10 ft
    (b) 12 ft
    (c) 15 ft
    (d) 18 ft

82. If a set of 120/240V overhead conductors terminates at a through-the-roof raceway or approved support, with less than 6 ft of these conductors passing over the roof overhang, the minimum clearance above the roof for these conductors is _____.

(a) 12 in.   (b) 18 in.   (c) 2 ft   (d) 5 ft

83. Overhead conductors to a building must maintain a vertical clearance of final spans above, or within _____ measured horizontally from the platforms, projections, or surfaces from which they might be reached.

(a) 3 ft   (b) 6 ft   (c) 8 ft   (d) 10 ft

84. Raceways on exterior surfaces of buildings or other structures must be arranged to drain, and in _____ locations must be raintight.

(a) damp   (b) wet   (c) dry   (d) all of these

85. A building or structure must be supplied by a maximum of _____ feeder(s) or branch circuit(s).

(a) one   (b) two   (c) three   (d) as many as desired

86. The building disconnecting means must be installed at a(n) _____ location.

(a) accessible   (b) readily accessible   (c) outdoor   (d) indoor

87. •There must be no more than _____ disconnects installed for each electric supply.

(a) two   (b) four   (c) six   (d) none of these

88. The one or more additional disconnecting means for fire pumps or for emergency, legally required standby or optional standby systems as permitted by 225.30, must be installed sufficiently remote from the one to six disconnecting means for normal supply to minimize the possibility of _____ interruption of supply.

(a) accidental   (b) intermittent   (c) simultaneous   (d) prolonged

89. In a multiple-occupancy building where electrical maintenance is provided by the building management under continuous building management supervision, the building disconnecting means supplying more than one occupancy can be accessible to authorized _____ only.

(a) inspectors   (b) tenants   (c) management personnel   (d) none of these

90. •The building or structure disconnecting means must plainly indicate whether it is in the _____ position.

(a) open or closed   (b) correct   (c) up or down   (d) none of these

91. For installations consisting of not more than two 2-wire branch circuits, the building disconnecting means must have a rating of not less than _____.

(a) 15A   (b) 20A   (c) 25A   (d) 30A

Article 230 Services

This article covers the installation requirements for service conductors and equipment. It's very important to know where the service begins and ends when applying Articles 230 and 250.

Conductors supplied from a battery, uninterruptible power supply, solar photovoltaic system, generator, or transformer are not considered service conductors; they are feeder conductors.

92. Additional services must be permitted for a single building or other structure sufficiently large to make two or more services necessary if permitted by _____.

    (a) architects   (b) special permission   (c) written authorization   (d) master electricians

93. Where a building or structure is supplied by more than one service, or a combination of branch circuits, feeders, and services, a permanent plaque or directory must be installed at each service disconnect location denoting all other _____ supplying that building or structure and the area served by each.

    (a) services   (b) feeders   (c) branch circuits   (d) all of these

94. •Conductors other than service conductors must not be installed in the same _____.

    (a) service raceway   (b) service cable   (c) enclosure   (d) a or b

95. Service conductors installed as unjacketed multiconductor cable must have a minimum clearance of _____ from windows that are designed to be opened, doors, porches, stairs, fire escapes, or similar locations.

    (a) 3 ft   (b) 4 ft   (c) 6 ft   (d) 10 ft

96. _____ must not be installed beneath openings through which materials may be moved, such as openings in farm and commercial buildings, and must not be installed where they will obstruct entrance to these building openings.

    (a) Overcurrent protection devices   (b) Overhead-service conductors
    (c) Grounding conductors   (d) Wiring systems

97. Service-drop conductors must have _____.

    (a) sufficient ampacity to carry the current for the load   (b) adequate mechanical strength
    (c) a or b   (d) a and b

98. Service drops installed over roofs must have a vertical clearance of _____ above the roof surface.

    (a) 8 ft   (b) 12 ft   (c) 15 ft   (d) 3 ft

99. The requirement for maintaining a 3 ft vertical clearance from the edge of the roof does not apply to the final conductor span where the service drop is attached to _____.

    (a) a service pole   (b) the side of a building   (c) an antenna   (d) the base of a building

100. The minimum clearance for service drops not exceeding 600V that pass over commercial areas subject to truck traffic is _____.

    (a) 10 ft   (b) 12 ft   (c) 15 ft   (d) 18 ft

(• Indicates that 75% or fewer of those who took this exam answered the question correctly.)

1. An insulated grounded conductor of _____ or smaller must be identified by a continuous white or gray outer finish, or by three continuous white stripes on other than green insulation along its entire length.

    (a) 3 AWG   (b) 4 AWG   (c) 6 AWG   (d) 8 AWG

2. _____ must not be installed beneath openings through which materials may be moved, such as openings in farm and commercial buildings, and must not be installed where they will obstruct entrance to these building openings.

    (a) Overcurrent protection devices   (b) Overhead branch-circuit and feeder conductors
    (c) Grounding conductors   (d) Wiring systems

3. •Service-entrance or feeder conductors whose demand load is determined by the optional calculation, as permitted in 220.88, are not permitted to have the neutral load determined by 220.61.

    (a) True   (b) False

4. A building or structure must be supplied by a maximum of _____ service(s).

    (a) one   (b) two   (c) three   (d) as many as desired

5. A receptacle connected to a small-appliance circuit can supply gas-fired ranges, ovens, or counter-mounted cooking units.

    (a) True   (b) False

6. A receptacle outlet for the laundry is not required in a dwelling unit in a multifamily building when laundry facilities that are available to all building occupants are provided on the premises.

    (a) True   (b) False

7. A receptacle outlet must be installed in dwelling units for every kitchen and dining area countertop space _____, and no point along the wall line can be more than 2 ft, measured horizontally, from a receptacle outlet in that space.

    (a) wider than 10 in.   (b) wider than 3 ft   (c) 18 in. or wider   (d) 12 in. or wider

8. A single piece of equipment consisting of a multiple receptacle comprised of _____ or more receptacles must be computed at not less than 90 VA per receptacle.

    (a) 1   (b) 2   (c) 3   (d) 4

9. All 15 and 20A, 125V single-phase receptacles installed in crawl spaces at or below grade level and in _____ of dwelling units must have GFCI protection for personnel.

    (a) unfinished attics   (b) finished attics   (c) unfinished basements   (d) finished basements

10. All ungrounded (hot) conductors from two or more branch circuits terminating on multiple devices or equipment on the same yoke must have a means to be disconnected simultaneously in _____ occupancies.

    (a) dwelling unit   (b) commercial   (c) industrial   (d) all of these

11. At least one receptacle outlet must be installed directly above a show window for each _____, or major fraction thereof, of show-window area measured horizontally at its maximum width.

    (a) 10 ft   (b) 12 ft   (c) 18 ft   (d) 24 ft

12. At least one wall switch-controlled lighting outlet must be installed in every habitable room and bathroom of a guest room or guest suite of hotels, motels, and similar occupancies. A receptacle outlet controlled by a wall switch may be used to meet this requirement in other than _____.

    (a) bathrooms   (b) kitchens   (c) sleeping areas   (d) both a and b

13. Dwelling unit or mobile home feeder conductors need not be larger than the service conductors and are permitted to be sized according to 310.15(B)(6).

    (a) True   (b) False

14. For other than dwelling units or guest rooms of hotels or motels, the feeder and service load calculation for track lighting is to be determined at 150 VA for every _____ of track installed.

    (a) 4 ft   (b) 6 ft   (c) 2 ft   (d) none of these

15. GFCI protection for personnel is required for all 15 and 20A, 125V single-phase receptacles installed _____ of commercial, industrial, and all other nondwelling occupancies.

    (a) in storage rooms   (b) in equipment rooms   (c) in warehouses   (d) in bathrooms

16. GFCI protection for personnel is required for all 15 and 20A, 125V single-phase receptacles installed in a dwelling unit _____.

    (a) attic   (b) garage   (c) laundry   (d) all of these

17. Ground-fault protection of equipment is required for the feeder disconnect if _____.

    (a) the feeder is rated 1,000A or more
    (b) it is a solidly-grounded wye system
    (c) it is more than 150 volts-to-ground, but not exceeding 600V phase-to-phase
    (d) all of these

18. Guest rooms in hotels, motels, and similar occupancies without permanent provisions for cooking must have receptacle outlets installed in accordance with 210.52(A) and 210.52(D).

    (a) True   (b) False

19. If a dwelling unit is served by a single single-phase, 3-wire, 120/240V or 120/208V set of service-entrance or feeder conductors with an ampacity of _____ or greater, it is permissible to compute the feeder and service loads in accordance with 220.82 instead of the method specified in Part III of Article 220.

    (a) 100   (b) 125   (c) 150   (d) 175

20. In a dwelling unit, the minimum required receptacle outlets must be in addition to receptacle outlets that are _____.

    (a) part of a luminaire or appliance   (b) located within cabinets or cupboards
    (c) located more than 5 1/2 ft above the floor   (d) all of these

21. In dwelling units, at least one wall receptacle outlet must be installed in bathrooms within _____ of the outside edge of each basin. The receptacle outlet must be located on a wall or partition that is adjacent to the basin or basin countertop.

    (a) 12 in.   (b) 18 in.   (c) 24 in.   (d) 36 in.

22. In other than dwelling units, GFCI protection is required _____.

    (a) for outdoor 15 and 20A, 125V single-phase receptacles accessible to the public
    (b) at an accessible location for HVAC equipment
    (c) both a and b
    (d) neither a nor b

23. Loads that are computed for dwelling unit small-appliance branch circuits can be included with the _____ load and subject to the demand factors permitted in Table 220.42 for the general lighting load.

    (a) general lighting　　　　(b) feeder　　　　(c) appliance　　　　(d) receptacle

24. More than one feeder or branch circuit is permitted to supply a single building or other structure sufficiently large to require two or more supplies if permitted by _____.

    (a) architects　　　　(b) special permission　　　　(c) written authorization　　　　(d) master electricians

25. Multioutlet circuits rated 15 or 20A can supply fixed appliances (utilization equipment fastened in place) as long as the fixed appliances do not exceed _____ percent of the circuit rating.

    (a) 125　　　　(b) 100　　　　(c) 75　　　　(d) 50

26. Overhead conductors installed over roofs must have a vertical clearance of _____ above the roof surface.

    (a) 8 ft　　　　(b) 12 ft　　　　(c) 15 ft　　　　(d) 3 ft

27. Overhead-service conductors to a building must maintain a vertical clearance of final spans above, or within, _____ measured horizontally from the platforms, projections, or surfaces from which they might be reached.

    (a) 3 ft　　　　(b) 6 ft　　　　(c) 8 ft　　　　(d) 10 ft

28. Receptacle outlets in floors are not counted as part of the required number of receptacle outlets to service dwelling unit wall spaces unless they are located within _____ of the wall.

    (a) 6 in.　　　　(b) 12 in.　　　　(c) 18 in.　　　　(d) close to the wall

29. Service conductors supplying a building or other structure must not _____ of another building or other structure.

    (a) be installed on the exterior walls　　　　(b) pass through the interior
    (c) a and b　　　　(d) none of these

30. Service-drop conductors must have a minimum of _____ vertical clearance from final grade over residential property and driveways, as well as those commercial areas not subject to truck traffic where the voltage is limited to 300 volts-to-ground.

    (a) 10 ft　　　　(b) 12 ft　　　　(c) 15 ft　　　　(d) 18 ft

31. The 3 VA per-square-foot general lighting load for dwelling units does not include _____.

    (a) open porches　　　　(b) garages
    (c) unused or unfinished spaces not adaptable for future use　　　　(d) all of these

32. The calculated load to which the demand factors of Table 220.84 apply must include 3 VA per _____ for general lighting and general-use receptacles.

    (a) inch　　　　(b) foot　　　　(c) square inch　　　　(d) square foot

33. The feeder demand load for nine 16 kW ranges is _____.

    (a) 15,000W   (b) 28,800W   (c) 20,000W   (d) 26,000W

34. The grounded conductor of a 3-wire branch circuit supplying a household electric range is permitted to be smaller than the ungrounded conductors when the maximum demand of a range of 8.75 kW or more rating has been computed according to Column C of Table 220.19. However, the ampacity of the grounded conductor must not be less than _____ percent of the branch-circuit rating and not be smaller than _____ AWG.

    (a) 50, 6   (b) 70, 6   (c) 50, 10   (d) 70, 10

35. The identification of _____ to which a grounded conductor is to be connected must be substantially white in color.

    (a) wire connectors   (b) circuit breakers   (c) terminals   (d) ground rods

36. The location of the arc-fault circuit interrupter can be at other than the origination of the branch circuit if _____.

    (a) the arc-fault circuit interrupter is installed within 6 ft of the branch-circuit overcurrent device
    (b) the circuit conductors up to the arc-fault circuit interrupter are in a metal raceway or a cable with a metallic sheath
    (c) both a and b
    (d) none of these

37. The minimum point of attachment of overhead conductors to a building must in no case be less than _____ above finished grade.

    (a) 8 ft   (b) 10 ft   (c) 12 ft   (d) 15 ft

38. The minimum size service-drop conductor permitted by the *Code* is _____ AWG copper or _____ AWG aluminum or copper-clad aluminum.

    (a) 8, 6   (b) 6, 8   (c) 6, 6   (d) 8, 8

39. The rating of a branch circuit is determined by the rating of the _____.

    (a) ampacity of the largest device connected to the circuit
    (b) average of the ampacity of all devices
    (c) branch-circuit overcurrent protection
    (d) ampacity of the branch-circuit conductors according to Table 310.16

40. The two to six disconnects as permitted by 225.33 must be _____. Each disconnect must be marked to indicate the load served.

    (a) the same size   (b) grouped   (c) in the same enclosure   (d) none of these

41. There must be a minimum of one _____ branch circuit for the laundry outlet(s) in a dwelling unit.

    (a) 15A   (b) 20A   (c) 30A   (d) b and c

42. To determine the feeder demand load for ten 3 kW household cooking appliances, use _____ of Table 220.19.

    (a) Column A   (b) Column B   (c) Column C   (d) none of these

43. What is the maximum cord-and-plug connected load permitted on a 15A receptacle that is supplied by a 20A circuit supplying multiple outlets?

    (a) 12A   (b) 16A   (c) 20A   (d) 24A

44. When applying the demand factors of Table 220.56, in no case can the feeder or service demand load be less than the sum of _____.

    (a) the total number of receptacles at 180 VA per receptacle outlet
    (b) the VA rating of all of the small-appliance circuits combined
    (c) the largest two kitchen equipment loads
    (d) the kitchen heating and air-conditioning loads

45. When breaks occur in dwelling unit kitchen countertop spaces for ranges, refrigerators, sinks, etc., each countertop surface is considered a separate counter space for determining receptacle placement.

    (a) True   (b) False

46. When considering lighting outlets in dwelling units, a vehicle door in a garage is considered an outdoor entrance.

    (a) True   (b) False

47. When the building disconnecting means is a power-operated switch or circuit breaker, it must be able to be opened by hand in the event of a _____.

    (a) ground fault   (b) short circuit   (c) power surge   (d) power-supply failure

48. Where grounded conductors of different wiring systems are installed in the same raceway, cable, or enclosure, each grounded conductor must be identified by a different one of the acceptable methods in order to distinguish the grounded conductors of each system from the other.

    (a) True   (b) False

49. Where more than one nominal voltage system exists in a building, each ungrounded conductor of a branch circuit, where accessible, must be identified by system. The identification can be _____ and must be permanently posted at each branch-circuit panelboard.

    (a) color-coding   (b) phase tape   (c) tagging   (d) any of these

50. Which rooms in a dwelling unit must have a switch-controlled lighting outlet?

    (a) Every habitable room   (b) Bathrooms   (c) Hallways and stairways   (d) all of these

(• Indicates that 75% or fewer of those who took this exam answered the question correctly.)

1. A permanently-mounted luminaire (fixture) in a commercial garage and located over lanes on which vehicles are commonly driven must be located not less than _____ above floor level.

    (a) 10 ft   (b) 12 ft   (c) 14 ft   (d) none of these

2. A pool capable of holding water to a maximum depth of _____ is a storable pool.

    (a) 18 in.   (b) 36 in.   (c) 42 in.   (d) none of these

3. A pool light junction box that has a raceway that extends directly to underwater pool light forming shells must be located not less than _____ from the outdoor pool or spa.

    (a) 2 ft   (b) 3 ft   (c) 4 ft   (d) 6 ft

4. A sealing fitting must be installed within _____ of either side of the boundary where a conduit leaves a Class I, Division 1 location. The sealing fitting must be designed and installed so as to minimize the amount of gas or vapor within the Division 1 portion of the conduit being communicated beyond the seal.

    (a) 5 ft   (b) 6 ft   (c) 8 ft   (d) 10 ft

5. A single receptacle is a single contact device with no other contact device on the same _____.

    (a) circuit   (b) yoke   (c) run   (d) equipment

6. A solderless pressure connector is a device that _____ between two or more conductors or between one or more conductors and a terminal by means of mechanical pressure and without the use of solder.

    (a) provides access   (b) protects the wiring   (c) is never needed   (d) establishes a connection

7. A standard circuit breaker mounted in a Class I, Division 2 location with make-and-break contacts, and not hermetically sealed or oil-immersed, must be installed in a Class I, Division 1 rated enclosure.

    (a) True   (b) False

8. A strut-type channel raceway is a metallic raceway intended to be mounted to the surface of, or suspended from, a structure with associated accessories for the installation of electrical conductors.

    (a) True   (b) False

9. A surface mount strut-type channel raceway must be secured to the mounting surface with retention straps external to the channel at intervals not exceeding _____ and within 3 ft of each outlet box, cabinet, junction box, or other channel raceway termination.

    (a) 3 ft   (b) 5 ft   (c) 6 ft   (d) 10 ft

10. A surge arrester is a protective device for limiting surge voltages by _____ or bypassing surge current.

    (a) decreasing   (b) discharging   (c) limiting   (d) derating

11. A transfer switch is required for all fixed or portable optional standby power systems for buildings or structures for which an electric-utility supply is either the normal or standby source.

(a) True   (b) False

12. A value assigned to a circuit or system for the purpose of conveniently designating its voltage class such as 120/240V is called _____ voltage.

(a) root-mean-square   (b) circuit   (c) nominal   (d) source

13. A wall-mounted luminaire weighing not more than _____ can be supported to a device box with no fewer than two No. 6 or larger screws.

(a) 4 lbs   (b) 6 lbs   (c) 8 lbs   (d) 10 lbs

14. A(n) _____ is intended to provide limited overcurrent protection for specific applications and utilization equipment, such as luminaires and appliances. This limited protection is in addition to the protection provided by the required branch-circuit overcurrent protective device.

(a) supplementary overcurrent protective device   (b) transient voltage surge suppressor
(c) arc-fault circuit interrupter   (d) Class A GFCI

15. AC circuits of less than 50V must be grounded if supplied by a transformer whose supply system exceeds 150 volts-to-ground.

(a) True   (b) False

16. Additional services are permitted for different voltages, frequencies, or phases, or for different uses such as for _____.

(a) gymnasiums   (b) different rate schedules
(c) flea markets   (d) special entertainment events

17. Agricultural buildings where excessive dust and dust with water may accumulate, are defined as including all areas of _____ confinement systems, where litter dust or feed dust, including mineral feed particles may accumulate.

(a) poultry   (b) livestock   (c) fish   (d) all of these

18. All 125-volt, single-phase, 15 and 20 ampere receptacles installed in aircraft hangars in areas where _____ is (are) used must have ground-fault circuit interrupter protection for personnel.

(a) electrical diagnostic equipment   (b) electrical hand tools
(c) portable lighting equipment   (d) any of these

19. All 15 and 20A, 125V single-phase receptacles _____ of commercial occupancies must have GFCI protection for personnel.

(a) in bathrooms   (b) on rooftops   (c) in kitchens   (d) all of these

20. All 15 and 20A, 125V single-phase receptacles installed in pits, in hoistways, on elevator car tops, and in escalator and moving walk wellways must be _____.

(a) on a GFCI-protected circuit (b) of the GFCI type   (c) a or b   (d) none of these

21. All 15 and 20A, 125V, single-phase general-purpose receptacles installed _____ of agricultural buildings must have ground-fault circuit-interrupter protection for personnel.

(a) in areas having an equipotential plane   (b) outdoors
(c) in dirt confinement areas for livestock   (d) any of these

22. All 15, 20, and 30A, 125V, single-phase receptacle outlets used by personnel for temporary power must have ground-fault circuit-interrupter protection for personnel. GFCI protection can be incorporated into a _____ or other devices incorporating listed GFCI protection for personnel identified for portable use.

    (a) circuit breaker   (b) receptacle   (c) cord set   (d) any of these

23. All accessible portions of abandoned CATV cable must be removed.

    (a) True   (b) False

24. All accessible portions of abandoned communications cable must be removed.

    (a) True   (b) False

25. All accessible portions of abandoned fire alarm cable must be removed.

    (a) True   (b) False

26. All applicable articles of the *Code* apply to intrinsically safe systems except where specifically modified by Article 504.

    (a) True   (b) False

27. All areas designated as hazardous (classified) must be properly _____ and the documentation must be available to those authorized to design, install, inspect, maintain, or operate electrical equipment at these locations.

    (a) cleaned   (b) documented   (c) maintained   (d) all of these

28. All branch circuits that supply 15 and 20A, 125V single-phase outlets installed in dwelling unit bedrooms must be protected by a(n) _____ listed to provide protection of the entire branch circuit.

    (a) AFCI   (b) GFCI   (c) a and b   (d) none of these

29. All cut ends of rigid metal conduit must be _____ or otherwise finished to remove rough edges.

    (a) threaded   (b) reamed   (c) painted   (d) galvanized

30. All electric equipment, including power-supply cords, used with storable pools must be protected by _____.

    (a) fuses   (b) circuit breakers   (c) double-insulation   (d) GFCIs

31. All electrical connections in marinas and boatyards must be located _____.

    (a) at least 12 in. above the deck of a floating pier   (b) not less than 12 in. above the deck of a fixed pier
    (c) not below the electrical datum plane   (d) all of these

32. All joints between lengths of rigid nonmetallic conduit, and between conduit and couplings, fittings, and boxes must be made by _____.

    (a) the authority having jurisdiction   (b) set screw fittings
    (c) an approved method   (d) expansion fittings

33. All receptacles for temporary branch circuits are required to be electrically connected to the _____ conductor.

    (a) grounded   (b) grounding   (c) equipment grounding   (d) grounding electrode

34. All threaded conduit or fittings referred to in hazardous (classified) locations must be made wrenchtight in order to _____.

(a) prevent sparking when a fault current flows
(b) ensure the explosionproof or flameproof integrity of the conduit system
(c) a and b
(d) none of these

35. All wiring for Class 1 circuits must be installed in accordance with Article 300 and the other appropriate articles in Chapter 4.

(a) True   (b) False

36. All wiring must be installed so that the completed system will be free from _____, other than required or permitted in Article 250.

(a) short circuits   (b) grounds   (c) a and b   (d) none of these

37. Aluminum cable trays must not be used as an equipment grounding conductor for circuits with ground-fault protection above _____.

(a) 2,000A   (b) 300A   (c) 500A   (d) 1,200A

38. Aluminum conductors, and copper-clad aluminum conductors are permitted only for branch-circuit wiring in mobile homes.

(a) True   (b) False

39. An 8 AWG or larger solid copper equipotential bonding conductor must be extended or attached to any remote panelboard or service equipment enclosure to eliminate voltage gradients in the pool area.

(a) True   (b) False

40. An 8 x 8 x 4 in. deep junction/splice box requires 6 in. of free conductor, measured from the point in the box where the conductors enter the enclosure. The 3 in. of conductor outside-the-box rule _____.

(a) does apply   (b) does not apply   (c) sometimes applies   (d) none of these

41. An alternate ac power source such as an onsite generator is not a separately derived system if the _____ is solidly interconnected to a service-supplied system neutral.

(a) ignition system   (b) fuel cell   (c) neutral   (d) line conductor

42. An electric vehicle connector is a device that, by insertion into an electric vehicle inlet, establishes an electrical connection to the electric vehicle for the purpose of charging and information exchange.

(a) True   (b) False

43. An equipment grounding conductor must be identified by _____.

(a) a continuous outer finish that is green
(b) being bare
(c) a continuous outer finish that is green with one or more yellow stripes
(d) any of these

44. An equipotential plane is an area where wire mesh or other conductive elements are embedded in or placed under concrete bonded to _____.

(a) all metal structures   (b) fixed nonelectrical equipment that may become energized
(c) the electrical grounding system   (d) all of these

45. An equipotential plane must be installed in all concrete floor confinement areas of livestock buildings and all outdoor confinement areas that contain metallic equipment that is accessible to animals and that may become energized.

    (a) True   (b) False

46. An exothermic or irreversible compression connection to fireproofed structural metal is required to be accessible.

    (a) True   (b) False

47. An exposed wiring system for indoor wet locations where walls are frequently washed must be mounted so that there is at least _____ between the mounting surface and the electrical equipment.

    (a) a 1/4 in. airspace   (b) separation by insulated bushings
    (c) separation by noncombustible tubing   (d) none of these

48. Any current in excess of the rated current of equipment, or the ampacity of a conductor, is called _____.

    (a) trip current   (b) faulted   (c) overcurrent   (d) shorted

49. Any pit or depression below a garage floor level of a lubrication or service room where Class I liquids are not transferred is considered to be a Class I, Division _____ location up to floor level and extending 18 in. above floor level and 3 ft horizontally.

    (a) 1   (b) 2   (c) 3   (d) not classified

50. Any pit or depression below the level of the aircraft hangar floor is classified as a _____ location that extends up to said floor level.

    (a) Class I, Division 1 or Zone 1   (b) Class I, Division 2
    (c) Class II, Division 1   (d) Class III

Understanding Alternating Current

Introduction

Direct-current (dc) circuits and alternating-current (ac) circuits have similarities as well as differences. Some similarities in how dc and ac circuits work in series, parallel, or series-parallel combination circuits were covered in the preceding unit. How to calculate the resistance, voltage, and current at different points of these circuits was also addressed. This unit focuses on the special characteristics of alternating current and how it is generated, distributed, and utilized.

The practical use of electric power depends on the efficient generation and distribution of power to the point of utilization. The principles of magnetism and induction are important in the generation and transformation of ac power.

Direct current is delivered from a source with a constant polarity, which provides current that always flows through the circuit in the same direction. Alternating current is delivered from a source that changes polarity many times per second, resulting in current that changes its direction of flow through the circuit many times per second. This changing current flow results in a changing magnetic field around ac circuit conductors.

The flow of direct current in a circuit is opposed by resistance, but because of the changing current flow of an ac circuit, ac is opposed by a property called impedance. Impedance is a combination of resistance, inductive reactance, and capacitive reactance.

Some of the topics in this unit (in the context of ac circuits) include impedance, reactance, capacitance, inductance, skin effect, eddy currents, frequency, three-phase power, phase relationships, power factor, and efficiency.

Be sure to study this unit carefully so you will understand the differences between ac and dc circuits. There are some types of equipment that rely on the characteristics of the changing magnetic field developed by ac power to function, such as the ac motors and transformers that will be covered in Unit 4.

PART A—UNDERSTANDING ALTERNATING CURRENT

Introduction

Because ac current is inexpensive to transmit compared to dc current, ac has become the dominant form of electricity in our modern infrastructure. In the early days of commercially available electric power, dc was dominant. But, economics won out. Applying ac safely or effectively, however, requires an understanding of certain concepts that border on the complex. All of those concepts build on what you have already learned.

3.1 Current Flow

In order for current to flow in a circuit, the power supply must apply sufficient electromotive force to cause the electrons to move. The movement of the electrons themselves does not produce any useful work; it's the effects that the moving electrons have on the loads they flow through that are important. The effects of electron movement are the same regardless of the direction of the current flow. Figure 3-1

Current Flow
Alternating Current alternately flows in both directions.

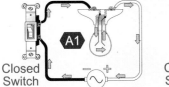 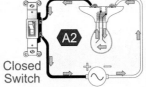

Alternating current (ac) rapidly changes polarity and magnitude. The polarity constantly changes causing the current to alternately flow in both directions.

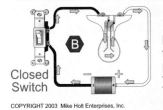

Direct Current Flows in One Direction
Direct current (dc) flows from the negative terminal of the power source to the positive terminal of the power source. The polarity of the voltage always remains the same.

COPYRIGHT 2003 Mike Holt Enterprises, Inc.

Figure 3–1

3.2 Why Alternating Current is Used

Alternating current is primarily used because it can be transmitted inexpensively due to the ease of transforming to high-transmission voltage and then transforming this voltage back to low distribution voltage. In addition, alternating current is used when direct current is not suitable for the application.

Direct-Current Use. There are other applications however, particularly inside electronic equipment, where only direct current can perform the desired function. This is accomplished by rectifying ac to dc to power these electronic loads. Figure 3–2

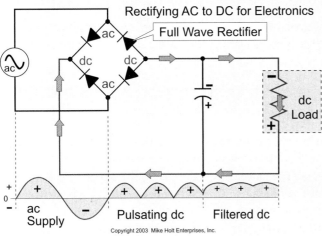

Rectifying AC to DC for Electronics
Full Wave Rectifier

Copyright 2003 Mike Holt Enterprises, Inc.

Direct current from a full-wave rectifier (supplied by ac) is very common inside electronic equipment where only dc can perform the desired function.

Figure 3–2

3.3 How Alternating Current is Produced

In 1831, Michael Faraday discovered that electricity could be produced from a source other than a battery. Faraday knew that electricity produced magnetism, and he wondered why magnetism couldn't produce electricity. Faraday discovered that when he moved a magnet inside a coil of wire, he got a pulse of electricity. When he pulled the magnet out, he got another pulse. He also got the same reaction when he moved the coil toward and away from the magnet.

Faraday's experiments revealed that when a magnetic field moves through a coil of wire, the lines of force of the magnetic field cause the electrons in the wire to flow in a specific direction. When the magnetic field moves in the opposite direction, electrons in the wire flow in the opposite direction. Electrons will flow only when there is motion of the conductors relative to the magnetic field. Figure 3–3

3.4 AC Generator

A simple ac generator consists of a loop of wire rotating between the lines of force between the opposite poles of a magnet. The halves of each conductor loop travel through the magnetic lines of force in opposite directions, causing the electrons within the conductor to move in a given direction. The magnitude of the voltage produced is dependent upon the number of turns of wire, the strength of the magnetic field, and the speed at which the coil rotates. Figure 3–4

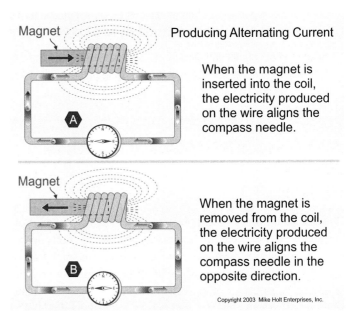

Producing Alternating Current

When the magnet is inserted into the coil, the electricity produced on the wire aligns the compass needle.

When the magnet is removed from the coil, the electricity produced on the wire aligns the compass needle in the opposite direction.

Copyright 2003 Mike Holt Enterprises, Inc.

Figure 3–3

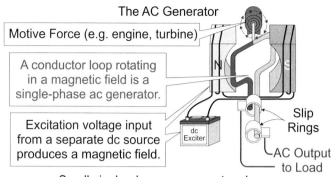

The AC Generator

Motive Force (e.g. engine, turbine)

A conductor loop rotating in a magnetic field is a single-phase ac generator.

Excitation voltage input from a separate dc source produces a magnetic field.

Slip Rings

AC Output to Load

Small single-phase ac generators have a conductor loop rotating inside a magnetic field.

Note: Larger ac generators have a rotating magnetic field inside stationary conductors.

Copyright 2003 Mike Holt Enterprises, Inc.

Figure 3–4

AUTHOR'S COMMENT: The rotating conductor loop is called a rotor or armature. Slip or collector rings and carbon brushes are used to connect the output voltage from the generator to an external circuit.

In generators that produce large quantities of electricity, the conductor coils are stationary and the magnetic field revolves within the coils. The magnetic field is produced by an electromagnet, instead of a permanent magnet. Use of electromagnets permit the strength of the magnetic field, and thus the lines of force, to be modified, thereby controlling the output voltage. Figure 3–5

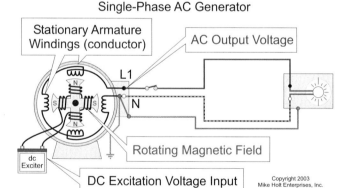

Single-Phase AC Generator

Stationary Armature Windings (conductor)

AC Output Voltage

L1

N

Rotating Magnetic Field

DC Excitation Voltage Input

Copyright 2003 Mike Holt Enterprises, Inc.

Most ac generators have a rotating magnetic field inside stationary armature windings. The voltage induced in the armature windings add to produce the ac output voltage.

Note: All ac generators are separately excited. Batteries or a small dc generator contained with the ac generator are typically used.

Figure 3–5

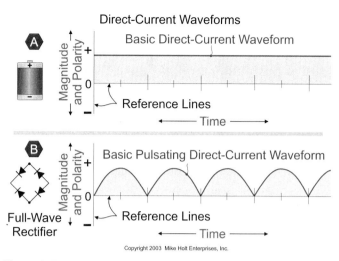

Direct-Current Waveforms

Ⓐ Basic Direct-Current Waveform

Magnitude and Polarity

Reference Lines

Time

Ⓑ Basic Pulsating Direct-Current Waveform

Magnitude and Polarity

Full-Wave Rectifier

Reference Lines

Time

Copyright 2003 Mike Holt Enterprises, Inc.

Figure 3–6

3.5 Waveform

A waveform image is used to display the level and direction of current and voltage.

Direct-Current Waveform

A direct-current waveform displays the direction (polarity) and magnitude of the current or voltage. Figure 3–6A and Figure 3–6B

Alternating-Current Waveform

The waveform for alternating-current circuits displays the level and direction of the current and voltage for every instant of time for one full revolution of the rotor. Figure 3–7

3.6 Sine Wave

Sinusoidal Waveform

The waveform for alternating-current circuits is symmetrical with positive above and negative below the zero reference level. For most alternating-current circuits, the waveform is called a sine wave.

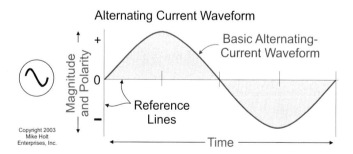

Alternating Current Waveform

Magnitude and Polarity

Basic Alternating-Current Waveform

Reference Lines

Time

Copyright 2003 Mike Holt Enterprises, Inc.

Figure 3–7

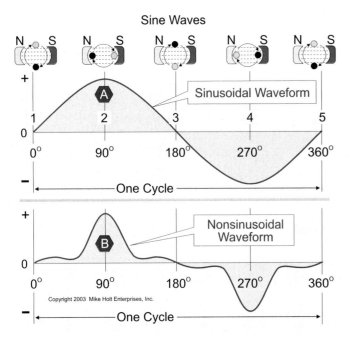

Sine Waves

Figure 3–8

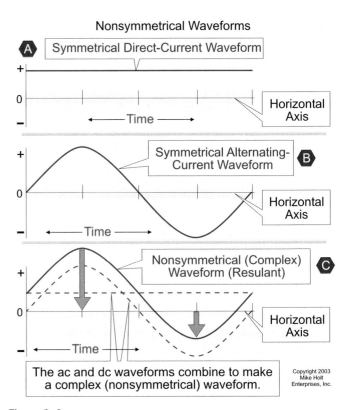

Nonsymmetrical Waveforms

The ac and dc waveforms combine to make a complex (nonsymmetrical) waveform.

Copyright 2003 Mike Holt Enterprises, Inc.

Figure 3–9

Figure 3–8A shows the relationship of the waveform and the rotor.

(1) The voltage starts at zero, when the rotor is not cutting any magnetic lines of force.

(2) As the rotor turns, the voltage increases from zero to a maximum value in one direction.

(3) It then decreases until it reaches zero.

(4) At zero, the voltage reverses polarity and increases until it reaches a maximum value at this opposite polarity.

(5) It decreases until it reaches zero again.

Nonsinusoidal Waveform

Figure 3–8B shows another ac waveform, but this one is nonsinusoidal. A nonsinusoidal waveform is created when nonlinear loads distort the sine wave.

Examples of nonlinear loads include computer power supplies and electronic ballasts for fluorescent lighting fixtures.

AUTHOR'S COMMENT: This topic is beyond the scope of this textbook.

3.7 Nonsymmetrical Waveform

The combination of alternating-current and direct-current waveforms results in a nonsymmetrical waveform. Figure 3–9

3.8 Frequency

The number of times the rotor turns in one second is called the frequency. Frequency is expressed as Hertz (Hz) or cycles per second, in honor of Heinrich Hertz. Most electrical power generated in the United States has a frequency of 60 Hz, Figure 3–10, whereas many other parts of the world use 50 Hz, and others use different power frequencies ranging from a low of 25 Hz to a high of 125 Hz.

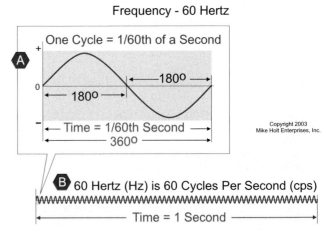

Frequency - 60 Hertz

60 Hertz (Hz) is 60 Cycles Per Second (cps)

Copyright 2003 Mike Holt Enterprises, Inc.

Figure 3–10

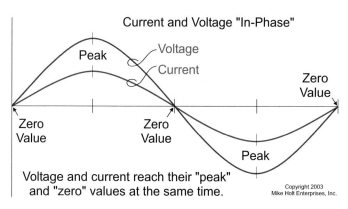

Figure 3–11

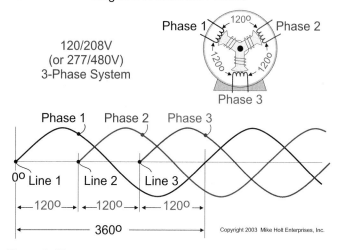

Figure 3–12

High-frequency electrical power, of 415 Hz, is often used for large computer systems and 400 Hz is used for airplane lighting. High-frequency power is often derived from motor-generator sets or other converters that operate at 60 Hz.

3.9 Phase

Phase is a term used to indicate the time or degree relationship between two waveforms, such as voltage-to-current or voltage-to-voltage. When two waveforms are in step with each other, they are said to be in-phase. In a purely resistive ac circuit, the current and voltage are in-phase. This means that, at every instant, the current is exactly in step with the applied voltage. They both reach their zero and peak values at the same time. Figure 3–11

3.10 Degrees

Phase differences are often expressed in degrees; one full waveform is equal to 360 degrees. For example, a three-phase generator has each of its windings out-of-phase with each other by 120 degrees. Figure 3–12

3.11 Lead or Lag

When describing the relationship between voltage and current, the reference waveform is always voltage—thus, a "lagging" waveform means that the voltage lags behind the current; a "leading" waveform means that the voltage leads the current.

Leading

It is easy to get confused as to which waveform leads and which one lags behind. The best way to remember this is to look at which waveform finishes its cycle first. In Figure 3–13A, the voltage waveform finishes its waveform cycle before the current waveform (designated by E_2 in Figure 3–13), so the voltage waveform "leads" the current waveform.

Lagging

In Figure 3–13B, the voltage waveform finishes its waveform cycle after the current waveform (designated by I_2 in Figure 3–13), in this case the voltage "lags" the current.

3.12 Values of Alternating Current

There are many important values in alternating-current waveforms. Some of the most important include instantaneous, peak, and effective. Figure 3–14

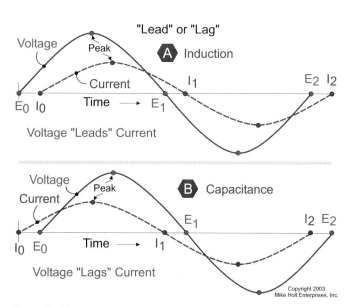

Figure 3–13

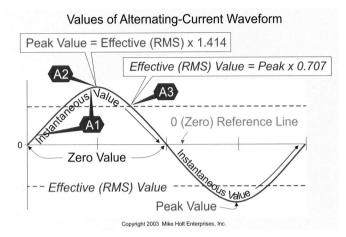

Values of Alternating-Current Waveform

Peak Value = Effective (RMS) x 1.414

Effective (RMS) Value = Peak x 0.707

Instantaneous Value

0 (Zero) Reference Line

Zero Value

Effective (RMS) Value

Peak Value

Copyright 2003 Mike Holt Enterprises, Inc.

Figure 3–14

Instantaneous Value

The value at a moment of time. Depending upon the instant selected, it can range anywhere from zero, to peak, to negative peak value. Figure 3–14A1

Peak Value

The maximum value the current or voltage waveform reaches. Figure 3–14A2

For a pure Sine wave:

Peak Value = Effective Value/0.707
Peak Value = Effective Value x 1.414
Effective Value = Peak Value x 0.707

Effective Value

Effective ac voltage or effective ac current is the equivalent value of dc voltage or dc current that would produce the same amount of heat in a resistor. Figure 3–14A3

For a pure sine wave:

Effective Value = RMS Value

RMS Value

Root-Mean-Square (RMS) describes the steps (in reverse) necessary to determine the effective voltage or current value. Figure 3–14A3

Step 1 Square the instant waveform values; this turns all of the negative portions into positive portions.

Step 2 Determine the Mean (average) of the instant values of the waveform.

Step 3 Calculate the square root value of the mean average in order to reverse the numerical effects of having squared the instant values (Step 1).

AUTHOR'S COMMENT: Actually it should be SMR, not RMS!

PART B—CAPACITANCE

Introduction

Capacitance is the property of an electrical circuit that enables it to store electrical energy by means of an electric field and to release that energy at a later time. Capacitance exists whenever an insulating material (dielectric) separates two conductors that have a difference of potential between them. Devices that intentionally introduce capacitance into circuits are called capacitors and are sometimes referred to as condensers. Figure 3-15

Capacitor Current Flow

Current does not flow through a capacitor. In an ac circuit, the electrons in the circuit move back and forth to alternately charge the capacitor, first in one direction, and then in the other. A capacitor permits current to flow because of its ability to store energy and then discharge the energy as the ac current flows in the opposite direction.

AUTHOR'S COMMENT: If a "full-wave rectifier" converts the ac voltage to filtered dc voltage, the capacitor will be continuously charged. Figure 3-16

3.13 Charged Capacitor

When a capacitor has a potential difference between the conductors (plates), the capacitor is charged. One plate has an excess of

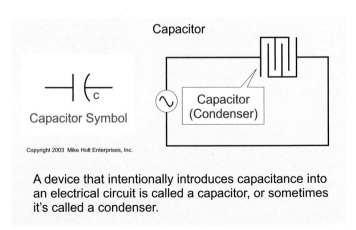

Capacitor

Capacitor Symbol

Capacitor (Condenser)

Copyright 2003 Mike Holt Enterprises, Inc.

A device that intentionally introduces capacitance into an electrical circuit is called a capacitor, or sometimes it's called a condenser.

Figure 3–15

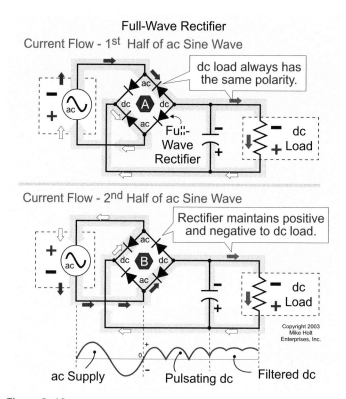

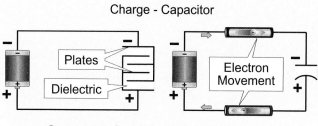

Full-Wave Rectifier
Current Flow - 1st Half of ac Sine Wave

dc load always has the same polarity.

Full-Wave Rectifier

dc Load

Current Flow - 2nd Half of ac Sine Wave

Rectifier maintains positive and negative to dc load.

dc Load

Copyright 2003 Mike Holt Enterprises, Inc.

ac Supply   Pulsating dc   Filtered dc

Figure 3–16

Charge - Capacitor

Plates

Dielectric

Electron Movement

Current can flow only when a capacitor is either charging or discharging.

Note: Except for a small amount of current leakage through the dielectric material, current does not flow through a charged capacitor.

Copyright 2003 Mike Holt Enterprises, Inc.

Figure 3–17

CAUTION: *Great care should be taken when working on a circuit that contains capacitors (such as those found in variable speed drives). Even when power is removed from the circuit, the capacitors can store large amounts of energy for a long period of time, and can discharge and arc if inadvertently shorted or grounded out.*

free electrons and the other plate has a lack of them. The plate with the excess electrons has an overall negative charge (-), while the plate from which electrons were removed has an overall positive charge (+). A difference of potential or voltage exists between the plates. Figure 3-17

3.14 Electrical Field

Though the electrons cannot flow, the force that attracts them still exists; this force is called the electrical field. The electrical field can be thought of as lines of electrical force that exist between the capacitor plates. Figure 3-18

The more the capacitor is charged, the stronger the electrical field. If the capacitor is overcharged, the electrons from the negative plate could be pulled through the insulation to the positive plate. If this happens, the capacitor is said to have broken down (shorted). Figure 3-19

3.15 Discharging a Capacitor

To discharge a capacitor, all that is required is a conducting path connected across the terminals of the capacitor. The free electrons on the negative plate will then flow through the external circuit to the positive plate.

3.16 Determining Capacitance

Factors that determine the capacitance of a capacitor are the surface area of the plates, the distance between the plates, and the insulating material or dielectric between the plates.

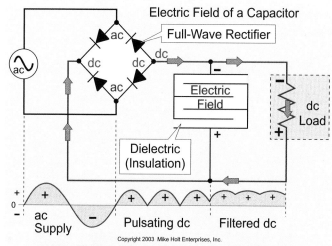

Electric Field of a Capacitor

Full-Wave Rectifier

Electric Field

dc Load

Dielectric (Insulation)

ac Supply   Pulsating dc   Filtered dc

Copyright 2003 Mike Holt Enterprises, Inc.

Although the electrons cannot flow through the capacitor, the force that attracts them still exists. This force is called the electric field.

Figure 3–18

"Shorted" Capacitor

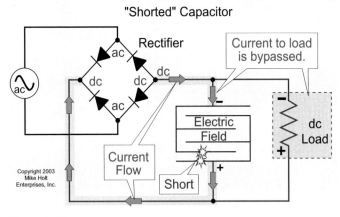

Figure 3–19

Plate Surface Area - Determining Capacitance

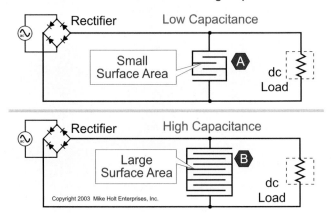

Figure 3–21

Plate Distance

Capacitance is inversely proportional to the distance between the capacitor plates. The closer the plates of the capacitor, the greater the capacitance and, conversely, the greater the distance between the plates, the lower the capacitance. Figure 3-20

Surface Area

Capacitance is directly proportional to the surface area. The greater the surface area of the plates, the greater the capacitance. Connecting capacitors in parallel has the effect of increasing the plate surface area, and increasing the capacitance by the sum of the capacitors. Connecting capacitors in series has the effect of increasing the dielectric, and decreasing the capacitance. Figure 3-21

Dielectric Strength

Dielectric strength indicates the maximum voltage that can be applied across the dielectric safely. Figure 3-22

3.17 Uses of Capacitors

One use of capacitors is to start single-phase ac motors and to prevent arcing across the contacts of electric switches. A capacitor connected across the switch contacts provides a path for current flow until the switch is fully open and the danger of arcing has passed. Figure 3-23

Electronic Power Supplies

One other very important use of capacitors is to smooth out pulsating dc waveforms, such as those which would be present through the dc load if the capacitor was not present. The full-wave bridge rectifier would transform the ac waveform from the source into a pulsating dc waveform—the presence of the capacitor smoothes out the waveform and makes a near-steady dc voltage across the dc load. Figure 3-24

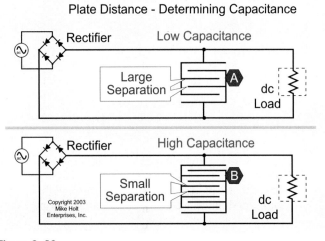

Figure 3–20

Dielectric (Insulation) Strength - Maximum Voltage

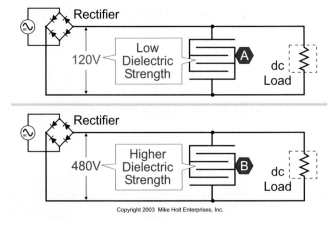

Figure 3–22

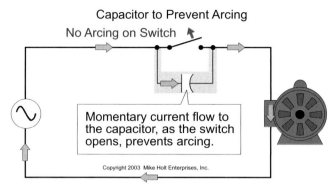

Capacitor to Prevent Arcing

No Arcing on Switch

Momentary current flow to the capacitor, as the switch opens, prevents arcing.

Copyright 2003 Mike Holt Enterprises, Inc.

Figure 3–23

3.18 Phase Relationship

A capacitor can be thought of as a device that resists changes in voltage. It supplies charge or accepts charge to this end. Because a capacitor introduces reactance to the circuit, it shifts the current waveform out-of-phase to the voltage waveform. Capacitive reactance causes the voltage waveform to lag the current waveform. Figure 3-25

One way to think of this is that the capacitor responds to changes in current by increasing or decreasing its own amount of charge. Therefore, the voltage waveform change lags the current waveform change. The opposition offered to the flow of ac current by

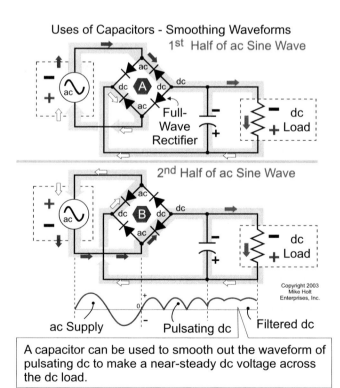

Uses of Capacitors - Smoothing Waveforms

1st Half of ac Sine Wave

Full-Wave Rectifier

dc Load

2nd Half of ac Sine Wave

dc Load

Copyright 2003 Mike Holt Enterprises, Inc.

ac Supply   Pulsating dc   Filtered dc

A capacitor can be used to smooth out the waveform of pulsating dc to make a near-steady dc voltage across the dc load.

Figure 3–24

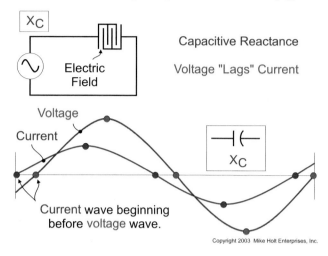

Phase Relationship - Capacitive Reactance (X_c)

X_C

Electric Field

Capacitive Reactance

Voltage "Lags" Current

X_C

Voltage

Current

Current wave beginning before voltage wave.

Copyright 2003 Mike Holt Enterprises, Inc.

Figure 3–25

a capacitor is called capacitive reactance. This is expressed in ohms and abbreviated X_C.

Capacitive reactance can be calculated by the equation:

$$X_C = 1/(2 \times \pi \times F \times C)$$

Where π is equal to 3.14, "F" is the frequency in hertz, "C" is the capacitance in farads, and "X_C" is expressed in ohms.

A capacitor can be thought of as a device that resists changes in current. Because a capacitor introduces reactance to the circuit, it shifts the current waveform to lead the applied voltage by 90 degrees.

PART C—INDUCTION

Introduction

Because electrons spin, they have their own magnetic fields. When electrons move, the magnetic fields of the individual electrons combine to produce an overall magnetic field. The overall magnetic field extends outside the conductor. The greater the current flow, the greater the overall magnetic field. The direction of the overall magnetic field around the conductor follows the left-hand rule, based on the electron current flow theory.

The movement of electrons caused by an external magnetic field is called induced current, and the associated potential that is established is called induced voltage. In order to induce voltage, all that is required is a conductor and an external magnetic field with relative motion between the two. This is the basis of the generator and transformer. Figure 3-26

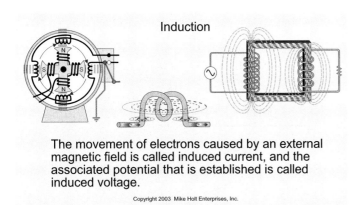

The movement of electrons caused by an external magnetic field is called induced current, and the associated potential that is established is called induced voltage.

Copyright 2003 Mike Holt Enterprises, Inc.

Figure 3–26

Inductance is the property of an electrical circuit that enables it to store electrical energy by means of an electromagnetic field and to release this energy at a later time.

3.19 Self-Induction

As the ac current through a conductor increases, an expanding electromagnetic field is created through the conductor. The expanding magnetic flux lines cut through the conductor itself (which, in effect, is in motion relative to the field), thus inducing a voltage within the conductor.

When the current within the conductor decreases, the electromagnetic field collapses, and again the magnetic flux lines through the conductor cut through the conductor itself. The voltage induced within the conductor caused by its own expanding and collapsing magnetic field is known as self-induced voltage. Figure 3-27

3.20 Induced Voltage and Applied Current

The induced voltage in a conductor carrying alternating current always opposes the change in current flowing through the conductor. The induced voltage that opposes the current flow is called "counter-electromotive force" (CEMF), or back-EMF.

The waveform of the induced voltage in the conductor (CEMF) is 90 degrees out-of-phase with the circuit current and it is 180 degrees out-of-phase with the applied voltage waveform. CEMF either opposes or aids the conductor current flow. Figure 3-28

Opposes Current Flow

When alternating current increases, the polarity of the induced voltage (CEMF) within the conductor opposes the conductor's current and tries to prevent the current from increasing. Figure 3-29A

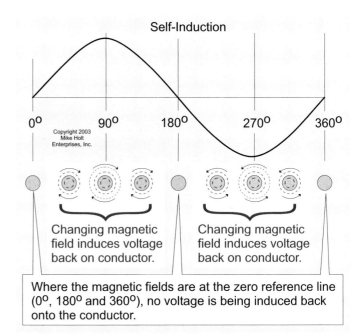

Self-Induction

Copyright 2003 Mike Holt Enterprises, Inc.

Changing magnetic field induces voltage back on conductor.

Changing magnetic field induces voltage back on conductor.

Where the magnetic fields are at the zero reference line (0°, 180° and 360°), no voltage is being induced back onto the conductor.

Figure 3–27

Aids the Current Flow

When the alternating current decreases, the polarity of the induced voltage within the conductor aids the conductor's current and tries to prevent the current from decreasing. Figure 3-29B

3.21 Conductor AC Resistance

In dc circuits, the only property that affects current and voltage flow is resistance. Conductor resistance is a physical property of the conductor. It is directly proportional to the conductor's length and inversely proportional to the conductor's cross-sectional

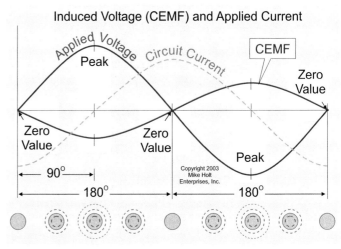

Induced Voltage (CEMF) and Applied Current

Applied Voltage
Circuit Current
Peak
CEMF
Zero Value
Zero Value
Zero Value
Peak
90°
Copyright 2003 Mike Holt Enterprises, Inc.
180°
180°

Figure 3–28

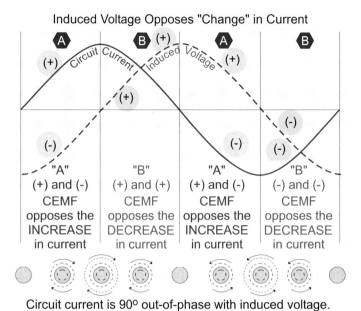

Induced Voltage Opposes "Change" in Current

"A" (+) and (−) CEMF opposes the INCREASE in current

"B" (+) and (+) CEMF opposes the DECREASE in current

"A" (+) and (−) CEMF opposes the INCREASE in current

"B" (−) and (−) CEMF opposes the DECREASE in current

Circuit current is 90° out-of-phase with induced voltage.

Copyright 2003 Mike Holt Enterprises, Inc.

Figure 3–29

area. This means that if the conductor's length is doubled, the total resistance is doubled; if the conductor's diameter is reduced, the resistance increases. Figure 3-30

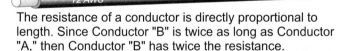

Conductor Resistance

Resistance is directly proportional to length.

A 500 ft 12 AWG = 0.965 ohms dc (1 ohm ac)

Both conductors have the same cross-sectional area but Conductor "B" is twice as long as Conductor "A."

B 1,000 ft 12 AWG = 1.93 ohms dc (NEC Table) 2 ohms ac (NEC Table)

The resistance of a conductor is directly proportional to length. Since Conductor "B" is twice as long as Conductor "A," then Conductor "B" has twice the resistance.

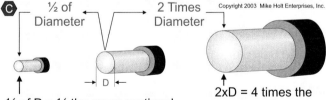

Resistance is inversely proportional to cross-sectional area.

C ½ of Diameter

2 Times Diameter

Copyright 2003 Mike Holt Enterprises, Inc.

½ of D = ¼ the cross-sectional area. This conductor has 4 times the resistance.

2xD = 4 times the cross-sectional area. This conductor has ¼ the resistance.

Figure 3–30

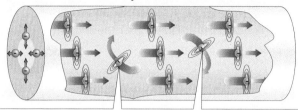

Eddy Currents

Eddy Currents are stray currents that consume power and oppose current flow. They are produced by the expanding and collapsing magnetic field of alternating-current circuits.

Copyright 2003 Mike Holt Enterprises, Inc.

Figure 3–31

For ac circuits, the ac resistance of a conductor must factor in the effects of eddy currents and skin effect (inductive reactance), in addition to resistance.

Eddy Currents

Eddy currents are small independent currents that are produced as a result of the expanding and collapsing magnetic field from an ac circuit. Eddy currents flow erratically through a conductor, consume power, and increase the opposition of current flow. Figure 3-31

Skin Effect

The expanding and collapsing magnetic field from an ac circuit induces a voltage in the conductors that repels the flowing electrons toward the surface of the conductor. This has the effect of decreasing the effective conductor cross-sectional area because more current (electrons) flows near the conductor surface than at the center. The decreased conductor cross-sectional area causes an increased opposition to current flow. Figure 3-32

3.22 Impedance

The total opposition to current flow (resistance and reactance) in ac circuits is called Impedance and it is measured in ohms. The abbreviation for the term Impedance is the letter "Z."

> **AUTHOR'S COMMENT:** I have no idea why the letter "Z" stands for impedance.

3.23 Conductor Shape

The physical shape of a conductor affects the amount of self-induced voltage within the conductor itself. When a conductor is

Skin Effect of Alternating Current

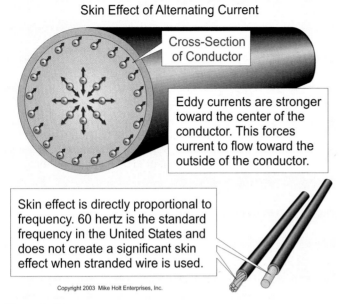

Cross-Section of Conductor

Eddy currents are stronger toward the center of the conductor. This forces current to flow toward the outside of the conductor.

Skin effect is directly proportional to frequency. 60 hertz is the standard frequency in the United States and does not create a significant skin effect when stranded wire is used.

Copyright 2003 Mike Holt Enterprises, Inc.

Figure 3–32

coiled into adjacent loops (helically wound), it is called a winding. The expanding and collapsing magnetic flux lines of ac current flowing through the conductor loops interact and add together to create a strong overall magnetic field. As the combined flux lines expand and collapse they cut additional conductor loops, creating greater self-inductance in each conductor loop. Figure 3-33

The amount of the self-induced voltage created within the winding is directly proportional to the current flow, the winding (conductor length and the number of turns), and the frequency at which the expanding and collapsing magnetic fields cut through the conductors of the winding.

Effect of Conductor Shape

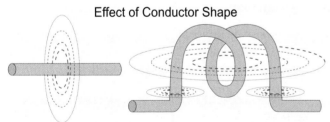

When the conductor is straight, the flux lines cut through only one part of the conductor.

When the conductor is coiled, the flux lines cut through the conductor at more than one point. This increases the CEMF by self-induction.

Copyright 2003 Mike Holt Enterprises, Inc.

Figure 3–33

Induction - Windings

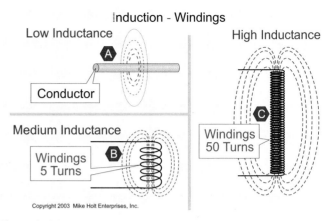

Low Inductance

Conductor

Medium Inductance

Windings 5 Turns

High Inductance

Windings 50 Turns

Copyright 2003 Mike Holt Enterprises, Inc.

Figure 3–34

Current

The greater the winding current, and the greater the alternating magnetic field, the greater the CEMF within the winding.

Winding

The greater the number of winding conductor loops (turns) and the closer the windings, the greater the CEMF produced within the winding. Figure 3-34

Frequency

Self-induced voltage is dependent upon the frequency at which the magnetic field expands or collapses. Therefore, the greater the frequency, the greater the CEMF induced within the winding.

3.24 Magnetic Cores

The core material also affects self-inductance in a winding (coil).

Core Material

Because an iron core provides an easy path for magnetic flux, windings with soft iron cores produce a greater self-inductance than windings with an air core. Figure 3-35

Core Length

Longer cores result in fewer flux lines; this results in reduced self-inductance. If the core length is doubled, the CEMF will be decreased by 50 percent. Figure 3-36

Core Area

Self-inductance (CEMF) is directly proportional to the cross-sectional area of the core, and inversely proportional to its length. This means that if the core area is doubled, the CEMF will be increased 200 percent. Figure 3-37

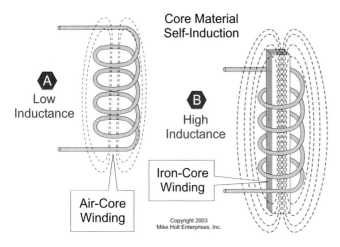

Figure 3–35

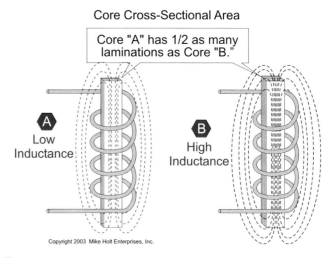

Figure 3–37

3.25 Self-Induced and Applied Voltage

A self-induced voltage waveform is 180 degrees out-of-phase with the applied voltage waveform. When the applied voltage increases or decreases, the polarity of the self-induced voltage is opposite that of the applied voltage. When the applied voltage is at its maximum in one direction, the induced voltage is at its maximum in the opposite direction. Figure 3-38

3.26 Current Flow

Alternating-current flow in a conductor is limited by the conductor's resistance and self-induced voltage (CEMF). Self-induced voltage (CEMF) acts to oppose the change in current flowing in the conductor. This property is called "inductive reactance" and it is measured in ohms.

Inductive Reactance

Inductive reactance is abbreviated X_L and can be calculated by the equation $X_L = 2 \times \pi \times F \times L$, where "F" is frequency with units of hertz, and "L" is inductance with units of Henrys.

> **AUTHOR'S COMMENT:** Just remember that ac current flow contains an additional element that opposes the flow of electrons, besides conductor resistance.

3.27 Phase Relationship

In a purely inductive circuit, the CEMF waveform is 90 degrees out-of-phase with the circuit current waveform and 180 degrees out-of-phase with the applied voltage waveform. As a result, the applied voltage waveform leads the current waveform by 90 degrees. Figure 3-39

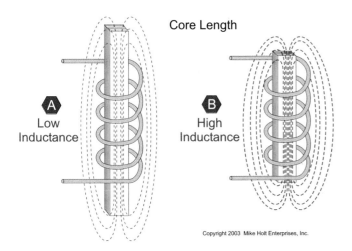

Figure 3–36

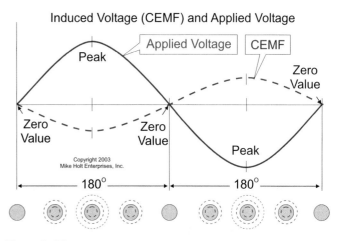

Figure 3–38

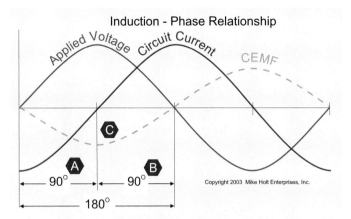

Induction - Phase Relationship

"A" - The applied voltage is 90° out-of-phase with the applied current.
"B" - The circuit current is 90° out-of-phase with the CEMF.
"C" - The applied voltage is 180° out-of-phase with the CEMF.

Figure 3–39

AUTHOR'S COMMENT: Just remember that an ac circuit contains inductive reactance because the voltage and current are "not in-phase with each other."

3.28 Uses of Induction

The major use of induction is in transformers, motors, and generators. Figure 3-40

AUTHOR'S COMMENT: Inductors are also used to increase the impedance in high-impedance grounding systems. This topic is beyond the scope of this textbook. Figure 3-41

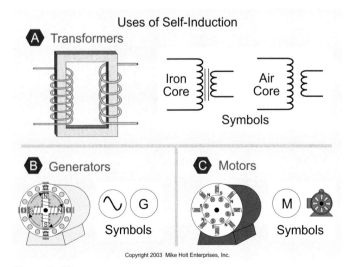

Uses of Self-Induction

Figure 3–40

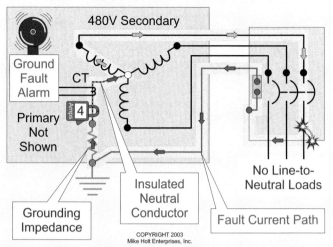

High-Impedance Grounded Neutral System

A high-impedance grounded neutral system will minimize the flow of fault current during a ground fault condition. An alarm will sound instead of the circuit breaker tripping.

Figure 3–41

PART D—POWER FACTOR

Introduction

The out-of-phase relationship between voltage and current in ac circuits that serve reactive loads often leads to a situation where more power is being delivered to the load than is actually used. This situation is very common in industrial plants where a large number of high horsepower motors are installed, resulting in a highly inductive load and a low power factor. Power suppliers typically impose penalties in their rate structure for customers with low power factor, so it becomes a topic of special interest for electricians to understand power factor and how to correct it in order to procure utility bill savings for their customers or their employer.

Inductors and Capacitors

Inductors and capacitors are energy storage devices in ac and dc circuits. The energy is stored in the electromagnetic field of an inductor and the electric field of a capacitor. Figure 3-42

3.29 Apparent Power (Volt-Amperes)

If you measure voltage and current in an inductive or capacitive circuit, and then multiply them together, you will obtain the apparent power supplied to the circuit by the source. Apparent power is expressed in volt-amperes (VA). Circuits and equipment must be sized to the circuit VA load. Apparent Power = Volts x Amperes

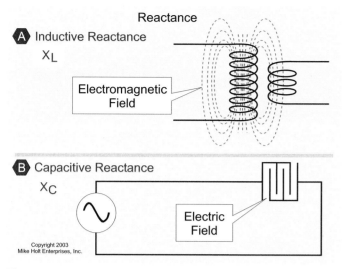

Figure 3–42

► **Example**

What is the apparent power in VA of a 1 hp, 115V motor that has a full-load current rating of 16A? **Figure 3-43**

    (a) 2,400 VA   (b) 1,320 VA
    (c) 1,840 VA   (d) 1,920 VA

    • Answer: (c) 1,840 VA
    VA = E x I
    VA = 115V x 16A
    VA = 1,840 VA

3.30 True Power (Watts)

True power is the energy consumed, expressed in the unit watts. Utility companies charge based on the total power consumed for one month, measured in units called kilowatt hours (kWh or 1,000 watts x 1 hour).

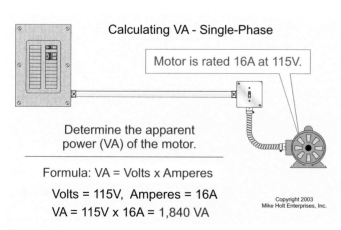

Figure 3–43

► **Example**

A 100W bulb, burning for 10 hours will use one kWh:

    100W x 10 hrs = 1,000 Wh = 1 kWh

Direct Current

To determine the true power consumed by a dc circuit, multiply the volts by the amperes (W = E x I).

Alternating Current

In an ac circuit, true power (W) is determined by multiplying the circuit volts (E), by the amperes (I), times the power factor (W = E x I x PF).

3.31 Power Factor

AC inductive or capacitive reactive loads cause the voltage and current sine waves to be out-of-phase with each other. Power factor is a measurement of how far the current waveform is out-of-phase with the voltage waveform. Power factor is equal to the ratio of circuit resistance to circuit impedance (capacitance reactance, inductive reactance, and resistance), and is expressed as a percentage. **Figure 3-44**

Power factor is defined as a ratio of true power (watts) to apparent power (VA).

    Power Factor (PF) = True Power (Watts)/
                               Apparent Power (VA)

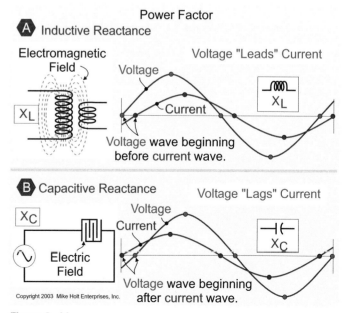

Figure 3–44

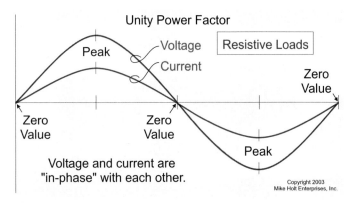

Figure 3–45

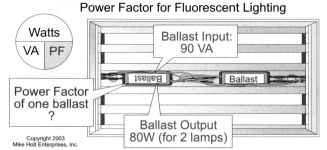

Electrical discharge lighting causes the voltage and current to be out-of-phase. "Unity Power Factor" would not apply to this kind of load.

Determine the power factor of each ballast.

$$PF = \frac{Watts}{(Volts \times Amperes)} = \frac{80W}{90\ VA} = 0.888\ or\ 89\% \ for\ Each\ Ballast$$

Or 4 Lamps = 160W, both ballasts = 180 VA

$$\frac{160W}{180\ VA} = 0.888\ or\ 89\%\ PF\ for\ Luminaire$$

Figure 3–46

3.32 Unity Power Factor

When an ac circuit supplies power to a purely resistive load, such as incandescent lighting, heating elements, etc., the circuit voltage and current will be in-phase with each other.

Because the voltage and current reach their zero and peak values at the same time, there is no leading or lagging of the voltage to the current. Therefore, the power factor of the load is 100 percent, and this condition is called "unity power factor." Figure 3-45

3.33 Power Factor Formulas

The relationship between True Power (watts), Apparent Power (VA), and Power Factor can be shown as:

Power Factor (PF) = True Power (Watts)/
Apparent Power (VA)

Apparent Power (VA) = True Power (W)/Power Factor (PF)

True Power (Watts) = Apparent Power (VA)
x Power Factor (PF)

▶ **Power Factor (PF) Example**

Assuming 100 percent efficiency, what is the power factor for each ballast rated 0.75A at 120V for a 2 x 4 fixture containing four 40W lamps (two lamps per ballast)? Figure 3-46

    (a) 69%   (b) 75%
    (c) 89%   (d) 95%

    • Answer: (c) 89%
    PF = W/VA
    PF = 80W/(0.75A x 120V)
    PF = 80W/(90VA)
    PF = 0.888 or 89%

▶ **Apparent Power (VA) Example**

What is the apparent power in VA of a fluorescent ballast that has a power factor of 89% when connected to two 40W lamps?

    (a) 70W   (b) 80 VA
    (c) 90 VA   (d) 100W

    • Answer: (c) 90 VA
    VA = W/PF
    VA = 80W/0.89 PF
    VA = 89.9 VA

Apparent power is expressed in VA; therefore, neither (a) nor (d) can be the answer.

▶ **True Power (Watts) Example**

What is the true power of a 16A load rated 120V, with a power factor of 85 percent?

    (a) 2,400W   (b) 1,920W
    (c) 1,632W   (d) none of these

    • Answer: (c) 1,632W
    Watts = VA x PF
    Watts = (120V x 16A) x 0.85 PF
    Watts = 1,632W

True power (watts) is equal to volts times amperes times power factor.

True power is always equal to or less than apparent power.

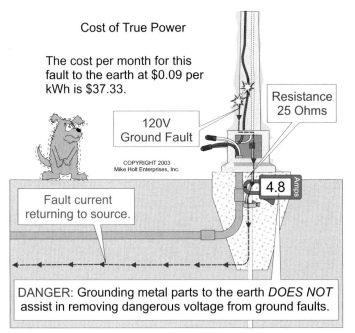

Cost of True Power

The cost per month for this fault to the earth at $0.09 per kWh is $37.33.

120V Ground Fault

Resistance 25 Ohms

COPYRIGHT 2003
Mike Holt Enterprises, Inc.

4.8 Amps

Fault current returning to source.

DANGER: Grounding metal parts to the earth *DOES NOT* assist in removing dangerous voltage from ground faults.

Figure 3–47

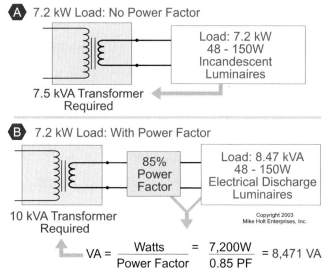

Effects of Power Factor

A 7.2 kW Load: No Power Factor

Load: 7.2 kW
48 - 150W
Incandescent
Luminaires

7.5 kVA Transformer Required

B 7.2 kW Load: With Power Factor

85% Power Factor

Load: 8.47 kVA
48 - 150W
Electrical Discharge
Luminaires

10 kVA Transformer Required

Copyright 2003
Mike Holt Enterprises, Inc.

$$VA = \frac{Watts}{Power\ Factor} = \frac{7,200W}{0.85\ PF} = 8,471\ VA$$

Figure 3–48

3.34 Cost of True Power

The cost of electrical power is based on the true power consumed during a month, multiplied by the cost per kWh (1,000W for a period of one hour).

▶ **Example**

What is the cost of power consumed per month (at $0.09 per kWh) for a 25 ohm ground rod having a ground-fault voltage of 120V? Figure 3-47

(a) $10   (b) $25
(c) $37   (d) $55

• Answer: (c) $37

Step 1   Power per hour = E^2/R

E = 120V
R = 25 ohms
P = (120V x 120V)/25 ohms
P = 576W

Step 2   Power consumed per day:
567W x 24 = 13,824W or 13.824 kWh

Step 3   Power consumed in 30 days:
13.824 kWh x 30 = 415 kWh

Step 4   Cost of power at $0.09 per kWh:
415 kWh x $0.09 = $37.33

3.35 Effects of Power Factor

The apparent power (VA) is used for sizing circuits and equipment. Because the VA of the load is greater than the watts of the load, fewer loads can be placed per circuit. More circuits and panels, and larger transformers might be required.

▶ **Example A**

What size transformer is required for forty-eight, 150W incandescent luminaires (noncontinuous load)? Figure 3-48A

(a) 3 kVA   (b) 5 kVA
(c) 7.5 kVA   (d) 10 kVA

• Answer: (c) 7.5 kVA
kW = (48 Fixtures x 150W)/1,000
kW = 7,200W/1,000
kW = 7.2 kW

AUTHOR'S COMMENT: Transformers are always sized based on kVA, not kW.

▶ **Example B**

What size transformer is required for forty-eight, 150W electric discharge luminaires that have a power factor of 85 percent (noncontinuous load)? Figure 3-48B

(a) 3 kVA   (b) 5 kVA
(c) 7.5 kVA   (d) 10 kVA

• Answer: (d) 10 kVA

kW = (48 x 150W)/1,000

kW = 7,200W/1,000

kW = 7.2 kW

Apparent Power = kW/PF

Apparent Power = 7.2kW/0.85PF

Apparent Power = 8.47 kVA

Transformers are sized for apparent power (kVA), not true power.

▶ **Example C**

How many 20A, 120V circuits are required for forty-eight, 150W luminaires (noncontinuous load)? **Figure 3-49A**

    (a) 2 circuits   (b) 3 circuits
    (c) 4 circuits   (d) 5 circuits

    • Answer: (b) 3 circuits

Each circuit has a capacity of: 120V x 20A = 2,400 VA

Each circuit can have: 2,400W/150W = 16 luminaires

The number of circuits required is:
48 luminaires/16 luminaires = 3 circuits

▶ **Example D**

How many 20A, 120V circuits are required for forty-eight, 150W luminaires (noncontinuous load) that have a power factor of 85 percent? **Figure 3-49B**

    (a) 4   (b) 6
    (c) 8   (d) 12

• Answer: (a) 4

Circuits are loaded according to VA, not watts!

VA of each luminaire is:
VA = Watts/PF
VA = 150W/0.85
VA = 176 VA

Each circuit has a capacity of: 120V x 20A = 2,400 VA

Each circuit can have: 2,400VA/176VA = 13 luminaires

The number of circuits required is:
48 luminaires/13 luminaires per circuit = 4 circuits

> **AUTHOR'S COMMENT:** If the building had 480 luminaires, we would need 40 circuits instead of 30 and the transformer would need to be rated at least 100 kVA, instead of 75 kVA.

PART E—EFFICIENCY

Introduction

Electricity is used because of its convenience in transferring energy to operate lighting, heating, controls, motors, etc. In the transfer of energy, there will be power losses in the conductors, the power supply, and the load itself. The degree of power loss in watts (waste) is indicated by the term "Efficiency."

Efficiency describes how much input energy is used for its intended useful purpose, expressed as a ratio of output true power to input true power. Naturally, the output power can never be greater than the input power. **Figure 3-50**

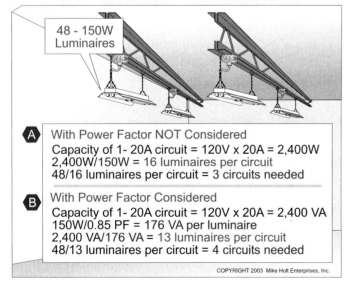

Effects of Power Factor on Inductive Lighting

48 - 150W Luminaires

Ⓐ With Power Factor NOT Considered
Capacity of 1- 20A circuit = 120V x 20A = 2,400W
2,400W/150W = 16 luminaires per circuit
48/16 luminaires per circuit = 3 circuits needed

Ⓑ With Power Factor Considered
Capacity of 1- 20A circuit = 120V x 20A = 2,400 VA
150W/0.85 PF = 176 VA per luminaire
2,400 VA/176 VA = 13 luminaires per circuit
48/13 luminaires per circuit = 4 circuits needed

COPYRIGHT 2003 Mike Holt Enterprises, Inc.

Figure 3–49

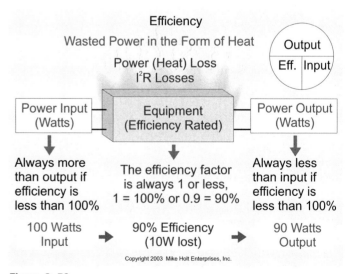

Efficiency

Wasted Power in the Form of Heat

Power (Heat) Loss
I²R Losses

Output
Eff. | Input

Power Input (Watts) — Equipment (Efficiency Rated) — Power Output (Watts)

Always more than output if efficiency is less than 100%

The efficiency factor is always 1 or less, 1 = 100% or 0.9 = 90%

Always less than input if efficiency is less than 100%

100 Watts Input ➡ 90% Efficiency (10W lost) ➡ 90 Watts Output

Copyright 2003 Mike Holt Enterprises, Inc.

Figure 3–50

If equipment is rated at 100 percent efficiency (there is none), this would mean that 100 percent of the input energy is consumed for its intended useful purpose.

When equipment is rated at 90 percent efficiency, this means that only 90 percent of the input power is used for its intended useful purpose. Another way of saying this is that 10 percent of the input power is wasted.

When energy is not used for its intended purpose, this condition is called power loss. Conductor resistance, mechanical friction, as well as many other factors can contribute to increased power losses, or reduced efficiency rating.

3.36 Efficiency Formulas

The formulas that are often used with efficiency calculations include:

Efficiency = Output Watts/Input Watts
Input Watts = Output Watts/Efficiency
Output Watts = Input Watts x Efficiency

► **Efficiency Example**

If the output of a load is 640W and the input is 800W, what is the efficiency of the equipment? Figure 3-51

(a) 60%   (b) 70%
(c) 80%   (d) 100%

• Answer: (c) 80%
  Efficiency is always less than 100%.
  Efficiency = Output Watts/Input Watts
  Efficiency = 640W/800W
  Efficiency = 0.80 or 80%

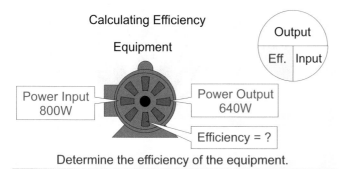

Calculating Efficiency

Determine the efficiency of the equipment.

Formula:
Efficiency = Output Watts / Input Watts
Answer must always be less than 100%.

Efficiency = 640W Output / 800W Input
Efficiency = 0.8 or 80%
Copyright 2003 Mike Holt Enterprises, Inc.

Figure 3–51

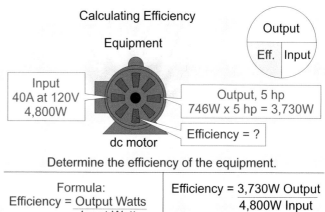

Calculating Efficiency

Determine the efficiency of the equipment.

Formula:
Efficiency = Output Watts / Input Watts
Answer must always be less than 100%.

Efficiency = 3,730W Output / 4,800W Input
Efficiency = 0.777 or 77.7%
Copyright 2003 Mike Holt Enterprises, Inc.

Figure 3–52

► **Efficiency Example B**

If the output of a 5 hp dc motor is 3,730W (746W x 5) and the input is 4,800W (40A at 120V), what is the efficiency of the motor? Figure 3-52

(a) 60%   (b) 78%
(c) 80%   (d) 100%

• Answer: (b) 78%
  Efficiency = Output Watts/Input Watts
  Efficiency = 3,730W/4,800W
  Efficiency = 0.777 or 77.7%

► **Input Example**

If the output is 250W and the equipment is 88 percent efficient, what is the input power rating in watts? Figure 3-53

(a) 200W   (b) 250W
(c) 285W   (d) 325W

• Answer: (c) 285W
  Input is always greater than the output.
  Input = Output Watts/Input Watts
  Input = 250W/0.88 Efficiency
  Input = 284W

Calculating Input Watts

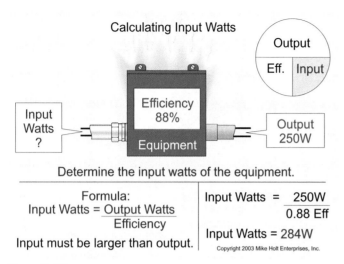

Determine the input watts of the equipment.

Formula:	Input Watts = $\dfrac{250W}{0.88\ \text{Eff}}$
Input Watts = $\dfrac{\text{Output Watts}}{\text{Efficiency}}$	
Input must be larger than output.	Input Watts = 284W

Copyright 2003 Mike Holt Enterprises, Inc.

Figure 3–53

Calculating Output Watts

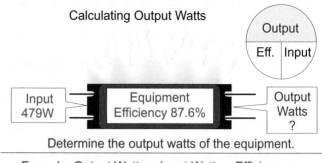

Determine the output watts of the equipment.

Formula: Output Watts = Input Watts x Efficiency

Output must be smaller than input.

Output = 479W x 0.876 Efficiency

Output = 419.6W

Copyright 2003 Mike Holt Enterprises, Inc.

Figure 3–54

▶ **Output Example**

If the input power to a load is 479W and the equipment is rated at 87.6 percent efficiency, what is the output power rating in watts? **Figure 3-54**

(a) 550W	(b) 500W
(c) 420W	(d) 350W

• Answer: (c) 420W
  Output is always less than input.
  Output Watts = Input Watts x Efficiency
  Output Watts = 479W x 0.876 Eff
  Output Watts = 419.6W

Unit 3 Conclusion

You now have a solid understanding of the basic concepts of alternating current. You know where it comes from and why it's used, plus you understand the various properties that characterize the current in a given circuit or system. The concepts of frequency, phase, and waveform are all critical to the field of power quality.

Your knowledge of what lead and lag mean will help you understand power factor. Remember that three-phase alternating current has three waveforms that, when conditions are perfect, have sinusoidal shapes and are 120 degrees out-of-phase with each other.

You now understand what a capacitor is, some uses for it, and why it works the way it does. You've also learned the equation for capacitive reactance. Capacitors have many uses, not all of which have been discussed here. For example, capacitors are often used in concert with inductors to form "tank circuits" in devices called power conditioners.

Induction, like capacitance and impedance, is one of the fundamental properties of electrical circuits. Now that you understand inductance, you are ready to learn the basic theory behind three important types of inductive devices—motors, generators, and transformers.

You know that no circuit is 100% efficient—all circuits and equipment have some power loss. The ability to calculate efficiency and power loss is now part of your skill set. While you don't normally have to use this skill, you may find it quite useful when troubleshooting or when deciding whether to replace old equipment.

You understand apparent power, true power, power factor, and unity power factor, and you know that it's possible to use capacitors to correct the power factor.

Unit 3 Calculation Practice Questions

(• Indicates that 75% or fewer of those who took this exam answered the question correctly.)

PART A—UNDERSTANDING ALTERNATING CURRENT

3.1 Current Flow

1. The movement of electrons themselves does not produce any useful work. It's the effects that the moving electrons have on the loads they flow through that are important.

    (a) True   (b) False

3.2 Why Alternating Current is Used

2. Alternating current is primarily used because it can be transmitted inexpensively.

    (a) True   (b) False

3.3 How Alternating Current is Produced

3. Faraday discovered that the lines of force of the magnetic field cause the electrons in the wire to flow in a specific direction. When the magnetic field moves in the opposite direction, electrons flow in the opposite direction.

    (a) True   (b) False

3.4 AC Generator

4. A simple ac generator consists of a loop of wire rotating between the lines of force between the opposite poles of a magnet.

    (a) True   (b) False

5. In ac generators that produce large quantities of electricity, the conductor coils are stationary and the magnetic field revolves within the coils.

    (a) True   (b) False

6. Output voltage of a generator is dependent upon the _____.

    (a) number of turns of wire   (b) strength of the magnetic field
    (c) speed at which the coil rotates   (d) all of these

3.5 Waveform

7. A waveform image is used to display the level and direction of current, but not voltage.

    (a) True   (b) False

8. The waveform for ac circuits displays the level and direction of the current and voltage for every instant of time for one full revolution of the rotor.

    (a) True   (b) False

3.6 Sine Wave

9.   The _____ wave is a waveform that is symmetrical with positive above and negative below the zero reference level.

(a) nonsinusoidal   (b) nonsymmetrical   (c) sine   (d) any of these

10.   A nonsinusoidal waveform is created when _____ loads distort the voltage and current sine wave.

(a) linear   (b) resistive   (c) inductive   (d) nonlinear

3.7 Nonsymmetrical Waveform

11.   The combination of alternating-current and direct-current waveforms results in a _____ waveform.

(a) nonsinusoidal   (b) nonsymmetrical   (c) sine   (d) any of these

3.8 Frequency

12.   The number of complete waveforms in one second is called the frequency. Frequency is expressed as _____ or cycles per second.

(a) degrees   (b) a sine wave   (c) phase   (d) Hertz

3.9 Phase

13.   The term "Phase" is used to indicate the time or degree relationship between two waveforms, such as voltage-to-current or voltage-to-voltage.

(a) True   (b) False

14.   In a purely resistive ac circuit, the current and voltage are _____. This means that they both reach their zero and peak values at the same time.

(a) in-phase   (b) out-of-phase   (c) a or b   (d) none of these

3.10 Degrees

15.   Phase differences are expressed in degrees; one full waveform is equal to _____.

(a) 90°   (b) 120°   (c) 180°   (d) 360°

16.   A three-phase generator has each of its windings out-of-phase with each other by _____.

(a) 90°   (b) 120°   (c) 180°   (d) 360°

17.   Phase differences are expressed in _____.

(a) sine waves   (b) phases   (c) Hertz   (d) degrees

3.11 Lead or Lag

18.   When describing the relationship between voltage and current, the reference waveform is always _____.

(a) current   (b) resistance   (c) voltage   (d) none of these

19.   If the voltage waveform finishes before the current waveform, the voltage is said to _____ the current waveform.

(a) lead   (b) lag   (c) be in-phase with   (d) none of these

20. When the current waveform finishes before the voltage waveform, the voltage _____ the current waveform.

    (a) leads   (b) lags   (c) is in-phase with   (d) none of these

3.12 Values of Alternating Current

21. _____ is the value of the voltage or current at a moment of time.

    (a) "Peak"   (b) "Root-mean-square"   (c) "Effective"   (d) "Instantaneous"

22. The peak value is equal to the effective value _____.

    (a) times 0.707   (b) times 1.41   (c) divided by 1.41   (d) none of these

23. _____ is the maximum value that ac current or voltage reaches, both for positive and negative polarity.

    (a) "Peak"   (b) "Root-mean-square"   (c) "Instantaneous"   (d) none of these

24. The effective value is equal to the peak value _____.

    (a) times 0.707   (b) times 1.41   (c) divided by 1.41   (d) none of these

25. Effective voltage or current value is the ac voltage or current that produces the same amount of heat in a resistor that would be produced by the same amount of dc voltage or current.

    (a) True   (b) False

26. _____ describes the steps necessary to determine the effective voltage or current value.

    (a) "Peak"   (b) "Root-mean-square"   (c) "Instantaneous"   (d) none of these

PART B—CAPACITANCE

Introduction

27. _____ is a property of an electrical circuit that enables it to store electrical energy by means of an electric field and to release this energy at a later time.

    (a) "Capacitance"   (b) "Induction"   (c) "Self-induction"   (d) none of these

28. A half-wave rectifier can be used to convert ac voltage into dc voltage to continuously charge a capacitor.

    (a) True   (b) False

3.13 Charged Capacitor

29. When a capacitor has a potential difference between the plates, it is said to be _____. One plate has an excess of free electrons, and the other plate has a lack of them.

    (a) induced   (b) charged   (c) discharged   (d) shorted

3.14 Electrical Field

30. If a capacitor is overcharged, the electrons from the negative plate could be pulled through the insulation to the positive plate. The capacitor is said to have _____.

    (a) charged   (b) discharged   (c) induced   (d) shorted

3.15 Discharging a Capacitor

31. To discharge a capacitor, all that is required is a(n) _____ path between the terminals of the capacitor. The free electrons on the negative plate then flow through the external circuit to the positive plate.

    (a) conductive   (b) insulating   (c) resistive   (d) semiconductor

32. Even when power is removed from the circuit, capacitors store large amounts of energy for a long period of time. They can discharge and arc if inadvertently shorted or grounded out.

    (a) True   (b) False

3.16 Determining Capacitance

33. Factors that determine the capacitance of a capacitor are the _____.

    (a) surface area of the plates   (b) distance between the plates
    (c) dielectric between the plates   (d) all of these

3.17 Uses of Capacitors

34. Capacitors are used to start single-phase ac motors and to prevent arcing across the contacts of electric switches.

    (a) True   (b) False

3.18 Phase Relationship

35. A capacitor can be thought of as a device that resists changes in current. Because a capacitor introduces reactance to the circuit, it shifts the current waveform to _____.

    (a) lead the applied voltage by 90°   (b) lag the applied voltage by 90°
    (c) lead the applied voltage by 180°   (d) lag the applied voltage by 180°

36. The opposition offered to the flow of ac current by a capacitor is called capacitive reactance, which is expressed in ohms and abbreviated _____.

    (a) X_C (b) X_L (c) Z   (d) none of these

PART C—INDUCTION

Introduction

37. When electrons move, the magnetic fields of the individual electrons combine to produce an overall magnetic field. The greater the current flow, the greater the overall magnetic field around the conductor.

    (a) True   (b) False

38. The direction of the overall magnetic field around the conductor follows the _____ rule, based on the electron current flow theory.

    (a) left-hand   (b) right-hand   (c) law of attraction   (d) none of these

39. The movement of electrons caused by an external magnetic field is called _____ current, and the associated potential that is established is called _____ voltage.

    (a) circuit   (b) applied   (c) induced   (d) none of these

40. In order to induce voltage, all that is required is relative motion between a conductor and a _____ field. This is the basis of the generator and transformer.

    (a) voltage   (b) current   (c) magnetic   (d) none of these

3.19 Self-Induction

41. As the ac current through a conductor increases, an expanding and collapsing electromagnetic field through the conductor induces a voltage within the conductor. This is known as _____ voltage.

    (a) applied   (b) circuit   (c) self-induced   (d) none of these

3.20 Induced Voltage and Applied Current

42. The induced voltage in a conductor carrying alternating current opposes the change in current flowing through the conductor. The induced voltage that opposes the current flow is called _____.

    (a) CEMF   (b) counter-electromotive force
    (c) back-EMF   (d) all of these

43. The waveform of the CEMF is _____ out-of-phase with the applied voltage.

    (a) 90°   (b) 120°   (c) 180°   (d) 360°

44. When alternating current increases, the polarity of the CEMF within the conductor tries to prevent the current from increasing.

    (a) True   (b) False

45. When alternating current decreases, the polarity of the induced voltage within the conductor tries to prevent the current from decreasing.

    (a) True   (b) False

3.21 Conductor AC Resistance

46. In dc circuits, the only property that affects current and voltage flow is _____.

    (a) impedance   (b) reactance   (c) resistance   (d) none of these

47. Conductor resistance is directly proportional to the conductor's length and cross-sectional area.

    (a) True   (b) False

48. For ac circuits, the ac _____ of a conductor must be taken into consideration.

    (a) eddy currents   (b) skin effect   (c) resistance   (d) all of these

49. Eddy currents are small independent currents induced within the conductor because of direct current.

    (a) True   (b) False

50. The expanding and collapsing magnetic field within the conductor induces a voltage in the conductors (CEMF) that repels the flowing electrons toward the surface of the conductor. This is called _____.

    (a) eddy currents   (b) induced voltage   (c) impedance   (d) skin effect

3.22 Impedance

51. The total opposition to current flow in ac circuits is called _____ and it is measured in ohms.

    (a) resistance   (b) reactance   (c) impedance   (d) skin effect

52. The abbreviation for impedance is _____.

    (a) X_L (b) X_C (c) Z   (d) none of these

3.23 Conductor Shape

53. The magnitude of self-induced voltage within a winding is directly proportional to the current flow, the winding, and the frequency at which magnetic fields cut through the winding.

    (a) True   (b) False

3.24 Magnetic Cores

54. Because an iron core provides an easy path for magnetic flux, windings with soft iron cores produce a greater self-inductance than windings with air cores.

    (a) True   (b) False

3.25 Self-Induced and Applied Voltage

55. Self-induced voltage is 180° out-of-phase with the _____. When the applied voltage is at its maximum in one direction, the induced voltage is at its maximum in the opposite direction.

    (a) applied current   (b) applied voltage   (c) induced voltage   (d) induced current

3.26 Current Flow

56. Self-induced voltage opposes the change in current flowing in the conductor. This is called inductive reactance and it is abbreviated _____.

    (a) X_L (b) X_C (c) Z   (d) none of these

3.27 Phase Relationship

57. In a purely inductive circuit, the CEMF waveform is _____ out-of-phase with the applied voltage waveform.

    (a) 90°   (b) 120°   (c) 180°   (d) 360°

58. In an inductive circuit, the CEMF waveform is 90° out-of-phase with the current waveform and 180° out-of-phase with the applied voltage waveform, making the voltage waveform lead the current waveform by _____.

    (a) 90°   (b) 120°   (c) 180°   (d) 360°

3.28 Uses of Induction

59. A common practical use of induction is for _____.

    (a) motors   (b) transformers   (c) generators   (d) all of these

PART D—POWER FACTOR

Introduction

60. Inductors and capacitors are electrical devices that store energy in the electromagnetic field of an inductor and the electric field of a capacitor.

(a) True   (b) False

3.29 Apparent Power (Volt-Amperes)

61. If you measure voltage and current in an inductive or capacitive circuit and then multiply them together, you obtain the circuit's _____.

(a) true power   (b) power factor   (c) apparent power   (d) none of these

3.30 True Power (Watts)

62. To determine the true power consumed by a dc circuit, multiply the volts by the amperes.

(a) True   (b) False

63. True power of an ac circuit equals the volts times the amperes.

(a) True   (b) False

3.31 Power Factor

64. AC inductive or capacitive reactive loads cause the voltage and current to be in-phase with each other.

(a) True   (b) False

65. Power factor is a measurement of how far the current is out-of-phase with the voltage.

(a) True   (b) False

3.32 Unity Power Factor

66. When an ac circuit supplies power to a purely _____ load, the circuit voltage and current will be in-phase with each other. This condition is called unity power factor.

(a) capacitive   (b) inductive   (c) resistive   (d) any of these

3.34 Cost of True Power

67. What does it cost per year (at 9 cents per kWh) for ten 150W recessed luminaires to operate if they are turned on for six hours a day?

(a) $150   (b) $300   (c) $500   (d) $800

3.35 Effects of Power Factor

68. Because apparent power (VA) is greater than the true power (W), more loads can be placed on a circuit, so fewer circuits and panels, and smaller transformers might be required.

(a) True   (b) False

69. When sizing circuits or equipment, always size the circuit components and transformers according to the apparent power (VA), not the true power (W).

    (a) True   (b) False

70. What is the true power of a 10A circuit operating at 120V with unity power factor?

    (a) 1,200 VA   (b) 2,400 VA   (c) 1,200W   (d) 2,400W

71. What size transformer is required for a 100A, 240V, single-phase noncontinuous load (unity power factor)?

    (a) 15 kVA   (b) 25 kVA   (c) 37.5 kVA   (d) 50 kVA

72. What size transformer is required for a 100A, 240V, single-phase noncontinuous load that has a power factor of 85 percent?

    (a) 15 kVA   (b) 25 kVA   (c) 37.5 kVA   (d) 50 kVA

73. How many 20A, 120V circuits are required for forty-two, 300W incandescent luminaires (noncontinuous load)?

    (a) 3 circuits   (b) 4 circuits   (c) 5 circuits   (d) 6 circuits

74. How many 20A, 120V circuits are required for forty-two, 300W luminaires (assume this is a noncontinuous load) that have a power factor of 85 percent?

    (a) 5 circuits   (b) 6 circuits   (c) 7 circuits   (d) 8 circuits

PART E—EFFICIENCY

Introduction

75. In the transfer of electrical energy, there is power loss in the conductors, the power supply, and the load itself.

    (a) True   (b) False

76. Efficiency describes how much input energy is used for its intended purpose.

    (a) True   (b) False

3.36 Efficiency Formulas

77. If the output is 1,320W and the input is 1,800W, what is the efficiency of the equipment?

    (a) 62%   (b) 73%   (c) 80%   (d) 100%

78. If the input of a 1 hp dc motor is 1,128W and the output is 746W, what is the efficiency of the motor?

    (a) 66%   (b) 74%   (c) 87%   (d) 100%

79. If the output is 1,600W and the equipment is 88 percent efficient, what are the input amperes at 120V?

    (a)10A   (b) 15A   (c) 20A   (d) 25A

80. If a transformer is 97 percent efficient, for every 1 kW input, there will be _____ output.

    (a) 970W   (b) 1,000W   (c) 1,030W   (d) 1,200W

Unit 3 Calculation Challenge Questions

(• Indicates that 75% or fewer of those who took this exam answered the question correctly.)

PART A—UNDERSTANDING ALTERNATING CURRENT

3.2 Why Alternating Current Is Used

1. The primary reason(s) for high-voltage transmission lines is(are) _____.

    (a) reduced voltage drop   (b) smaller wire   (c) smaller equipment   (d) all of these

2. One of the advantages of a higher-voltage system as compared to a lower-voltage system (for the same wattage loads) is _____.

    (a) reduced voltage drop   (b) reduced power use   (c) large currents   (d) lower electrical pressure

3. The advantage of ac over dc is that ac provides for _____.

    (a) better speed control   (b) ease of voltage variation
    (c) lower resistance at high currents   (d) none of these

3.5 Waveform

4. A waveform represents _____.

    (a) the magnitude and direction of current or voltage   (b) how current or voltage can vary with time
    (c) how output voltage can vary with the generator armature   (d) all of these

3.8 Frequency

5. The frequency of an ac waveform is the number of times the current or voltage goes through 360 degrees in _____.

    (a) 1/10 second   (b) 5 seconds   (c) 1 second   (d) 60 seconds

6. How much time does it take for 60 Hz ac to travel through 180 degrees?

    (a) 1/90 second   (b) 1/40 second   (c) 1/180 second   (d) none of these

3.12 Values of Alternating Current

7. •The heating effects of 10A of ac as compared with 10A of dc is _____.

    (a) the same   (b) less   (c) greater   (d) none of these

8. If the peak value of an ac system is 50A, the RMS value would be approximately _____.

    (a) 25A   (b) 30A   (c) 35A   (d) 40A

9. •The maximum value of 120V dc is equal to the peak value of an equivalent 120V ac.

    (a) True   (b) False

Mike Holt Enterprises, Inc. • www.NECcode.com • 1.888.NEC.CODE

10. •120V is the reading shown on a voltmeter. This is an indication of the _____ value of the voltage source.

    (a) average   (b) peak   (c) effective   (d) instantaneous

PART B—CAPACITANCE
3.16 Determining Capacitance

11. The insulating material between the surface plates of a capacitor is called the _____.

    (a) inhibitor   (b) electrolyte   (c) dielectric   (d) regulator

12. If three capacitors are to be connected together, which connection will provide the highest capacitance?

    (a) Connect all three in series.
    (b) Connect all three in parallel.
    (c) Connect the capacitors in a combination of series and parallel.
    (d) none of these

3.17 Uses of Capacitors

13. •In a circuit that has only capacitive reactance (X_C), the voltage and current are said to be out-of-phase to each other because the voltage _____.

    (a) leads the current by 90°   (b) lags the current by 90°
    (c) leads the current   (d) none of these

14. Resonance occurs when _____.

    (a) only resistance occurs in the system   (b) the power factor is equal to zero
    (c) $X_L = X_C$ (d) when R = Z

3.18 Phase Relationship

15. Capacitive reactance is measured in _____.

    (a) ohms   (b) volts   (c) watts   (d) henrys

PART C—INDUCTION
3.20 Induced Voltage and Applied Current

16. _____ Law states that a change in current produces a counter-electromotive force whose direction is such that it opposes the change in current.

    (a) Kirchoff's Second   (b) Kirchoff's First   (c) Lenz's   (d) Hertz's

17. Inductive reactance is abbreviated as _____.

    (a) I^2R (b) L_X (c) X_L (d) Z

18. Inductive reactance changes proportionately with frequency.

    (a) True   (b) False

19. Inductive reactance is measured in _____.

    (a) farads   (b) watts   (c) ohms   (d) coulombs

20. •If the frequency is constant, the inductive reactance of a circuit will _____.

    (a) remain constant regardless of the current and voltage changes
    (b) vary directly with the voltage
    (c) vary directly with the current
    (d) not affect the impedance

3.22 Impedance

21. The total opposition to current flow in an ac circuit is expressed in ohms and is called _____.

    (a) impedance   (b) conductance   (c) reluctance   (d) none of these

22. Impedance is present in _____ type circuit(s).

    (a) resistance   (b) direct-current   (c) alternating-current   (d) none of these

23. Conductor resistance to ac flow is _____ the resistance to dc.

    (a) higher than   (b) lower than   (c) the same as   (d) none of these

PART D—POWER FACTOR

3.29 Apparent Power (Volt-Amperes)

24. If you multiply the voltage by the current in an inductive or capacitive circuit, the answer will be the _____ of the circuit.

    (a) watts   (b) true power   (c) apparent power   (d) all of these

25. The apparent power of a 19.2A, 120V load is _____.

    (a) 0.23 kVA   (b) 2.3 kVA   (c) 2.3 VA   (d) 230 kVA

3.30 True Power (Watts)

26. •A wattmeter is connected in _____ in the circuit.

    (a) series   (b) parallel   (c) series-parallel   (d) none of these

27. •True power is always voltage times current for _____.

    (a) all ac circuits   (b) dc circuits
    (c) ac circuits at unity power factor   (d) b and c

28. Power consumed (watts) in either a single-phase ac or dc system is always equal to _____.

    (a) $I \times R^2$ (b) $E \times R$ (c) $I^2 \times R$ (d) $E/(I \times R)$

29. •The power consumed by a 208V, 76A, three-phase circuit that has a power factor of 89 percent is _____.

    (a) 27,379W   (b) 35,808W   (c) 24,367W   (d) 12,456W

110. •The true power of a single-phase, 2.1 kVA load with a power factor of 91 percent is _____.

   (a) 2.1 kW   (b) 1.91 kW   (c) 1.75 kW   (d) 0.191 kW

3.31 Power Factor

111. Power factor in an ac circuit is unity (100 percent), if the circuit contains only _____.

   (a) induction motors   (b) transformers   (c) reactance coils   (d) resistive loads

112. •Three 8 kW electric-discharge lighting bank circuits, which have a 92 percent power factor, are connected to a 230V, three-phase source. The current flow of these lights is _____.

   (a) 37A   (b) 50A   (c) 65A   (d) 75A

PART E—EFFICIENCY

3.36 Efficiency Formulas

113. •Motor efficiency can be determined by which of the following formulas?

   (a) hp x 746W   (b) hp x 746W/VA Input
   (c) hp x 746W/W Input   (d) Input W/(hp x 746W)

114. The efficiency ratio of a 4,000 VA transformer winding with a secondary VA of 3,600 VA is _____.

   (a) 80%   (b) 70%   (c) 90%   (d) 110%

(• Indicates that 75% or fewer of those who took this exam answered the question correctly.)

Article 230 Services (continued)

1. The minimum point of attachment of the service-drop conductors to a building must in no case be less than _____ above finished grade.

   (a) 8 ft   (b) 10 ft   (c) 12 ft   (d) 15 ft

2. Service-lateral conductors are required to be insulated except for the grounded conductor when it is _____.

   (a) bare copper used in a raceway
   (b) bare copper and part of a cable assembly that is identified for underground use
   (c) copper-clad aluminum
   (d) a or b

3. Underground copper service conductors must not be smaller than _____ AWG copper.

   (a) 3   (b) 4   (c) 6   (d) 8

4. When two to six service disconnecting means in separate enclosures are grouped at one location and supply separate loads from one service drop or lateral, _____ set(s) of service-entrance conductors are permitted to supply each or several such service equipment enclosures.

   (a) one   (b) two   (c) three   (d) four

5. Service conductors must be sized no less than _____ percent of the continuous load, plus 100 percent of the noncontinuous load.

   (a) 100   (b) 115   (c) 125   (d) 150

6. Cable tray systems are permitted to support service-entrance conductors. Cable trays used to support service-entrance conductors can contain only service-entrance conductors _____.

   (a) unless a solid fixed barrier separates the service-entrance conductors
   (b) only for under 300V
   (c) only in industrial locations
   (d) only for over 600V

7. Service-entrance conductors can be spliced or tapped by clamped or bolted connections at any time as long as _____.

   (a) the free ends of conductors are covered with an insulation that is equivalent to that of the conductors or with an insulating device identified for the purpose
   (b) wire connectors or other splicing means installed on conductors that are buried in the earth are listed for direct burial
   (c) no splice is made in a raceway
   (d) all of these

8. Service cables that are subject to physical damage must be protected by _____.

   (a) rigid metal conduit   (b) intermediate metal conduit
   (c) schedule 80 rigid nonmetallic conduit   (d) any of these

9.   Service cables mounted in contact with a building must be supported at intervals not exceeding _____.

  (a) 4 ft   (b) 3 ft   (c) 30 in.   (d) 24 in.

10. Where individual open conductors are not exposed to the weather, the conductors must be mounted on _____ knobs.

  (a) door   (b) insulated metal   (c) glass or porcelain   (d) none of these

11. When individual open conductors enter a building or other structure, they must enter through roof bushings or through the wall in an upward slant through individual, noncombustible, nonabsorbent insulating _____.

  (a) tubes   (b) raceways   (c) chases   (d) standoffs

12. Service cables must be equipped with a raintight _____.

  (a) raceway   (b) service head   (c) cover   (d) all of these

13. Service heads must be located _____.

  (a) above the point of attachment   (b) below the point of attachment
  (c) even with the point of attachment   (d) none of these

14. Service-drop conductors and service-entrance conductors must be arranged so that _____ will not enter the service raceway or equipment.

  (a) dust   (b) vapor   (c) water   (d) none of these

15. The service disconnecting means must be installed at a(n) _____ location.

  (a) dry   (b) readily accessible   (c) outdoor   (d) indoor

16. Each service disconnecting means must be permanently marked to identify it as a service disconnecting means.

  (a) True   (b) False

17. Each service disconnecting means must be suitable for _____.

  (a) hazardous locations   (b) wet locations   (c) dry locations   (d) the prevailing conditions

18. Disconnecting means used solely for power monitoring equipment, transient voltage surge suppressors, or the control circuit of the ground-fault protection system or power-operable service disconnecting means, installed as part of the listed equipment, are not considered a service disconnecting means.

  (a) True   (b) False

19. The additional service disconnecting means for fire pumps or for emergency, legally required standby, or optional standby services permitted by 230.2, must be installed remote from the one to six service disconnecting means for normal service to minimize the possibility of _____ interruption of supply.

  (a) accidental   (b) intermittent   (c) simultaneous   (d) prolonged

20. In a multiple-occupancy building where electric service and electrical maintenance are provided by the building management under continuous building management supervision, the service disconnecting means supplying more than one occupancy can be accessible to authorized _____ only.

  (a) inspectors   (b) tenants   (c) management personnel   (d) none of these

21.   •The service disconnecting means must plainly indicate whether it is in the _____ position.

(a) open or closed   (b) tripped   (c) up or down   (d) correct

22.   For installations consisting of not more than two 2-wire branch circuits, the service disconnecting means must have a rating of not less than _____.

(a) 15A   (b) 20A   (c) 25A   (d) 30A

23.   The service conductors must be connected to the service disconnecting means by _____ or other approved means.

(a) pressure connectors   (b) clamps   (c) solder   (d) a or b

24.   _____ for power-operable service disconnects can be connected on the supply side of the service disconnecting means, if suitable overcurrent protection and disconnecting means are provided.

(a) Control circuits   (b) Distribution panels   (c) Grounding conductors (d) none of these

25.   In a service, overcurrent protection devices must never be placed in the grounded service conductor with the exception of a circuit breaker that simultaneously opens all conductors of the circuit.

(a) True   (b) False

26.   Where necessary to prevent tampering, an automatic overcurrent protection device that protects service conductors supplying only a specific load, such as a water heater, are permitted to be _____ where located so as to be accessible.

(a) locked   (b) sealed   (c) a or b   (d) none of these

27.   As defined by 230.95, the rating of the service disconnect is considered to be the rating of the largest _____ that can be installed or the highest continuous-current trip setting for which the actual overcurrent protection device installed in a circuit breaker is rated or can be adjusted.

(a) fuse   (b) circuit   (c) wire   (d) all of these

28.   The maximum setting of the ground-fault protection in a service disconnecting means must be _____.

(a) 800A   (b) 1,000A   (c) 1,200A   (d) 2,000A

29.   Ground-fault protection that functions to open the service disconnect _____ protect(s) service conductors or the service equipment on the line side.

(a) will   (b) will not   (c) adequately   (d) totally

30.   Where ground-fault protection is provided for the _____ disconnect and interconnection is made with another supply system by a transfer device, means or devices may be needed to ensure proper ground-fault sensing by the ground-fault protection equipment.

(a) circuit   (b) service
(c) switch and fuse combination   (d) b and c

Article 240 Overcurrent Protection

This article provides the general requirements for overcurrent protection and overcurrent protective devices. Overcurrent protection for conductors and equipment is provided to open the circuit if the current reaches a value that will cause an excessive or dangerous temperature on the conductors or conductor insulation.

31. Overcurrent protection for conductors and equipment is designed to _____ the circuit if the current reaches a value that will cause an excessive or dangerous temperature in conductors or conductor insulation.

     (a) open   (b) close   (c) monitor   (d) record

32. Conductor overload protection is not required where the interruption of the _____ would create a hazard, such as in a material-handling magnet circuit or fire-pump circuit. However, short-circuit protection is required.

     (a) circuit   (b) line   (c) phase   (d) system

33. 240.4(E) allows tap conductors to be protected against overcurrent in accordance with other *Code* sections that deal with the specific situation outside Article 240.

     (a) True   (b) False

34. Where flexible cord is used in listed extension cord sets, the conductors are considered protected against overcurrent when used within _____.

     (a) indoor installations   (b) non-hazardous locations
     (c) the extension cord's listing requirements (d) 50 ft of the branch-circuit panelboard

35. The standard ampere ratings for fuses and inverse-time circuit breakers are listed in 240.6(A). Additional standard ratings for fuses include _____.

     (a) 1A   (b) 6A   (c) 601A   (d) all of these

36. Supplementary overcurrent protection _____.

     (a) must not be used in luminaires
     (b) may be used as a substitute for a branch-circuit overcurrent protection device
     (c) may be used to protect internal circuits of equipment
     (d) must be readily accessible

37. When an orderly shutdown is required to minimize hazard(s) to personnel and equipment, a system of coordination based on two conditions is permitted. Those two conditions are _____ short-circuit protection, and _____ indication based on monitoring systems or devices.

     (a) uncoordinated, overcurrent   (b) coordinated, overcurrent
     (c) coordinated, overload   (d) none of these

38. A(n) _____ is considered equivalent to an overcurrent trip unit.

     (a) current transformer   (b) overcurrent relay   (c) a and b   (d) a or b

39. Circuit breakers must _____ all ungrounded conductors of the circuit.

     (a) open   (b) close   (c) isolate   (d) inhibit

40. Single-pole breakers with identified handle ties can be used to protect each ungrounded conductor for line-to-line connected loads.

     (a) True   (b) False

41. A feeder tap of 10 ft or less can be made without overcurrent protection at the tap when the rating of the overcurrent device on the line side of the tap conductors does not exceed _____ times the ampacity of the tap conductor.

    (a) 10   (b) 5   (c) 125   (d) 25

42. One of the requirements that permit conductors supplying a transformer to be tapped, without overcurrent protection at the tap, is that the conductors supplied by the _____ of a transformer must have an ampacity, when multiplied by the ratio of the primary-to-secondary voltage, of at least one-third the rating of the overcurrent device protecting the feeder conductors.

    (a) primary   (b) secondary   (c) tertiary   (d) none of these

43. The "next size up protection rule" of 240.4(B) is permitted for transformer secondary tap conductors.

    (a) True   (b) False

44. No overcurrent protection device can be connected in series with any conductor that is intentionally grounded except where the overcurrent protection device opens all conductors of the circuit, including the _____ conductor, and is designed so that no pole can operate independently (except as allowed for motor overload protection in 430.36 or 430.37).

    (a) ungrounded   (b) grounding   (c) grounded   (d) none of these

45. Overcurrent protection devices must be _____.

    (a) accessible (as applied to wiring methods)   (b) accessible (as applied to equipment)
    (c) readily accessible   (d) inaccessible to unauthorized personnel

46. Overcurrent protection devices are not permitted to be located _____.

    (a) where exposed to physical damage   (b) near easily ignitible materials, such as in clothes closets
    (c) in bathrooms of dwelling units   (d) all of these

47. Handles or levers of circuit breakers, and similar parts that may move suddenly in such a way that persons in the vicinity are likely to be injured by being struck by them, must be _____.

    (a) guarded   (b) isolated   (c) a and b   (d) a or b

48. Plug fuses of the Edison-base type have a maximum rating of _____.

    (a) 20A   (b) 30A   (c) 40A   (d) 50A

49. Fuseholders of the Edison-base type must be installed only where they are made to accept _____ fuses by the use of adapters.

    (a) Edison-base   (b) medium-base   (c) heavy-duty base   (d) Type S

50. Type _____ fuse adapters must be designed so that once inserted in a fuseholder they cannot be removed.

    (a) A   (b) E   (c) S   (d) P

51. Dimensions of Type S fuses, fuseholders, and adapters must be standardized to permit interchangeability regardless of the _____.

    (a) model   (b) manufacturer   (c) amperage   (d) voltage

52. Fuseholders for cartridge fuses must be so designed that it is difficult to put a fuse of any given class into a fuseholder that is designed for a _____ lower or a _____ higher than that of the class to which the fuse belongs.

    (a) voltage, wattage   (b) wattage, voltage   (c) voltage, current   (d) current, voltage

53. Cartridge fuses and fuseholders must be classified according to _____ ranges.

    (a) voltage   (b) amperage   (c) voltage or amperage   (d) voltage and amperage

54.   Circuit breakers must be capable of being closed and opened by manual operation. Their normal method of operation by other means, such as electrical or pneumatic must be permitted if means for _____ operation are also provided.

      (a) automated   (b) timed   (c) manual   (d) shunt trip

55.   A(n) _____ must be of such design that any alteration of its trip point (calibration) or the time required for its operation will require dismantling of the device or breaking of a seal for other than intended adjustments.

      (a) Type S fuse   (b) Edison-base fuse   (c) circuit breaker   (d) fuseholder

56.   Circuit breakers must be marked with their ampere rating in a manner that will be durable and visible after installation. Such marking can be made visible by removal of a _____.

      (a) trim   (b) cover   (c) box   (d) a or b

57.   Circuit breakers having an interrupting current rating of other than _____ must have their interrupting rating marked on the circuit breaker.

      (a) 50,000A   (b) 10,000A   (c) 15,000A   (d) 5,000A

58.   Circuit breakers used to switch high-intensity discharge lighting circuits must be listed and marked as _____.

      (a) SWD   (b) HID   (c) a or b   (d) a and b

59.   A circuit breaker with a straight voltage rating (240V or 480V) can be used on a circuit where the nominal voltage between any two conductors does not exceed the circuit breaker's voltage rating.

      (a) True   (b) False

Article 250 Grounding and Bonding

Article 250 covers the requirements for providing a low-impedance path to conduct undesired high voltage to the earth, and requirements for the low-impedance fault-current path necessary to facilitate the operation of overcurrent protection devices.

60.   A ground-fault current path is an electrically conductive path from the point of a line-to-case fault extending to the _____.

      (a) ground   (b) earth   (c) electrical supply source   (d) none of these

61.   An effective ground-fault current path is an intentionally constructed low-impedance path designed and intended to carry fault current from the point of a line-to-case fault on a wiring system to _____.

      (a) ground   (b) earth
      (c) the electrical supply source   (d) none of these

62.   Electrical systems that are grounded must be connected to earth in a manner that will _____.

      (a) limit voltages due to lightning, line surges, or unintentional contact with higher voltage lines
      (b) stabilize the voltage-to-ground during normal operation
      (c) facilitate overcurrent protection device operation in case of ground faults
      (d) a and b

63.   Electrical systems are grounded to the _____ to stabilize the system voltage.

      (a) ground   (b) earth   (c) electrical supply source   (d) none of these

64.   For grounded systems, the metal parts of electrical equipment in a building or structure must be connected to the _____ for the purpose of limiting the voltage to ground on these materials.

      (a) ground   (b) earth   (c) electrical supply source   (d) none of these

65. For grounded systems, the electrical equipment and wiring, and other electrically conductive material likely to become energized, are installed in a manner that creates a permanent, low-impedance circuit capable of safely carrying the maximum ground-fault current likely to be imposed on it from where a ground fault may occur to the _____.

    (a) ground   (b) earth   (c) electrical supply source   (d) none of these

66. For grounded systems, the earth can be considered as an effective ground-fault current path.

    (a) True   (b) False

67. The grounding of electrical systems, circuit conductors, surge arresters, and conductive noncurrent-carrying materials and equipment must be installed and arranged in a manner that will prevent objectionable current over the grounding conductors or grounding paths.

    (a) True   (b) False

68. •Currents that introduce noise or data errors in electronic equipment are considered objectionable currents.

    (a) True   (b) False

69. Sheet-metal screws can be used to connect grounding (or bonding) conductors or connection devices to enclosures.

    (a) True   (b) False

70. _____ on equipment to be grounded must be removed from contact surfaces to ensure good electrical continuity.

    (a) Paint   (b) Lacquer   (c) Enamel   (d) any of these

71. AC systems of 50 to 1,000V that supply premises wiring systems must be grounded where the system can be grounded so that the maximum voltage-to-ground on the ungrounded conductors does not exceed _____.

    (a) 1,000V   (b) 300V   (c) 150V   (d) 50V

72. AC systems of 50 to 1,000V that supply premises wiring systems must be grounded where supplied by a three-phase, 4-wire, delta-connected system.

    (a) True   (b) False

73. •When grounding service-supplied alternating-current systems, the grounding electrode conductor must be connected (bonded) to the grounded service conductor (neutral) at _____.

    (a) the load end of the service drop   (b) the meter equipment
    (c) the service disconnect   (d) any of these

74. A grounding connection must not be made to any grounded circuit conductor on the _____ side of the service disconnecting means except as permitted for separately derived systems or separate buildings.

    (a) supply   (b) power   (c) line   (d) load

75. The grounded conductor brought to service equipment must be routed with the phase conductors and must not be smaller than specified in Table _____ when the service-entrance conductors are not larger than 1,100 kcmil copper.

    (a) 250.66   (b) 250.122   (c) 310.16   (d) 430.52

76. Where the service-entrance phase conductors are installed in parallel, the size of the grounded conductor in each raceway must be based on the size of the ungrounded service-entrance conductor in the raceway, but not smaller than _____ AWG.

    (a) 6   (b) 1   (c) 1/0   (d) none of these

77.   A main bonding jumper must be a _____ or similar conductor.

(a) wire   (b) bus   (c) screw   (d) any of these

78.   The grounding electrode conductor for a single separately derived system must connect the grounded conductor of the derived system to the grounding electrode.

(a) True   (b) False

79.   Grounding electrode taps from a separately derived system to a common grounding electrode conductor are permitted when a building or structure has multiple separately derived systems.

(a) True   (b) False

80.   Where a grounded conductor is installed and the neutral-to-case bond is not at the source of the separately derived system, the grounded conductor must be routed with the derived phase conductors and must not be smaller than the required grounding electrode conductor specified in Table 250.66, but must not be required to be larger than the largest ungrounded derived phase conductor.

(a) True   (b) False

81.   A grounding electrode at a separate building or structure is required where one multiwire branch circuit serves the building or structure.

(a) True   (b) False

82.   When supplying a grounded system at a separate building or structure, if the equipment grounding conductor is not run with the supply conductors and there are no continuous metallic paths bonded to the grounding system in both buildings involved, and ground-fault protection of equipment has not been installed on the common ac service, then the grounded circuit conductor must be connected to the building disconnecting means and to the grounding electrode at the separate building.

(a) True   (b) False

83.   The frame of a portable generator is not required to be grounded and is not to be connected to a(n) _____ for a system supplied by cord and plug using receptacles mounted on the generator with the grounding terminals of the receptacles bonded to the generator frame.

(a) grounding electrode   (b) grounded conductor
(c) ungrounded conductor   (d) equipment grounding conductor

84.   Where none of the items in 250.52(A)(1) through (A)(6) are present for use as a grounding electrode, one or more of the following must be installed and used as the grounding electrode: _____.

(a) a ground ring   (b) rod and pipe electrodes or plate electrodes
(c) local metal underground systems or structures (d) any of these

85.   Interior metal water piping located more than _____ from the point of entrance to the building cannot be used as a part of the grounding electrode system, or as a conductor to interconnect electrodes that are part of the grounding electrode system.

(a) 2 ft   (b) 4 ft   (c) 5 ft   (d) 6 ft

86.   A bare 4 AWG copper conductor installed near the bottom of a concrete foundation or footing that is in direct contact with the earth may be used as a grounding electrode when the conductor is at least _____ in length.

(a) 25 ft   (b) 15 ft   (c) 10 ft   (d) 20 ft

87. Electrodes of pipe or conduit must not be smaller than _____ and, where of iron or steel, must have the outer surface galvanized or otherwise metal-coated for corrosion protection.

    (a) 1/2 in.　　　　(b) 3/4 in.　　　　(c) 1 in.　　　　(d) none of these

88. A metal underground water pipe must be supplemented by an additional electrode of a type specified in 250.52(A)(2) through (A)(7). Where the supplemental electrode is a rod, pipe, or plate electrode, that portion of the bonding jumper that is the sole connection to the supplemental grounding electrode is not required to be larger than _____ AWG copper wire.

    (a) 8　　　　(b) 6　　　　(c) 4　　　　(d) 1

89. Ground rod electrodes must be installed so that at least _____ of the length is in contact with the soil. Where rock bottom is encountered, the rod must be driven at an angle not to exceed 45 degrees.

    (a) 8 ft　　　　(b) 5 ft　　　　(c) 1/2　　　　(d) 80 percent

90. When driving a ground rod electrode, if rock bottom is encountered, the rod is allowed to be bent over in a trench and buried or shortened with a hack saw.

    (a) True　　　　(b) False

91. The supplementary electrode allowed by the *Code* is different from a supplemental electrode, and is allowed to be connected to the equipment grounding conductors but cannot be used in place of an effective ground-fault current path for electrical equipment.

    (a) True　　　　(b) False

92. When multiple ground rods are used for a grounding electrode, they must be separated not less than _____ apart.

    (a) 6 ft　　　　(b) 8 ft　　　　(c) 20 ft　　　　(d) 12 ft

93. Where separate services supply a building and are required to be connected to a grounding electrode, the same grounding electrode must be used. Two or more grounding electrodes that are _____ are considered as a single grounding electrode system in this sense.

    (a) effectively bonded together　　　　(b) spaced no more than 6 ft apart
    (c) a and b　　　　(d) none of these

94. The grounding electrode conductor must be made of which of the following materials?

    (a) Copper　　　　(b) Aluminum　　　　(c) Copper-clad aluminum　　　　(d) any of these

95. Grounding electrode conductors smaller than _____ must be in rigid metal conduit, intermediate metal conduit, rigid nonmetallic conduit, electrical metallic tubing, or cable armor.

    (a) 6 AWG　　　　(b) 8 AWG　　　　(c) 10 AWG　　　　(d) 4 AWG

96. The grounding electrode conductor must be installed in one continuous length without a splice or joint, unless spliced _____.

    (a) by connecting to a busbar
    (b) by irreversible compression-type connectors listed as grounding and bonding
    (c) by the exothermic welding process.
    (d) any of these

97.   The grounding electrode conductor can be run to any convenient grounding electrode available in the grounding electrode system or to one or more grounding electrodes individually.

  (a) True   (b) False

98.   •The largest size grounding electrode conductor required for any service is a _____ copper.

  (a) 6 AWG   (b) 1/0 AWG   (c) 3/0 AWG   (d) 250 kcmil

99.   In an ac system, the size of the grounding electrode conductor to a concrete-encased electrode is not required to be larger than _____ copper wire.

  (a) 4 AWG   (b) 6 AWG   (c) 8 AWG   (d) 10 AWG

100. Grounding electrode conductor connections to a concrete-encased or buried grounding electrode are required to be readily accessible.

  (a) True   (b) False

(• Indicates that 75% or fewer of those who took this exam answered the question correctly.)

1. Where raceway-type service masts are used, all raceway fittings must be _____ for use with service masts.

    (a) identified   (b) approved   (c) heavy-duty   (d) listed

2. •A service that contains 12 AWG service-entrance conductors, as permitted by 230.23(B) Ex., requires a grounding electrode conductor sized no less than _____.

    (a) 6 AWG   (b) 4 AWG   (c) 8 AWG   (d) 10 AWG

3. •Where the resistance-to-ground of a single rod electrode exceeds 25 ohms, _____.

    (a) other means besides made electrodes must be used in order to provide grounding
    (b) at least one additional electrode must be added
    (c) no additional electrodes are required
    (d) the electrode can be omitted

4. •Which of the following statements about Type S fuses is (are) true?

    (a) Adapters must fit Edison-base fuseholders.   (b) Adapters are designed to be easily removed.
    (c) Type S fuses must be classified as not over 125V and 30A.   (d) a and c

5. A circuit breaker with a slash rating (120/240V or 277/480V) can be used on a solidly grounded circuit where the nominal voltage of any conductor to _____ does not exceed the lower of the two values, and the nominal voltage between any two conductors does not exceed the higher value.

    (a) another conductor   (b) an enclosure   (c) earth   (d) ground

6. A device that, when interrupting currents in its current-limiting range, will reduce the current flowing in the faulted circuit to a magnitude substantially less than that obtainable in the same circuit if the device were replaced with a solid conductor having comparable impedance, is defined as a(n) _____ protective device.

    (a) short-circuit   (b) overload   (c) ground-fault   (d) current-limiting

7. AC systems of 50 to 1,000V that supply premises wiring systems must be grounded where supplied by a three-phase, 4-wire, wye-connected system.

    (a) True   (b) False

8. Air terminal conductors or electrodes used for grounding air terminals _____ be used as the grounding electrodes required by 250.50 for grounding wiring systems and equipment.

    (a) must   (b) must not   (c) can   (d) any of these

9. An 800A fuse rated at 600V _____ on a 250V system.

    (a) must not be used   (b) must be used   (c) can be installed   (d) none of these

10. An effective ground-fault current path is created when all electrically conductive materials that are likely to be energized are bonded together and to the _____.

(a) ground   (b) earth   (c) electrical supply source   (d) none of these

11. Branch-circuit overcurrent protection devices are not required to be accessible to occupants of guest rooms of hotels and motels if maintenance is provided in a facility that is under continuous building management.

(a) True   (b) False

12. Breakers or fuses can be used in parallel when _____.

(a) they are factory assembled in parallel   (b) they are listed as a unit
(c) a and b   (d) a or b

13. Cartridge fuses and fuseholders of the 300V type are not permitted on circuits exceeding 300V _____.

(a) between conductors   (b) to ground   (c) or less   (d) a or c

14. Circuit breakers must be marked with their _____ rating in a manner that will be durable and visible after installation.

(a) voltage   (b) ampere   (c) type   (d) all of these

15. Circuit breakers used as switches in 120V or 277V fluorescent-lighting circuits must be listed and marked _____.

(a) UL   (b) SWD or HID   (c) Amps   (d) VA

16. Except where limited by 210.4(B), individual single-pole circuit breakers, with or without approved handle ties, are permitted as the protection for each ungrounded conductor of multiwire branch circuits that serve only single-phase line-to-neutral loads.

(a) True   (b) False

17. Flexible cords approved for and used with a specific listed appliance or portable lamp are considered to be protected when _____.

(a) not more than 6 ft in length   (b) 20 AWG and larger
(c) applied within the listing requirements   (d) 16 AWG and larger

18. For grounded systems, electrical equipment and wiring, and other electrically conductive material likely to become energized, must be installed in a manner that creates a _____ from any point on the wiring system where a ground fault may occur to the electrical supply source.

(a) permanent path
(b) low-impedance path
(c) path capable of safely carrying the ground-fault current likely to be imposed on it
(d) all of these

19. For grounded systems, noncurrent-carrying conductive materials enclosing electrical conductors or equipment, or forming part of such equipment, must be connected to earth so as to limit the voltage-to-ground on these materials.

(a) True   (b) False

20. For industrial installations only, a tap can be made without overcurrent protection when the transformer secondary conductors have a total length of not more than _____. The tap conductors must have an ampacity not less than the secondary current rating of the transformer and the sum of the ratings of the overcurrent devices.

(a) 8 ft   (b) 25 ft   (c) 35 ft   (d) 75 ft

21. For installations that supply only limited loads of a single branch circuit, the service disconnecting means must have a rating of not less than _____.

    (a) 15A   (b) 20A   (c) 25A   (d) 30A

22. Ground-fault protection at service equipment may make it necessary to review the overall wiring system for proper selective over-current protection _____.

    (a) rating   (b) coordination   (c) devices   (d) none of these

23. Ground-fault protection of equipment must be provided for solidly grounded wye electrical services of more than 150 volts-to-ground, but not exceeding 600V phase-to-phase for each service disconnecting means rated _____ or more.

    (a) 1,000A   (b) 1,500A   (c) 2,000A   (d) 2,500A

24. Ground-fault protection of equipment must be provided in accordance with the provisions of 230.95 for solidly grounded wye electrical systems of more than 150 volts-to-ground, but not exceeding 600V phase-to-phase for each individual device used as a building or structure main disconnecting means rated _____, or more.

    (a) 1,000A   (b) 1,500A   (c) 2,000A   (d) 2,500A

25. Grounding electrode conductor fittings must be protected from physical damage by being enclosed in _____ where there may be a possibility of physical damage.

    (a) metal   (b) wood   (c) the equivalent of a or b   (d) none of these

26. Grounding electrode conductors _____ and larger that are not subject to physical damage can be run exposed along the surface, if securely fastened to the construction.

    (a) 6 AWG   (b) 8 AWG   (c) 10 AWG   (d) 4 AWG

27. Grounding electrodes consisting of stainless-steel rods or nonferrous rods that are less than 5/8 in. in diameter must be listed and cannot be less than _____ in diameter.

    (a) 1/2 in.   (b) 3/4 in.   (c) 1 in.   (d) 1 1/4 in.

28. In a multiple-occupancy building, each occupant must have access to the occupant's _____.

    (a) service disconnecting means (b) service drops   (c) distribution transformer   (d) lateral conductors

29. Meter disconnect switches that have a short-circuit current rating equal to or greater than the available short-circuit current are permitted ahead of the service-disconnecting means.

    (a) True   (b) False

30. Overcurrent protection for tap conductors not over 25 ft is not required at the point where the conductors receive their supply providing the _____.

    (a) ampacity of the tap conductors is not less than one-third the rating of the overcurrent device protecting the feeder conductors being tapped
    (b) tap conductors terminate in a single circuit breaker or set of fuses that limit the load to the ampacity of the tap conductors
    (c) tap conductors are suitably protected from physical damage
    (d) all of these

31. Plug fuses of 15A or less must be identified by a(n) _____ configuration of the window, cap, or other prominent part to distinguish them from fuses of higher ampere ratings.

  (a) octagonal   (b) rectangular   (c) hexagonal   (d) triangular

32. Service cables, where subject to physical damage, must be protected.

  (a) True   (b) False

33. Service disconnecting means must not be installed in bathrooms.

  (a) True   (b) False

34. Service heads for service raceways must be _____.

  (a) raintight   (b) weatherproof   (c) rainproof   (d) watertight

35. Service lateral conductors that supply power to limited loads of a single branch circuit must not be smaller than _____.

  (a) 4 AWG copper   (b) 8 AWG aluminum   (c) 12 AWG copper   (d) none of these

36. Temporary current flowing on the effective ground-fault current path during a ground fault condition is considered by the *Code* to be objectionable current.

  (a) True   (b) False

37. The connection of the grounding electrode conductor to a buried grounding electrode (driven ground rod) must be made with a listed terminal device that is accessible.

  (a) True   (b) False

38. The frame of a vehicle-mounted generator is not required to be connected to a(n) _____ for a system supplied by cord and plug using receptacles mounted on the vehicle or the generator when the grounding terminals of the receptacles are bonded to the generator frame and the generator frame is bonded to the vehicle frame.

  (a) grounding electrode   (b) grounded conductor
  (c) ungrounded conductor   (d) equipment grounding conductor

39. The grounding electrode conductor at the service is permitted to terminate on an equipment grounding terminal bar if a (main) bonding jumper is installed between the grounded conductor bus and the equipment grounding terminal.

  (a) True   (b) False

40. The grounding electrode for a separately derived system must be as near as practicable to, and preferably in the same area as, the grounding electrode conductor connection to the system. The grounding electrode must be the nearest one of the following:

  (a) An effectively grounded metal member of the building structure.
  (b) An effectively grounded metal water pipe, but only if it's within 5 ft from the point of entrance into the building.
  (c) Any metal structure that is effectively grounded.
  (d) a or b

41. The metal frame of a building where one of the four *Code*-prescribed methods of making an earth connection has been met may serve as part of the grounding electrode system.

  (a) True   (b) False

42. There must be no more than _____ disconnects installed for each service or for each set of service-entrance conductors as permitted in 230.2 and 230.40.

    (a) two   (b) four   (c) six   (d) none of these

43. To prevent water from entering service equipment, service-entrance conductors must _____.

    (a) be connected to service-drop conductors below the level of the service head
    (b) have drip loops formed on the service-entrance conductors
    (c) a or b
    (d) a and b

44. When driving a ground rod electrode, if rock bottom is encountered, the rod must be driven at an angle not to exceed 45 degrees. Where rock bottom is encountered when driving at an angle up to 45 degrees, the electrode is permitted to be buried in a trench that is at least _____ deep.

    (a) 4 ft   (b) 30 in.   (c) 8 ft   (d) 18 in.

45. When service-entrance conductors exceed 1,100 kcmil for copper, the required grounded conductor for the service must be sized not less than _____ percent of the area of the largest ungrounded service-entrance (phase) conductor.

    (a) 15   (b) 19   (c) 12 1/2   (d) 25

46. When supplying a grounded system at a separate building or structure, if the equipment grounding conductor is run with the supply conductors and connected to the building disconnecting means, there must be no connection made between the grounded conductor and the equipment grounding conductor at the separate building.

    (a) True   (b) False

47. Where a main bonding jumper is a screw only, the screw must be identified with _____ that must be visible with the screw installed.

    (a) a silver or white finish   (b) an etched ground symbol   (c) a green tag   (d) a green finish

48. Where exposed to _____, service conductors must be mounted on insulators or on insulating supports attached to racks, brackets, or other approved means. Where not exposed to the weather, the conductors must be mounted on glass or porcelain knobs.

    (a) a corrosive environment   (b) the weather   (c) the general public   (d) any inspector

49. Where the service overcurrent devices are locked or sealed or are not readily accessible to the _____, branch-circuit overcurrent devices must be installed on the load side, must be mounted in a readily accessible location, and must be of lower ampere rating than the service overcurrent device.

    (a) inspector   (b) electrician   (c) occupant   (d) all of these

50. Wiring methods permitted for service conductors include _____.

    (a) rigid metal conduit   (b) electrical metallic tubing   (c) rigid nonmetallic conduit   (d) all of these

(• Indicates that 75% or fewer of those who took this exam answered the question correctly.)

1. Armored cable is limited or not permitted _____.

   (a) in damp or wet locations
   (b) where subject to physical damage
   (c) where exposed to corrosive fumes or vapors
   (d) all of these

2. Armored cable used for the connection of recessed luminaires or equipment within an accessible ceiling does not need to be secured for lengths up to _____.

   (a) 2 ft
   (b) 3 ft
   (c) 4 ft
   (d) 6 ft

3. Article 604 contains all requirements for the installation of manufactured wiring systems, no other *Code* articles will apply.

   (a) True
   (b) False

4. At carnivals, circuses, and similar events, electrical service equipment must not be installed in a location that is accessible to unqualified persons, unless the equipment is _____.

   (a) lockable
   (b) operating at under 600V
   (c) weatherproof
   (d) arc-fault protected

5. At least _____ 125V, single-phase, duplex receptacle(s) must be provided in each machine room and machinery space.

   (a) one
   (b) two
   (c) three
   (d) four

6. Attachment plugs, cord connectors, and flanged-surface devices, must be listed with the manufacturer's name or identification and voltage and ampere ratings.

   (a) True
   (b) False

7. Audio cables installed exposed on the surface of ceilings and sidewalls must be supported by the structural components of the building in such a manner that the cable will not be damaged by normal building use. Such cables must be supported by _____ designed and installed so as not to damage the cable.

   (a) straps
   (b) staples
   (c) hangers
   (d) any of these

8. Automatic transfer switches on legally required standby systems must be electrically operated and _____ held.

   (a) electrically
   (b) mechanically
   (c) gravity
   (d) any of these

9. Ballasts, transformers, and electronic power supplies for electric signs must be located where accessible and must be securely fastened in place. Where they are not installed in the sign, a working space at least _____ must be provided.

   (a) 3 ft high, 3 ft wide by 3 ft deep
   (b) 4 ft high, 3 ft wide by 3 ft deep
   (c) 6 ft high, 3 ft wide by 3 ft deep
   (d) none of these

10. Bare aluminum or copper-clad aluminum grounding conductors must not be used where in direct contact with masonry, the earth, or where subject to corrosive conditions. Where used outside, aluminum or copper-clad aluminum grounding electrode conductors must not be terminated within _____ of the earth.

    (a) 6 in.
    (b) 12 in.
    (c) 15 in.
    (d) 18 in.

11. Bends in ITC cable must be made _____.

    (a) so as not to exceed 45 degrees   (b) so as not to damage the cable
    (c) not less than 5 times the diameter of the cable   (d) using listed bending tools

12. Bends made in UF cable must be made so that the cable will not be damaged. The radius of the curve of the inner edge of any bend during or after installation must not be less than _____ the diameter of the cable.

    (a) 5 times   (b) 7 times   (c) 10 times   (d) 125% of

13. Boxes and fittings must be _____ where installed in a Class III, Division 1 or 2 hazardous (classified) location.

    (a) explosionproof   (b) dust-ignitionproof   (c) dusttight   (d) weatherproof

14. Boxes and fittings used for taps, joints, or terminal connections must be _____ where installed in a Class II, Division 1 hazardous (classified) location.

    (a) explosionproof   (b) identified for Class II locations (dust-ignitionproof)
    (c) dusttight   (d) weatherproof

15. Boxes can be supported from a multiconductor cord or cable, provided the conductors are protected from _____.

    (a) strain   (b) temperature   (c) sunlight   (d) abrasion

16. Boxes, enclosures, fittings, and joints are not required to be explosionproof in a Class I, Division 2 location. However, if arcs or sparks (such as from make-and-break contacts) can result from equipment being utilized, that equipment must be installed in an explosionproof enclosure meeting the requirements for Class I, Division 1 locations.

    (a) True   (b) False

17. Branch-circuit conductors for data-processing equipment must have an ampacity not less than _____ of the total connected load.

    (a) 80 percent   (b) 100 percent   (c) 125 percent   (d) the sum

18. Branch-circuit conductors supplying a single motor-compressor must have an ampacity not less than _____ percent of either the motor-compressor rated-load current or the branch-circuit selection current, whichever is greater.

    (a) 125   (b) 100   (c) 250   (d) 80

19. Branch-circuit conductors that supply a continuous load, or any combination of continuous and noncontinuous loads, must have an ampacity of not less than 125 percent of the continuous load, plus 100 percent of the noncontinuous load.

    (a) True   (b) False

20. Cable or nonmetallic raceway-type wiring methods installed in a groove, to be covered by wallboard, siding, paneling, carpeting, or similar finish must be protected by 1/16 in. thick _____ or by not less than 1 1/4 in. of free space for the full length of the groove. A thinner plate that provides equal or better protection may be used if listed and marked.

    (a) steel plate   (b) steel sleeve   (c) PVC bushing   (d) a or b

21. Cable splices or terminations in power-limited fire alarm systems must be made in listed _____ or utilization equipment.

    (a) fittings   (b) boxes or enclosures   (c) fire alarm devices   (d) all of these

22. Cable trays and their associated fittings must be _____ for the intended use.

    (a) listed   (b) approved   (c) identified   (d) none of these

23. Cable trays must be _____ except as permitted by 392.6(G).

(a) exposed   (b) accessible   (c) concealed   (d) a and b

24. Cable wiring methods must not be used as a means of support for _____.

(a) other cables   (b) raceways   (c) nonelectrical equipment   (d) a, b, or c

25. Capable of being removed or exposed without damaging the building structure or finish, or not permanently closed in by the structure or finish of the building defines _____.

(a) accessible (equipment)   (b) accessible (wiring methods)
(c) accessible, readily   (d) all of these

26. Circuit breakers and fuses must be readily accessible and they must be installed so the center of the grip of the operating handle of the fuse switch or circuit breaker, when in its highest position, isn't more than _____ above the floor or working platform.

(a) 6 ft 7 in.   (b) 2 ft   (c) 5 ft   (d) 4 ft 6 in.

27. Circuit breakers must clearly indicate whether they are in the open "off" or closed "on" position. Where the circuit breaker handles are operated vertically the "up" position of the handle must be the _____.

(a) "on" position   (b) "off" position   (c) tripped position   (d) any of these

28. Circuit breakers rated at _____ amperes or less and _____ volts or less must have the ampere rating molded, stamped, etched, or similarly marked into their handles or escutcheon areas.

(a) 100, 600   (b) 600, 100   (c) 1,000, 6,000   (d) 6,000, 1,000

29. Circuits used only for the operation of fire alarms, other protective signaling systems, or the supply to fire pump equipment are permitted to be connected on the _____ of the service overcurrent protection device where separately provided with overcurrent protection.

(a) base   (b) load side   (c) supply side   (d) top

30. Class 1 and nonpower-limited fire alarm circuits can occupy the same cable, enclosure, or raceway, provided all conductors are insulated for the maximum voltage of any conductor.

(a) True   (b) False

31. Class 1 power-limited circuits must be supplied from a source having a rated output of not more than 30V. If the voltage rating were 25V, the maximum VA of the circuit would be _____.

(a) 750 VA   (b) 700 VA   (c) 1,000 VA   (d) 1,200 VA

32. Class 2 and Class 3 plenum cables listed as suitable for use in ducts, plenums, and other spaces used for environmental air are _____.

(a) CL2P and CL3P   (b) CL2R and CL3R   (c) CL2 and CL3   (d) PLCT

33. Coaxial cables used for CATV systems must not be strapped, taped, or attached by any means to the exterior of any _____ as a means of support.

(a) conduit
(b) raceway
(c) raceway-type mast intended for overhead spans of such cables
(d) a or b

34. Communications wiring such as telephone, antenna, and CATV wiring within a building is not required to comply with the installation requirements of Chapters 1 through 7, except where it is specifically referenced therein.

    (a) True   (b) False

35. Composite optical fiber cables contain optical fibers and current-carrying electrical conductors. They are permitted to contain noncurrent-carrying conductive members such as metallic _____. Composite optical fiber cables are classified as electrical cables in accordance with the type of electrical conductors.

    (a) strength members   (b) vapor barriers   (c) none of these   (d) a and b

36. Concrete-encased electrodes of _____ are not required to be part of the grounding electrode system where the steel reinforcing bars or rods aren't accessible for use without disturbing the concrete.

    (a) hazardous locations   (b) health care facilities
    (c) existing buildings or structures   (d) agricultural buildings with equipotential planes

37. Conductors and cables of intrinsically safe circuits not in raceways or cable trays must be separated by at least _____ and secured from conductors and cables of any nonintrinsically safe circuits.

    (a) 6 in.   (b) 2 in.   (c) 18 in.   (d) 12 in.

38. Conductors for an appliance circuit supplying more than one appliance or appliance receptacle in an installation operating at less than 50V must not be smaller than _____ AWG copper or equivalent.

    (a) 18   (b) 14   (c) 12   (d) 10

39. Conductors in metal raceways and enclosures must be so arranged as to avoid heating the surrounding metal by alternating-current induction. To accomplish this, the _____ conductor(s) must be grouped together.

    (a) phase   (b) grounded   (c) ungrounded   (d) all of these

40. Conductors installed in conduit exposed to direct sunlight in close proximity to rooftops have been shown, under certain conditions, to experience an increase in temperature of _____°F above ambient temperature.

    (a) 70   (b) 10   (c) 30   (d) 40

41. Conductors larger than that for which the wireway is designed may be installed in any wireway.

    (a) True   (b) False

42. Conductors must have their ampacity determined using the _____ column of Table 310.16 for circuits rated 100A or less or marked for 14 AWG through 1 AWG conductors, unless the equipment terminals are listed for use with higher temperature rated conductors.

    (a) 60°C   (b) 75°C   (c) 30°C   (d) 90°C

43. Conductors smaller than 1/0 AWG can be connected in parallel to supply control power, provided _____.

    (a) they are all contained within the same raceway or cable
    (b) each parallel conductor has an ampacity sufficient to carry the entire load
    (c) the circuit overcurrent protection device rating does not exceed the ampacity of any individual parallel conductor
    (d) all of these

44. Conduits, cable trays, and open wiring used for intrinsically safe systems must be identified with permanently affixed labels with the wording "Intrinsic Safety Wiring." The labels must be visible after installation and the spacing between labels must not exceed _____ ft.

    (a) 3   (b) 10   (c) 25   (d) 50

45. Connection of conductors to terminal parts must ensure a thoroughly good connection without damaging the conductors and must be made by means of _____.

    (a) solder lugs   (b) pressure connectors   (c) splices to flexible leads   (d) any of these

46. Constant-voltage generators must be protected from overloads by _____ or other acceptable overcurrent protective means suitable for the conditions of use.

    (a) inherent design   (b) circuit breakers   (c) fuses   (d) any of these

47. Continuous duty is defined as _____.

    (a) when the load is expected to continue for three hours or more
    (b) operation at a substantially constant load for an indefinite length of time
    (c) operation at loads and for intervals of time, both of which may be subject to wide variations
    (d) operation at which the load may be subject to maximum current for six hours or more

48. Cord connectors for carnivals, circuses, and fairs can be laid on the ground when the connectors are _____ for a wet location, but they must not be placed in audience traffic paths or within areas accessible to the public unless guarded.

    (a) listed   (b) labeled   (c) approved   (d) all of these

49. Cord-and-plug connected equipment must be grounded by means of _____.

    (a) an equipment grounding conductor in the cable assembly   (b) a separate flexible wire or strap
    (c) either a or b   (d) none of these

50. Each _____ service conductor must have overload protection.

    (a) overhead   (b) underground   (c) ungrounded   (d) none of these

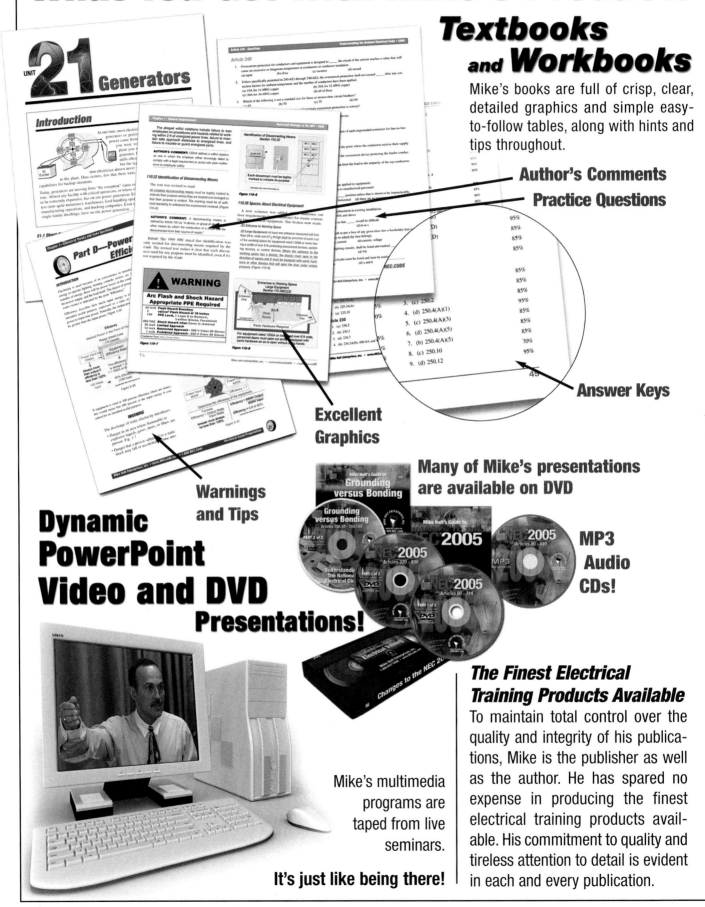

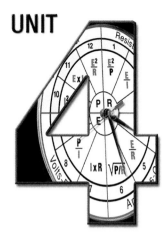

UNIT 4

Motors and Transformers

Introduction

Electric motors are equipment used to convert electrical energy into mechanical energy that can be used to do work and accomplish a productive goal. Motors are an essential component of industrialized society, so it is important for electricians to understand the basic operational characteristics of motors and how to properly install and connect them.

There are many different types of specialized motors available. This unit will discuss the most commonly used direct-current (dc) motors and alternating-current (ac) motors. Some of the important things covered in this unit include the differences between full-load current rating, full-load ampere rating, and locked-rotor current.

Generators are equipment used to convert mechanical energy into electrical energy. DC generators, single-phase ac generators, and three-phase ac generators are introduced in this unit. Generators can be found everywhere from very large units at utility generating plants, to emergency standby generators at hospitals and manufacturing plants, to small residential standby units.

The ability to distribute high-voltage alternating-current (ac) with low line losses and then transform that ac current to lower voltages for local distribution systems and utilization equipment is, quite possibly, one of the most attractive features of using ac as opposed to dc for distribution systems. Transformers are also used within premises wiring systems to provide the necessary voltages for utilization equipment and applications such as control circuits.

Transformers operate using the principle of mutual induction, which accomplishes the transfer of energy from one system to a second system with no physical connection between the two. In this unit we'll explain some basic transformer principles and you'll be introduced to three-phase transformer configurations.

PART A—MOTORS

Introduction

The electric motor is one of the most prevalent loads on the electrical system of commercial and industrial occupancies. Think of the sheer number of things that must move in some way. Every pump, fan, compressor, conveyor, or other device that moves material or objects, requires either a motor or an engine. A motor is a device that converts energy into motion; an engine is a device that burns fuel to release energy that it turns into motion. Computers contain many small motors (in the fans, DVDs, CD drives, hard drives, and other devices), as do automobiles (which have steadily been replacing vacuum-operated and fluid-operated motors with electrically-operated motors). Where there's motion, there's probably an electric motor.

An electrician typically works with various configurations of motors that are powered by 120V, 240V, or 480V supplies. A solid understanding of motor basics, motor calculations, motor circuits, and motor controls is essential for success as an electrician. The goal of this unit is to provide you with that basic understanding and prepare you for learning more about this important subject.

4.1 Motor Principles

A motor must have two opposing magnetic fields in order to rotate.

Stator

The stationary field winding of a motor is mounted on the stator, which is the part of the motor that does not turn. For permanent magnet motors, there is no field winding because the field is produced by permanent magnets.

Rotor

The rotating part of the motor is referred to as either the "rotor" or the "armature."

4.2 Dual-Voltage AC Motors

Dual-voltage ac motors are made with two field windings, each rated for the lower of two possible operating voltages. The field windings are connected in parallel for low-voltage operation and in series for high-voltage operation.

For example, a 460/230V dual-rated motor has its windings in series if connected to a 460V source, or the windings will be in parallel if connected to a 230V source. Figure 4–1

> **AUTHOR'S COMMENT:** According to the *NEC*, voltages are described as either nominal voltage or rated voltage. Nominal voltage is in reference to the approximate expected utility voltage, for example a 120/240V system. However, because of circuit voltage drop, the actual voltage at the load will be less than 120V or 240V. Therefore, the rated voltage of equipment will have a value less than the nominal system voltage (for example 115V/230V).

4.3 Motor Horsepower Rating

Motors are used to convert electrical energy into mechanical work. The output mechanical work of a motor is measured or rated in horsepower.

> **AUTHOR'S COMMENT:** The conversion of mechanical work to electrical energy is measured in watts, where one horsepower = 746W.

> **CAUTION:** *The 746W per horsepower is the electrical output value for each horsepower. This value is not the input electrical rating required to calculate the motor nameplate current rating.*

▶ **Horsepower Example**

What size motor, in horsepower, is used to produce a 15 kW output? Figure 4–2

    (a) 5 hp   (b) 10 hp
    (c) 20 hp   (d) 30 hp

   • Answer: (c) 20 hp
     Horsepower = Output Watts/746
     Horsepower = 15,000W/746W
     Horsepower = 20 hp

▶ **Output Watts Example**

What is the output watts rating of a 10 hp, ac, 480V, three-phase motor with an efficiency of 75 percent and power factor of 70 percent? Figure 4–3

    (a) 5 kW   (b) 7.5 kVA
    (c) 7.5 kW   (d) none of these

   • Answer: (c) 7.5 kW
     Output Watts = hp x 746W
     Output Watts = 10 hp x 746W
     Output Watts = 7,460W

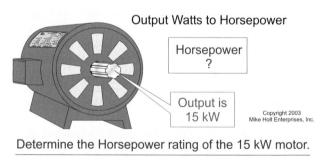

Output Watts to Horsepower

Determine the Horsepower rating of the 15 kW motor.

HP is based on output watts only.
Input factors are not considered.
One hp is equal to 746W, 15 kW x 1,000 = 15,000W

$$hp = \frac{\text{Output Watts}}{746W} \quad \frac{15,000W}{746W} = 20 \text{ hp}$$

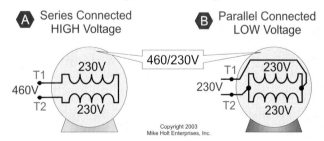

Dual-Voltage Motor Windings - 1-Phase

A Series Connected HIGH Voltage   B Parallel Connected LOW Voltage

460/230V

Copyright 2003
Mike Holt Enterprises, Inc.

Figure 4–1

Figure 4–2

Output Horsepower to Watts

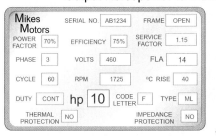
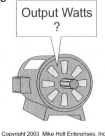

Determine the output watts of the 10 hp motor.

Output Watts = hp x 746
Output watts are based on hp only,
input factors are not considered.
1 hp is equal to 746W.
Output Watts = 10 hp x 746W = 7,460W
7,460W/1,000 = 7.46 kW

Figure 4–3

Efficiency, power factor, phases, and voltage have nothing to do with determining the output watts of a motor!

Calculating motor output watts can, however, help you understand how motor nameplate current numbers are developed.

4.4 Motor Current Ratings

Motor Full-Load Ampere (FLA) Rating

The motor nameplate full-load ampere rating is identified as FLA. The FLA rating is the current rating in amperes that the motor draws while carrying its rated horsepower load at its rated voltage. Figure 4–4

Actual Motor Current

The actual current drawn by the motor is dependent upon the load on the motor and the actual operating voltage at the motor terminals. That is, if the load increases, the current also increases and/or if the motor operates at a voltage below its nameplate rating, the operating current will increase.

> CAUTION: To prevent damage to motor windings from excessive heat (because of excessive current), never place a load on a motor above its horsepower rating and/or be sure the voltage source matches the motor's voltage rating.

Motor Full-Load Current (FLC) Rating

The motor nameplate FLA rating is not to be used when sizing motor conductor size or circuit protection. According to the

Motor Full-Load Amperes (FLA)

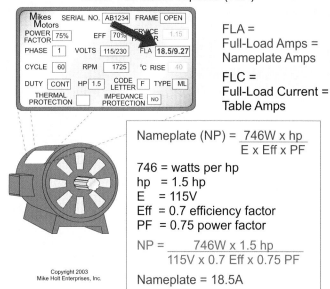

FLA =
Full-Load Amps =
Nameplate Amps

FLC =
Full-Load Current =
Table Amps

Nameplate (NP) = $\dfrac{746W \times hp}{E \times Eff \times PF}$

746 = watts per hp
hp = 1.5 hp
E   = 115V
Eff = 0.7 efficiency factor
PF = 0.75 power factor

NP = $\dfrac{746W \times 1.5\ hp}{115V \times 0.7\ Eff \times 0.75\ PF}$

Nameplate = 18.5A

Figure 4–4

Code, we must size these electrical components in accordance with the motor Full-Load Current (FLC) rating as listed in the *NEC* Tables. Figure 4–5

> AUTHOR'S COMMENT: This topic is covered in Unit 7.

4.5 Calculating Motor FLA

The motor nameplate full-load ampere (FLA) rating can be determined by:

FLC Versus Nameplate Amperes

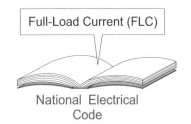
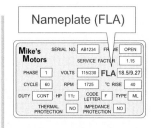

Table FLC is used to size:
• conductors and disconnects
• short-circuit and ground-fault
  protection devices

Motor nameplate
is used to size
overload protection

COPYRIGHT 2003 Mike Holt Enterprises, Inc.

Figure 4–5

Single-Phase

FLA = (Motor hp x 746W)/(E x Eff x PF)

Three-Phase

FLA = (Motor hp x 746W)/(E x 1.732 x Eff x PF)

▶ **Single-Phase Motor FLA Example**

What is the motor nameplate FLA rating for a 7.5 hp motor, 230V, single-phase, having an efficiency of 93 percent and a power factor of 87 percent? **Figure 4–6**

    (a) 16A   (b) 24A

    (c) 19A   (d) 30A

     • Answer: (d) 30A

Step 1   Determine the motor output watts:

        Output Watts = hp x 746W

        Output Watts = 7.5 hp x 746W

        Output Watts = 5,595W

Step 2   Determine the motor input watts:

        Input = Output/Eff

        Input = 5,595W/0.93 Eff

        Input = 6,016W

Step 3   Determine the motor input VA:

        VA = Watts/PF

        VA = 6,016W/0.87 PF

        VA = 6,915 VA

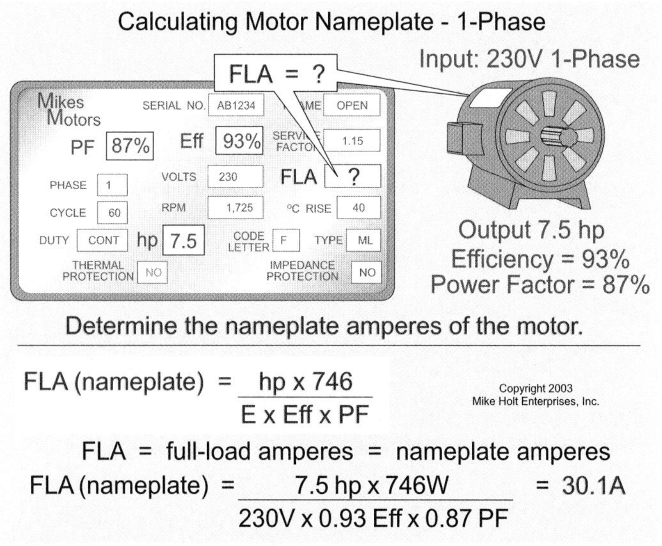

Calculating Motor Nameplate - 1-Phase

Input: 230V 1-Phase

FLA = ?

Mikes Motors

SERIAL NO. AB1234 |ME | OPEN

PF 87%   Eff 93%   SERVICE FACTOR 1.15

PHASE 1   VOLTS 230   FLA ?

CYCLE 60   RPM 1,725   °C RISE 40

DUTY CONT   hp 7.5   CODE LETTER F   TYPE ML

THERMAL PROTECTION NO   IMPEDANCE PROTECTION NO

Output 7.5 hp
Efficiency = 93%
Power Factor = 87%

Determine the nameplate amperes of the motor.

$$\text{FLA (nameplate)} = \frac{\text{hp x 746}}{\text{E x Eff x PF}}$$

Copyright 2003
Mike Holt Enterprises, Inc.

FLA = full-load amperes = nameplate amperes

$$\text{FLA (nameplate)} = \frac{\text{7.5 hp x 746W}}{\text{230V x 0.93 Eff x 0.87 PF}} = 30.1\text{A}$$

Figure 4–6

Step 4   Determine the motor amperes:

        FLA = VA/E

        FLA = 6,915W/230V

        FLA = 30A

OR

        FLA = (hp x 746W)/(E x Eff x PF)

        FLA = (7.5 hp x 746W)/(230V x 0.93 Eff x 0.87 PF)

        FLA = 30A

▶ **Three-Phase Motor FLA Example**

What is the motor FLA rating for a 40 hp, 208V, three-phase motor, having an efficiency rating of 80 percent and a power factor of 90 percent?

    (a) 76A   (b) 84A

    (c) 99A   (d) 115A

     • Answer: (d) 115A

Step 1   Determine the motor output watts:

        Output Watts = hp x 746W

        Output Watts = 40 hp x 746W

        Output Watts = 29,840W

Step 2   Determine the motor input watts:

        Input Watts = Output/Eff

        Input Watts = 29,840W/0.80 Eff

        Input Watts = 37,300W

Step 3   Determine the motor input VA:

        VA = Watts/PF

        VA = 37,300W/0.90 PF

        VA = 41,444 VA

Step 4   Determine the motor amperes:

        FLA = VA/(E x 1.732)

        FLA = 41,444VA/(208V x 1.732)

        FLA = 115A

OR

        FLA = (hp x 746W)/(E x 1.732 x Eff x PF)

        FLA = (40 hp x 746W)/

                (208V x 1.732 x 0.80 Eff x 0.90 PF)

        FLA = 115A

4.6 Motor-Starting Current

When voltage is first applied to the field winding of an induction motor, only the conductor resistance opposes the flow of current through the motor winding. Because the conductor resistance is so low, the motor will have a very large inrush current (a minimum of six times the full-load ampere rating). **Figure 4–7A**

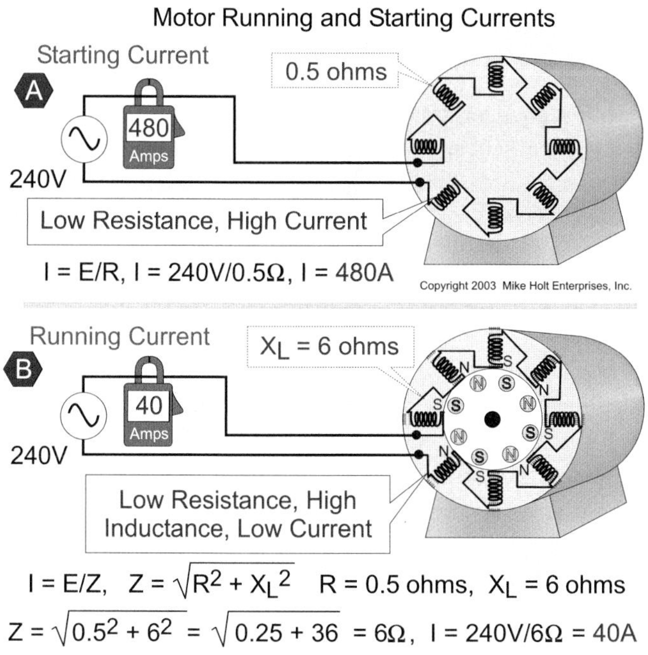

Motor Running and Starting Currents

Starting Current

A

240V

480 Amps

0.5 ohms

Low Resistance, High Current

$I = E/R$, $I = 240V/0.5\Omega$, $I = 480A$

Copyright 2003 Mike Holt Enterprises, Inc.

Running Current

B

240V

40 Amps

$X_L = 6$ ohms

Low Resistance, High Inductance, Low Current

$I = E/Z$, $Z = \sqrt{R^2 + X_L^2}$ $R = 0.5$ ohms, $X_L = 6$ ohms

$Z = \sqrt{0.5^2 + 6^2} = \sqrt{0.25 + 36} = 6\Omega$, $I = 240V/6\Omega = 40A$

Figure 4–7

4.7 Motor-Running Current

However, once the rotor begins turning, the rotor-bars (winding) will be increasingly cut by the stationary magnetic field, resulting in an increasing counter-electromotive force. **Figure 4–7B**

We learned previously that the CEMF opposes the applied voltage, resulting in an increased opposition to current flow within the conductor. This is called inductive reactance. The increase in inductive reactance, because of self-induction, causes the impedance of the conductor winding to increase and this results in a reduction of current flow.

4.8 Motor Locked-Rotor Current (LRC)

If the rotating part of the motor winding (armature) becomes jammed so that it cannot rotate, no CEMF will be produced in the motor winding. This results in a decrease in conductor impedance to the point that it's effectively a short circuit. Result—the motor operates at locked-rotor current (LRC), which is about six times the running current value, and this will cause the motor winding to overheat to the point that it will be destroyed if the current is not quickly stopped.

> **AUTHOR'S COMMENT:** The *National Electrical Code* requires most motors to be provided with overcurrent protection to prevent damage to the motor winding because of locked-rotor current.

4.9 Motor Overload Protection

Motors must be protected against excessive winding heat. Motors must not be overloaded, they must operate near their nameplate voltage, and measures must be taken to prevent the motor from jamming (LRC). If a motor is overloaded or if it operates at a voltage below its rating, the operating current can increase to a value above the motor full-load amperes (FLA) rating. The excessive operating current may damage the motor winding from excessive heat.

Figure 4–8 shows a type of overload device called a melting-alloy type of overload. There are other types of overload devices that provide motor overload protection, but they do it in different ways. These include the dashpot type and bimetallic type, as well as solid-state overload relays.

> **AUTHOR'S COMMENT:** Motors are designed to operate with an inrush current of six to eight times the motor-rated FLA for short periods of time without damage to the motor windings. **Figure 4–9**
>
> However, if a motor operates at LRC for a prolonged period of time, the motor insulation and lubrication can be destroyed by excessive heat. Most motors can operate at 600 percent of motor FLA satisfactorily for a period of less than one minute or 300 percent of the motor FLA for not more than three minutes.

NEC Requirement

To protect against excessive heat from an overload, the *National Electrical Code* requires standard overload protection devices to be sized at 115 to 125 percent of the motor FLA rating. **Figure 4–10**

4.10 Direct-Current Motor Principles

DC motors use brushes (pieces of conductive carbon) with springs to hold them in contact with a commutator. A commutator is a ring around the rotor shaft that has segments with insulation between them.

Motor Overloads - Magnetic Motor Starter

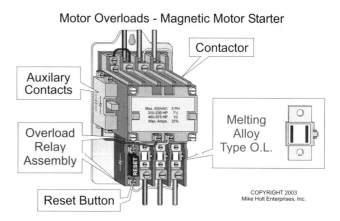

Contactor

Auxilary Contacts

Max. 600VAC 3 PH
200-230 HP 7½
460-575 HP 10
Max. Amps. 27A.

Overload Relay Assembly

Melting Alloy Type O.L.

Reset Button

COPYRIGHT 2003
Mike Holt Enterprises, Inc.

Figure 4–8

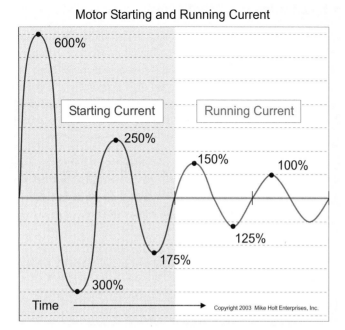

Figure 4–9

A commutator is necessary for a dc motor because the maximum torque on the rotor is developed when the active rotor winding opposes the magnetic field of the stator. As the winding passes this point, less torque is developed. As the commutator turns, the carbon brushes come into contact with the next set of rotor windings, which are in the proper position to oppose the stator field and keep the rotor moving. As the rotor turns, the brush-commutator set always supplies power to the rotor windings that are in the correct position to develop maximum torque.

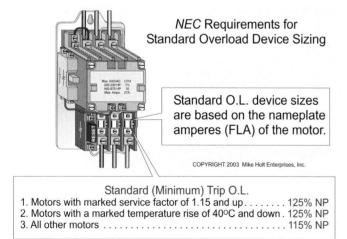

Figure 4–10

4.11 Direct-Current Motor Types

Shunt-Wound DC Motor

One of the great advantages of the shunt-wound dc motor (whose armature and field are in parallel) is its ability to maintain a constant speed under load. If the speed of a dc motor begins to increase, the armature will cut through the electromagnetic field at an increasing rate. This results in a greater armature CEMF, which acts to cut down on the increased armature current, resulting in the motor slowing back down.

Placing a load on a dc motor causes the motor to slow down, which reduces the rate at which the armature is cut by the field flux lines. As a result, the armature CEMF decreases, resulting in an increase in the applied armature voltage and current. The increase in current results in an increase in motor speed. This gives shunt-wound dc motors a built-in system for regulating their own speed. For these reasons, computer disk drives and recording equipment use dc motors exclusively.

Series-Wound DC Motor

Series-wound dc motors (those in which the field winding and the armature winding are connected in series) have poor speed regulation, and slow down considerably when a load is applied. When unloaded, they often run at very high rpms. However, series dc motors have very good torque characteristics. One of the best examples of a series-wound dc motor is the starter motor on your automobile, which has very high torque to start the engine and is connected to a load so that it does not overspeed.

4.12 Reversing the Rotation of a DC Motor

To reverse the rotation of a dc motor, you must reverse either the stator field or the armature magnetic field. This is accomplished by reversing either the field or armature current. Because most dc motors have the field and armature windings fed from the same dc power supply, reversing the polarity of the power supply will change the field and armature simultaneously. This will result in the motor continuing to run in the same direction. Figure 4–11

4.13 AC Induction Motor

In the ac induction motor, the stator produces a rotating magnetic field.

The rotor is a series of coils (windings) that are connected in a closed loop. The rotating magnetic field of the stator induces (thus, induction motor) currents flowing in the rotor windings. These rotor currents generate a magnetic field in opposition to the magnetic field of the stator, thereby causing the rotor to turn.

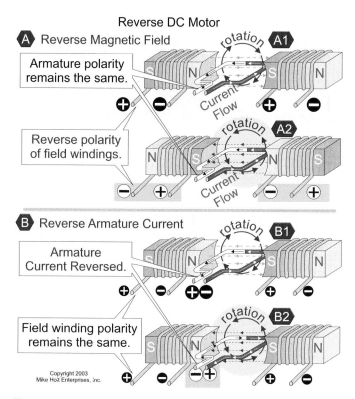

Reverse DC Motor

A Reverse Magnetic Field

Armature polarity remains the same.

Reverse polarity of field windings.

B Reverse Armature Current

Armature Current Reversed.

Field winding polarity remains the same.

Copyright 2003
Mike Holt Enterprises, inc.

Figure 4–11

It is also for this reason that the rotor of an induction motor always turns with an rpm slightly less than the rpm of the stator's magnetic field.

4.14 Alternating-Current Motor Types

Squirrel-Cage Induction Motor

The most prevalent type of an ac motor is the induction motor, which uses no physical connection between its rotating member (the rotor), and the stationary member surrounding it (the stator).

The three-phase ac squirrel-cage induction motor is used in almost all major industrial applications. It is called a squirrel-cage motor because the rotor consists of bars that are either parallel to the shaft or at a slight angle and are connected together at the ends by shorting rings. These bars would resemble a hamster or squirrel cage if you were to remove the core material around them.

As the magnetic field from the stator of an induction motor rotates, the field induces voltage in the rotor bars as it cuts across them. Conditions for generator action exist—a conductor (rotor bars), a magnetic field (from the field winding), and relative motion between them. The generated voltage causes current to flow from bar to bar through the shorting rings. The conditions for motor action are now present—a conductor (each rotor bar)

has current flowing through it in a magnetic field (from the stator field). This produces torque in the rotor causing it to turn.

Synchronous Motor

In a synchronous motor, the rotor is actually locked in step with the rotating stator field and is dragged along at the synchronous speed of the rotating magnetic field. Synchronous motors maintain their speed with a high degree of accuracy.

They are often found in large industrial facilities driving loads such as compressors, crushers, and large pumps. Sometimes they are operated unloaded, meaning that nothing is attached to their shafts. In this application, the synchronous motor is being operated "overexcited," meaning that a large amount of dc current is being fed into the rotor through the slip rings. The synchronous motor acts as though it were a large capacitor when it is in this condition and can be used for power factor correction.

Wound-Rotor Motor

Wound-rotor induction motors are used only in special applications because of their complexity. Wound-rotor induction motors only operate on three-phase ac power. They are similar to an induction motor; however, the rotor windings are connected in a wye configuration and the points of the wye are brought out through slip rings to an external controller. Resistors are usually inserted into the rotor winding circuit during start-up in order to reduce the inrush current. As the motor increases speed, the value of the resistance is changed to lower values. Ultimately, the rotor windings are shorted, thereby allowing the motor to achieve full speed.

The wound-rotor motor can also be used in applications that require some speed control. Today, however, it is much more customary to use a Variable Speed Drive coupled to an induction motor.

Universal Motor

Universal motors are fractional horsepower motors that operate equally well on ac and dc. They are used for vacuum cleaners, electric drills, mixers, and light household appliances. These motors have the inherent disadvantages associated with dc motors, which is the need for commutation. The problem with commutation is that as the motor operates, motor parts rub against each other and the motor wears itself out. Induction-type ac motors do not depend on commutation for operation.

4.15 Reversing the Rotation of an AC Motor

Swapping any two of the three line conductors can reverse a three-phase ac motor's rotation. Industry practice is to reverse Line 1 and Line 3. Figure 4–12

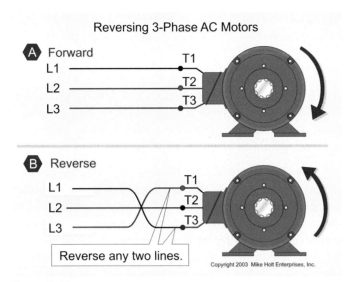

Figure 4–12

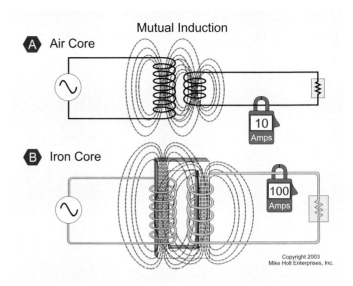

Figure 4–13

PART B—TRANSFORMERS

Introduction

A transformer is a stationary device used to raise or lower voltage. It has the ability to transfer electrical energy (power) from one system to another with no physical connection between the two systems.

Some transformers, called isolation transformers, do not raise or lower the voltage. They are simply for the purpose of decoupling the primary from the secondary. This topic is beyond the scope of this textbook.

4.16 Transformer Basics

Primary versus Secondary

The transformer winding connected to the voltage source is called the primary winding. The transformer winding connected to the load is called the secondary. Transformers are reversible, meaning that either winding can be used as the primary or secondary.

Mutual Induction

The energy transfer of a transformer is accomplished because the electromagnetic lines of force from the primary winding induce a voltage in the secondary winding. This process is called mutual induction. Figure 4–13

The voltage level that can be induced in the secondary winding, from the primary magnetic field, is a function of the number of secondary conductor loops (turns) that are cut by the primary electromagnetic field.

4.17 Secondary Induced Voltage

Voltage induced in the secondary winding of a transformer is equal to the sum of the voltages induced in each loop of the secondary winding.

For example, if a transformer had three windings on the secondary and each secondary winding had 80V induced, the secondary voltage would be 240V. Figure 4–14

The induced voltage in each loop of the secondary winding is dependent on the number of secondary conductor loops (turns), as compared to the number of primary turns. Figure 4–15

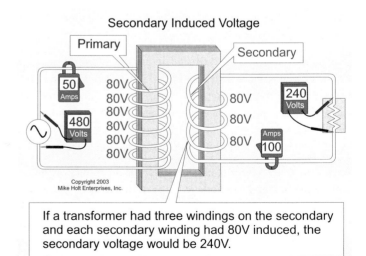

If a transformer had three windings on the secondary and each secondary winding had 80V induced, the secondary voltage would be 240V.

Figure 4–14

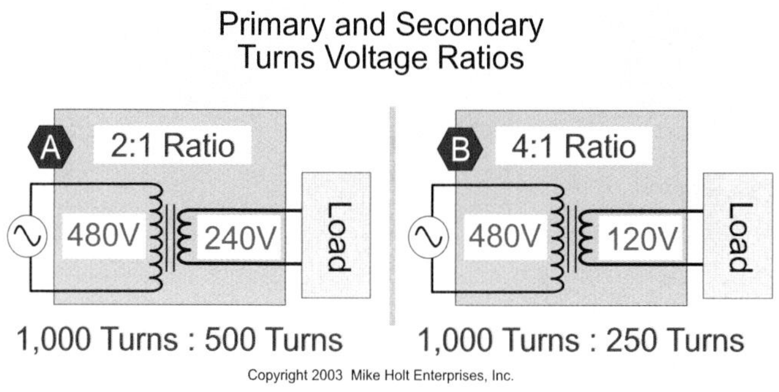

Primary and Secondary Turns Voltage Ratios

A 2:1 Ratio   480V 240V Load
1,000 Turns : 500 Turns

B 4:1 Ratio   480V 120V Load
1,000 Turns : 250 Turns

Copyright 2003 Mike Holt Enterprises, Inc.

Figure 4–15

If both windings have the same number of turns, and if all of the magnetism set up by the primary passes through the secondary, the secondary will deliver the same voltage and power as the primary. **Figure 4–16**

4.18 Autotransformers

Autotransformers use a common winding for both the primary and secondary and their purpose is to step the voltage up or down.

Autotransformers are often used to step the voltage up from 208V to 240V, or down from 240V to 208V. **Figure 4–17**

Step-Down Transformer

The secondary winding of a step-down transformer has fewer turns than the primary winding, resulting in a lower secondary voltage as compared to the primary.

Primary and Secondary With Same Number of Turns

1:1 Ratio   480V 480V Load
1,000 Turns : 1,000 Turns

Copyright 2003 Mike Holt Enterprises, Inc.

If both windings have the same number of turns, and if all of the magnetism set up by the primary passes through the secondary, the secondary will deliver the same voltage and power as the primary.

Figure 4–16

Autotransformers

Step-Up   208V 240V Load

Step-Down   240V 208V Load

A Step-Up Autotransformer   **B** Step-Down Autotransformer

Copyright 2003 Mike Holt Enterprises, Inc.

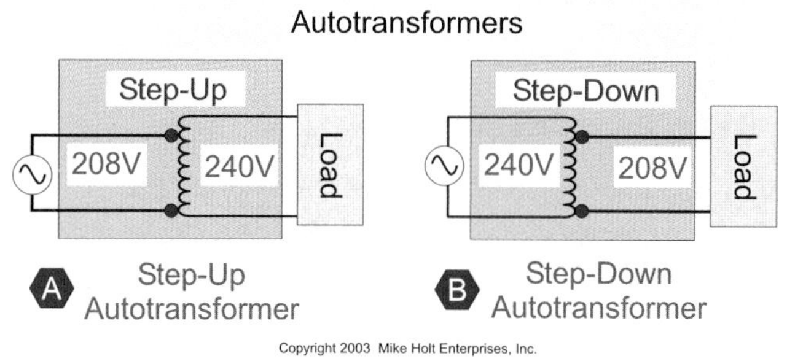

Figure 4–17

Step-Up Transformer

The secondary winding of a step-up transformer has more turns than the primary winding, resulting in a higher secondary voltage as compared to the primary.

> **AUTHOR'S COMMENT:** The disadvantage of an autotransformer is the lack of isolation between the primary and secondary conductors, but they are often used because they are inexpensive.

4.19 Power Losses

In an ideal transformer, all the primary power is transferred from the primary winding to the secondary winding, but real-world transformers have power losses because of conductor resistance, flux leakage, eddy currents, and hysteresis losses.

Conductor Resistance Loss

Transformer primary and secondary windings are generally made of many turns of copper. Conductor resistance is directly

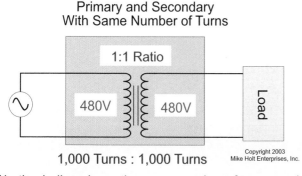

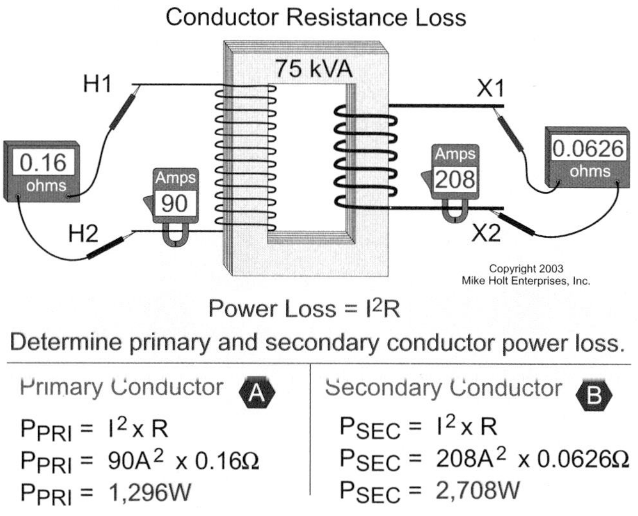

Conductor Resistance Loss

75 kVA

H1   0.16 ohms   Amps 90   Amps 208   0.0626 ohms   X1

H2   X2

Copyright 2003 Mike Holt Enterprises, Inc.

$$\text{Power Loss} = I^2 R$$

Determine primary and secondary conductor power loss.

Primary Conductor **A**	Secondary Conductor **B**
$P_{PRI} = I^2 \times R$	$P_{SEC} = I^2 \times R$
$P_{PRI} = 90A^2 \times 0.16\Omega$	$P_{SEC} = 208A^2 \times 0.0626\Omega$
$P_{PRI} = 1,296W$	$P_{SEC} = 2,708W$

Figure 4–18

proportional to the length of the conductor and inversely proportional to the cross-sectional area of the conductor.

▶ **Primary Power Loss Example**

What is the primary conductor power loss of a 75 kVA transformer if the primary current rating is 90A and the winding has a resistance of 0.16 ohms? **Figure 4–18A**

    (a) 400W   (b) 800W
    (c) 1,100W   (d) 1,300W

  • Answer: (d) 1,300W
    Power = I^2 x R
    I = 90A
    R = 0.16 ohms
    P = $90A^2$ x 0.16 ohms
    P = 1,296W

▶ **Secondary Power Loss Example**

What is the secondary conductor power loss of a 75 kVA transformer if the secondary current rating is 208A and the winding has a resistance of 0.0626 ohms? **Figure 4–18B**

    (a) 1,400W   (b) 1,800W
    (c) 2,100W   (d) 2,700W

  • Answer: (d) 2,700W
    Power = I^2 x R
    I = 208A
    R = 0.0626 ohms
    P = $208A^2$ x 0.0626 ohms
    P = 2,708W

Flux Leakage Loss

The leakage of the electromagnetic flux lines between the primary and secondary windings also represents wasted energy. **Figure 4–19**

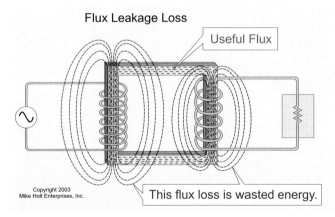

Flux Leakage Loss
Useful Flux
This flux loss is wasted energy.
Copyright 2003
Mike Holt Enterprises, Inc.

Figure 4–19

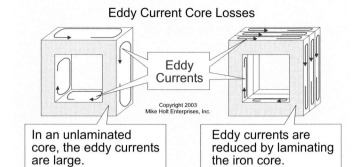

Eddy Current Core Losses
Eddy Currents
Copyright 2003
Mike Holt Enterprises, Inc.

In an unlaminated core, the eddy currents are large.

Eddy currents are reduced by laminating the iron core.

Figure 4–20

Eddy Currents

Iron is the only metal used for transformer cores because of the relative ease with which the material can be magnetized. However, the expanding and collapsing electromagnetic field from alternating current induces a voltage in the iron core. Wasteful circulating eddy currents in the iron core cause the core to heat up without any useful purpose. To reduce losses because of eddy currents, long laminated iron cores, separated by insulation (usually lacquer), are used. **Figure 4–20**

Hysteresis Losses

As current flows through the transformer, the iron core is temporarily magnetized by the electromagnetic field created by the alternating current. Each time the primary magnetic field expands and collapses, the core molecules realign themselves to the changing polarity of the electromagnetic field. The energy required to realign the core molecules to the changing electromagnetic field is called the hysteresis loss of the core. **Figure 4–21**

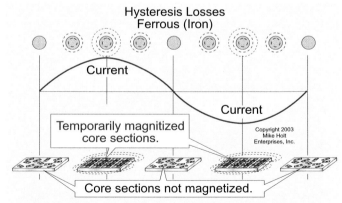

Hysteresis Losses
Ferrous (Iron)
Current
Current
Temporarily magnitized core sections.
Core sections not magnetized.
Copyright 2003
Mike Holt Enterprises, Inc.

The molecules of the core material align and realign with the expanding and collapsing electromagnetic field. The energy that does this realignment is wasted energy and is called Hysteresis Loss.

Figure 4–21

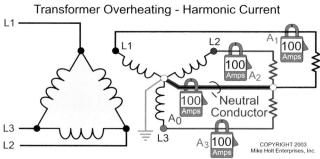

Transformer Overheating - Harmonic Current

In 3-phase, 4-wire delta/wye transformers, odd triplen harmonic currents from nonlinear loads can cause excessive heating of the primary winding.

Figure 4–22

Hysteresis losses are directly proportional to the alternating-current frequency. The greater the frequency, the more times per second the molecules must realign. Hysteresis loss is one of the main reasons why iron-core transformers are not used in applications involving high frequencies and nonlinear loads.

4.20 Harmonic Current

Three-phase, 4-wire wye-connected systems, such as 120/208V or 277/480V that supply nonlinear line-to-neutral loads, can overheat because of circulating odd triplen harmonic currents (3rd, 9th, 15th, 21st, etc.). Figure 4–22

Additional losses may occur in some transformers where harmonic currents are present, resulting in increased heat in the transformer above its rating. The heating from harmonic currents is proportional to the square of the harmonic current. Figure 4–23

> **AUTHOR'S COMMENT:** Both of these topics are beyond the scope of this textbook.

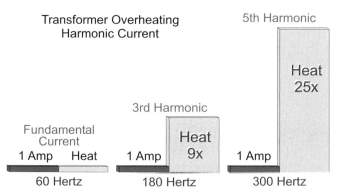

Transformer Overheating Harmonic Current

Harmonic currents from nonlinear loads can increase the heating in a transformer. Ventilation may not be adequate.

COPYRIGHT 2003 Mike Holt Enterprises, Inc.

Figure 4–23

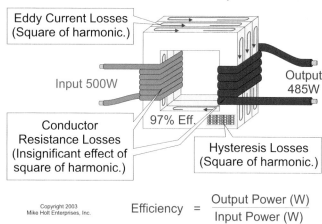

Transformer Efficiency

$$\text{Efficiency} = \frac{\text{Output Power (W)}}{\text{Input Power (W)}}$$

Figure 4–24

4.21 Efficiency

Because of conductor resistance, flux leakage, eddy currents, and hysteresis losses, not all of the input power is transferred to the secondary winding for useful purposes. Figure 4–24

> **AUTHOR'S COMMENT:** For most practical purposes, transformer efficiency can be ignored.

4.22 Transformer Turns Ratio

The relationship of the primary winding voltage to the secondary winding voltage is the same as the relationship between the number of turns of wire on the primary as compared to the number of turns on the secondary. This relationship is called turns ratio. Figure 4–25

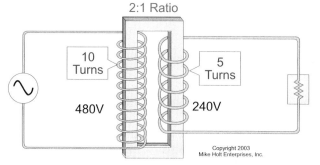

Primary - Secondary Turns Ratio

Ratio of number of primary turns to number of secondary turns.

Figure 4–25

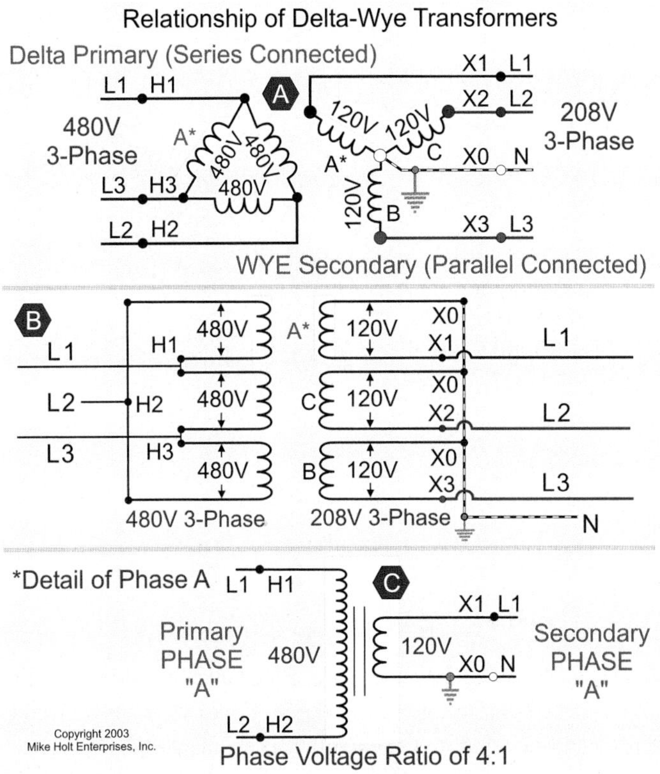

Relationship of Delta-Wye Transformers

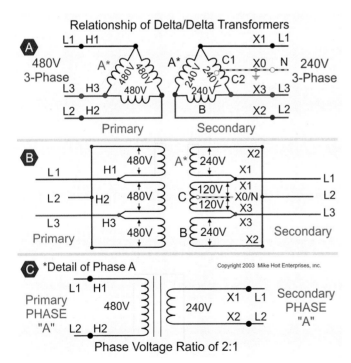

Figure 4–26

Relationship of Delta/Delta Transformers

Figure 4–27

▶ **Delta/Wye Example**

What is the turns ratio of the delta/wye transformer shown in Figure 4–26 if the primary phase voltage is 480V and the secondary is 120V?

    (a) 4:1   (b) 1:4   (c) 2:1   (d) 1:2

    • Answer: (a) 4:1

▶ **Delta/Delta Example**

What is the turns ratio of the delta/delta transformer shown in Figure 4–27 if the primary phase voltage is 480V and the secondary is 240V?

    (a) 4:1   (b) 1:4   (c) 2:1   (d) 1:2

    • Answer: (c) 2:1

▶ **Primary Voltage Example**

What is the primary voltage of the transformer shown in Figure 4–28 if the turns ratio is 20:1 and the secondary voltage is 6V?

    (a) 6V   (b) 24V

    (c) 48V   (d) none of these

    • Answer: (d) none of these

The turns ratio is 20:1. This means the voltage ratio is also 20:1. Since the secondary voltage is 6V, the primary voltage is 20 times larger, 20 x 6V = 120V.

▶ **Secondary Voltage Example**

What is the secondary voltage of the transformer shown in Figure 4–29 if the turns ratio is 10:1 and the primary voltage is 240V?

    (a) 6V   (b) 24V

    (c) 48V   (d) none of these

    • Answer: (b) 24V

Transformer Ratios - Primary Voltage

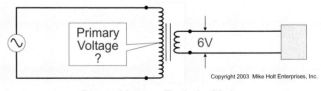

Phase Voltage Ratio is 20:1
Determine the primary voltage.

Voltage ratio is 20:1, secondary voltage is 6V.
Primary voltage is 20 times higher than secondary voltage.
6V x 20 = 120V on primary

Figure 4–28

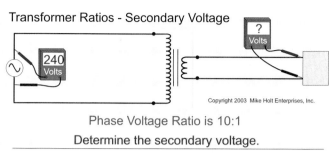

Figure 4–29

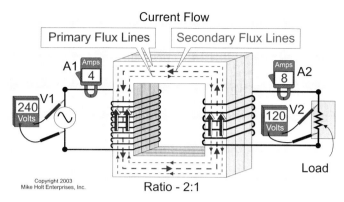

Figure 4–31

Since the primary voltage is 240V, the secondary voltage is 10 times smaller, 240V/10 = 24V.

4.23 Transformer kVA Rating

Transformers are rated in kilovolt-amperes (kVA), where 1 kilo-volt-ampere = 1,000 volt-amperes = 1,000 VA.

Figure 4–30 lists some standard transformer sizes, although some transformers get much, much larger than those listed in this figure.

4.24 Current Flow

The following steps explain the process of primary and secondary current flow in a transformer.

Step 1 When a load is connected to the secondary of a transformer, secondary voltage induced from the primary magnetic field will cause current to flow through the secondary conductor winding.

Step 2 The secondary current flow in the secondary winding creates an electromagnetic field that opposes the primary electromagnetic field.

Step 3 The flux lines from the secondary magnetic field effectively reduce the strength of the primary flux lines, and as a result, less CEMF is generated in the primary winding conductors. With less CEMF to oppose the primary applied voltage, the primary current increases in direct proportion to the secondary current. Figure 4–31

4.25 Current Rating

The primary current rating can be determined by the formulas:

Single-Phase	Three-Phase
$I = VA/E$	$I = VA/(E \times 1.732)$

▶ **Single-Phase Example**

What is the maximum primary and secondary line current at full load for a 480/240V, 25 kVA transformer? Figure 4–32

   (a) 52/104A   (b) 104/52A
   (c) 104/208A   (d) 208/104A

• Answer: (a) 52/104A
I primary = VA/E
I primary = 25,000 VA/480V
I primary = 52A

I secondary = VA/E
I secondary = 25,000 VA/240V
I secondary = 104A

Standard Transformer Ratings - In kVA

Single-Phase	Three-Phase
1.0	3.0
1.5	6.0
2.0	9.0
3.0	15.0
5.0	22.5
7.5	25.0
10.0	30.0
15.0	37.5
25.0	45.0
37.5	50.0
50.0	75.0
75.0	112.5
100.0	150.0
125.0	225.0

Copyright 2003 Mike Holt Enterprises, Inc.

Figure 4–30

Primary and Secondary Line Current - Single Phase

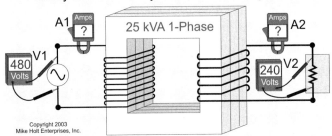

Copyright 2003
Mike Holt Enterprises, Inc.

Determine the primary and secondary line current.

Primary Current	Secondary Current
I = P/E	I = P/E
P = 25 kVA/1,000	P = 25 kVA/1,000
P = 25,000 VA	P = 25,000 VA
E = 480V	E = 240V
I = 25,000 VA/480V	I = 25,000 VA/240V
I = 52A	I = 104A

Figure 4–32

▶ **Three-Phase Example**

What is the maximum primary and secondary line current at full load for a 480/208V, 37.5 kVA transformer? Figure 4–33

    (a) 45/104A   (b) 104/40A

    (c) 208/140A   (d) 140/120A

     • Answer: (a) 45/104A

Primary and Secondary Line Currents Delta/Wye Transformer

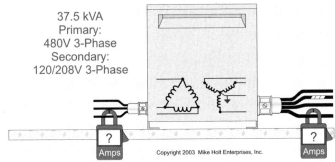

37.5 kVA
Primary:
480V 3-Phase
Secondary:
120/208V 3-Phase

Copyright 2003 Mike Holt Enterprises, Inc.

Determine the primary and secondary line current.

Formula:
$$I_{LINE} = \frac{\text{Line Power}}{(\text{Line Volts} \times \sqrt{3})} = \frac{VA}{(E \times \sqrt{3})}$$

Primary Current	Secondary Current
$I_{LINE} = \dfrac{37{,}500\ VA}{(480V \times 1.732)} = 45A$	$I_{LINE} = \dfrac{37{,}500\ VA}{(208V \times 1.732)} = 104A$

Figure 4–33

I primary = VA/(E x 1.732)
I primary = 37,500 VA/(480V x 1.732)
I primary = 45A

I secondary = VA/(E x 1.732)
I secondary = 37,500 VA/(208V x 1.732)
I secondary = 104A

Unit 4 Conclusion

Article 430 of the *National Electrical Code* addresses motors, motor circuits, and motor controllers. It is the largest of all the *NEC* articles. Now that you have studied basic motor theory, motor calculations, motor circuits, and motor controls, you can see why this is so. Although you have learned much here, you would benefit from learning even more, especially if you are going to do much commercial or industrial work.

You now have a basic understanding of transformers, the various types, the standard sizes, how they're rated, and how they work. You will encounter transformers often in your work. What you have learned here will help determine how successful you are in that work.

Unit 4 Calculation Practice Questions

(• Indicates that 75% or fewer of those who took this exam answered the question correctly.)

PART A—MOTORS

4.1 Motor Principles

1. A motor must have two opposing magnetic fields in order to rotate. The stationary field winding is mounted on the stator, and the rotating part is referred to as the armature.

   (a) True   (b) False

4.2 Dual-Voltage AC Motors

2. Dual-voltage ac motors are made with two field windings. The field windings are connected in _____ for low-voltage operation and in _____ for high-voltage operation.

   (a) series, parallel   (b) parallel, series   (c) series, series   (d) parallel, parallel

3. For a dual-voltage 230/460V motor, the field windings are connected in parallel for _____ operation and in series for _____ operation.

   (a) 230V, 460V   (b) 460V, 230V   (c) 230V, 230V   (d) 460V, 460V

4.3 Motor Horsepower Rating

4. Motors are used to convert electrical energy into mechanical work and the output mechanical work of a motor is rated in horsepower. 1 hp = _____.

   (a) 476W   (b) 674W   (c) 746W   (d) 840W

5. What size motor, in horsepower, is required to produce approximately 30 kW of output?

   (a) 20 hp   (b) 30 hp   (c) 40 hp   (d) 50 hp

6. What is the approximate output of a 15 hp motor?

   (a) 11 kW   (b) 15 kW   (c) 22 kW   (d) 31 kW

7. What is the approximate output of a 5 hp, 480V, three-phase motor?

   (a) 3.75 kW   (b) 4.75 kW   (c) 6.75 kW   (d) 7.75 kW

4.4 Motor Current Ratings

8. The nameplate motor FLA rating describes the motor current rating when it carries its rated horsepower load at its rated _____.

   (a) power   (b) resistance   (c) CEMF   (d) voltage

9. The actual motor current is dependent upon the load on the motor and the operating voltage at the motor terminals.

   (a) True   (b) False

10. The motor FLA rating is used when sizing motor conductors or circuit protection.

     (a) True   (b) False

4.5 Calculating Motor FLA

11. What is the nameplate FLA for a 5 hp, 230V, single-phase motor, with 93 percent power factor and 87 percent efficiency?

     (a) 10A   (b) 20A   (c) 28A   (d) 35A

12. What is the nameplate FLA for a 20 hp, 208V, three-phase motor with 90 percent power factor and 80 percent efficiency?

     (a) 51A   (b) 58A   (c) 65A   (d) 80A

4.6 Motor-Starting Current

13. When a motor starts, the current drawn is at least _____ times the motor FLA; this is known as motor locked-rotor amperes (LRA).

     (a) 1.25   (b) 0.80   (c) 3   (d) 6

4.7 Motor-Running Current

14. Once a motor begins turning, the rotor winding will be increasingly cut by the stationary magnetic field, resulting in an increasing counter-electromotive force.

     (a) True   (b) False

4.8 Motor Locked-Rotor Current (LRC)

15. If the rotating part of the motor winding is jammed so that it cannot rotate, no CEMF will be produced in the motor winding. As a result, the motor operates at _____ and the windings will be destroyed by excessive heat.

     (a) FLA   (b) FLC   (c) LRC   (d) any of these

4.9 Motor Overload Protection

16. Motors must be protected against excessive winding heat by a properly sized overload protection device, based on the motor _____ current rating.

     (a) FLA   (b) FLC   (c) LRC   (d) any of these

4.10 Direct-Current Motor Principles

17. DC motors use brushes with springs to hold them in contact with a(n) _____.

     (a) rotor   (b) stator   (c) armature   (d) commutator

4.11 Direct-Current Motor Types

18. If the speed of a shunt-wound dc motor is increased, the armature cuts through the field at an increasing rate, resulting in a lower CEMF that acts to cut down on the increased armature current, which slows the motor back down.

     (a) True   (b) False

19. Placing a load on a shunt-wound dc motor causes the motor to slow down, which increases the rate at which the field flux lines are being cut by the armature. As a result, the armature CEMF increases resulting in an increase in the applied armature voltage and current. The increase in current results in increased motor speed.

    (a) True   (b) False

4.12 Reversing the Rotation of a DC Motor

20. To reverse the rotation of a dc motor, you must reverse the _____.

    (a) stator field   (b) rotor field   (c) a and b   (d) a or b

4.13 AC Induction Motor

21. In an ac induction motor, the stator produces a rotating magnetic field that induces current in the rotor windings. The rotor current generates a magnetic field in opposition to the magnetic field of the stator, thereby causing the rotor to turn.

    (a) True   (b) False

4.14 Alternating-Current Motor Types

22. In a(n) _____ motor, the rotor is actually locked in step with the rotating stator field and is dragged along at the speed of the rotating magnetic field.

    (a) wound-rotor   (b) induction   (c) synchronous   (d) squirrel-cage

23. _____ motors are fractional horsepower motors that operate equally well on ac and dc and are used for vacuum cleaners, electric drills, mixers, and light household appliances.

    (a) AC   (b) Universal   (c) Wound-rotor   (d) Synchronous

4.15 Reversing the Rotation of an AC Motor

24. Swapping _____ of the line conductors can reverse a three-phase ac motor's rotation.

    (a) one   (b) two   (c) three   (d) none of these

PART B—TRANSFORMERS
4.16 Transformer Basics

25. A _____ is used to raise or lower voltage and it has the ability to transfer electrical energy from one system to another with no physical connection between the two systems.

    (a) capacitor   (b) motor   (c) relay   (d) transformer

26. The transformer winding that is connected to the source is called the _____ winding and the transformer winding that is connected to the load is called the _____.

    (a) secondary, primary   (b) primary, secondary   (c) depends on the wiring (d) none of these

27. The energy transfer ability of a transformer is accomplished because the primary electromagnetic lines of force induce a voltage in the secondary winding.

    (a) True   (b) False

4.17 Secondary Induced Voltage

28.　Voltage induced in the secondary winding of a transformer is dependent on the number of secondary turns as compared to the number of primary turns.

　　(a) True　　　　　　　　　　(b) False

4.18 Autotransformers

29.　Autotransformers use separate windings for the primary and secondary.

　　(a) True　　　　　　　　　　(b) False

4.19 Power Losses

30.　Wasteful circulating _____ in the iron core cause(s) the core to heat up without any useful purpose.

　　(a) conductor resistance　　　(b) flux leakage　　　　(c) eddy currents　　　　(d) hysteresis losses

31.　_____ can be reduced by dividing the core into many flat sections or laminations.

　　(a) Conductor resistance　　　(b) Flux leakage　　　　(c) Eddy currents　　　　(d) Hysteresis losses

32.　As current flows through the transformer, the iron core is temporarily magnetized. The energy required to realign the core molecules to the changing electromagnetic field is called _____ loss.

　　(a) conductor resistance　　　(b) flux leakage　　　　(c) eddy currents　　　　(d) hysteresis

33.　The leakage of electromagnetic flux lines between the primary and secondary windings of a transformer represents wasted energy.

　　(a) True　　　　　　　　　　(b) False

4.20 Harmonic Current

34.　Three-phase, _____, wye-connected systems can overheat because of circulating odd triplen harmonic currents.

　　(a) 2-wire　　　　　　　　　(b) 3-wire　　　　　　　(c) 4-wire　　　　　　　　(d) none of these

35.　The heating from harmonic currents is proportional to the square of the harmonic current.

　　(a) True　　　　　　　　　　(b) False

4.21 Efficiency

36.　Because of conductor resistance, flux leakage, eddy currents, and hysteresis losses, not all of the input power is transferred to the secondary winding for useful purposes.

　　(a) True　　　　　　　　　　(b) False

37.　For most practical purposes, transformer efficiency can be ignored.

　　(a) True　　　　　　　　　　(b) False

4.22 Transformer Turns Ratio

38.   The relationship of the number of turns of wire on the _____ as compared to the number of turns on the _____ is called turns ratio.

(a) primary, secondary   (b) secondary, primary   (c) primary, primary   (d) secondary, secondary

39.   If the primary phase voltage is 480V and the secondary phase voltage is 240V, the turns ratio is _____.

(a) 1:2   (b) 2:1   (c) 4:1   (d) 1:4

4.23 Transformer kVA Rating

40.   Transformers are rated in _____.

(a) VA   (b) kW   (c) W   (d) kVA

4.24 Current Flow

41.   The primary electromagnetic field induces a voltage in the secondary. As the secondary current flows, it produces an electromagnetic field that reduces the strength of the primary flux lines. This results in an increase in primary current.

(a) True   (b) False

42.   Current flow in a secondary transformer winding creates an electromagnetic field that opposes the primary electromagnetic field resulting in less primary CEMF. The primary current automatically increases in direct proportion to the secondary current.

(a) True   (b) False

Unit 4 Calculation Challenge Questions

(• Indicates that 75% or fewer of those who took this exam answered the question correctly.)

PART A—MOTORS

4.3 Motor Horsepower Rating

1. The input VA of a 5 hp (15.2A), 230V, three-phase motor is closest to _____.

   (a) 7,500 VA   (b) 6,100 VA   (c) 5,300 VA   (d) 4,600 VA

2. The input VA of a 1 hp (16A), 115V, single-phase motor is _____.

   (a) 2,960 VA   (b) 1,840 VA   (c) 3,190 VA   (d) 1,650 VA

4.11 Direct-Current Motor Types

3. A(n) _____ type of electric motor tends to "run away" if it is not always connected to its load.

   (a) dc series   (b) dc shunt   (c) ac induction   (d) ac synchronous

4. •A(n) _____ motor has a wide speed range.

   (a) ac   (b) dc   (c) synchronous   (d) induction

4.14 Alternating-Current Motor Types

5. The _____ induction motor is used only in special applications and is always operated on three-phase ac power.

   (a) compound   (b) synchronous   (c) split phase   (d) wound rotor

6. •The rotating part of a dc motor or generator is called the _____.

   (a) shaft   (b) rotor   (c) armature   (d) b or c

4.15 Reversing the Rotation of an AC Motor

7. •If the two line (supply) leads of a dc series motor are reversed, the motor will _____.

   (a) not run   (b) run backwards   (c) run the same as before   (d) become a generator

8. •To reverse a dc series motor, we may simply reverse the supply (power) leads.

   (a) True   (b) False

PART B—TRANSFORMERS

4.19 Power Losses

9. •When the current in the steel core of a transformer has risen to a point where high flux density has been reached and additional increases in current produce few additional flux lines, the metal core is said to be _____.

   (a) maximized   (b) saturated   (c) full   (d) none of these

Mike Holt Enterprises, Inc. • www.NECcode.com • 1.888.NEC.CODE

10. •Magnetomotive-force (MMF) can be increased by increasing the _____.

    (a) number of ampere-turns   (b) current in the coils   (c) number of coils   (d) all of these

4.22 Transformer Turns Ratio

11. •A transformer winding has a voltage turns ratio of 2:1. The current flowing through the secondary winding will be _____ the current flowing through the primary winding.

    (a) higher than   (b) lower than   (c) the same as   (d) none of these

12. •The primary winding of a transformer has 100 turns and the secondary winding has 10 turns. What is the current flowing through the primary winding if the current flowing through the secondary winding is 5A?

    (a) 25A   (b) 10A   (c) 5A   (d) 0.5A

13. •Which winding of a current transformer (CT) carries more current?
    Tip: An induction clamp-on ammeter (CT) operates on the principle where the meter acts as the secondary winding.

    (a) Primary   (b) Secondary   (c) Interwinding   (d) Tertiary

14. If a transformer primary winding has 900 turns and the secondary winding has 90 turns, which winding of the transformer has a larger conductor?

    (a) Primary   (b) Secondary   (c) Interwinding   (d) Autowinding

15. If the primary transformer winding operates at 480V and the secondary at 240V, which winding has a larger conductor?

    (a) Tertiary   (b) Secondary   (c) Primary   (d) Windings are equal

16. If the transformer winding voltage turns ratio is 5:1 and the current flowing through the secondary winding is 10A, the current flowing through the primary winding will be _____.

    (a) 25A   (b) 10A   (c) 2A   (d) 1A

17. A transformer primary winding operates at 240V, the secondary winding operates at 12V and the secondary load is two 100W lamps. What is the secondary current flow if the transformer winding is 80 percent efficient?

    (a) 1A   (b) 17A   (c) 28A   (d) none of these

18. A transformer primary winding operates at 240V, the secondary at 120V and the load is 1,500W. If the transformer is 92 percent efficient, what is the current flowing through the primary winding of this transformer?

    (a) 6.8A   (b) 8.6A   (c) 9.9A   (d) 7.8A

19. •The approximate primary kVA of a transformer that supplies a 208V, 100A, three-phase load is _____. (See **Figure 4-34**.)

    (a) 72.5 kVA   (b) 42 kVA   (c) 30 kVA   (d) 21 kVA

20. •The primary current of this transformer is _____. (See **Figure 4-34**.)

    (a) 90A   (b) 50A   (c) 25A   (d) 12A

21. •The secondary voltage of this transformer is _____. (See Figure **4-35**.)

    (a) 6V   (b) 12V   (c) 24V   (d) 30V

22. The primary load in watts for a transformer (95 percent efficient) that supplies a 500W load is _____. (See **Figure 4-36**.)

    (a) 526W   (b) 400W   (c) 475W   (d) 550W

23. The primary current of the transformer is _____. (See **Figure 4-36**.)

    (a) 0.416A   (b) 4.38A   (c) 3.56A   (d) 41.6A

24. The primary winding of a transformer operates at 240V, the secondary at 12V and the load consists of two 100W lamps. What is the load on the secondary winding if the transformer winding is 92 percent efficient?

    (a) 200 VA   (b) The same as the primary VA
    (c) Cannot be calculated   (d) none of these

25. •The secondary winding of a transformer operates at 24V and it supplies a load that has a rating of 5A. If the transformer is 90 percent efficient, what is the secondary VA load rating?

    (a) 120 VA   (b) The same as the primary VA
    (c) Cannot be calculated   (d) a and b

26. A primary transformer winding operates at 240V, the secondary at 12V and the load is two 100W lamps. What is the primary VA load if the transformer is 92 percent efficient?

    (a) 185 VA   (b) 217 VA   (c) 0.217 VA   (d) 275 VA

27. The input power for a 20 kW load will be approximately _____ if it operates at an efficiency level of 65 percent.

    (a) 11 kW   (b) 20 kW   (c) 31 kW   (d) 33 kW

4.23 Transformer kVA Rating

28. What is the primary kVA rating for a transformer winding that is 100 percent efficient if a 5A load on the secondary operates at 12V?

    (a) 600 kVA   (b) 30 kVA   (c) 6 kVA   (d) 0.06 kVA

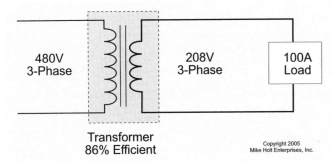

Transformer
86% Efficient

Figure 4–34

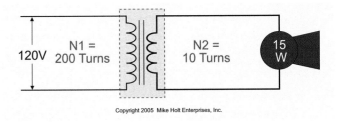

Figure 4–35

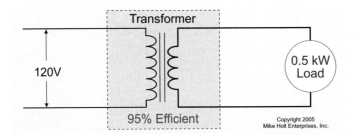

Figure 4–36

(• Indicates that 75% or fewer of those who took this exam answered the question correctly.)

Article 250 Grounding and Bonding (continued)

1. The connection (attachment) of the grounding electrode conductor to a grounding electrode must _____.

    (a) be accessible   (b) be made in a manner that will ensure a permanent and effective grounding path
    (c) a and b   (d) none of these

2. The grounding conductor connection to the grounding electrode must be made by _____.

    (a) listed lugs   (b) exothermic welding   (c) listed pressure connectors   (d) any of these

3. A metal elbow that is installed in an underground installation of rigid nonmetallic conduit and is isolated from possible contact by a minimum cover _____ to any part of the elbow, is not required to be grounded.

    (a) of 6 in.   (b) of 12 in.
    (c) of 18 in.   (d) as specified in Table 300.5

4. Metal enclosures and raceways for conductors added to existing installations of _____, which do not provide an equipment ground are not required to be grounded if they are less than 25 ft long, they are free from probable contact with grounded conductive material, and are guarded against contact by persons.

    (a) nonmetallic-sheathed cable (b) open wiring   (c) knob-and-tube wiring   (d) all of these

5. Bonding must be provided where necessary to ensure _____ and the capacity to conduct safely any fault current likely to be imposed.

    (a) electrical continuity   (b) fiduciary responsibility   (c) listing requirements   (d) electrical demand

6. Service equipment, service raceways, and service conductor enclosures must be bonded _____.

    (a) to the grounded service conductor
    (b) by threaded raceways into enclosures, couplings, hubs, conduit bodies, etc.
    (c) by listed bonding devices with bonding jumpers
    (d) any of these

7. Service metal raceways and metal clad cables are considered effectively bonded when using threadless couplings and connectors that are _____.

    (a) nonmetallic   (b) made up tight
    (c) sealed   (d) these are never allowed for bonding

8. An accessible means external to enclosures for connecting intersystem _____ conductors must be provided at the service equipment and at the disconnecting means.

    (a) bonding   (b) grounding   (c) secondary   (d) a and b

9.   When bonding enclosures, metal raceways, frames, fittings, and other metal noncurrent-carrying parts, any nonconductive paint, enamel, or similar coating must be removed at _____.

(a) contact surfaces   (b) threads   (c) contact points   (d) all of these

10.   For circuits over 250 volts-to-ground (277/480V), electrical continuity can be maintained between a box or enclosure where no oversized, concentric, or eccentric knockouts are encountered, and a metal conduit by _____.

(a) threadless fittings for cables with metal sheath
(b) double locknuts on threaded conduit (one inside and one outside the box or enclosure)
(c) fittings that have shoulders that seat firmly against the box with a locknut on the inside or listed fittings identified for the purpose.
(d) all of these

11.   Regardless of the voltage of the electrical system, the electrical continuity of noncurrent-carrying metal parts of equipment, raceways, and other enclosures in any hazardous (classified) location as defined in Article 500 must be ensured by any of the methods specified in 250.92(B)(2) through (B)(4). One or more of these _____ methods must be used whether or not supplementary equipment grounding conductors are installed.

(a) grounded   (b) securing   (c) sealing   (d) bonding

12.   Equipment bonding jumpers on the supply side of the service must be no smaller than the sizes shown in _____.

(a) Table 250.66   (b) Table 250.122   (c) Table 310.16   (d) Table 310.15(B)(6)

13.   A service is supplied by three metal raceways. Each raceway contains 600 kcmil ungrounded (phase) conductors. Determine the size of the service bonding jumper for each raceway.

(a) 1/0 AWG   (b) 2/0 AWG   (c) 225 kcmil   (d) 500 kcmil

14.   What is the minimum size copper bonding jumper for a service raceway containing 4/0 THHN aluminum conductors?

(a) 6 AWG aluminum   (b) 3 AWG copper   (c) 4 AWG aluminum   (d) 4 AWG copper

15.   The equipment bonding jumper can be installed on the outside of a raceway providing the length of the run is not more than _____ and the bonding jumper is routed with the raceway.

(a) 12 in.   (b) 24 in.   (c) 36 in.   (d) 72 in.

16.   The metal water piping system(s) must be bonded to the _____.

(a) grounded conductor at the service
(b) service equipment enclosure
(c) equipment grounding bar or bus at any panelboard within the building
(d) a or b

17.   A building or structure that is supplied by a feeder must have the interior metal water piping system bonded with a conductor sized from _____.

(a) Table 250.66   (b) Table 250.122   (c) Table 310.16   (d) none of these

18.   Exposed structural metal that is interconnected to form a steel building frame, that is not intentionally grounded and is likely to become energized, must be bonded to:

(a) The service equipment enclosure.
(b) The grounded conductor at the service.
(c) The grounding electrode conductor where of sufficient size.
(d) any of these

19. Lightning protection system ground terminals _____ be bonded to the building grounding electrode system.

(a) must   (b) must not   (c) can   (d) none of these

20. Exposed noncurrent-carrying metal parts of fixed equipment likely to become energized must be grounded where _____.

(a) within 8 ft vertically or 5 ft horizontally of ground or grounded metal objects
(b) located in wet or damp locations and not isolated
(c) in electrical contact with metal
(d) any of these

21. Electrical equipment that is permanently mounted on skids themselves, and the skids, must be grounded with an equipment bonding jumper sized as required by _____.

(a) 250.50   (b) 250.66   (c) 250.122   (d) 310.15

22. An equipment grounding conductor run with, or enclosing, the circuit conductors must be _____ or metal raceway as listed in 250.118.

(a) a copper conductor   (b) an aluminum conductor
(c) a copper-clad aluminum conductor   (d) any of these

23. For flexible metal conduit (FMC) and liquidtight flexible metal conduit (LFMC), an equipment grounding conductor is required regardless of the size of the overcurrent protection if the FMC or LFMC is installed for the reason of _____.

(a) physical protection   (b) flexibility
(c) protection from moisture   (d) communications systems

24. Liquidtight flexible metal conduit (LFMC) in trade sizes 3/4 through 1 1/4 can be used as the equipment grounding conductor if the length in any ground return path does not exceed 6 ft and the circuit conductors contained in the conduit are protected by overcurrent devices rated at _____ or less when the conduit is not installed for flexibility.

(a) 15A   (b) 20A   (c) 30A   (d) 60A

25. Conductors with insulation that is _____ cannot be used for ungrounded or grounded conductors.

(a) green   (b) green with one or more yellow stripes
(c) a or b   (d) white

26. Equipment grounding conductors for feeder taps must be sized in accordance with _____ based on the ampere rating of the circuit protection device ahead of the feeder, but in no case is it required to be larger than the circuit conductors.

(a) Table 250.66   (b) Table 250.94   (c) Table 250.122   (d) Table 220.19

27. The equipment grounding conductor must not be smaller than shown in Table 250.122, but it must not be required to be larger than the circuit conductors supplying the equipment.

(a) True   (b) False

28. When a single equipment grounding conductor is used for multiple circuits in the same raceway or cable, the single equipment grounding conductor must be sized according to _____.

(a) the combined rating of all the overcurrent protection devices
(b) the largest overcurrent protection device of the multiple circuits
(c) the combined rating of all the loads
(d) any of these

29. The terminal of a wiring device for the connection of the equipment grounding conductor must be identified by a green-colored, _____.

    (a) not readily removable terminal screw with a hexagonal head
    (b) hexagonal, not readily removable terminal nut
    (c) pressure wire connector
    (d) any of these

30. When considering whether equipment is effectively grounded, the structural metal frame of a building is permitted to be used as the required equipment grounding conductor for ac equipment.

    (a) True   (b) False

31. Ranges and clothes dryers for existing branch-circuit installations that were installed with the frame grounded by the grounded circuit conductor are allowed to continue this practice if all conditions of the exception to 250.140 are met.

    (a) True   (b) False

32. A grounded circuit conductor must not be used for grounding noncurrent-carrying metal parts of equipment on the load side of _____.

    (a) the service disconnecting means
    (b) the separately derived system disconnecting means
    (c) overcurrent protection devices for separately derived systems not having a main disconnecting means
    (d) all of these

33. An _____ must be used to connect the grounding terminal of a grounding-type receptacle to a grounded box.

    (a) equipment bonding jumper   (b) equipment grounding jumper
    (c) a or b   (d) a and b

34. An equipment bonding jumper must be used to connect the grounding terminal of a grounding-type receptacle to a grounded box. Where the box is surface-mounted, direct metal-to-metal contact between the device yoke and the box can be permitted to ground the receptacle to the box.

    (a) True   (b) False

35. Receptacle yokes designed and _____ as self-grounding are permitted to establish the bonding path between the device yoke and a grounded outlet box.

    (a) approved   (b) advertised   (c) listed   (d) installed

36. Contact devices or yokes designed and listed as self-grounding are permitted in conjunction with the supporting screws to establish the grounding circuit between the device yoke and flush-type boxes.

    (a) True   (b) False

37. Where circuit conductors are spliced within a box, or terminated on equipment within or supported by a box, any equipment grounding conductors associated with those circuit conductors must be spliced or joined within the box or to the box with devices suitable for the use.

    (a) True   (b) False

38. When equipment grounding conductor(s) are installed in a metal box, an electrical connection is required between the equipment grounding conductor and the metal box enclosure by means of a _____.

    (a) grounding screw   (b) soldered connection   (c) listed grounding device   (d) a or c

39.　The secondary circuits of current and potential instrument transformers must be grounded where the primary windings are connected to circuits of _____ or more to ground and, where on switchboards, must be grounded irrespective of voltage.

(a) 300V　　　　　　(b) 600V　　　　　　(c) 1,000V　　　　　　(d) 150V

40.　The grounding conductor for secondary circuits of instrument transformers and for instrument cases must not be smaller than _____ AWG copper.

(a) 18　　　　　　(b) 16　　　　　　(c) 14　　　　　　(d) 12

Article 280 Surge Arresters

This article covers general requirements, installation requirements, and connection requirements for surge arresters installed on the line side of service equipment.

41.　Line and ground-connecting conductors for a surge arrester must not be smaller than _____ AWG copper.

(a) 14　　　　　　(b) 12　　　　　　(c) 10　　　　　　(d) 8

Article 285 Transient Voltage Surge Suppressors (TVSSs)

This article covers general requirements, installation requirements, and connection requirements for transient voltage surge suppressors (TVSSs) permanently installed on the load side of service equipment. It doesn't apply to cord-and-plug connected units, such as "computer power strips."

42.　Article 285 covers surge arresters.

(a) True　　　　　　(b) False

43.　A TVSS is listed to limit transient voltages by diverting or limiting surge current.

(a) True　　　　　　(b) False

44.　TVSSs must be marked with their short-circuit current rating, and they must not be installed where the available fault current is in excess of that rating.

(a) True　　　　　　(b) False

45.　A TVSS can be connected anywhere on the premises wiring system.

(a) True　　　　　　(b) False

CHAPTER 3 WIRING METHODS AND MATERIALS

Article 300 Wiring Methods

Article 300 contains the general requirements for all wiring methods included in the *NEC*, except for signaling and communications systems, which are covered in Chapters 7 and 8.

46.　Unless specified elsewhere in the *Code*, Chapter 3 must be used for voltages of _____.

(a) 600 volts-to-ground or less　　　　　　(b) 300V between conductors or less
(c) 600V, nominal, or less　　　　　　(d) 600V RMS

47. All conductors of a circuit, including the grounded and equipment grounding conductors, must be contained within the same _____.

    (a) raceway   (b) cable   (c) trench   (d) all of these

48. In both exposed and concealed locations, where a cable or nonmetallic raceway-type wiring method is installed through bored holes in joists, rafters, or wood members, holes must be bored so that the edge of the hole is _____ the nearest edge of the wood member.

    (a) not less than 1 1/4 in. from   (b) immediately adjacent to
    (c) not less than 1/ 16 in. from   (d) 90°away from

49. Cables laid in wood notches require protection against nails or screws by using a steel plate at least _____ thick, installed before the building finish is applied. A thinner plate that provides equal or better protection may be used if listed and marked.

    (a) 1/16 in.   (b) 1/8 in.   (c) 1/2 in.   (d) none of these

50. Where NM cable passes through factory or field openings in metal members, it must be protected by _____ bushings or _____ grommets that cover metal edges. The protection fitting must be securely fastened in the opening prior to the installation of the cable.

    (a) approved   (b) identified   (c) listed   (d) none of these

51. Wiring methods installed behind panels that allow access, such as the space above a dropped ceiling, are required to be _____ according to their applicable Articles.

    (a) supported   (b) painted   (c) in a metal raceway   (d) all of these

52. When unable to maintain the minimum required distance from the edge of a wood framing member when installing a cable or nonmetallic raceway parallel to framing members, the cable or raceway must be protected from penetration by screws or nails by a steel plate or bushing at least _____ and of appropriate length and width to cover the area of the wiring. A thinner plate that provides equal or better protection may be used if listed and marked.

    (a) 1/4 in. thick   (b) 1/8 in. thick   (c) 1/16 in. thick   (d) 24 gauge

53. Where underground conductors and cables emerge from underground, they must be protected by enclosures or raceways to a point _____ above finished grade. In no case can the protection be required to exceed 18 in. below grade.

    (a) 3 ft   (b) 6 ft   (c) 8 ft   (d) 10 ft

54. What is the minimum cover requirement in inches for direct burial UF cable installed outdoors that supplies power to a 120V, 30A circuit?

    (a) 6 in.   (b) 12 in.   (c) 18 in.   (d) 24 in.

55. •When installing raceways underground in rigid nonmetallic conduit and other approved raceways, there must be a minimum of _____ of cover.

    (a) 6 in.   (b) 12 in.   (c) 18 in.   (d) 22 in.

56. UF cable used with a 24V landscape lighting system is permitted to have a minimum cover of _____.

    (a) 6 in.   (b) 12 in.   (c) 18 in.   (d) 24 in.

57. Direct-buried conductors or cables can be spliced or tapped without the use of splice boxes when the splice or tap is made in accordance with 110.14(B).

    (a) True   (b) False

58. Conduits or raceways through which moisture may contact live parts must be _____ at either or both ends.

(a) sealed   (b) plugged   (c) bushed   (d) a or b

59. All conductors of the same circuit are required to be _____.

(a) in the same raceway or cable   (b) in close proximity in the same trench
(c) the same size   (d) a or b

60. Cables or raceways installed using directional boring equipment must be _____ for this purpose.

(a) marked   (b) listed   (c) labeled   (d) approved

61. Which of the following metal parts must be protected from corrosion both inside and out?

(a) Ferrous metal raceways   (b) Metal elbows   (c) Boxes   (d) all of these

62. Metal raceways, boxes, fittings, supports, and support hardware can be installed in concrete or in direct contact with the earth or other areas subject to severe corrosive influences, where _____ approved for the conditions, or where provided with corrosion protection approved for the purpose.

(a) the soil is   (b) made of material   (c) the qualified installer is   (d) none of these

63. Nonmetallic raceways, cable trays, cablebus, auxiliary gutters, boxes, cables with a nonmetallic outer jacket and internal metal armor or jacket, cable sheathing, cabinets, elbows, couplings, nipples, fittings, supports and support hardware must be made of material _____.

(a) listed for the condition   (b) approved for the condition   (c) both a and b   (d) either a or b

64. Nonmetallic raceways, cable trays, cablebus, auxiliary gutters, boxes, and cables with a nonmetallic outer jacket must be made of material approved for the condition and where exposed to chemicals, the materials or coatings must be _____.

(a) listed as inherently resistant to chemicals   (b) identified for the specific chemical reagent
(c) both a and b   (d) either a or b

65. In general, areas where _____ are handled and stored may present severe corrosive conditions, particularly when wet or damp.

(a) laboratory chemicals and acids   (b) acids and alkali chemicals
(c) acids and water   (d) chemicals and water

66. Raceways must be provided with expansion fittings where necessary to compensate for thermal expansion and contraction.

(a) True   (b) False

67. •Metal raceways, cable armor, and other metal enclosures for conductors must be _____ joined together to form a continuous electrical conductor.

(a) electrically   (b) permanently   (c) metallically   (d) none of these

68. Where independent support wires of a ceiling assembly are used to support raceways, cable assemblies, or boxes above a ceiling, they must be secured at both ends. Cables and raceways must _____.

(a) be identified for this purpose   (b) not be supported by ceiling grids
(c) not contain conductors larger than 14 AWG   (d) be identified by painting them orange

69. The independent support wires for wiring in a fire-rated ceiling assembly must be distinguishable from fire-rated suspended-ceiling framing support wires by _____.

    (a) color   (b) tagging   (c) other effective means   (d) any of these

70. Raceways are allowed to be used as a means of support when the raceway contains electrical power supply conductors for electrically controlled equipment and the raceway is used to support Class 2 circuit conductors or cables that connect to the same equipment.

    (a) True   (b) False

71. Metal or nonmetallic raceways, cable armors, and cable sheaths _____ between cabinets, boxes, fittings or other enclosures or outlets.

    (a) can be attached with electrical tape   (b) are allowed gaps for expansion
    (c) must be continuous   (d) none of these

72. In multiwire circuits, the continuity of the _____ conductor must not be dependent upon the device connections.

    (a) ungrounded   (b) grounded   (c) grounding   (d) a and b

73. When the opening to an outlet, junction, or switch point is less than 8 in. in any dimension, each conductor must be long enough to extend at least _____ outside the opening of the enclosure.

    (a) 0 in.   (b) 3 in.   (c) 6 in.   (d) 12 in.

74. A box or conduit body is not required where cables enter or exit from conduit or tubing that is used to provide cable support or protection against physical damage. A fitting must be provided on the end(s) of the conduit or tubing to _____.

    (a) allow for the future connection of a box   (b) be used for a future pull point
    (c) protect the cable from abrasion   (d) allow the coupling of another section of conduit

75. Splices and taps are permitted in cabinets or cutout boxes if the conductors, splices, and taps do not fill the wiring space at any cross-section to more than _____ percent.

    (a) 20   (b) 40   (c) 60   (d) 75

76. A bushing is permitted in lieu of a box or terminal where conductors emerge from a raceway and enter or terminate at equipment, such as open switchboards, unenclosed control equipment, or similar equipment.

    (a) True   (b) False

77. The number of conductors permitted in a raceway must be limited to _____.

    (a) permit heat to dissipate   (b) prevent damage to insulation during installation
    (c) prevent damage to insulation during removal of conductors   (d) all of these

78. Prewired raceway assemblies are permitted only where specifically permitted in the *Code* for the applicable wiring method.

    (a) True   (b) False

79. Metal raceways must not be _____ by welding to the raceway unless specifically designed to be, or otherwise specifically permitted to be, by the *Code*.

    (a) supported   (b) terminated   (c) connected   (d) all of these

80. A vertical run of 4/0 AWG copper must be supported at intervals not exceeding _____.

    (a) 80 ft   (b) 100 ft   (c) 120 ft   (d) 40 ft

81. _____ is a nonferrous, nonmagnetic metal that has no heating due to inductive hysteresis heating.

    (a) Steel   (b) Iron   (c) Aluminum   (d) all of these

82. Openings around electrical penetrations through fire-resistant-rated walls, partitions, floors, or ceilings must _____ to maintain the fire resistance rating.

    (a) be documented   (b) not be allowed
    (c) be firestopped using approved methods   (d) be enlarged

83. Equipment and devices are permitted within ducts or plenum chambers used to transport environmental air only if necessary for their direct action upon, or sensing of, the _____.

    (a) contained air   (b) air quality   (c) air temperature   (d) none of these

84. One wiring method that is permitted in ducts or plenums used for environmental air is _____.

    (a) flexible metal conduit of any length   (b) electrical metallic tubing
    (c) armored cable (Type AC)   (d) nonmetallic-sheathed cable

85. The space above a hung ceiling used for environmental air-handling purposes is an example of _____ and the wiring limitations of _____ apply.

    (a) a plenum, 300.22(B)   (b) other spaces, 300.22(C)   (c) a duct, 300.22(B)   (d) none of these

86. Electric wiring in the air-handling area beneath raised floors for data-processing systems is permitted in accordance with Article 645.

    (a) True   (b) False

Article 310 Conductors for General Wiring

This article contains the general requirements for conductors, such as insulation markings, ampacity ratings, and conductor use. Article 310 doesn't apply to conductors that are part of cable assemblies, flexible cords, fixture wires, or conductors that are an integral part of equipment [90.6 and 300.1(B)].

87. Conductors must be insulated except where specifically allowed by the *NEC* to be bare, such as for equipment grounding or bonding purposes.

    (a) True   (b) False

88. In general, the minimum size phase, neutral, or grounded conductor permitted for use in parallel installations is _____ AWG.

    (a) 10   (b) 1   (c) 1/0   (d) 4

89. When conductors are run in parallel, the currents should be evenly divided between the individual parallel conductors so that each conductor is evenly heated. This is accomplished by ensuring that each of the conductors within a parallel set has the same _____ and all conductors terminate in the same manner.

    (a) length   (b) material   (c) cross-sectional area   (d) all of these

90. It is not the intent of 310.4 to require that conductors of one phase, neutral, or grounded circuit conductor be the same as those of another phase, neutral, or grounded circuit conductor to achieve _____.

    (a) polarity   (b) balance   (c) grounding   (d) none of these

91. The minimum size conductor permitted in any building for branch circuits under 600V is _____ AWG.

    (a) 14   (b) 12   (c) 10   (d) 8

92. •Insulated conductors used in wet locations must be _____.

    (a) moisture-impervious metal-sheathed   (b) RHW, TW, THW, THHW, THWN, XHHW
    (c) listed for wet locations   (d) any of these

93. Where conductors of different insulation are associated together, the limiting temperature of any conductor must not be exceeded.

    (a) True   (b) False

94. There are four principal determinants of conductor operating temperature, one of which is _____ generated internally in the conductor as the result of load current flow.

    (a) friction   (b) magnetism   (c) heat   (d) none of these

95. Letters used to designate the number of conductors within a cable are _____.

    (a) D - Two insulated conductors laid parallel   (b) M - Two or more insulated conductors twisted spirally
    (c) T - Two or more insulated conductors twisted in parallel   (d) a and b

96. TFE-insulated conductors are manufactured in sizes from 14 through _____ AWG.

    (a) 2   (b) 1   (c) 2/0   (d) 4/0

97. Lettering on conductor insulation indicates its intended condition of use. THWN is rated _____.

    (a) 75°C   (b) for wet locations   (c) a and b   (d) not enough information

98. The ampacities listed in the Tables of Article 310 are based on temperature alone and do not take _____ into consideration.

    (a) continuous loads   (b) voltage drop   (c) insulation   (d) wet locations

99. Where six current-carrying conductors are run in the same conduit or cable, the ampacity of each conductor must be adjusted to a factor of _____ percent of its value.

    (a) 90   (b) 60   (c) 40   (d) 80

100. Conductor derating factors do not apply to conductors in nipples having a length not exceeding _____

    (a) 12 in.   (b) 24 in.   (c) 36 in.   (d) 48 in.

(• Indicates that 75% or fewer of those who took this exam answered the question correctly.)

1. When an underground metal water-piping system is used as a grounding electrode, effective bonding must be provided around insulated joints and around any equipment that is likely to be disconnected for repairs or replacement. Bonding conductors must be of _____ to permit removal of such equipment while retaining the integrity of the bond.

   (a) stranded wire   (b) flexible conduit   (c) sufficient length   (d) none of these

2. •Cases or frames of instrument transformers are not required to be grounded _____.

   (a) when accessible to qualified persons only
   (b) for current transformers where the primary is not over 150 volts-to-ground and that are used exclusively to supply current to meters
   (c) for potential transformers where the primary is less than 150 volts-to-ground
   (d) a or b

3. •Circuit conductors that operate at 277V (with 600V insulation) may occupy the same enclosure or raceway with 48V dc conductors that have an insulation rating of 300V.

   (a) True   (b) False

4. •What is the minimum cover requirement in inches for UF cable supplying power to a 120V, 15A GFCI-protected circuit outdoors under a driveway of a one-family dwelling?

   (a) 12 in.   (b) 24in.   (c) 16 in.   (d) 6 in.

5. •Where circuit conductors are spliced within a box, or terminated on equipment within or supported by a box, any equipment grounding conductors associated with those circuit conductors must be spliced or joined in the box or to the box with devices suitable for the use. This does not apply to insulated equipment grounding conductors for isolated ground receptacles for electronic equipment.

   (a) True   (b) False

6. •Wiring methods permitted in the hung ceiling area used for environmental air include _____.

   (a) electrical metallic tubing
   (b) flexible metal conduit of any length
   (c) rigid metal conduit without an overall nonmetallic covering
   (d) all of these

7. A 100 ft vertical run of 4/0 AWG copper requires the conductors to be supported at _____ locations.

   (a) 4   (b) 5   (c) 2   (d) none of these

8. A grounding-type receptacle can replace a nongrounding-type receptacle at an outlet box that does not contain an equipment grounding conductor if the equipment grounding conductor is connected to the _____.

   (a) grounding electrode system as described in 250.50
   (b) grounding electrode conductor
   (c) equipment grounding terminal bar within the enclosure where the branch circuit for the receptacle originates
   (d) any of these

9. A TVSS device must be listed.

    (a) True   (b) False

10. An equipment bonding jumper for a grounding-type receptacle must be installed between the receptacle and a flush-mounted outlet box, even when the contact device is listed as self-grounding.

    (a) True   (b) False

11. Backfill used for underground wiring must not _____.

    (a) damage the wiring method   (b) prevent compaction of the fill
    (c) contribute to the corrosion of the raceway   (d) all of these

12. Bonding jumpers must be used around _____ knockouts that are punched or otherwise formed so as to impair the electrical connection to ground. Standard locknuts or bushings cannot be the sole means for this bonding.

    (a) concentric   (b) eccentric   (c) field-punched   (d) a or b

13. Ceiling-support wires used for the support of electrical raceways and cables within nonfire-rated assemblies are required to be distinguishable from the suspended-ceiling framing support wires.

    (a) True   (b) False

14. Conductors in raceways must be _____ between outlets, boxes, devices, and so forth.

    (a) continuous   (b) installed   (c) copper   (d) in conduit

15. Direct buried conductors, cables, or raceways, which are subject to movement by settlement or frost, must be arranged to prevent damage to the _____ or to equipment connected to the raceways.

    (a) siding of the building mounted on   (b) landscaping around the cable or raceway
    (c) the enclosed conductors   (d) expansion fitting

16. Each current-carrying conductor of a paralleled set of conductors must be counted as a current-carrying conductor for the purpose of applying the adjustment factors of 310.15(B)(2)(a).

    (a) True   (b) False

17. Electrical installations in hollow spaces, vertical shafts, and ventilation or air-handling ducts must be made so that the possible spread of fire or products of combustion will not be _____.

    (a) substantially increased   (b) allowed   (c) inherent   (d) possible

18. Equipment bonding jumpers must be of copper or other corrosion-resistant material. A bonding jumper must be a _____ or similar suitable conductor.

    (a) wire   (b) bus   (c) screw   (d) any of these

19. Fittings and connectors must be used only with the specific wiring methods for which they are designed and listed.

    (a) True   (b) False

20. In both exposed and concealed locations, where a cable or nonmetallic raceway-type wiring method is installed parallel to framing members such as joists, rafters, or studs or furring strips, the nearest outside surface of the cable or raceway must be _____ the nearest edge of the framing member where nails or screws are likely to penetrate.

(a) not less than 1 1/4 in. from
(b) immediately adjacent to
(c) not less than 1/16 in. from
(d) 90°away from

21. Liquidtight flexible metal conduit (LFMC) up to trade size 1/2 can be used as the equipment grounding conductor if the length in any ground return path does not exceed 6 ft and the circuit conductors contained in the conduit are protected by overcurrent devices rated at _____ or less when the conduit is not installed for flexibility.

(a) 15A
(b) 20A
(c) 30A
(d) 60A

22. Metal enclosures and raceways for other than service conductors must be grounded except as permitted by 250.112(I).

(a) True
(b) False

23. Metal gas piping can be considered bonded by the circuit's equipment grounding conductor of the circuit that is likely to energize the piping.

(a) True
(b) False

24. Metal raceways, enclosures, frames, and other noncurrent-carrying metal parts of electric equipment installed on a building equipped with a lightning protection system may require spacing from the lightning protection conductors, typically 6 ft through air or ___ through dense materials, such as concrete, brick, wood, etc.

(a) 2 ft
(b) 3 ft
(c) 4 ft
(d) 6 ft

25. Metric designators and trade sizes for conduit, tubing, and associated fittings and accessories are designated in Table _____.

(a) 250.66
(b) 250.122
(c) 300.1(C)
(d) 310.16

26. Nonmetallic raceways, cable trays, cablebus, auxiliary gutters, boxes, and cables with a nonmetallic outer jacket must be made of material approved for the condition and where exposed to sunlight, the materials must be _____.

(a) listed as sunlight resistant
(b) identified as sunlight resistant
(c) both a and b
(d) either a or b

27. Raceways must be _____ between outlet, junction, or splicing points prior to the installation of conductors.

(a) installed complete
(b) tested for ground faults
(c) a minimum of 80 percent completed
(d) none of these

28. Raceways, cable assemblies, boxes, cabinets, and fittings must be securely fastened in place. Support wires and associated fittings that provide secure support and that are installed in addition to the ceiling grid support wires are permitted as the sole support.

(a) True
(b) False

29. Solid dielectric insulated conductors operated above 2,000V in permanent installations must have _____ insulation and must be shielded.

(a) ozone-resistant
(b) asbestos
(c) high-temperature
(d) perfluoro-alkoxy

30. The _____ is defined as the area between the top of direct-burial cable and the finished grade.

(a) notch
(b) cover
(c) gap
(d) none of these

31. The _____ rating of a conductor is the maximum temperature, at any location along its length, which the conductor can withstand over a prolonged period of time without serious degradation.

    (a) ambient   (b) temperature   (c) maximum withstand   (d) short-circuit

32. The conductor between a surge arrester and the line and the grounding connection must not be smaller than _____ AWG copper for installations operating at 1 kV or more.

    (a) 4   (b) 6   (c) 8   (d) 2

33. The equipment bonding jumper on the supply side of services (service raceway) must be sized according to the _____.

    (a) calculated load
    (b) service-entrance conductor size
    (c) service-drop size
    (d) load to be served

34. The general rule for equipment bonding jumpers installed on the outside of a raceway or enclosure is that they are not permitted to be longer than 6 ft, but an equipment bonding jumper can be longer than 6 ft at outside pole locations for the purpose of bonding or grounding isolated sections of metal raceways or elbows installed in exposed risers of metal conduit or other metal raceways.

    (a) True   (b) False

35. The grounded circuit conductor is permitted to ground noncurrent-carrying metal parts of equipment, raceways, and other enclosures at the supply side or within the enclosure of the ac service-disconnecting means.

    (a) True   (b) False

36. The noncurrent-carrying metal parts of service equipment, such as _____, must be effectively bonded together.

    (a) service raceways, cable trays, or service cable armor
    (b) service equipment enclosures containing service conductors, including meter fittings, boxes, or the like, interposed in the service raceway or armor
    (c) the metallic raceway or armor enclosing a grounding electrode conductor
    (d) all of these

37. THW insulation has a _____ rating when installed within electric-discharge lighting equipment, such as through fluorescent luminaires.

    (a) 60°C   (b) 75°C   (c) 90°C   (d) none of these

38. Type AC cable can be installed in ducts or plenums that are used for environmental air.

    (a) True   (b) False

39. When ungrounded conductors are increased in size, the equipment grounding conductor is not required to be increased because it is not a current-carrying conductor.

    (a) True   (b) False

40. Where _____ conductors are run in separate raceways or cables, the same number of conductors must be used in each raceway or cable.

    (a) parallel   (b) control   (c) communication   (d) aluminum

41. Where a metal box is surface-mounted, direct metal-to-metal contact between the device yoke and the box is permitted to ground the receptacle to the box. Unless the receptacle is listed as _____, at least one of the insulating retaining washers must be removed from the receptacle to ensure direct metal-to-metal contact between the device yoke and metal outlet box.

(a) self-grounding   (b) weatherproof   (c) metal contact sufficient   (d) isolated grounding

42. Where accessible only to qualified persons, a box or conduit body is not required for conductors in _____ when installed in accordance with applicable *Code* provisions.

(a) manholes   (b) handhole enclosures   (c) a or b   (d) elevator pits

43. Where an equipment grounding conductor consists of a raceway, cable tray, cable armor, cablebus framework, or cable sheath, it must be installed _____.

(a) in accordance with applicable *Code* provisions
(b) using fittings for joints and terminations approved for the use
(c) with all connections, joints, and fittings made tight using suitable tools
(d) all of these

44. Where corrosion protection is necessary and the conduit is threaded in the field, the threads must be coated with a(n) _____, electrically conductive, corrosion-resistance compound.

(a) marked   (b) listed   (c) labeled   (d) approved

45. Where installed in raceways, conductors _____ AWG and larger must be stranded.

(a) 10   (b) 6   (c) 8   (d) 4

46. Where NM cables pass through cut or drilled slots or holes in metal members, the cable needs to be protected by _____ securely covering all metal edges fastened in the opening prior to installation of the cable.

(a) listed bushings   (b) listed grommets   (c) plates   (d) a or b

47. Where portions of a cable raceway or sleeve are subjected to different temperatures and where condensation is known to be a problem, as in cold storage areas of buildings or where passing from the interior to the exterior of a building, the _____ must be filled with an approved material to prevent the circulation of warm air to a colder section of the raceway or sleeve.

(a) raceways   (b) sleeve   (c) a or b   (d) none of these

48. Where required to reduce electric noise for electronic equipment, electrical continuity of the metal raceway is not required and the metal raceway can terminate to a(n) _____ nonmetallic fitting(s) or spacer on the electronic equipment.

(a) listed   (b) labeled   (c) identified   (d) marked

49. Which conductor has an insulation temperature rating of 90°C?

(a) RH   (b) RHW   (c) THHN   (d) TW

50. Which of the following appliances installed in residential occupancies need not be grounded?

(a) Toaster   (b) Aquarium   (c) Dishwasher   (d) Refrigerator

(• Indicates that 75% or fewer of those who took this exam answered the question correctly.)

1. Each dispensing device must be provided with a means to remove all external voltage sources, including feedback, during periods of maintenance and service of the dispensing equipment. The disconnecting means must be either inside or adjacent to the dispensing device.

    (a) True   (b) False

2. Each doorway leading into a transformer vault from the building interior must be provided with a tight-fitting door having a minimum fire rating of _____ hours.

    (a) 2   (b) 4   (c) 5   (d) 3

3. Each length of HDPE must be clearly and durably marked not less than every _____ ft, as required in 110.21.

    (a) 10   (b) 3   (c) 5   (d) 20

4. Each service disconnecting means must be permanently _____ to identify it as a service disconnect.

    (a) identified   (b) positioned   (c) marked   (d) none of these

5. Electrical systems that are grounded, including transformers and generators, must be connected to the _____ for the purpose of limiting the voltage imposed by lightning, line surges, or unintentional contact with higher voltage lines.

    (a) ground   (b) earth   (c) electrical supply source   (d) none of these

6. Electrical wiring and equipment located at or serving motor fuel dispensing equipment in marinas or boatyards must be in accordance with Article 514, in addition to the requirements of Article 555. All electrical wiring for_____ must be installed on the side of the wharf, pier, or dock opposite from the liquid piping system.

    (a) power   (b) lighting   (c) dispensing equipment   (d) all of these

7. Electrical wiring within the cavity of a fire-rated floor-ceiling or roof-ceiling assembly cannot be supported by the ceiling assembly or ceiling support wires. An independent means of support must be provided which _____.

    (a) is permitted to be attached to the ceiling assembly   (b) cannot be attached to the ceiling assembly
    (c) can be nonmetallic material   (d) none of these

8. Electronic organs or other electronic musical instruments are included in the scope of equipment and wiring covered by Article 640.

    (a) True   (b) False

9. Emergency lighting and/or emergency power in a building or group of buildings must be available within the time period required for the application, but not to exceed _____ seconds.

    (a) 5   (b) 10   (c) 30   (d) 60

10. Emergency systems may also provide power for such functions as ventilation where essential to maintain life, fire detection and alarm systems, elevators, fire pumps, public safety communications systems, industrial processes where current interruption would produce serious _____, and similar functions.

    (a) production slowdowns   (b) life, safety, or health hazards
    (c) a and b   (d) a or b

11. EMT must not be used where _____.

(a) subject to severe physical damage
(c) used for the support of luminaires

(b) protected from corrosion only by enamel
(d) any of these

12. Enclosures and fittings installed in areas of agricultural buildings where excessive dust may be present must be designed to minimize the entrance of dust and must have no openings through which dust can enter the enclosure. Only dust-ignitionproof enclosures and fittings can be used for this purpose.

(a) True

(b) False

13. Enclosures for overcurrent protection devices must be mounted in a _____ position unless that is shown to be impracticable.

(a) vertical

(b) horizontal

(c) vertical or horizontal

(d) there are no requirements

14. ENT and fittings can be _____, provided fittings identified for this purpose are used.

(a) encased in poured concrete
(b) embedded in a concrete slab on grade where the tubing is placed on sand or approved screenings
(c) either a or b
(d) none of these

15. ENT must be securely fastened in place every _____.

(a) 12 in.

(b) 18 in.

(c) 24 in.

(d) 36 in.

16. ENT must not be used where exposed to the direct rays of the sun, unless identified as _____.

(a) high-temperature rated

(b) sunlight resistant

(c) schedule 80

(d) never can be

17. Equipment bonding jumpers are not required for receptacles listed as self-grounding that have mounting screws to provide the grounding continuity between the metal yoke and the flush box.

(a) True

(b) False

18. Equipment grounding conductors must be the same size as the circuit conductors for _____ circuits.

(a) 15A

(b) 20A

(c) 30A

(d) all of these

19. Equipment is required to be identified not only for the class of location but also for the explosive, combustible, or ignitible properties of the specific _____ that will be present.

(a) gas or vapor

(b) dust

(c) fiber or flyings

(d) all of these

20. Equipment listed by a qualified electrical testing laboratory is not required to have the factory-installed _____ wiring inspected at the time of installation except to detect alterations or damage.

(a) external

(b) associated

(c) internal

(d) all of these

21. Examples of assembly occupancies include, but are not limited to _____.

(a) restaurants

(b) conference rooms

(c) pool rooms

(d) all of these

22. Exposed CATV cables must be secured by straps, staples, hangers, or similar fittings designed and installed so as not to damage the cable.

(a) True

(b) False

23. Exposed Class 1, 2, and 3 cables must be supported by straps, staples, hangers, or similar fittings designed and installed so as not to damage the cable.

   (a) True   (b) False

24. Exposed communications cables must be secured by straps, staples, hangers, or similar fittings designed and installed so as not to damage the cable.

   (a) True   (b) False

25. Exposed vertical risers of IMC for industrial machinery or fixed equipment can be supported at intervals not exceeding _____ if the conduit is made up with threaded couplings, firmly supported at the top and bottom of the riser, and no other means of support is available.

   (a) 10 ft   (b) 12 ft   (c) 15 ft   (d) 20 ft

26. Exposed vertical risers of RMC for industrial machinery or fixed equipment can be supported at intervals not exceeding _____ if the conduit is made up with threaded couplings, firmly supported at the top and bottom of the riser, and no other means of support is available.

   (a) 6 ft   (b) 10 ft   (c) 20 ft   (d) none of these

27. Feeder and branch-circuit conductors installed for sensitive electronic equipment systems must be identified _____ by color, marking, tagging, or other effective means, and the means of identification must be posted at each branch-circuit panelboard and at the disconnecting means for the building.

   (a) at splices   (b) at terminations   (c) only on the blueprints   (d) a and b

28. Feeder conductors to the mobile home must consist of _____.

   (a) a listed cord   (b) a permanently installed feeder consisting of 4 color-coded, insulated conductors
   (c) either a or b   (d) none of these

29. Feeders for temporary installations may be within cable assemblies or within multiconductor cords or cables identified for hard usage or extra-hard usage. Type NM and Type NMC cables are permitted to be used in any dwelling, building, or structure not more than 3 floors high for temporary feeders.

   (a) True   (b) False

30. Field-installed skeleton tubing and outline lighting consisting of listed luminaires are not required to be listed when installed in conformance with the *Code*.

   (a) True   (b) False

31. Flexible cords and cables must be connected to devices and to fittings so that tension will not be transmitted to joints or terminal screws. This must be accomplished by _____.

   (a) knotting the cord   (b) winding the cord with tape
   (c) fittings designed for the purpose (d) any of these

32. Flexible cords and flexible cables used for temporary wiring must _____.

   (a) be protected from accidental damage   (b) be protected where passing through doorways
   (c) avoid sharp corners and projections   (d) all of these

33. Flexible cords immersed in or exposed to water in a fountain must be _____.

(a) of the hard-service type   (b) marked water resistant   (c) encased in at least 2 in. of concrete   (d) a and b

34. Flexible cords must not be used as a substitute for _____ wiring unless specifically permitted in 400.7.

(a) temporary   (b) fixed   (c) overhead   (d) none of these

35. Flexible metal conduit can be used as the equipment grounding conductor if the length in any ground return path does not exceed 6 ft and the circuit conductors contained in the conduit are protected by overcurrent devices rated at _____ or less.

(a) 15A   (b) 20A   (c) 30A   (d) 60A

36. FMC must be supported and secured _____.

(a) at intervals not exceeding 4 1/2 ft   (b) within 8 in. on each side of a box where fished
(c) where fished   (d) at intervals not exceeding 6 ft at motor terminals

37. For a cabinet or cutout box constructed of sheet steel, the metal must not be thinner than _____ uncoated.

(a) 0.53 in.   (b) 0.035 in.   (c) 0.053 in.   (d) 1.35 in.

38. For a cover mounted receptacle, direct metal-to-metal contact of the receptacle yoke and the metal cover is always considered to be sufficiently bonded and no equipment bonding jumper is required.

(a) True   (b) False

39. For a grounded system, an unspliced _____ must be used to connect the equipment grounding conductor(s) and the service disconnect enclosure to the grounded conductor of the system within the enclosure for each service disconnect.

(a) grounding electrode   (b) main bonding jumper
(c) bus bar only   (d) insulated copper conductor only

40. For a single separately derived system, the grounding electrode conductor connects the grounding electrode to the grounded conductor of the derived system at the same point on the separately derived system where the _____ is installed.

(a) metering equipment   (b) transfer switch   (c) bonding jumper   (d) largest circuit breaker

41. For a transformer rated 600V, nominal, or less, if the primary overcurrent protection device is sized at 250 percent of the primary current, what size secondary overcurrent protection device is required if the secondary current is 42A?

(a) 40A   (b) 70A   (c) 60A   (d) 90A

42. For electrical equipment supplementary electrodes:

(a) A bond to the grounding electrode system is not required.
(b) The bonding jumper to the supplementary electrode can be any size.
(c) The 25 ohm resistance requirement of 250.56 does not apply.
(d) All of the above are true

43. For grounded systems, noncurrent-carrying conductive materials enclosing electrical conductors or equipment, or forming part of such equipment, must be connected together and to the _____ in a manner that establishes an effective ground-fault current path.

(a) ground   (b) earth   (c) electrical supply source   (d) none of these

44. For pendants used in an aircraft hangar, not installed in a Class I location, cords are not required to include a separate equipment grounding conductor.

    (a) True   (b) False

45. For permanently connected appliances rated over _____ or 1/8 hp, the branch-circuit switch or circuit breaker is permitted to serve as the disconnecting means where the switch or circuit breaker is within sight from the appliance or is capable of being locked in the open position with a permanently installed locking provision.

    (a) 200 VA   (b) 300 VA   (c) 400 VA   (d) 500 VA

46. For ungrounded systems, noncurrent-carrying conductive materials enclosing electrical conductors or equipment, or forming part of such equipment, must be connected to earth in a manner that will limit the voltage imposed by lightning or unintentional contact with higher-voltage lines.

    (a) True   (b) False

47. Fuses are required to be marked with _____.

    (a) ampere and voltage rating   (b) interrupting rating where other than 10,000A
    (c) the name or trademark of the manufacturer   (d) all of these

48. General-purpose optical fiber cables listed as suitable for general-purpose use, with the exception of risers and plenums are Types _____.

    (a) OFNP and OFCP   (b) OFNR and OFCR   (c) OFNG and OFCG   (d) OFN and OFC

49. GFCI protection for personnel must be provided for electrically heated floors in _____ locations.

    (a) bathroom   (b) hydromassage bathtub   (c) kitchen   (d) a and b

50. GFCI protection is required for all 15 and 20A, 125V single-phase receptacles located within an arc measurement of 6 ft from the dwelling unit _____.

    (a) laundry sink   (b) utility sink   (c) wet bar sink   (d) all of these

UNIT 5

Raceway and Box Calculations

Introduction

Anyone who has ever pulled wire into a conduit understands the reason for maximum limits on the wire fill for raceways. Trying to pull too many conductors into a raceway can result in damage to the conductor insulation due to the friction and mechanical abuse that can occur due to exceeding physical size limits. We have all heard a joke about tying a wire-pulling rope onto the hitch of the service truck and "locking in the hubs." At least, we hope this is a joke, not an accurate recounting of an installation.

Chapter 9, Table 1 provides the maximum limits the *Code* recognizes for wire fill in terms of percentage of the raceway's interior cross-sectional area. This unit explains those limits and provides instruction regarding the use of the associated tables in Chapter 9 to figure conductor fill. How to use the tables in Annex C when all of the conductors in the raceway are the same size (total cross-sectional area including insulation) is also covered.

The *Code* provides a limit to the number of conductors allowed in outlet boxes, based on Table 314.16(A). This limit is often joked about as being the "maximum number of conductors that can be installed in the outlet box while using the persuasion of your hammer handle." This method does not follow the *NEC's* guidance set forth in 314.16(B). In this unit, you will learn how to properly calculate the maximum number of conductors and "conductor equivalents" to be installed in an outlet box. Be sure to read this material carefully so you'll understand what the *Code* means by "conductor equivalents."

An explanation of the sizing requirements of 314.28(A)(1) and (2) for larger pull boxes and junction boxes, enclosing conductors 4 AWG and larger rounds out the information provided here in Unit 5.

PART A—RACEWAY FILL

5.1 Understanding the *NEC*, Chapter 9 Tables

Table 1—Conductor Percent Fill

The maximum percentage of allowable conductor fill is listed in Chapter 9, Table 1. It is based on common conditions where the length of the conductor and number of raceway bends are within reasonable limits [Chapter 9, Table 1, Fine Print Note 1]. Figure 5–1

Table 1, Note 1—Conductors all the Same Size and Insulation

When all conductors are the same size and insulation, the number of conductors permitted in a raceway can be determined by simply looking at the tables located in Annex C—Conduit and Tubing Fill Tables for Conductors and Fixture Wires of the Same Size.

Raceway Fill Limitation
Chapter 9, Table 1

53% — Cable is treated as 1 conductor 53% fill, Note 9

40% — Three or more conductors 40% fill

53% — One conductor 53% fill

60% — Nipple: (24 in. or less) 60% fill Note 4

31% — Two conductors 31% fill

COPYRIGHT 2005 Mike Holt Enterprises, Inc.

When different size conductors are installed in a raceway, conductor fill is limited to the above percentages

Figure 5–1

Tables C.1 through C.12(A) are based on maximum percent fill as listed in Chapter 9, Table 1.

- Table C.1—Conductors and fixture wires in electrical metallic tubing (EMT)
- Table C.1(A)—Compact conductors in electrical metallic tubing (EMT)
- Table C.2—Conductors and fixture wires in electrical non-metallic tubing (ENT)
- Table C.2(A)—Compact conductors in electrical non-metallic tubing (ENT)
- Table C.3—Conductors and fixture wires in flexible metal conduit (FMC)
- Table C.3(A)—Compact conductors in flexible metal conduit (FMC)
- Table C.4—Conductors and fixture wires in intermediate metal conduit (IMC)
- Table C.4(A)—Compact conductors in intermediate metal conduit (IMC)
- Table C.5—Conductors and fixture wires in liquidtight flexible nonmetallic conduit (gray type) (LFNC-B)
- Table C.5(A)—Compact conductors in liquidtight flexible nonmetallic conduit (gray type) (LFNC-B)
- Table C.6—Conductors and fixture wires in liquidtight flexible nonmetallic conduit (orange type) (LFNC-A)
- Table C.6(A)—Compact conductors in liquidtight flexible nonmetallic conduit (orange type) (LFNC-A)
  Note: The annex does not have a table for LFNC of the black type.
- Table C.7—Conductors and fixture wires in liquidtight flexible metallic conduit (LFMC)
- Table C.7(A)—Compact conductors in liquidtight flexible metal conduit (LFMC)
- Table C.8—Conductors and fixture wires in rigid metal conduit (RMC)
- Table C.8(A)—Compact conductors in rigid metal conduit (RMC)
- Table C.9—Conductors and fixture wires in rigid nonmetallic conduit (RNC) Schedule 80
- Table C.9(A)—Compact conductors in rigid nonmetallic conduit (RNC) Schedule 80
- Table C.10—Conductors and fixture wires in rigid nonmetallic conduit (RNC) Schedule 40
- Table C.10(A)—Compact conductors in rigid nonmetallic conduit (RNC) Schedule 40
- Table C.11—Conductors and fixture wires in Type A, rigid PVC conduit
- Table C.11(A)—Compact conductors in Type A, rigid PVC conduit
- Table C.12—Conductors and fixture wires in Type EB, PVC conduit
- Table C.12(A)—Compact conductors in Type EB, PVC conduit

Table 1 of Chapter 9, Maximum Percent Conductor Fill	
Number of Conductors	Percent Fill Permitted
1 conductor	53% fill
2 conductors	31% fill
3 or more conductors	40% fill
Raceway 24 inches or less	60% fill Note 4

▶ **Annex C—Table C.1 — EMT**

How many 14 RHH conductors (without cover) can be installed in trade size 1 EMT? Figure 5–2

(a) 25 conductors
(b) 16 conductors
(c) 13 conductors
(d) 19 conductors

- Answer: (b) 16 conductors
  Annex C, Table C.1

AUTHOR'S COMMENT: Note 2 at the end of Annex C, Table C.1 indicates that an asterisk (*) with conductor insulation types RHH*, RHW*, and RHW-2* do not have an outer covering. Insulation types RHH, RHW, and RHW-2 (without the asterisk) do have an outer cover.

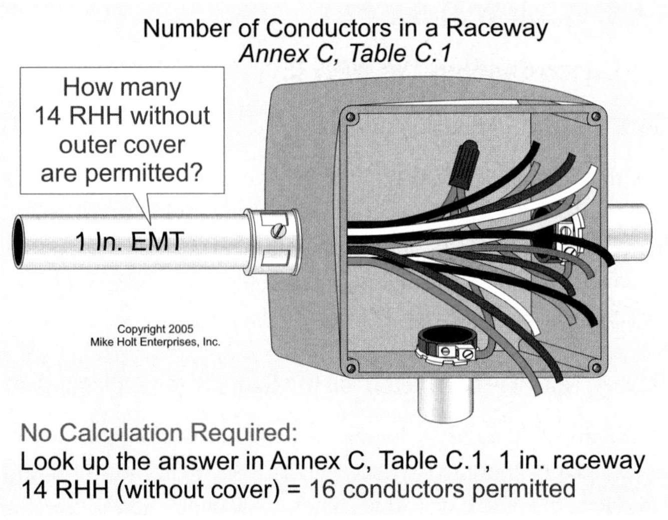

Number of Conductors in a Raceway
Annex C, Table C.1

How many 14 RHH without outer cover are permitted?

1 In. EMT

Copyright 2005
Mike Holt Enterprises, Inc.

No Calculation Required:
Look up the answer in Annex C, Table C.1, 1 in. raceway 14 RHH (without cover) = 16 conductors permitted

Figure 5–2

▶ **Annex C—Table C.2A — Compact Conductors in ENT**

How many 6 XHHW compact conductors can be installed in trade size 1 1/4 ENT?

(a) 10 conductors   (b) 6 conductors
(c) 16 conductors   (d) 13 conductors

• Answer: (a) 10 conductors
  Annex C, Table C.2A

AUTHOR'S COMMENT: Unless the question specifically states compact conductors, assume that the conductors are not the compact type.

▶ **Annex C—Table C.3 — FMC**

If trade size 1 1/4 FMC has three THHN conductors (not compact), what is the largest conductor permitted to be installed? Figure 5–3

(a) 1 THHN   (b) 1/0 THHN
(c) 2/0 THHN   (d) 3/0 THHN

• Answer: (a) 1 THHN
  Annex C, Table C.3

▶ **Annex C—Table C.4 — IMC**

How many 4/0 RHH conductors can be installed in trade size 2 IMC?

Note: Since there is no asterisk (*) with 4/0 RHH, assume RHH insulation with outer cover.

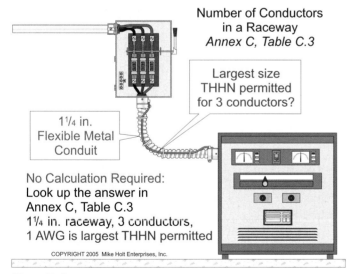

Number of Conductors in a Raceway
Annex C, Table C.3

Largest size THHN permitted for 3 conductors?

1¹/4 in. Flexible Metal Conduit

No Calculation Required:
Look up the answer in Annex C, Table C.3
1¹/4 in. raceway, 3 conductors, 1 AWG is largest THHN permitted

COPYRIGHT 2005 Mike Holt Enterprises, Inc.

Figure 5–3

Determining the Number of Fixture Wires in a Raceway
Annex C, Table C.7

3/4 Inch Liquidtight

How many 18 TFFN permitted?

18 AWG TFFN

COPYRIGHT 2005 Mike Holt Enterprises, Inc.

No calculation required:
Look up answer in Annex C, Table C.7

18 TFFN, 3/4 in. liquidtight = 39 conductors

Figure 5–4

(a) 2 conductors   (b) 1 conductor
(c) 3 conductors   (d) 4 conductors

• Answer: (c) 3 conductors
  Annex C, Table C.4

▶ **Annex C—Table C.7 — Fixture Wire in LFMC**

How many 18 TFFN conductors can be installed in trade size 3/4 LFMC? Figure 5–4

(a) 40 conductors   (b) 26 conductors
(c) 30 conductors   (d) 39 conductors

• Answer: (d) 39 conductors
  Annex C, Table C.7

Table 1, Note 3—Equipment Grounding (Bonding) Conductors

When equipment grounding (bonding) conductors are installed in a raceway, the actual area of the conductor must be used to calculate raceway fill, Figure 5–5. Chapter 9, Table 5 can be used to determine the cross-sectional area of insulated conductors and Chapter 9, Table 8 can be used to determine the cross-sectional area of bare conductors [Chapter 9, Table 1, Note 8].

Table 1, Note 4—Nipples, Raceways not Exceeding 24 Inches

The cross-sectional areas of conduit and tubing are found in Chapter 9, Table 4. When a conduit or tubing raceway does not exceed 24 in. in length, it is called a nipple. Nipples are permitted to be filled to 60% of their total cross-sectional area. Figure 5–6

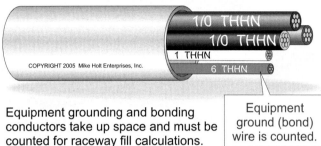

Equipment Grounding and Bonding Conductors
Chapter 9, Table 1, Note 3

Equipment grounding and bonding conductors take up space and must be counted for raceway fill calculations.

Equipment ground (bond) wire is counted.

Figure 5–5

Table 1, Note 7

When the calculated number of conductors (all of the same size and insulation) results in a decimal of 0.80 or larger, the next higher whole number can be used. But, be careful—this only applies when the conductors are all the same size (cross-sectional area including insulation) and for raceways over 24 in. in length.

Table 1, Note 8

The dimensions for bare conductors are listed in Chapter 9, Table 8.

Table 4—Conduit and Tubing Cross-Sectional Area

The sixth column of this table (Total Area 100%) gives the total cross-sectional area in square inches of the raceway. There are also 31% (2 wires), 40% (3 or more wires), 53% (1 wire), and 60% (nipple) cross-sectional area columns based on the number of conductors in accordance with Chapter 9, Table 1.

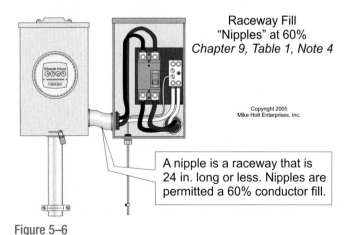

Raceway Fill
"Nipples" at 60%
Chapter 9, Table 1, Note 4

A nipple is a raceway that is 24 in. long or less. Nipples are permitted a 60% conductor fill.

Figure 5–6

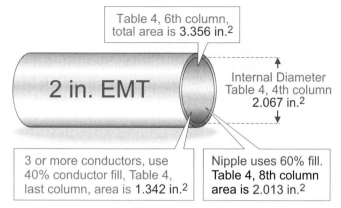

Measurements of Raceway Cross-Section
Chapter 9 - Table 4

Table 4, 6th column, total area is 3.356 in.²

Internal Diameter
Table 4, 4th column
2.067 in.²

3 or more conductors, use 40% conductor fill, Table 4, last column, area is 1.342 in.²

Nipple uses 60% fill.
Table 4, 8th column
area is 2.013 in.²

Figure 5–7

▶ **Conduit Cross-Sectional Area**

What is the cross-sectional area of permitted conductor fill for a trade size 2 EMT raceway having a length of only 20 inches?
Figure 5–7

(a) 2.067 sq in.   (b) 3.356 sq in.
(c) 2.013 sq in.   (d) 1.342 sq in.

• Answer: (c) 2.013 sq in.
  Chapter 9, Table 1, Note 4 and Table 4, 60% column

What is the cross-sectional area of permitted conductor fill for a trade size 2 EMT raceway having a length of only 30 in. and containing four conductors?

(a) 2.067 sq in.   (b) 3.356 sq in.
(c) 2.013 sq in.   (d) 1.342 sq in.

• Answer: (d) 1.342 sq in.
  Chapter 9, Table 1 and Table 4, 40% column

Table 5—Dimensions of Insulated Conductors and Fixture Wires

Chapter 9, Table 5 lists the cross-sectional area of insulated conductors and fixture wires. See Table 5–1.

▶ **Table 5—THHN**

What is the cross-sectional area for one 14 THHN conductor?
Figure 5–8

(a) 0.0206 sq in.   (b) 0.0172 sq in.
(c) 0.0097 sq in.   (d) 0.0278 sq in.

• Answer: (c) 0.0097 sq in.

Table 5–1: Commonly Used Conductor Cross-Sectional Area

	RHH/RHW With Cover	RHH/RHW Without Cover	TW or THW	THHN THWN	XHHW	BARE Stranded Conductors
			Chapter 9, Table 5			Chapter 9, Table 8
Column 1	Column 2	Column 3	Column 4	Column 5	Column 6	
Size AWG/kcmil			Approximate Cross-Sectional Area – Square Inches			
14	0.0293	0.0209	0.0139	0.0097	0.0139	**0.004**
12	0.0353	0.0260	0.0181	0.0133	0.0181	**0.006**
10	0.0437	0.0333	0.0243	0.0211	0.0243	**0.011**
8	0.0835	0.0556	0.0437	0.0366	0.0437	**0.017**
6	0.1041	0.0726	0.0726	0.0507	0.0590	**0.027**
4	0.1333	0.0973	0.0973	0.0824	0.0814	**0.042**
3	0.1521	0.1134	0.1134	0.0973	0.0962	**0.053**
2	0.1750	0.1333	0.1333	0.1158	0.1146	**0.067**
1	0.2660	0.1901	0.1901	0.1562	0.1534	**0.087**
0	0.3039	0.2223	0.2223	0.1855	0.1825	**0.109**
00	0.3505	0.2624	0.2624	0.2233	0.2190	**0.137**
000	0.4072	0.3117	0.3117	0.2679	0.2642	**0.173**
0000	0.4754	0.3718	0.3718	0.3237	0.3197	**0.219**

Cross-Sectional Area of a Conductor
Chapter 9 - Table 5
Cross-section of a conductor
Area in sq in.?
14 THHN 600V
The area of one 14 THHN is 0.0097 sq in.
Copyright 2005 Mike Holt Enterprises, Inc.

Figure 5–8

► Table 5—RHW With an Outer Cover

What is the cross-sectional area for one 12 RHW conductor with an outer cover?

(a) 0.0206 sq in. (b) 0.0172 sq in.
(c) 0.0353 sq in. (d) 0.0278 sq in.

• Answer: (c) 0.0353 sq in.

► Table 5—RHH Without an Outer Cover

What is the cross-sectional area for one 10 RHH without an outer cover?

(a) 0.0117 sq in. (b) 0.0333 sq in.
(c) 0.0252 sq in. (d) 0.0278 sq in.

• Answer: (b) 0.0333 sq in.

AUTHOR'S COMMENT: The note at the end of Table 5 states that conductor Types RHH, RHW, and RHW-2 without outer covering are identified with an asterisk (*).

Table 5A—Compact Aluminum Building Wire Nominal Dimensions and Areas

Chapter 9, Table 5A, lists the cross-sectional areas for compact aluminum building wires. We will not use this table for this unit.

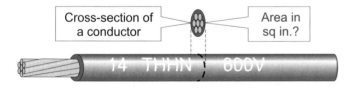

Table 8—Conductor Properties

Chapter 9, Table 8 contains conductor properties such as cross-sectional area in circular mils, number of strands per conductor, cross-sectional area in sq in. for bare conductors, and dc resistance at 75°C for both copper and aluminum conductors.

▶ **Bare Conductor—Cross-Sectional Area**

What is the cross-sectional area for one 10 AWG bare conductor with seven strands? **Figure 5–9**

(a) 0.008 sq in.   (b) 0.011 sq in.
(c) 0.038 sq in.   (d) a or b

• Answer: (b) 0.011 sq in.

Table 9—AC Impedance for Conductors in Conduit or Tubing

Chapter 9, Table 9, contains the ac impedance for copper and aluminum conductors when there are three single conductors in a conduit.

5.2 Raceway and Nipple Calculations

Annex C—Tables 1 through 12 cannot be used to determine raceway sizing when conductors of different sizes are installed in the same raceway. When this situation is encountered, the following steps can be used to determine the raceway size and nipple size:

Step 1: Determine the cross-sectional area (in square inches) for each conductor from Chapter 9, Table 5 for insulated conductors and from Chapter 9, Table 8 for bare conductors.

Step 2: Determine the total cross-sectional area for all conductors.

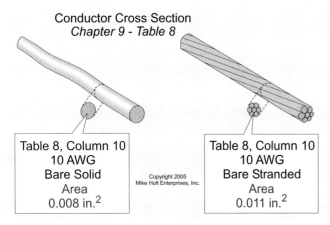

Conductor Cross Section
Chapter 9 - Table 8

Table 8, Column 10
10 AWG
Bare Solid
Area
0.008 in.²

Copyright 2005
Mike Holt Enterprises, Inc.

Table 8, Column 10
10 AWG
Bare Stranded
Area
0.011 in.²

Figure 5–9

Step 3: Size the raceway according to the percent fill as listed in Chapter 9, Table 1. Table 4 of Chapter 9 includes the various types of raceways with columns representing the allowable percentage fills; such as 40% for three or more conductors, and 60% for raceways 24 in. or less in length (nipples).

▶ **Raceway Size**

A 400A feeder is installed in Schedule 40 RNC. This raceway contains three 500 kcmil THHN conductors, one 250 kcmil THHN conductor, and one 3 THHN conductor. What size raceway is required for these conductors? **Figure 5–10**

(a) Trade size 2   (b) Trade size 2 1/2
(c) Trade size 3   (d) Trade size 3 1/2

• Answer: (c) Trade size 3

Step 1: Determine the cross-sectional area of the conductors, Chapter 9, Table 5.

500 THHN 0.7073 sq in. x 3 wires = 2.1219 sq in.
250 THHN 0.3970 sq in. x 1 wire = 0.3970 sq in.
3 THHN 0.0973 sq in. x 1 wire = 0.0973 sq in.

Step 2: Total cross-sectional area of all conductors = 2.6162 sq in.

Step 3: Size the conduit at 40% fill [Chapter 9, Table 1] using Table 4.

Trade size 3 Schedule 40 RNC has an allowable cross-sectional area of 2.907 sq in. for over 2 conductors in the 40% column.

Determining Raceway Size
Chapter 9, Tables 4 and 5

Schedule 40 RNC

500,000 THHN
500,000 THHN
500,000 THHN
250 THHN
3 THHN

Determine the raceway size for these conductors.

Determine the area in sq in. of the conductors; Chapter 9, Table 5.

1- 500 kcmil THHN = 0.7073 in² x 3 conductors = 2.1219 in²
1- 250 kcmil THHN = 0.3970 in² x 1 conductor = 0.3970 in²
1- 3 THHN = 0.0973 in² x 1 conductor = 0.0973 in²
Total area of the conductors = 2.6162 in²
Chapter 9, Table 4, assume 40% fill [Chapter 9, Table 1].

3 in. raceway required at 2.907 sq in.

COPYRIGHT 2005 Mike Holt Enterprises, Inc.

Figure 5–10

▶ Nipple Size

What size RMC nipple is required for three 3/0 THHN conductors, one 1 THHN conductor, and one 6 THHN conductor? Figure 5–11

(a) Trade size 1/2   (b) Trade size 1

(c) Trade size 1 1/2   (d) Trade size 2

• Answer: (c) Trade size 1 1/2

Step 1:   Determine the cross-sectional area of the conductors, Chapter 9, Table 5.

3/0 THHN 0.2679 sq in. x 3 wires = 0.8037 sq in.
1 THHN 0.1562 sq in. x 1 wire = 0.1562 sq in.
6 THHN 0.0507 sq in. x 1 wire = 0.0507 sq in.

Step 2:   Total cross-sectional area of the conductors = 1.0106 sq in.

Step 3:   Size the conduit at 60% fill [Chapter 9, Table 1, Note 4] using Table 4.

Trade size 1 1/4 nipple = 0.0916 sq in., too small
Trade size 1 1/2 nipple = 1.243 sq in., just right
Trade size 2 nipple = 2.045 sq in., larger than required

5.3 Existing Raceway Calculations

There are times when we need to add conductors to an existing raceway. This can be accomplished by using the following steps when all conductors to be added are the same size:

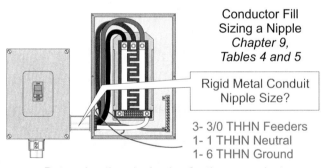

Conductor Fill
Sizing a Nipple
*Chapter 9,
Tables 4 and 5*

Rigid Metal Conduit
Nipple Size?

3- 3/0 THHN Feeders
1- 1 THHN Neutral
1- 6 THHN Ground

Determine the nipple size for these conductors.

Area in sq in. of conductors, Chapter 9, Table 5:

1- 3/0 THHN = 0.2679 in² x 3 conductors = 0.8037 in²
1- 1 THHN = 0.1562 in² x 1 conductor = 0.1562 in²
1- 6 THHN = 0.0507 in² x 1 conductor = 0.0507 in²
Total area of the conductors = 1.0106 in²

Chapter 9, Table 1, Note 4, nipple is 60% fill
Chapter 9, Table 4 RMC, 60% fill (last column):

Use a 1½ in. nipple

Copyright 2005 Mike Holt Enterprises, Inc.

Figure 5–11

Part 1—Determine the raceway cross-sectional available spare space area.

Step 1:   Determine the raceway's cross-sectional area for conductor fill [Chapter 9, Tables 1 and 4].

Step 2:   Determine the area of the existing conductors [Chapter 9, Table 5].

Step 3:   Subtract the cross-sectional area of the existing conductors (Step 2) from the area of permitted conductor fill (Step 1).

Part 2—Determine the number of conductors permitted in the spare space area.

Step 1:   Determine the cross-sectional area of each of the conductors to be added [Chapter 9, Table 5 for insulated conductors, and Chapter 9, Table 8 for bare conductors].

Step 2:   Divide the spare space area by the conductor's individual cross-sectional area.

▶ Spare Space Area

An existing trade size 1 LFMC contains two 12 THW conductors, two 10 THW conductors, and one 12 AWG bare conductor with seven strands. What is the area remaining for additional conductors? Figure 5–12

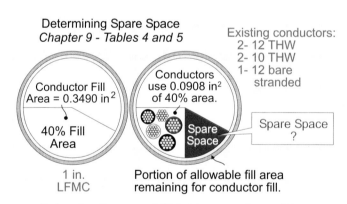

Determining Spare Space
Chapter 9 - Tables 4 and 5

Existing conductors:
2- 12 THW
2- 10 THW
1- 12 bare
stranded

Conductor Fill
Area = 0.3490 in²

40% Fill
Area

Conductors
use 0.0908 in²
of 40% area.

Spare
Space

Spare Space
?

1 in.
LFMC

Portion of allowable fill area
remaining for conductor fill.

Determine the area of fill (spare space) remaining.

Spare Space = Allowable fill area - Existing conductor space used

Allowable Fill Area: Chapter 9, Table 4
1 in. LFMC, 3 or more conductors = 40% = 0.3490 sq in.

Space Used: Chapter 9, Table 5
One 12 THW = 0.0181 in.² x 2 conductors = 0.0362 sq in.
One 10 THW = 0.0243 in.² x 2 conductors = 0.0486 sq in.
One 12 bare stranded, Chapter 9, Tbl 8 = 0.0060 sq in.
Allowable fill area used = 0.0908 sq in.

Spare Space = 0.3490 in.² - 0.0908 in.² = 0.2582 sq in.
Remaining fill area

Copyright 2005 Mike Holt Enterprises, Inc.

Figure 5–12

(a) Raceway 0.2582 sq in.

(b) Nipple 0.4332 sq in.

(c) there is no spare space

(d) a and b

• Answer: (d) a and b

Step 1: Raceway cross-sectional area, LFMC [Chapter 9, Table 1, Note 4 and Chapter 9, Table 4].

Raceway: 40 percent column = 0.349 sq in.
Nipple: 60 percent column = 0.524 sq in.

Step 2: Cross-sectional area of existing conductors [Chapter 9, Tables 5 and 8].

12 THW 0.0181 sq in. x 2 wires	0.0362 sq in.
10 THW 0.0243 sq in. x 2 wires	0.0486 sq in.
12 bare 0.006 sq in. x 1 wire	0.0060 sq in.
Total cross-sectional area	0.0908 sq in.

Note: Ground wires must be counted for raceway fill—Chapter 9, Table 1, Note 3.

Step 3: Subtract the area of the existing conductors from the permitted area of conductor fill.

Raceway: 0.349 sq in. – 0.0908 sq in. = 0.2582 sq in.
Nipple: 0.524 sq in. – 0.0908 sq in. = 0.4332 sq in.

▶ **Conductors in Spare Space Area**

An existing trade size 1 EMT conduit contains two 12 THHN conductors, two 10 THHN conductors, and one 12 AWG bare, 7-stranded conductor. How many additional 8 THHN conductors can be added to this raceway? **Figure 5–13**

(a) 7 conductors if raceway

(b) 12 conductors if nipple

(c) 15 conductors regardless of raceway length

(d) a and b

• Answer: (d) a and b

Step 1: Cross-sectional area of trade size 1 EMT permitted for conductor fill [Chapter 9, Table 1, Note 4 and Chapter 9, Table 4].

Raceway: 0.3460 sq in.
Nipple: 0.5190 sq in.

Step 2: Cross-sectional area of existing conductors. [Chapter 9, Table 5 for insulated conductors, or Chapter 9, Table 8 for bare conductors]

10 THHN 0.0211 sq in. x 2	0.0422 sq in.
12 THHN 0.0133 sq in. x 2	0.0266 sq in.
12 bare 0.0060 sq in. x 1	+ 0.0060 sq in.
Total cross-sectional area	0.0748 sq in.

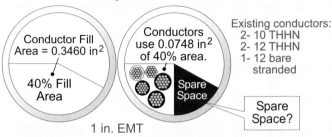

Adding Conductors to Spare Space
Chapter 9 - Tables 4 and 5

Conductor Fill Area = 0.3460 in^2

40% Fill Area

Conductors use 0.0748 in^2 of 40% area.

Spare Space

Existing conductors:
2- 10 THHN
2- 12 THHN
1- 12 bare stranded

Spare Space?

1 in. EMT
How many 8 THHN are permitted in spare space?

Spare Space = Allowable fill area - Existing conductor space used

Allowable Fill Area: Chapter 9, Table 4
1 in. EMT, 3 or more conductors = 40% = 0.3460 sq in.

Space Used: Chapter 9, Table 5
One 10 THHN = 0.0211 in.^{2} x 2 conductors = 0.0422 sq in.
One 12 THHN = 0.0133 in.^{2} x 2 conductors = 0.0266 sq in.
One 12 bare stranded, Chapter 9, Tbl 8 = 0.0060 sq in.
Conductor fill used = 0.0748 sq in.

Spare Space = 0.3460 in.^{2} - 0.0748 in.^{2} = 0.2712 sq in.
Chapter 9, Table 5: 8 THHN = 0.0366 sq in.
0.2712 in^2/0.0366 in.^{2} = 7.4 = 7- 8 THHN can be added

Copyright 2005 Mike Holt Enterprises, Inc.

Figure 5–13

Note: Equipment grounding (bonding) conductors must be counted for raceway fill. See Chapter 9, Table 1, Note 3.

Step 3: Subtract the area of the existing conductors from the permitted area of conductor fill.

Raceway: 0.346 sq in. – 0.0748 sq in. = 0.2712 sq in.
Nipple: 0.519 sq in. – 0.0748 sq in. = 0.4442 sq in.

Step 4: Cross-sectional area of the conductor to be installed [Chapter 9, Table 5].

8 THHN = 0.0366 sq in.

Step 5: Divide the spare space area (Step 3) by the conductor area.

Raceway: 0.2712 sq in./0.0366 sq in. =
7.4 or 7 conductors
Nipple: 0.4442 sq in./0.0366 sq in. =
12.1 or 12 conductors

Note: We must round down to 7 conductors for the raceway (12 conductors for the nipple) because Note 7 of Table 1 only applies if all of the conductors are the same size and have the same insulation.

5.4 Tips for Raceway Calculations

Tip 1: Take your time.

Tip 2: Use a ruler or a straightedge when using tables, and highlight key words and important sections.

Tip 3: Watch out for different types of raceways and conductor insulation, particularly RHH/RHW with or without an outer cover.

PART B—OUTLET BOX FILL CALCULATIONS [314.16]

Boxes must be of sufficient size to provide free space for all conductors. An outlet box is generally used for the attachment of devices and luminaires and has a specific amount of space (volume) for conductors, devices, and fittings. The volume taken up by conductors, devices, and fittings in a box must not exceed the box fill capacity. The volume of a box is the total volume of its assembled parts, including plaster rings, industrial raised covers, and extension rings. The total volume includes only those parts that are marked with their volumes in cubic inches [314.16(A)] or included in Table 314.16(A). Figure 5–14

5.5 Sizing Box—Conductors All the Same Size [Table 314.16(A)]

When all of the conductors in an outlet box are the same size (insulation doesn't matter), Table 314.16(A) of the *NEC* can be used to:

(1) Determine the number of conductors permitted in the outlet box, or

(2) Determine the size outlet box required for the given number of conductors.

> **AUTHOR'S COMMENT:** Table 314.16(A) only applies if the outlet box contains no switches, receptacles, luminaire studs, luminaire hickeys, manufactured cable clamps, or grounding conductors (not likely).

▶ **Outlet Box Size**

What size outlet box is required for six 12 THHN conductors and three 12 THW conductors? Figure 5–15

(a) 4 x 1 1/4 in. square   (b) 4 x 1 1/2 in. square
(c) 4 x 1 1/4 in. round   (d) 4 x 1 1/2 in. round

- Answer: (b) 4 x 1 1/2 in. square
  Table 314.16(A) permits nine 12 AWG conductors; insulation is not a factor.

▶ **Number of Conductors in an Outlet Box**

Using Table 314.16(A), how many 14 THHN conductors are permitted in a 4 x 1 1/2 in. round box?

(a) 7 conductors   (b) 9 conductors
(c) 10 conductors   (d) 11 conductors

- Answer: (a) 7 conductors

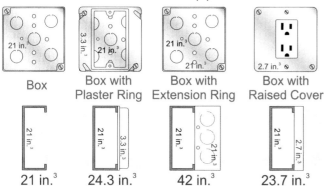

Box Volume Calculations
Section 314.16(A)

Box — 21 in.³
Box with Plaster Ring — 24.3 in.³
Box with Extension Ring — 42 in.³
Box with Raised Cover — 23.7 in.³

The volume of a box includes the volume of its assembled parts that are marked with their cu in. or are made from boxes listed in Table 314.16(A).

COPYRIGHT 2005 Mike Holt Enterprises, Inc.

Figure 5–14

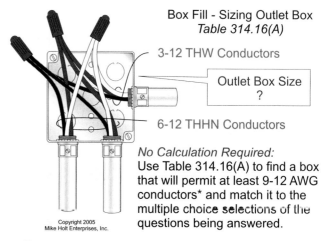

Box Fill - Sizing Outlet Box
Table 314.16(A)

3-12 THW Conductors

Outlet Box Size ?

6-12 THHN Conductors

Copyright 2005
Mike Holt Enterprises, Inc.

No Calculation Required:
Use Table 314.16(A) to find a box that will permit at least 9-12 AWG conductors* and match it to the multiple choice selections of the questions being answered.

*Note: Insulation is not a factor for box fill calculations.

Figure 5–15

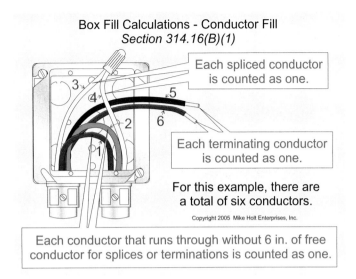

Box Fill Calculations - Conductor Fill
Section 314.16(B)(1)

Each spliced conductor is counted as one.

Each terminating conductor is counted as one.

For this example, there are a total of six conductors.

Copyright 2005 Mike Holt Enterprises, Inc.

Each conductor that runs through without 6 in. of free conductor for splices or terminations is counted as one.

Figure 5–16

5.6 Conductor Equivalents [314.16(B)]

Table 314.16(A) does not take into consideration the fill requirements of clamps, support fittings, devices, or equipment grounding (bonding) conductors within the outlet box. In no case can the volume of the box and its assembled sections be less than the fill calculation as listed below:

Conductor Fill. *Conductors Terminating in the Box.* Each conductor that originates outside the box and terminates or is spliced within the box is counted as one conductor [314.16(B)(1)]. Figure 5–16

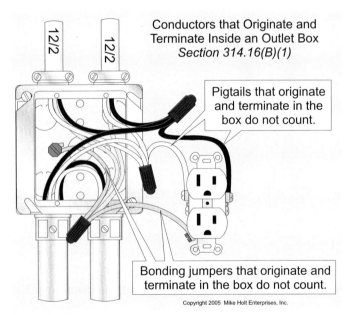

Conductors that Originate and Terminate Inside an Outlet Box
Section 314.16(B)(1)

Pigtails that originate and terminate in the box do not count.

Bonding jumpers that originate and terminate in the box do not count.

Copyright 2005 Mike Holt Enterprises, Inc.

Figure 5–17

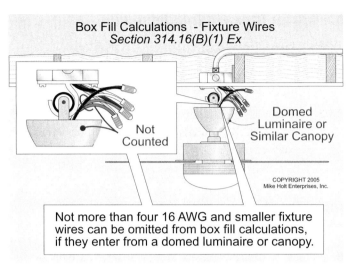

Box Fill Calculations - Fixture Wires
Section 314.16(B)(1) Ex

Not Counted

Domed Luminaire or Similar Canopy

COPYRIGHT 2005 Mike Holt Enterprises, Inc.

Not more than four 16 AWG and smaller fixture wires can be omitted from box fill calculations, if they enter from a domed luminaire or canopy.

Figure 5–18

Conductor Running Through the Box. Each conductor that runs through the box without a splice or termination is counted as one conductor as long as it does not make a loop in the box exceeding 12 in. If it is long enough to make a 12 in. loop, it is counted as 2 conductors. See Figure 5–16. Conductors that are completely contained within the box are not counted. This includes equipment bonding jumpers and pigtails [314.16(B)(1)]. Figure 5–17

An exception allows for four or fewer fixture wires smaller than 14 AWG from a domed luminaire or similar canopy to not be counted. Figure 5–18

Cable Clamp Fill. One or more internal cable clamps in the box are counted as a single conductor volume in accordance with the volume listed in Table 314.16(B), based on the largest conductor that enters the outlet box [314.16(B)2)]. Figure 5–19

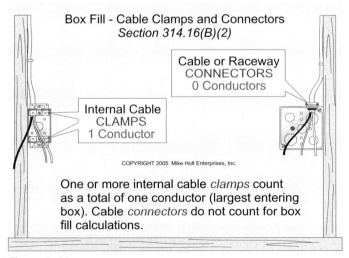

Box Fill - Cable Clamps and Connectors
Section 314.16(B)(2)

Cable or Raceway CONNECTORS
0 Conductors

Internal Cable CLAMPS
1 Conductor

COPYRIGHT 2005 Mike Holt Enterprises, Inc.

One or more internal cable *clamps* count as a total of one conductor (largest entering box). Cable *connectors* do not count for box fill calculations.

Figure 5–19

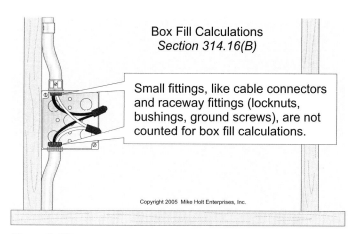

Box Fill Calculations
Section 314.16(B)

Small fittings, like cable connectors and raceway fittings (locknuts, bushings, ground screws), are not counted for box fill calculations.

Copyright 2005 Mike Holt Enterprises, Inc.

Figure 5–20

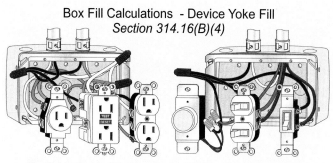

Box Fill Calculations - Device Yoke Fill
Section 314.16(B)(4)

Each device yoke counts as two conductors, based on the largest conductor terminating on the device.

COPYRIGHT 2005 Mike Holt Enterprises, Inc.

Figure 5–22

AUTHOR'S COMMENT: A cable or raceway connector that attaches to a box is not counted because it isn't an internal clamp (same as a raceway connector) [314.16(B)(2)]. Small fittings such as locknuts, ground screws, and bushings aren't counted [314.16(B)]. Figure 5–20

Support Fittings Fill. One or more luminaire studs or hickeys (crow's foot) within the box are counted as one conductor volume for each type, based on the largest conductor that enters the outlet box. [314.16(B)(3)] Figure 5–21

Device or Equipment Fill. Each yoke or strap containing one or more devices or equipment is counted as two conductors, based on the largest conductor that terminates on the yoke. [314.16(B)(4)] Figure 5–22

Equipment Grounding (Bonding) Conductors. One or more equipment grounding (bonding) conductors are counted as one conductor in accordance with the volume of the largest equipment grounding (bonding) conductor that enters the outlet box. [314.16(B)(5)] Figures 5–23 and 5–24

AUTHOR'S COMMENT: Fixture ground wires smaller than 14 AWG from a domed luminaire or similar canopy are not counted [314.16(B)(1) Ex].

What's Not Counted. Wire connectors, cable connectors, raceway fittings, and conductors that originate and terminate within the outlet box (such as equipment bonding jumpers and pigtails) are not counted for box fill calculations [314.16(B)].

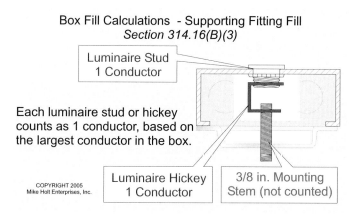

Box Fill Calculations - Supporting Fitting Fill
Section 314.16(B)(3)

Luminaire Stud
1 Conductor

Each luminaire stud or hickey counts as 1 conductor, based on the largest conductor in the box.

COPYRIGHT 2005
Mike Holt Enterprises, Inc.

Luminaire Hickey
1 Conductor

3/8 in. Mounting
Stem (not counted)

Figure 5–21

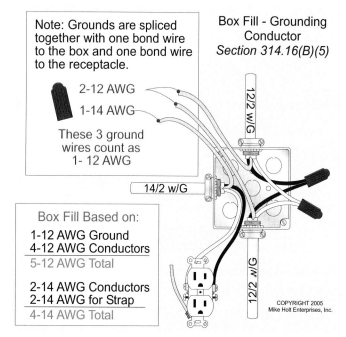

Note: Grounds are spliced together with one bond wire to the box and one bond wire to the receptacle.

2-12 AWG
1-14 AWG

These 3 ground wires count as 1- 12 AWG

Box Fill - Grounding Conductor
Section 314.16(B)(5)

12/2 w/G

14/2 w/G

12/2 w/G

Box Fill Based on:
1-12 AWG Ground
4-12 AWG Conductors
5-12 AWG Total

2-14 AWG Conductors
2-14 AWG for Strap
4-14 AWG Total

COPYRIGHT 2005
Mike Holt Enterprises, Inc.

Figure 5–23

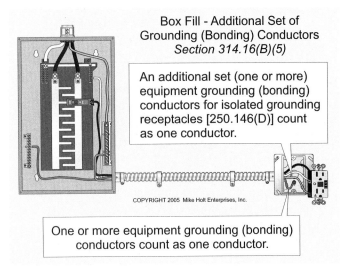

Box Fill - Additional Set of
Grounding (Bonding) Conductors
Section 314.16(B)(5)

An additional set (one or more)
equipment grounding (bonding)
conductors for isolated grounding
receptacles [250.146(D)] count
as one conductor.

COPYRIGHT 2005 Mike Holt Enterprises, Inc.

One or more equipment grounding (bonding)
conductors count as one conductor.

Figure 5–24

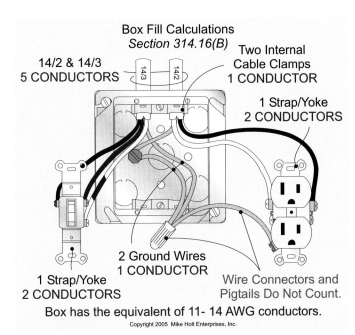

Box Fill Calculations
Section 314.16(B)

14/2 & 14/3
5 CONDUCTORS

Two Internal
Cable Clamps
1 CONDUCTOR

1 Strap/Yoke
2 CONDUCTORS

2 Ground Wires
1 CONDUCTOR

1 Strap/Yoke
2 CONDUCTORS

Wire Connectors and
Pigtails Do Not Count.

Box has the equivalent of 11- 14 AWG conductors.

Copyright 2005 Mike Holt Enterprises, Inc.

Figure 5–25

▶ **Number of Conductors**

What is the total number of conductors used for the box fill calculations in **Figure 5–25**?

(a) 5 conductors   (b) 7 conductors   (c) 9 conductors   (d) 11 conductors

• Answer: (d) 11 conductors

Switch	5 – 14 AWG, two conductors for the device and three conductors terminating
Receptacles	4 – 14 AWG, two conductors for the device and two conductors terminating
Ground wires	1 – 14 AWG
Cable clamps	1 – 14 AWG
Total	11 – 14 AWG

5.7 Sizing Box—Different Size Conductors [314.16(B)]

To determine the size of the outlet box when the conductors are of different sizes (insulation is not a factor), follow these steps:

Step 1:   Determine the number and size of conductor equivalents in the box.

Step 2:   Determine the volume of the conductor equivalents from Table 314.16(B).

Step 3:   Size the box by using Table 314.16(A).

▶ **Example: Calculating Different Size Conductors**

What size square outlet box is required for one 14/3 Type NM cable that terminates on a 3-way switch, and one 12/2 Type NM cable that terminates on a receptacle? The box has internally installed cable clamps. **Figure 5–26**

(a) 4 x 1 1/4 square   (b) 4 x 1 1/2 square   (c) 4 x 2 1/8 square   (d) any of these

• Answer: (c) 4 x 2 1/8 square

Box Fill Calculations - Different Size Conductors
Table 314.16(B)

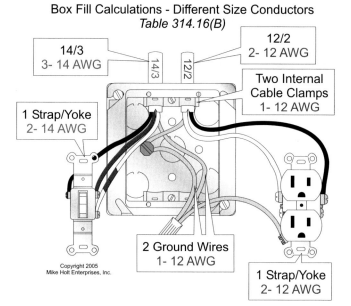

Copyright 2005
Mike Holt Enterprises, Inc.

Box has the equivalent of:
5- 14 AWG conductors and 6- 12 AWG conductors

Figure 5–26

Step 1: Determine the number of each size conductor.

14 AWG

14/3 NM =	3 – 14 AWG
Switch	2 – 14 AWG
Total	5 – 14 AWG

12 AWG

12/2 NM	2 – 12 AWG
Cable Clamp	1 – 12 AWG
Receptacle	2 – 12 AWG
Ground Wire	1 – 12 AWG
Total	6 – 12 AWG

AUTHOR'S COMMENT: All equipment grounding (bonding) conductors count as one conductor, based on the largest entering the box [314.16(B)(5)].

Step 2: Determine the volume of the conductors [Table 314.16(B)].

14 AWG	2 cu in. each
2 cu in. x 5 conductors	10 cu in.
12 AWG	2.25 cu in. each
2.25 cu in. x 6 conductors	13.5 cu in.
Total Volume	10 cu in. + 13.5 cu in.
Total Volume	23.5 cu in.

Step 3: Select the outlet box from Table 314.16(A).

4 x 1 1/2 square, 21 cu in.—too small
4 x 2 1/8 square, 30.3 cu in.—best selection

▶ **Domed Fixture Canopy [314.16(B)(1) Ex]**

A round 4 x 1/2 in. box has a total volume of 7 cubic inches and has factory-installed internal cable clamps. Can this pancake box be used with a lighting luminaire that has a domed canopy? The branch-circuit wiring is 14/2 NM cable, and the luminaire has three fixture wires and one ground wire all smaller than 14 AWG. Figure 5–27

(a) Yes   (b) No

• Answer: (b) No
The box is limited to 7 cu in., and the conductor equivalents total 8 cu in. [314.16(B)(1) Ex].

Step 1: Determine the number and size of conductors within the box.

Fixture wires, including the fixture ground wire are not counted when the fixture has a domed canopy.

14/2 NM	2 – 14 AWG
Cable clamps	1 – 14 AWG
Ground wire	1 – 14 AWG
Total	4 – 14 AWG conductors

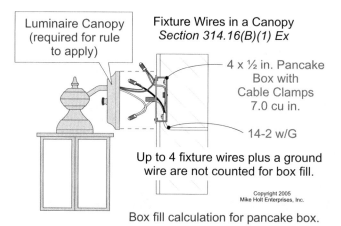

Fixture Wires in a Canopy
Section 314.16(B)(1) Ex

Luminaire Canopy (required for rule to apply)

4 x ½ in. Pancake Box with Cable Clamps 7.0 cu in.

14-2 w/G

Up to 4 fixture wires plus a ground wire are not counted for box fill.

Copyright 2005
Mike Holt Enterprises, Inc.

Box fill calculation for pancake box.

Number of Conductors in Box: [314.16(B)]
14-2 NM Cable = 2 conductors
14-2 Ground = 1 conductor
Cable Clamps = 1 conductor
Fixture Wires = 0 conductors, [314.16(B)(1) Ex.]
Total = 4-14 AWG conductors

Volume of Conductors: Table 314.16(B)
1-14 AWG = 2 cu in. x 4 conductors = 8 cu in.

Volume of box is 7 cu in. (too small).
This installation is a VIOLATION.

Figure 5–27

Step 2: Determine the volume of the conductors [Table 314.16(B)].

14 AWG = 2 cu in.
Four 14 AWG conductors = 4 wires x 2 cu in. = 8 cu in.

▶ **Conductors Added to an Existing Box**

How many 14 THHN conductors can be pulled through a 4 x 2 1/8 square box that has a plaster ring of 3.6 cu in.? The box already contains two receptacles, five 12 THHN conductors, and one 12 AWG bare grounding conductor. Figure 5–28

(a) 4 conductors   (b) 5 conductors

(c) 6 conductors   (d) 7 conductors

• Answer: (b) 5 conductors

Step 1: Determine the number and size of the existing conductors.

Two Receptacles	4 – 12 AWG conductors
	(2 yokes x 2 conductors)
Five 12 AWG	5 – 12 AWG conductors
One ground	1 – 12 AWG conductor
Total	10 – 12 AWG conductors

Step 2: Determine the volume of the existing conductors [Table 314.16(B)].

12 AWG conductor = 2.25 cu in.
10 wires x 2.25 cu in. = 22.5 cu in.

Step 3: Determine the space remaining for the additional 14 AWG conductors.

Remaining space = Total space less existing conductors
Total space = 30.3 cu in. (box) [Table 314.16(A)]
  + 3.6 cu in. (ring) = 33.9 cu in.
Remaining space = 33.9 cu in. – 22.5 cu in.
  (ten 12 AWG conductors)
Remaining space = 11.4 cu in.

Step 4: Determine the number of 14 AWG conductors permitted in the spare space.

Conductors added = Remaining space/
  added conductors' volume
Conductors added = 11.4 cu in./2 cu in.
  = 5.7 [Table 314.16(B)]
Conductors added = 5
  (Rounding up does not apply to box fill.)

PART C—PULL BOXES, JUNCTION BOXES, AND CONDUIT BODIES

Pull boxes, junction boxes, and conduit bodies must be sized to permit conductors to be installed so that the conductor insulation will not be damaged. For conductors 4 AWG and larger, pull boxes, junction boxes, and conduit bodies must be sized in accordance with 314.28. Figure 5–29

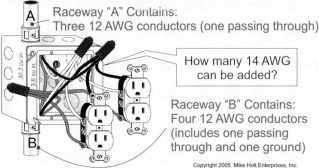

Box Fill Calculation - Adding Conductors
Section 314.16(B)

Raceway "A" Contains:
Three 12 AWG conductors (one passing through)

How many 14 AWG can be added?

Raceway "B" Contains:
Four 12 AWG conductors (includes one passing through and one ground)

Copyright 2005 Mike Holt Enterprises, Inc.

How many 14 AWG conductors can you add to the box?

Step 1. Volume of existing conductors:
  One 12 AWG = 2.25 cu in. x 10 conductors = 22.5 cu in.
Step 2. Volume of box and ring:
  30.3 cu in. + 3.6 cu in. = 33.9 cu in.
Step 3. Determine spare space:
  33.9 cu in. - 22.5 cu in. = 11.4 cu in. space for fill
Step 4. Number of 14 AWG added:
  Table 314.16(B), one 14 AWG = 2 cu in.
  11.4 cu in./2 cu in. = Five 14 AWG can be added

Figure 5–28

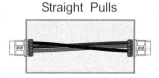

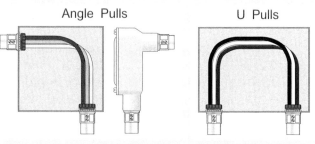

Pull and Junction Boxes - 4 AWG and Larger
Section 314.28

Straight Pulls

314.28 is used to size pull boxes, junction boxes, and conduit bodies when conductor sizes 4 AWG and larger are used.

Angle Pulls   U Pulls

COPYRIGHT 2005 Mike Holt Enterprises

Figure 5–29

Pull Box Sizing - Straight Pull
Section 314.28(A)(1)

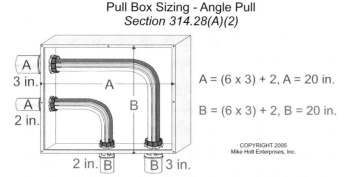

The distance from the conductors' entry to the opposite wall must not be less than 8X the largest raceway.

Figure 5–30

5.8 Pull and Junction Box Size Calculations

Straight-Pull Calculation [314.28(A)(1)]

A straight-pull calculation applies when 4 AWG and larger conductors enter one side of a box and leave through the opposite wall of the box. The minimum distance from where the raceway enters to the opposite wall must not be less than eight times the trade size of the largest raceway. Figure 5–30

Angle-Pull Calculation [314.28(A)(2)]

An angle-pull calculation applies when 4 AWG and larger conductors enter one wall and leave the enclosure not opposite the wall of the conductor entry. The distance for angle-pull calculations from where the raceway enters to the opposite wall must not be less than six times the trade diameter of the largest raceway, plus the sum of the diameters of the remaining raceways on the same wall and row. Figure 5–31

Pull Box Sizing - Angle Pull
Section 314.28(A)(2)

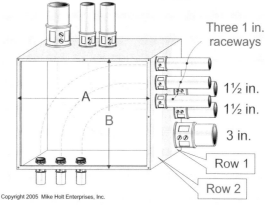

A = (6 x 3) + 2, A = 20 in.

B = (6 x 3) + 2, B = 20 in.

For angle pulls, the distance (measured from conductor wall entry to the opposite wall) must not be less than 6X the largest raceway, plus the sum of the diameters of the remaining raceways on the same wall and row.

Figure 5–31

Sizing Junction/Pull Boxes for Angle Conductor Pulls
Determining Largest Row
Section 314.28(A)(2)

Three 1 in.
raceways

1½ in.

1½ in.

3 in.

Row 1

Row 2

When there is more than one row of conduit entries on the same wall, each row must be calculated separately and the larger answer used.
Row 1 = (6 x 3 in.) + 1½ + 1½ = 21 in.
Row 2 = (6 x 1 in.) + 1 in. + 1 in. = 8 in. (omit)
Dimension A = 21 in.

Figure 5–32

When there is more than one row of raceways or cables, each row must be calculated separately and the row with the largest calculation must be considered the minimum angle-pull dimension. Figure 5–32

U-Pull Calculations [314.28(A)(2)]

A U-pull calculation applies when the 4 AWG and larger conductors enter and leave from the same wall. The distance from where the raceways enter to the opposite wall must not be less than six times the trade diameter of the largest raceway, plus the sum of the diameters of the remaining raceways on the same wall. Figure 5–33

> **AUTHOR'S COMMENT:** The width of the pull box in Figure 5–33 must be sufficient to accommodate the distance required between raceways containing the same conductor, in this case, 18 in. (Dimension C—covered next), plus the raceway fittings.

Distance Between Raceways Containing the Same Conductor Calculation [314.28(A)(2)]

After sizing the pull box, the raceways must be installed so that the distance between raceways enclosing the same conductors is not less than six times the trade diameter of the largest raceway. This distance is measured from the nearest edge of one raceway to the nearest edge of the other raceway. Figures 5-33 and 5-34

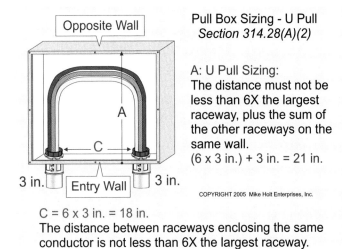

Pull Box Sizing - U Pull
Section 314.28(A)(2)

A: U Pull Sizing:
The distance must not be less than 6X the largest raceway, plus the sum of the other raceways on the same wall.
(6 x 3 in.) + 3 in. = 21 in.

COPYRIGHT 2005 Mike Holt Enterprises, Inc.

C = 6 x 3 in. = 18 in.
The distance between raceways enclosing the same conductor is not less than 6X the largest raceway.

Figure 5–33

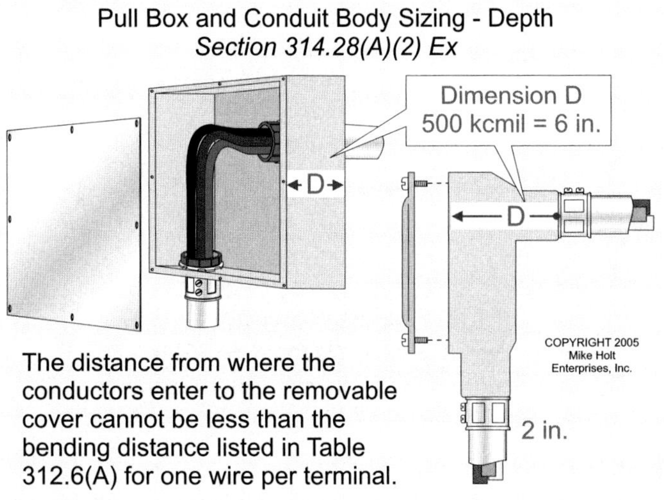

Pull Box and Conduit Body Sizing - Depth
Section 314.28(A)(2) Ex

Dimension D
500 kcmil = 6 in.

COPYRIGHT 2005
Mike Holt
Enterprises, Inc.

The distance from where the conductors enter to the removable cover cannot be less than the bending distance listed in Table 312.6(A) for one wire per terminal.

Figure 5–35

5.9 Depth of Box and Conduit Body Sizing [314.28(A)(2) Ex]

When conductors enter an enclosure opposite a removable cover, such as the back of a pull box, conduit body, or hand-hole enclosure, the distance from where the conductors enter to the removable cover must not be less than the distances listed in Table 312.6(A); one wire per terminal. Figure 5–35

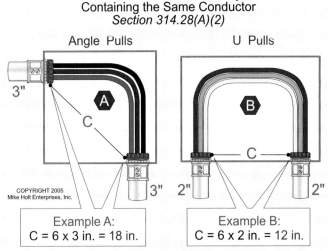

Distance Between Raceways
Containing the Same Conductor
Section 314.28(A)(2)

Angle Pulls

U Pulls

COPYRIGHT 2005
Mike Holt Enterprises, Inc.

Example A:
C = 6 x 3 in. = 18 in.

Example B:
C = 6 x 2 in. = 12 in.

The distance between raceways containing the same conductor must not be less than 6 times the diameter of the larger raceway.

Figure 5–34

▶ Depth of Pull or Junction Box

A 24 x 24 in. pull box has two trade size 2 conduits that enter the back of the box containing 4/0 AWG conductors. What is the minimum depth of the box?

(a) 4 in.　　　　　　　(b) 6 in.
(c) 8 in.　　　　　　　(d) 10 in.

• Answer: (a) 4 in., Table 312.6(A)

5.10 Junction and Pull Box Sizing Tips

When sizing pull and junction boxes, follow these suggestions:

Step 1: Always draw out the problem.

Step 2: Calculate the HORIZONTAL distance(s):

　• Left to right straight calculation
　• Left to right angle or U-pull calculation
　• Right to left straight calculation
　• Right to left angle or U-pull calculation

Step 3: Calculate the VERTICAL distance(s):

　• Top to bottom straight calculation
　• Top to bottom angle or U-pull calculation
　• Bottom to top straight calculation
　• Bottom to top angle or U-pull calculation

Pull (Junction) Box Sizing
Section 314.28
314.28 is used to size junction boxes for conductor sizes 4 AWG and larger and the distance between conductors containing the same conductor.

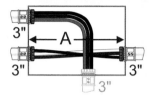

A: Horizontal Dimension
Straight Pull:
Left to Right: 8 x 3 in. = 24 in.
Right to Left: 8 x 3 in. = 24 in.
Angle Pull:
Left to Right: (6 x 3 in.) + 3 in. = 21 in.
Right to Left: No Calculation
Largest Calculation = 24 in.

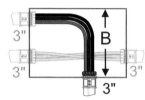

B: Vertical Dimension
Straight Pull:
Top to Bottom: No Calculation
Bottom to Top: No Calculation
Angle Pull:
Top to Bottom: (No Calculation)
Bottom to Top: 6 x 3 in. = 18 in.
Largest Calculation = 18 in.

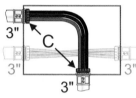

C: Distance Between Raceways
(Containing the same conductor)
Angle Pull is the only application
6 x 3 in. = 18 in.

COPYRIGHT 2005 Mike Holt Enterprises, Inc.

Figure 5–36

5.11 Pull Box Examples

Pull Box Sizing

A junction box contains two trade size 3 raceways on the left side and one trade size 3 raceway on the right side. The conductors from one of the trade size 3 raceways on the left wall are pulled through a trade size 3 raceway on the right wall. The conductors from the other trade size 3 raceways on the left wall are pulled through a trade size 3 raceway at the bottom of the pull box. Figure 5–36

▶ **Horizontal Dimension**

What is the horizontal dimension of this box?

(a) 18 in.   (b) 21 in.
(c) 24 in.   (d) 30 in.

• Answer: (c) 24 in.
  [314.28], **Figure 5–36A**

Left to right angle pull	(6 x 3 in.) + 3 in. = 21 in.
Left to right straight pull	8 x 3 in. = 24 in.
Right to left angle pull	No calculation
Right to left straight pull	8 x 3 in. = 24 in.

▶ **Vertical Dimension**

What is the vertical dimension of this box?

(a) 18 in.   (b) 21 in.
(c) 24 in.   (d) 30 in.

• Answer: (a) 18 in.
  [314.28], **Figure 5–36B**

Top to bottom angle	No calculation
Top to bottom straight	No calculation
Bottom to top angle	6 x 3 in. = 18 in.
Bottom to top straight	No calculation

▶ **Distance Between Raceways**

What is the minimum distance between the two trade size 3 raceways that contain the same conductors?

(a) 18 in.   (b) 21 in.
(c) 24 in.   (d) none of these

• Answer: (a) 18 in.
  6 x 3 in., 314.28 **Figure 5–36C**

Pull Box Sizing

A pull box contains two trade size 4 raceways on the left side and two trade size 2 raceways on the top.

▶ **Horizontal Dimension**

What is the horizontal dimension of the box?

(a) 28 in.   (b) 21 in.
(c) 24 in.   (d) none of these

• Answer: (a) 28 in., 314.28(A)(2)

Left to right angle pull	(6 x 4 in.) + 4 in. = 28 in.
Left to right straight pull	No calculation
Right to left angle pull	No calculation
Right to left straight pull	No calculation

▶ **Vertical Dimension**

What is the vertical dimension of the box?

(a) 18 in.   (b) 21 in.
(c) 26 in.   (d) 14 in.

• Answer: (d) 14 in., 314.28(A)(2)

Top to bottom angle	(6 x 2 in.) + 2 in. = 14 in.
Top to bottom straight	No calculation
Bottom to top angle	No calculation
Bottom to top straight	No calculation

▶ Distance Between Raceways

If the two trade size 4 raceways contain the same conductors, what is the minimum distance between these raceways?

(a) 18 in.   (b) 21 in.   (c) 24 in.   (d) none of these

• Answer: (c) 24 in.
  6 x 4 in. = 24 in. [314.28(A)(2)]

AUTHOR'S COMMENT: In this junction box example, the vertical dimension came out to be 14 in. based on the two trade size 2 raceways on the top. The correct answer is 14 in. based on that information. Since the last question changed the variables, 24 in. is the correct answer in this case.

Unit 5 Conclusion

The importance of protecting the insulation of conductors during installation is certainly understood by every electrician. The principles covered in this unit have gone far towards helping you achieve that goal.

In this unit, you learned how to use the tables in Chapter 9 when calculating raceway fill. First, the area of the conductor is found, using Chapter 9, Table 5 for insulated conductors or Chapter 9, Table 8 for bare conductors. Then after totaling the cross-sectional area of all the conductors, the raceway trade size from Chapter 9, Table 4 is selected using the available cross-sectional area of the raceway. Be cautious by taking your time when working out these calculations to select the correct insulation type and the correct raceway for your problem.

Annex C provides a quicker method for sizing raceways than the Chapter 9 Tables when the conductors are all the same AWG size, and the same size in cross-sectional area (including the insulation). There are numerous tables in Annex C, based on the raceway type, that can be used to reduce the time spent in calculations, so once again be sure to take your time and be certain you are using the correct table.

Maintaining proper outlet box fill is important as you rough-in the installation. There are a number of details that were covered in determining the correct box size to be used that will be important on an exam. Be sure to remember what items are counted in box fill calculations, and review the information if necessary.

Junction box and pull box calculations only come into play when the conductors are 4 AWG and larger. Straight pulls, angle pulls, and U pulls were all covered in this unit, as well as an often forgotten requirement that applies to two raceways that contain the same conductors. Always draw out a problem involving junction or pull boxes so that you'll be able to visualize it and properly apply the calculations you have learned.

(• Indicates that 75% or fewer of those who took this exam answered the question correctly.)

PART A—RACEWAY FILL

5.1 Understanding the *NEC*, Chapter 9 Tables

1. When all the conductors are the same size (total cross-sectional area including insulation), the number of conductors permitted in a raceway can be determined by simply looking at the Tables listed in _____.

    (a) Chapter 9   (b) Annex B   (c) Annex C   (d) Annex D

2. When equipment grounding conductors are installed in a raceway, the actual area of the conductor must be used when calculating raceway fill.

    (a) True   (b) False

3. When a raceway does not exceed 24 in. in length, the raceway is permitted to be filled to _____ of its cross-sectional area.

    (a) 53%   (b) 31%   (c) 40%   (d) 60%

4. How many 16 TFFN conductors can be installed in trade size 3/4 electrical metallic tubing?

    (a) 40   (b) 26   (c) 30   (d) 29

5. How many 6 RHH conductors (without outer cover) can be installed in trade size 1 1/4 electrical nonmetallic tubing?

    (a) 25   (b) 16   (c) 13   (d) 7

6. How many 1/0 XHHW conductors can be installed in trade size 2 flexible metal conduit?

    (a) 7   (b) 6   (c) 16   (d) 13

7. How many 12 RHH conductors (with outer cover) can be installed in a trade size 1 IMC raceway?

    (a) 7   (b) 11   (c) 5   (d) 4

8. Three THHN compact conductors are needed in a trade size 2 rigid metal conduit. What is the largest compact conductor that can be installed?

    (a) 4/0 AWG   (b) 250 kcmil   (c) 350 kcmil   (d) 500 kcmil

9. The actual area of conductor fill is dependent on the raceway size and the number of conductors installed. If there are three or more conductors installed in a raceway, the total area of conductor fill is limited to _____.

    (a) 53%   (b) 31%   (c) 40%   (d) 60%

10. •What is the cross-sectional area in sq in. for 10 THW?

    (a) 0.0243   (b) 0.0172   (c) 0.0252   (d) 0.0278

11. What is the cross-sectional area in sq in. for 14 RHW (without an outer cover)?

    (a) 0.0209 (b) 0.0172 (c) 0.0252 (d) 0.0278

12. What is the cross-sectional area in sq in. for 10 THHN?

    (a) 0.0117 (b) 0.0172 (c) 0.0252 (d) 0.0211

13. What is the cross-sectional area in sq in. for 12 RHH (with an outer cover)?

    (a) 0.0117 (b) 0.0353 (c) 0.0252 (d) 0.0327

14. •What is the cross-sectional area in sq in. for an 8 AWG bare solid conductor?

    (a) 0.013 (b) 0.027 (c) 0.038 (d) 0.045

5.2 Raceway and Nipple Calculations

15. The number of conductors permitted in a raceway is dependent on the _____.

    (a) area of the raceway
    (b) percent area fill as listed in Chapter 9, Table 1
    (c) area of the conductors as listed in Chapter 9, Tables 5 and 8
    (d) all of these

16. A 200A feeder installed in schedule 80 rigid nonmetallic conduit has three 3/0 THHN conductors, one 2 THHN conductor, and one 6 THHN conductor. What size raceway is required?

    (a) Trade size 2 (b) Trade size 2 1/2 (c) Trade size 3 (d) Trade size 3 1/2

17. What size rigid metal nipple is required for three 4/0 THHN conductors, one 1/0 THHN conductor, and one 4 THHN conductor?

    (a) Trade size 1 1/2 (b) Trade size 2 (c) Trade size 2 1/2 (d) none of these

5.3 Existing Raceway Calculations

18. •An existing trade size 3/4 rigid metal conduit nipple contains four 10 THHN conductors and one 10 AWG (bare stranded) ground wire. How many additional 10 THHN conductors can be installed?

    (a) 5 (b) 7 (c) 9 (d) 11

PART B—OUTLET BOX FILL CALCULATIONS [314.16]

5.5 Sizing Box—Conductors all the Same Size [Table 314.16(A)]

19. What size box is required for six 14 THHN conductors and three 14 THW conductors?

    (a) 4 x 1 1/4 square (b) 4 x 1 1/2 round (c) 4 x 1 1/4 round (d) none of these

20. How many 10 THHN conductors are permitted in a 4 x 1 1/2 square box?

    (a) 8 conductors (b) 9 conductors (c) 10 conductors (d) 11 conductors

5.6 Conductor Equivalents [314.16(B)]

21. Table 314.16(A) does not take into consideration the volume of _____.

    (a) switches and receptacles
    (b) luminaire studs and hickeys
    (c) internal cable clamps
    (d) all of these

22. When determining the number of conductors for box fill calculations, which of the following statements is/are true?

    (a) A luminaire stud or hickey is considered as one conductor for each type, based on the largest conductor that enters the outlet box.
    (b) Internal factory cable clamps are considered as one conductor for one or more cable clamps, based on the largest conductor that enters the outlet box.
    (c) The device yoke is considered as two conductors, based on the largest conductor that terminates on the strap (device mounting fitting).
    (d) all of these

23. •When determining the number of conductors for box fill calculations, which of the following statements is/are true?

    (a) Each conductor that runs through the box without loop (without splice) is considered as one conductor.
    (b) Each conductor that originates outside the box and terminates in the box is considered as one conductor.
    (c) Wirenuts, cable connectors, raceway fittings, and conductors that originate and terminate within the outlet box (equipment bonding jumpers and pigtails) are not counted for box fill calculations.
    (d) all of these

24. It is permitted to omit one equipment grounding conductor and not more than _____ that enter a box from a luminaire canopy.

    (a) five fixture wires
    (b) four 16 AWG fixture wires
    (c) four 18 AWG fixture wires
    (d) b and c

25. Can a round 4 x 1/2 in. box marked as 8 cu in. with manufactured cable clamps supplied with 14/2 NM be used with a luminaire that has two 18 TFN conductors and a canopy cover?

    (a) Yes
    (b) No

5.7 Sizing Box—Different Size Conductors [314.16(B)]

26. •What size outlet box is required for one 12/2 NM cable that terminates on a switch, one 12/3 NM cable that terminates on a receptacle, and the box has manufactured cable clamps?

    (a) 4 x 1 1/4 square
    (b) 4 x 1 1/2 square
    (c) 4 x 2 1/8 square
    (d) none of these

27. •How many 14 THHN conductors can be pulled through a 4 x 1 1/2 square box with a plaster ring marked 3.6 cu in.? The box contains two duplex receptacles, five 14 THHN conductors, and two grounding conductors.

    (a) 1
    (b) 2
    (c) 3
    (d) 4

PART C—PULL BOXES, JUNCTION BOXES, AND CONDUIT BODIES
5.8 Pull and Junction Box Size Calculations

28. When conductors 4 AWG and larger are installed in boxes and conduit bodies, the enclosure must be sized according to which of the following requirements?

(a) The minimum distance for straight-pull calculations from where the conductors enter to the opposite wall must not be less than eight times the trade size of the largest raceway.

(b) The distance for angle-pull calculations from the raceway entry to the opposite wall must not be less than six times the trade size diameter of the largest raceway, plus the sum of the diameters of the remaining raceways on the same wall and row.

(c) The distance between raceways enclosing the same conductor(s) must not be less than six times the trade size diameter of the largest raceway.

(d) all of these

29. When conductors enter an enclosure opposite a removable cover, the distance from where the conductors enter to the removable cover must not be less than _____.

(a) six times the largest raceway   (b) eight times the largest raceway
(c) a or b   (d) none of these

The following information applies to the next three questions.
A junction box contains two trade size 2 1/2 raceways on the left side and one trade size 2 1/2 raceway on the right side. The conductors from one trade size 2 1/2 raceway (left wall) are pulled through the raceway on the right wall. The other trade size 2 1/2 raceway conductors (on the side) are pulled through a trade size 2 1/2 raceway at the bottom of the pull box.

30. What is the distance from the left wall to the right wall?

(a) 18 in.   (b) 21 in.   (c) 24 in.   (d) 20 in.

31. •What is the distance from the bottom wall to the top wall?

(a) 18 in.   (b) 21 in.   (c) 24 in.   (d) 15 in.

32. What is the distance between the raceways that contain the same conductors?

(a) 18 in.   (b) 21 in.   (c) 24 in.   (d) 15 in.

The following information applies to the next three questions.
A junction box contains two trade size 2 raceways on the left side and two trade size 2 raceways on the top.

33. What is the distance from the left wall to the right wall?

(a) 28 in.   (b) 21 in.   (c) 24 in.   (d) 14 in.

34. What is the distance from the bottom wall to the top wall?

(a) 18 in.   (b) 21 in.   (c) 24 in.   (d) 14 in.

35. What is the distance between the trade size 2 raceways that contain the same conductors?

(a) 18 in.   (b) 21 in.   (c) 24 in.   (d) 12 in.

Unit 5 Calculation Challenge Questions

(• Indicates that 75% or fewer of those who took this exam answered the question correctly.)

PART A—RACEWAY FILL

5.3 Existing Raceway Calculations

1. •A trade size 3 schedule 40 RNC (PVC) raceway contains seven 1 RHW conductors without outer cover. How many 2 THW conductors may be installed in this raceway with the existing conductors?

    (a) 11   (b) 15   (c) 20   (d) 25

PART B—BOX FILL CALCULATIONS [314.16]

5.7 Sizing Box—Different Size Conductors [314.16(B)]

2. •Determine the minimum cubic inches required for two 10 TW conductors passing through a box, four 14 THHN conductors spliced in the box, two 12 TW conductors terminating to a receptacle, and one 12 AWG equipment bonding jumper from the receptacle to the box.

    (a) 18.5 cu in.   (b) 22 cu in.   (c) 20 cu in.   (d) 21.75 cu in.

3. •When determining the number of conductors in a box fill that has two 18 AWG fixture wires from a domed luminaire, one 14/3 nonmetallic-sheathed cable with ground, one duplex switch and two internal cable clamps, the count will equal _____.

    (a) 7 conductors   (b) 8 conductors   (c) 10 conductors   (d) 6 conductors

PART C—PULL BOXES, JUNCTION BOXES, AND CONDUIT BODIES

5.8 Pull and Junction Box Size Calculations

Figure 5-37 applies to the next four questions.

4. The minimum horizontal dimension for the junction box shown in the diagram in Figure 5-37 is _____.

    (a) 21 in.   (b) 18 in.
    (c) 24 in.   (d) 20 in.

5. •The minimum vertical dimension for the junction box shown in Figure 5-37 is _____.

    (a) 16 in.   (b) 18 in.
    (c) 20 in.   (d) 24 in.

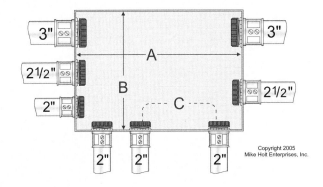

Figure 5–37

6. The minimum distance between the two trade size 2 raceways that contain the same conductor C, as illustrated in **Figure 5-37** is _____.

    (a) 12 in.   (b) 18 in.   (c) 24 in.   (d) 30 in.

7. •If a trade size 3 raceway entry (250 kcmil) is in the wall opposite a removable cover, the distance from that wall to the cover must not be less than _____. **Figure 5-37**

    (a) 4 in.   (b) 4 1/2 in.   (c) 5 in.   (d) 6 in.

(• Indicates that 75% or fewer of those who took this exam answered the question correctly.)

Article 310 Conductors for General Wiring (continued)

1. •When bare grounding conductors are allowed, their ampacities are limited to _____.

    (a) 60°C
    (b) 75°C
    (c) 90°C
    (d) those permitted for the insulated conductors of the same size

2. On a three-phase, 4-wire, wye circuit, where the major portion of the load consists of electrical discharge lighting, data-processing equipment, or other harmonic current inducting loads, the grounded conductor must be counted when applying 310.15(B)(2) adjustment factors.

    (a) True
    (b) False

3. Service and feeder conductors may be sized using Table 310.15(B)(6) for_____.

    (a) any kind of service under 400 amps
    (b) only multifamily dwelling services
    (c) only 120/240 volt, 3-wire, single-phase services for individual dwelling units
    (d) commercial services only

4. In designing circuits, the current-carrying capacity of conductors should be corrected for heat at room temperatures above _____.

    (a) 30°F
    (b) 86°F
    (c) 94°F
    (d) 75°F

5. The ampacity of a single insulated 1/0 THHN copper conductor in free air is _____.

    (a) 260A
    (b) 300A
    (c) 185A
    (d) 215A

6. As used in the *Code*, thermal resistivity refers to the heat _____ capability through a substance by conduction.

    (a) assimilation
    (b) generation
    (c) transfer
    (d) dissipation

7. Table 310.70 provides the ampacities of insulated single aluminum conductors isolated in air. If the conductor size is 8 AWG, MV-90, and the voltage range is 2,001 through 5,000, then the ampacity is _____.

    (a) 64A
    (b) 85A
    (c) 115A
    (d) 150A

Article 312 Cabinets, Cutout Boxes, and Meter Socket Enclosures

Article 312 covers the installation and construction specifications for cabinets, cutout boxes, and meter socket enclosures.

8. Cabinets or cutout boxes installed in wet locations must be _____.

    (a) waterproof
    (b) raintight
    (c) weatherproof
    (d) watertight

9. Where raceways or cables enter above the level of uninsulated live parts of an enclosure in a wet location, a(n) _____ must be used.

    (a) fitting listed for wet locations
    (b) explosion proof seal-off
    (c) fitting listed for damp locations
    (d) insulated fitting

10. Plaster, drywall, or plasterboard surfaces that are broken or incomplete must be repaired so there will be no gaps or open spaces greater than _____ at the edge of a cabinet or cutout box employing a flush-type cover.

    (a) 1/4 in   (b) 1/2 in   (c) 1/8 in   (d) 1/16 in

11. Each cable entering a cutout box _____.

    (a) must be secured to the cutout box   (b) can be sleeved through a chase
    (c) must have a maximum of two cables per connector   (d) all of these

12. A switch enclosure (cabinet) must not be used as a junction box, except where adequate space is provided so that the conductors don't fill the wiring space at any cross-section to more than 40 percent of the cross-sectional area of the space, and so that _____ don't fill the wiring space at any cross-section to more than 75 percent of the cross-sectional area of the space.

    (a) splices   (b) taps   (c) conductors   (d) all of these

Article 314 Outlet, Device, Pull and Junction Boxes, Conduit Bodies, and Handhole Enclosures

Article 314 contains installation requirements for outlet boxes, pull and junction boxes, as well as conduit bodies, and handhole enclosures.

13. Round boxes must not be used where conduits or connectors requiring the use of locknuts or bushings are to be connected to the side of the box.

    (a) True   (b) False

14. Metallic boxes are required to be _____.

    (a) metric   (b) installed   (c) grounded   (d) all of these

15. Short-radius conduit bodies such as capped elbows, and service-entrance elbows that enclose conductors 6 AWG and smaller are intended to enable the installation of the raceway and the contained conductors and must not contain _____.

    (a) splices   (b) taps   (c) devices   (d) any of these

16. According to the *NEC*, the volume of a 3 x 2 x 2 in. device box is _____

    (a) 12 cu in.   (b) 14 cu in.   (c) 10 cu in.   (d) 8 cu in.

17. When counting the number of conductors in a box, a conductor running through the box with an unbroken loop not less than twice the minimum length required for free conductors in 300.14 is counted as _____ conductor(s).

    (a) one   (b) two   (c) zero   (d) none of these

18. When determining the number of conductors in a box, and one or more factory or field-supplied internal cable clamps are present in the box, a double volume allowance for the clamps, in accordance with Table 314.16(B), must be made based on the largest conductor present in the box.

    (a) True   (b) False

19. Each yoke or strap containing one or more devices or equipment counts as _____ conductor(s), based on the largest conductor that terminates on that device.

    (a) 1   (b) 2   (c) 3   (d) none

20. When a box contains three equipment grounding conductors that originated outside the box, the three grounding conductors are counted as _____ conductor(s) when determining the number of conductors in a box for box fill calculations.

    (a) 3   (b) 6   (c) 1   (d) 0

21. Splices and taps can be made in conduit bodies that are durably and legibly marked by the manufacturer with their volume and the maximum number of conductors as computed in accordance with Table 314.16(B)

    (a) True   (b) False

22. •In noncombustible walls or ceilings, the front edge of a box, plaster ring, extension ring, or listed extender may be set back not more than _____ from the finished surface.

    (a) 3/8 in.   (b) 1/8 in.   (c) 1/2 in.   (d) 1/4 in.

23. Plaster, drywall, or plasterboard surfaces that are broken or incomplete around boxes employing a flush-type cover or faceplate must be repaired so there will be no gaps or open spaces larger than _____ at the edge of the box.

    (a) 1/4 in.   (b) 1/2 in.   (c) 1/8 in.   (d) 1/16 in.

24. •Only a _____ wiring method can be used for a surface extension from a cover, and the wiring method must include an equipment grounding conductor.

    (a) solid   (b) flexible   (c) rigid   (d) cord

25. Nails or screws can fasten boxes to structural members of a building using brackets on the outside of the enclosure, or they can pass through the interior within _____ of the back or ends of the enclosure. Screws are not permitted to pass through the box unless exposed threads in the box are protected using approved means to avoid abrasions of conductor insulation.

    (a) 1/8 in   (b) 1/16 in   (c) 1/4 in   (d) 1/2 in

26. When mounting an enclosure in a finished surface, the enclosure must be _____ secured to the surface by clamps, anchors, or fittings identified for the application.

    (a) temporarily   (b) partially   (c) never   (d) rigidly

27. Outlet boxes can be secured to independent support wires, which are taut and secured at both ends, if the box is supported to the independent support wires using methods identified for the purpose.

    (a) True   (b) False

28. •Enclosures not over 100 cu in. that have threaded entries that support luminaires or contain devices are considered adequately supported where two or more conduits are threaded wrenchtight into the enclosure where each conduit is supported within _____ of the enclosure.

    (a) 12 in.   (b) 18 in.   (c) 24 in.   (d) 30 in.

29. •The minimum size box that is to contain a flush device must not be less than _____ deep.

    (a) 15/16 in.   (b) 8/15 in.   (c) 1 in.   (d) 1 1/2 in.

30. Outlet boxes used at luminaire or lampholder outlets must be _____.

    (a) designed for the purpose   (b) metal only
    (c) plastic only   (d) mounted using bar hangers only

31. Luminaires must be supported independently of the outlet box where the weight exceeds _____

    (a) 60 lbs   (b) 50 lbs   (c) 40 lbs   (d) 30 lbs

32. When installing floor boxes, boxes _____ must be used.

    (a) made only of metal   (b) listed specifically for this application
    (c) fed by metal raceways only   (d) fed by nonmetallic cable only

33. Listed outlet boxes, or outlet box systems that are identified for the purpose are permitted to support ceiling-suspended fans that weigh more than 35 lbs but no more than _____ if the allowable weight is marked on the box.

    (a) 50 lbs   (b) 60 lbs   (c) 70 lbs   (d) none of these

34. Pull boxes or junction boxes that have any dimension over _____ must have all conductors cabled or racked in an approved manner.

    (a) 3 ft   (b) 6 ft   (c) 9 ft   (d) 12 ft

35. Listed boxes designed for underground installation can be directly buried when covered by _____ if their location is identified and accessible.

    (a) concrete   (b) gravel
    (c) noncohesive granulated soil   (d) b or c

36. Handhole enclosures must be sized in accordance with 314.28(A) for conductors operating at 600V and below. For handhole enclosures without bottoms, the measurement to the removable cover is taken from the _____.

    (a) end of the conduit or cable assembly   (b) lowest point in the hole
    (c) leveling marks provided   (d) highest possible ground water level

37. Where handhole enclosures without bottoms are installed, all enclosed conductors and any splices or terminations, if present, must be listed as _____.

    (a) suitable for wet locations   (b) suitable for damp locations
    (c) handhole ready   (d) general duty

38. Handhole enclosure covers must require the use of tools to open, or they must weigh over _____. Metal covers and other exposed conductive surfaces must be bonded to an effective ground-fault current path.

    (a) 45 lbs   (b) 100 lbs   (c) 70 lbs   (d) 200 lbs

39. Metal boxes over _____ in size must be constructed so as to be of ample strength and rigidity. Sheet steel must not be less than 0.053 in. thick.

    (a) 50 cu in.   (b) 75 cu in.   (c) 100 cu in.   (d) 125 cu in.

40. For systems over 600V, the length of a pull box for a straight pull must not be less than _____ entering the box.

    (a) 18 times the diameter of the largest raceway
    (b) 48 times the diameter of the largest raceway
    (c) 48 times the outside diameter of the largest shielded conductor or cable
    (d) 36 times the largest conductor

41. •For angle or U-pulls, the distance between the shielded conductor entry (for systems over 600V, nominal) and the opposite wall of the box must not be less than _____ times the outside diameter of the largest cable or conductor.

    (a) 6   (b) 12   (c) 24   (d) 36

Article 320 Armored Cable (Type AC)

Armored cable is an assembly of insulated conductors, 14 AWG through 1 AWG, that are individually wrapped with waxed paper. The conductors are contained within a flexible spiral metal (steel or aluminum) sheath that interlocks at the edges. Armored cable looks like flexible metal conduit. Many electricians call this metal cable BX®.

42. •The use of Type AC cable is permitted in _____ installations.

    (a) wet   (b) cable tray   (c) exposed   (d) b and c

43. Exposed runs of Type AC cable must closely follow the surface of the building finish or of running boards. Exposed runs are also permitted to be installed on the underside of joists where supported at each joist and located so as not to be subject to physical damage.

    (a) True   (b) False

44. Where run across the top of floor joists, or within 7 ft of floor or floor joists, across the face of rafters or studding in attics and roof spaces that are accessible by permanent stairs or ladders, Type AC cable must be protected by substantial guard strips that are _____.

    (a) at least as high as the cable   (b) constructed of metal   (c) made for the cable   (d) none of these

45. When armored cable is run parallel to the sides of rafters, studs, or floor joists in an accessible attic, the cable must be protected with running boards.

    (a) True   (b) False

46. Type AC cable must be supported and secured at intervals not exceeding 4 1/2 ft and the cable must be secured within _____ of every outlet box, cabinet, conduit body, or other armored cable termination.

    (a) 4 in.   (b) 8 in.   (c) 9 in.   (d) 12 in.

47. At all Type AC cable terminations, a(n) _____ must be provided.

    (a) fitting (or box design) that protects the wires from abrasion
    (b) insulating bushing between the conductors and the cable armor
    (c) both a and b
    (d) none of these

48. Type AC cable must provide _____ for equipment grounding as required by Article 250.

    (a) an adequate path
    (b) a green terminal on all Type AC fittings
    (c) a solid copper insulated green conductor in all Type AC cables
    (d) a bonding locknut on all Type AC fittings

Article 322 Flat Cable Assemblies (Type FC)

This article covers the use, installation, and construction specifications for flat cable assemblies, Type FC.

49. Flat cable assemblies are suitable to supply tap devices for _____ loads. The rating of the branch circuit must not exceed 30A.

    (a) lighting   (b) small appliance   (c) small power   (d) all of these

50. Flat cable assemblies must not be installed _____.

    (a) where subject to corrosive vapors unless suitable for the application
    (b) in hoistways
    (c) in any hazardous (classified) location
    (d) all of these

51. Tap devices used in Type FC assemblies must be rated at not less than _____ or more than 300 volts-to-ground, and they must be color-coded in accordance with the requirements of 322.120(C).

    (a) 20A   (b) 15A   (c) 30A   (d) 40A

52. Flat cable assemblies must have conductors of _____ AWG special stranded copper wires.

    (a) 14   (b) 12   (c) 10   (d) all of these

Article 324 Flat Conductor Cable (Type FCC)

This article covers a field-installed wiring system for branch circuits incorporating Type FCC cable and associated accessories as defined by the article. The wiring system is designed for installation under carpet squares.

53. Type FCC cable consists of _____ copper conductors placed edge-to-edge and separated and enclosed within an insulating assembly.

    (a) 3 or more square   (b) 2 or more round   (c) 3 or more flat   (d) 2 or more flat

54. The maximum voltage permitted between ungrounded conductors of flat conductor cable systems is _____.

    (a) 600V   (b) 300V   (c) 250V   (d) 150V

55. Use of Type FCC cable systems are permitted on wall surfaces in _____.

    (a) surface metal raceways   (b) cable trays   (c) busways   (d) any of these

56. Floor-mounted flat conductor cable and fittings must be covered with carpet squares no larger than _____.

    (a) 36 sq in. area   (b) 36 inches square   (c) 30 sq in. area   (d) 24 inches square

57. No more than _____ layers of flat conductor cable can cross at any one point.

    (a) 2   (b) 3   (c) 4   (d) none of these

58. The top shield installed over all floor-mounted Type FCC cable must completely _____ all cable runs, corners, connectors, and ends.

    (a) cover   (b) encase   (c) protect   (d) none of these

59. Each Type FCC transition assembly must incorporate means for _____.

    (a) facilitating the entry of the Type FCC cable into the assembly
    (b) connecting the Type FCC cable to the grounded conductors
    (c) electrically connecting the assembly to the metal cable shields and equipment grounding conductors
    (d) all of these

60. Type FCC cable must be clearly and durably marked _____.

    (a) on the top side at intervals not exceeding 30 in.
    (b) on both sides at intervals not exceeding 24 in.
    (c) with conductor material, maximum temperature, and ampacity
    (d) b and c

Article 328 Medium Voltage Cable (Type MV)

This article covers the use, installation, and construction specifications for medium voltage cable, Type MV.

61. Type MV cable is defined as a single or multiconductor solid dielectric insulated cable rated _____V or higher.

    (a) 601   (b) 1,001   (c) 2,001   (d) 6,001

Article 330 Metal-Clad Cable (Type MC)

Metal-clad cable encloses one or more insulated conductors in a metal sheath of either corrugated or smooth copper or aluminum tubing, or spiral interlocked steel or aluminum. The physical characteristics of type MC cable make it a versatile wiring method that is permitted in almost any location and for almost any application. The most common type of MC cable is the interlocking type, which looks similar to armored cable or flexible metal conduit.

62. Type MC cable installed through, or parallel to, framing members must be protected against physical damage from penetration by screws or nails by 1 1/4 in. separation or protected by a suitable metal plate.

    (a) True   (b) False

63. Type MC cable installed in accessible attics or roof spaces must comply with the same requirements as given for AC cable in 320.24. This includes the installation of guard strips to protect the cable when run across the top of floor joists within _____of the nearest edge of the scuttle hole or attic entrance if the space is not accessible by permanent stairs or ladders.

    (a) 6 ft   (b) 7 ft   (c) 1 1/4 in.   (d) 18 in.

64. Bends made in interlocked or corrugated sheath metal clad cable must maintain a bending radius of at least _____ the external diameter of the metallic sheath.

    (a) 5 times   (b) 7 times   (c) 10 times   (d) 125% of

65. Type MC cable containing four or fewer conductors, sized no larger than 10 AWG, must be secured within _____ of every box, cabinet, fitting, or other cable termination.

    (a) 8 in.   (b) 18 in.   (c) 12 in.   (d) 24 in.

66. Fittings used for connecting Type MC cable to boxes, cabinets, or other equipment must _____.

    (a) be nonmetallic only   (b) be listed and identified for such use
    (c) be listed and identified as weatherproof   (d) include anti-shorting bushings (red heads)

67. Where MC cable is used for equipment grounding it must comply with 250.118(10), which allows the metallic sheath alone of interlocked metal tape-type MC cable to be used as an equipment grounding conductor.

    (a) True   (b) False

Article 332 Mineral-Insulated, Metal-Sheathed Cable (Type MI)

This article covers the use, installation, and construction specifications for mineral-insulated, metal-sheathed cable, Type MI cable.

68. The outer sheath of Type MI cable is made of _____.

    (a) aluminum   (b) steel alloy   (c) copper   (d) b or c

69. Bends in Type MI cable must be made so that the cable will not be _____.

    (a) damaged   (b) shortened   (c) a and b   (d) none of these

70. The radius of the inner edge of any bend in Type MI cable must not be less than _____ times the external diameter of the metallic sheath for any cable having a diameter greater than 3/4 in., but not more than 1 in.

    (a) 6   (b) 3   (c) 8   (d) 10

71. Where single-conductor Type MI cables are used, all ungrounded (phase) conductors and, when used, the _____ conductor, must be grouped together to minimize induced voltage on the metal sheath.

    (a) larger   (b) grounded neutral (c) grounding   (d) largest

72. Type MI cable conductors must be made of _____, nickel, or nickel-coated copper with a resistance corresponding to standard AWG and kcmil sizes.

    (a) solid copper   (b) solid or stranded copper   (c) stranded copper   (d) solid copper or aluminum

73. The conductor insulation of Type MI cable must be a highly-compressed refractory mineral that will provide proper _____ for all conductors.

    (a) covering   (b) spacing   (c) resistance   (d) none of these

Article 334 Nonmetallic-Sheathed Cable (Types NM and NMC)

Nonmetallic-sheathed cable encloses two, three, or four insulated conductors, 14 AWG through 2 AWG, within a nonmetallic outer jacket. Because this cable is nonmetallic, it contains a separate equipment grounding conductor. Nonmetallic-sheathed cable is a common wiring method used for residential and commercial branch circuits. Most electricians call this plastic cable Romex®.

74. Types NM and NMC nonmetallic-sheathed cables can be used in _____.

    (a) one-family dwellings   (b) multifamily dwellings   (c) other structures   (d) all of these

75. Type NM cable can be installed in multifamily dwellings of Types III, IV, and V construction except as prohibited in 334.12.

    (a) True   (b) False

76. Type NM cable must not be used _____.

    (a) in commercial buildings   (b) in the air void of masonry block not subject to excessive moisture
    (c) for exposed work   (d) embedded in poured cement, concrete, or aggregate

77. When installed in _____, nonmetallic-sheathed cable must be protected from physical damage where necessary by RMC, IMC, schedule 80 rigid nonmetallic conduit, EMT, guard strips, or other means.

    (a) hazardous locations of commercial garages   (b) exposed work
    (c) service-entrance applications   (d) motion picture studios

78. NM cable on a wall of an unfinished basement is permitted to be installed in a listed raceway. A _____ must be installed at the point where the cable enters the raceway. Metal conduit and tubing and metal outlet boxes must be grounded.

    (a) nonmetallic bushing or adapter   (b) sealing fitting
    (c) bonding bushing   (d) junction box

79. Nonmetallic-sheathed cable installed in accessible attics or roof spaces must comply with the same requirements as given for AC cable in 320.24. This includes the installation of _____ to protect the cable when run across the top of floor joists if the space is accessible by permanent stairs or ladders.

    (a) GFCI protection   (b) arc-fault protection   (c) rigid metal conduit   (d) guard strips

80. Bends made in nonmetallic-sheathed cable must be made so that the cable will not be damaged. The radius of the curve of the inner edge of any bend during or after installation must not be less than _____ the external diameter of the cable.

    (a) 5 times   (b) 7 times   (c) 10 times   (d) 12 times

81. Flat two-conductor Type NM cables cannot be stapled on edge.

    (a) True   (b) False

82. Type NM cables run horizontally through framing are considered supported and secured where such support does not exceed 4 1/2 ft intervals and the Type NM cable is securely fastened in place within 12 in. of each box, cabinet, or conduit body.

    (a) True   (b) False

83. Switch, outlet, and tap devices of insulating material can be used without boxes in exposed cable wiring of Type NM or Type NMC cable.

    (a) True   (b) False

84. Where more than two NM cables containing two or more current-carrying conductors are bundled together and pass through wood framing that is to be fire- or draft-stopped using thermal insulation or sealing foam, the allowable ampacity of each conductor is _____.

    (a) no more than 20A   (b) adjusted in accordance with 310.15(B)(2)(a)

    (c) limited to 30A   (d) calculated by an engineer

85. •The difference in the construction specifications between Type NM cable and Type NMC cable is that Type NMC cable is _____, which Type NM is not.

    (a) corrosion-resistant   (b) flame-retardant   (c) fungus-resistant   (d) a and c

Article 336 Power and Control Tray Cable (Type TC)

Power and control cable tray is a factory assembly of two or more insulated conductors under a nonmetallic sheath for installation in cable trays, in raceways, or where supported by a messenger wire.

86. Type TC tray cable must not be installed _____.

    (a) where it will be exposed to physical damage   (b) outside of a raceway or cable tray system

    (c) direct buried unless identified for such use   (d) all of these

Article 338 Service-Entrance Cable (Types SE and USE)

Service-entrance cable can be a single-conductor or multiconductor assembly within an overall nonmetallic covering. This cable is used primarily for services not over 600V, but is also permitted for feeders and branch circuits.

87. Type USE cable used for service laterals can emerge from the ground outside at termination in meter bases or other enclosures where protected in accordance with 300.5(D).

    (a) True   (b) False

88. Type SE service-entrance cables are permitted for use for branch circuits or feeders where the insulated conductors are used for circuit wiring and the uninsulated conductor is used only for _____ purposes.

    (a) grounded neutral connection   (b) equipment grounding

    (c) remote control and signaling   (d) none of these

89. Bends made in USE and SE cable must be made so that the cable will not be damaged. The radius of the curve of the inner edge of any bend during or after installation must not be less than _____ the diameter of the cable.

    (a) 5 times   (b) 7 times   (c) 10 times   (d) 125% of

Article 340 Underground Feeder and Branch-Circuit Cable (Type UF)

Underground feeder cable is a moisture-, fungus-, and corrosion-resistant cable suitable for direct burial in the earth, and it comes in sizes 14 AWG through 4/0 AWG [340.104]. Multiconductor UF cable is covered in molded plastic that encapsulates the insulated conductors.

90. Type UF cable must not be used where subject to physical damage. When this cable is subject to physical damage, it must be protected by a suitable method as described in 300.5.

    (a) True   (b) False

91. Underground Feeder and branch-circuit (Type UF) cable is allowed to be used in commercial garages.

    (a) True   (b) False

92. Type UF cable must not be used _____.

(a) in any hazardous (classified) location
(b) embedded in poured cement, concrete, or aggregate
(c) where exposed to direct rays of the sun, unless identified as sunlight-resistant
(d) all of these

93. The ampacity of Type UF cables must be that of _____ in accordance with 310.15.

(a) 90°C conductors   (b) 75°C conductors   (c) 60°C conductors   (d) none of these

94. The overall covering of Type UF cable must be _____.

(a) flame retardant   (b) moisture, fungus, and corrosion resistant
(c) suitable for direct burial in the earth   (d) all of these

Article 342 Intermediate Metal Conduit (Type IMC)

Intermediate metal conduit is a circular metal raceway with the same outside diameter as rigid metal conduit. The wall thickness of intermediate metal conduit is less than that of rigid metal conduit, so it has a greater interior cross-sectional area. Intermediate metal conduit is lighter and less expensive than rigid metal conduit, but it's permitted in all the same locations as rigid metal conduit. Intermediate metal conduit also uses a different steel alloy, which makes it stronger than rigid metal conduit, even though the walls are thinner.

95. Materials such as straps, bolts, screws, etc. that are associated with the installation of IMC in wet locations are required to be _____.

(a) weatherproof   (b) weathertight   (c) corrosion-resistant   (d) none of these

96. Trade Size 1 IMC raceway containing three or more conductors must not exceed _____ percent conductor fill.

(a) 53   (b) 31   (c) 40   (d) 60

97. A run of IMC must not contain more than the equivalent of _____ quarter bends including all offsets between pull points such as conduit bodies and boxes.

(a) 1   (b) 2   (c) 3   (d) 4

98. Trade Size 1 IMC must be supported every _____.

(a) 8 ft   (b) 10 ft   (c) 12 ft   (d) 14 ft

99. Horizontal runs of IMC supported by openings through framing members at intervals not exceeding 10 ft and securely fastened within 3 ft of terminations is permitted.

(a) True   (b) False

100. Threadless couplings and connectors must not be used on threaded IMC ends unless the fittings are listed for the purpose.

(a) True   (b) False

(• Indicates that 75% or fewer of those who took this exam answered the question correctly.)

1. In a balanced 120/208V, 4-wire, three-phase system, the grounded conductor will carry _____ amperes if the loads supplied are linear loads and no harmonic currents are present.

    (a) full load   (b) zero   (c) fault-current   (d) none of these

2. •Nonmetallic boxes are permitted for use with _____.

    (a) flexible nonmetallic conduit   (b) liquidtight nonmetallic conduit
    (c) nonmetallic cables and raceways   (d) all of these

3. •Type USE or SE cable must have a minimum of _____ conductors (including the uninsulated one) in order for one of the conductors to be uninsulated.

    (a) one   (b) two   (c) three   (d) four

4. •What is the total volume, in cubic inches, for box fill calculations for two internal cable clamps, six 12 THHN conductors, and one single-pole switch?

    (a) 2.00 cu in.   (b) 4.50 cu in.   (c) 14.50 cu in.   (d) 20.25 cu in.

5. A luminaire that weighs more than 50 lbs is permitted to be supported by an outlet box or fitting that is designed and listed for the weight of the luminaire.

    (a) True   (b) False

6. A wood brace that is used for mounting a box must have a cross-section not less than nominal _____.

    (a) 1 x 2 in   (b) 2 x 2 in   (c) 2 x 3 in   (d) 2 x 4 in

7. All bare Type FCC cable ends must _____.

    (a) be sealed   (b) be insulated   (c) use listed insulating ends   (d) all of these

8. All boxes and conduit bodies, covers, extension rings, plaster rings, and the like must be durably and legibly marked with the manufacturer's name or trademark.

    (a) True   (b) False

9. Boxes, conduit bodies, and fittings installed in wet locations do not need to be listed for use in wet locations.

    (a) True   (b) False

10. Cables with entirely nonmetallic sheaths are permitted to enter the top of a surface-mounted enclosure through one or more non-flexible raceways not less than 18 in. or more than _____ ft in length if all of the required conditions are met.

    (a) 3   (b) 10   (c) 25   (d) 100

11. Enclosures not over _____ in size, having threaded entries and that do not contain a device(s) or support a luminaire(s) or other equipment, is considered to be adequately supported where two or more conduits are threaded wrenchtight into the enclosure and each conduit secured within 3 ft.

    (a) 50 cu in.   (b) 75 cu in.   (c) 100 cu in.   (d) 125 cu in.

12. Equipment grounding conductor(s), and not more than _____ fixture wires (smaller than 14 AWG) can be omitted from the calculations where they enter the box from a domed luminaire or similar canopy and terminate within that box.

    (a) 2   (b) 3   (c) 4   (d) none of these

13. Flat cable assemblies must consist of _____ conductors.

    (a) 2   (b) 3   (c) 4   (d) any of these

14. Flat cable assemblies must not be installed outdoors or in wet or damp locations unless _____ for the use.

    (a) special permission is granted   (b) approved
    (c) identified   (d) none of these

15. For conductors rated 2,001V to 35,000V, thermal resistively is the reciprocal of thermal conductivity, is designated Rho, and is expressed in units of _____.

    (a) °F-cm/volt   (b) °F-cm/watt   (c) °C-cm/volt   (d) °C-cm/watt

16. For individual dwelling units of _____ dwellings, Table 310.15(B)(6) can be used to size 3-wire, single-phase, 120/240V service or feeder conductors that serve as the main power feeder.

    (a) one-family   (b) two-family   (c) multifamily   (d) any of these

17. Handhole enclosure covers must have an identifying _____ that prominently identifies the function of the enclosure, such as "electric."

    (a) mark   (b) logo   (c) a or b   (d) manual

18. Handhole enclosures must be designed and installed to withstand _____.

    (a) 3,000 lbs   (b) 6,000 lbs   (c) all loads likely to be imposed   (d) 600 lbs

19. IMC must be firmly fastened within _____ of each outlet box, junction box, device box, fitting, cabinet, or other conduit termination.

    (a) 12 in.   (b) 18 in.   (c) 2 ft   (d) 3 ft

20. In completed installations, each outlet box must have a _____.

    (a) cover   (b) faceplate   (c) canopy   (d) any of these

21. In walls constructed of wood or other _____ material, electrical cabinets must be flush with the finished surface or project therefrom.

    (a) nonconductive   (b) porous   (c) fibrous   (d) combustible

22. Metal shields for flat conductor cable must be electrically continuous to the _____.

    (a) floor   (b) cable
    (c) equipment grounding conductor   (d) none of these

23. Nonmetallic-sheathed cable installed in accessible attics or roof spaces must comply with the same requirements as given for AC cable in 320.24. This includes the installation of guard strips to protect the cable when run across the top of floor joists within _____ of the nearest edge of the scuttle hole or attic entrance if the space is not accessible by permanent stairs or ladders.

    (a) 6 ft   (b) 7 ft   (c) 1 1/4 in.   (d) 18 in.

24. Sections of Type NM cable protected from physical damage by a raceway are not required to be _____ within the raceway.

(a) covered   (b) insulated   (c) secured   (d) unspliced

25. Smooth-sheath Type MC cable with an external diameter of not greater than 1 in. must have a bending radius of not more than _____ times the cable external diameter.

(a) 5   (b) 10   (c) 12   (d) 13

26. Surface extensions from a flush-mounted box must be made by mounting and mechanically securing an extension ring over the flush box.

(a) True   (b) False

27. Table 310.71 provides ampacities of an insulated three-conductor copper cable isolated in air, based on conductor temperature of 90°C (194°F) and ambient air temperature of 40°C (104°F). If the conductor size is 4/0 AWG, MV-105, and the voltage range is 2,001 through 5,000, then the ampacity is _____.

(a) 250A   (b) 285A   (c) 320A   (d) 325A

28. The ampacity of Type NM cable must be that of 60°C conductors, as listed in 310.15. However, the 90°C rating can be used for ampacity derating purposes provided the final derated ampacity does not exceed that of a _____ rated conductor.

(a) 120°C   (b) 60°C   (c) 90°C   (d) none of these

29. The distance between a shielded cable or conductor entry and its exit from the box must be not less than _____ times the outside diameter of that cable or conductor on a system of over 600V.

(a) 16   (b) 18   (c) 36   (d) 40

30. The maximum size of conductors in Underground Feeder (Type UF) cable is _____ AWG.

(a) 14   (b) 10   (c) 1/0   (d) 4/0

31. The metallic sheath of metal-clad cable must be continuous and _____.

(a) flame-retardant   (b) weatherproof   (c) close fitting   (d) all of these

32. The radius of the curve of the inner edge of any bend must not be less than _____ for AC cable.

(a) five times the largest conductor within the cable   (b) three times the diameter of the cable
(c) five times the diameter of the cable   (d) six times the outside diameter of the conductors

33. The radius of the inner edge of any bend in Type MI cable must not be less than five times the external diameter of the metallic sheath for cable not more than _____ in external diameter.

(a) 1/2 in.   (b) 3/4 in.   (c) 5/8 in.   (d) 1 1/2 in.

34. Threadless couplings approved for use with IMC in wet locations must be _____.

(a) rainproof   (b) listed for wet locations   (c) moistureproof   (d) concrete-tight

35. Type AC cable installed through, or parallel to, framing members must be protected against physical damage from penetration by screws or nails.

(a) True   (b) False

36. Type FCC systems are permitted both for general-purpose and appliance branch circuits; they are not permitted for individual branch circuits.

    (a) True　　　　　　　　　　(b) False

37. Type MC cable can be unsupported where it is:

    (a) Fished between concealed access points in finished buildings or structures and support is impracticable.
    (b) Not more than 2 ft in length at terminals where flexibility is necessary.
    (c) Not more than 6 ft from the last point of support within an accessible ceiling for the connection of luminaires.
    (d) a or c

38. Type MC cable must not be used where exposed to the following destructive corrosive condition(s), unless the metallic sheath is suitable for the condition(s) or is protected by material suitable for the condition(s):

    (a) Direct burial in the earth　　(b) In concrete　　　　　(c) In cinder fill　　　　　(d) all of these

39. Type NM cable can be installed as open runs in dropped or suspended ceilings in other than one- and two-family and multifamily dwellings.

    (a) True　　　　　　　　　　(b) False

40. Type NM cable must be _____.

    (a) marked　　　　　　　　　(b) approved　　　　　　　(c) identified　　　　　　　(d) listed

41. Type SE service-entrance cable is permitted for use as _____ in wiring systems where all of the circuit conductors of the cable are of the rubber-covered or thermoplastic type.

    (a) branch circuits　　　　　(b) feeders　　　　　　　　(c) a or b　　　　　　　　　(d) neither a or b

42. Type TC cable can be used _____.

    (a) for power and lighting circuits　　　　　　　　　　(b) in cable trays in hazardous locations
    (c) in Class 1 control circuits　　　　　　　　　　　　(d) all of these

43. Type UF cable must not be used in _____.

    (a) motion picture studios　　(b) storage battery rooms　　(c) hoistways　　　　　　　(d) all of these

44. Use of Type FCC systems in damp locations _____.

    (a) are restricted　　　　　　　　　　　　　　　　　　(b) are permitted
    (c) are permitted provided the system is encased in concrete　(d) must be approved by special permission

45. When NM cable is used with nonmetallic boxes no larger than 2 1/4 x 4 in., securing the cable to the box is not required if the cable is fastened within _____ of that box.

    (a) 6 in.　　　　　　　　　　(b) 8 in.　　　　　　　　　(c) 10 in.　　　　　　　　　(d) 12 in.

46. When sizing a pull box in a straight run which contains conductors of 4 AWG or larger, the length of the box must not be less than _____ for systems not over 600V.

    (a) 8 times the diameter of the largest raceway
    (b) 6 times the diameter of the largest raceway
    (c) 48 times the outside diameter of the largest shielded conductor
    (d) 36 times the largest conductor

47.   When Type AC cable is installed in thermal insulation, it must have conductors that are rated at 90°C. The ampacity of the cable in this application is _____.

   (a) based on 90°C column   (b) as labeled by the manufacturer
   (c) based on the 60°C column   (d) none of these

48.   Where practicable, contact of dissimilar metals must be avoided anywhere in an IMC raceway installation to prevent _____.

   (a) corrosion   (b) galvanic action   (c) shorts   (d) none of these

49.   Where Type MI cable terminates, a(n) _____ must be installed immediately after stripping to prevent the entrance of moisture into the insulation.

   (a) bushing   (b) connector   (c) flexible fitting   (d) end seal fitting

50.   Where Type NMC cable is run at angles with joists in unfinished basements, it is permissible to secure cables not smaller than _____ conductors directly to the lower edges of the joist.

   (a) two, 6 AWG   (b) three, 8 AWG   (c) three, 10 AWG   (d) a or b

(• Indicates that 75% or fewer of those who took this exam answered the question correctly.)

1. Grounded conductors _____ and larger must be identified by a continuous white or gray outer finish along their entire length, by three continuous white stripes along their entire length, or by distinctive white or gray markings such as tape, paint, or other effective means at their terminations.

    (a) 10 AWG   (b) 8 AWG   (c) 6 AWG   (d) 4 AWG

2. Grounding and bonding conductors cannot be connected by _____.

    (a) pressure connections   (b) solder   (c) lugs   (d) approved clamps

3. Grounding electrodes that are driven rods require a minimum of _____ in contact with the soil.

    (a) 10 ft   (b) 8 ft   (c) 6 ft   (d) 12 ft

4. Grounding-type attachment plugs must be used only with a cord having a(n) _____ conductor.

    (a) equipment grounding   (b) isolated   (c) computer circuit   (d) insulated

5. Hazards often occur because of _____.

    (a) overloading of wiring systems by methods or usage not in conformity with this *Code*
    (b) initial wiring not providing for increases in the use of electricity
    (c) a and b
    (d) none of these

6. HDPE is allowed only in trade sizes _____.

    (a) 3/4 to 4   (b) 1/2 to 4   (c) 1 to 5   (d) 1 to 3

7. HDPE is permitted to be installed _____.

    (a) where subject to chemicals for which the conduit is listed   (b) in cinder fill
    (c) in direct burial installations in earth or concrete   (d) all of these

8. How many 12 XHHW conductors, not counting a bare ground wire, are allowed in trade size 3/8 FMC (maximum of 6 ft) with outside fittings?

    (a) 4   (b) 3   (c) 2   (d) 5

9. Hydromassage bathtubs and their associated electrical components must be GFCI protected.

    (a) True   (b) False

10. If required by the authority having jurisdiction, a diagram showing feeder details must be provided _____ of the feeders.

    (a) after the installation   (b) prior to the installation   (c) before the final inspection   (d) diagrams are not required

11. If the motor disconnecting means is a motor-circuit switch, it must be rated in _____.

    (a) horsepower   (b) watts   (c) amperes   (d) locked-rotor current

12. IMC can be installed in or under cinder fill subject to permanent moisture _____.

   (a) where the conduit is not less than 18 in. under the fill
   (b) when protected on all sides by 2 in. of noncinder concrete
   (c) where protected by corrosion protection judged suitable for the condition
   (d) any of these

13. In a Class II, Division 1 location, switches, circuit breakers, motor controllers, and fuses, including pushbuttons, relays, and similar devices that are intended to interrupt current during normal operation or that are installed where combustible dusts of an electrically conductive nature may be present, are required to be provided with identified _____ enclosures.

   (a) explosionproof   (b) dust-ignitionproof   (c) dusttight   (d) weatherproof

14. In a Class III hazardous (classified) location, pendant luminaires suspended by stems longer than _____ ft must be provided with a fitting or flexible connector approved for the location.

   (a) 1   (b) 2   (c) 3   (d) 4

15. In a dwelling unit, illumination on the exterior side of outdoor entrances or exits that have grade-level access can be controlled by _____.

   (a) home automation devices   (b) motion sensors   (c) photocells   (d) any of these

16. In a multiple-occupancy building, each occupant must have access to his or her own _____.

   (a) disconnecting means   (b) building drops
   (c) building-entrance assembly   (d) lateral conductors

17. In areas used for patient care, the grounding terminals of all receptacles and all noncurrent-carrying conductive surfaces of fixed electric equipment _____ must be grounded by an insulated copper equipment grounding conductor.

   (a) operating at over 100V   (b) likely to become energized
   (c) subject to personal contact   (d) all of these

18. In assembly occupancies, NM cable, type AC cable, electrical nonmetallic tubing, and rigid nonmetallic conduit are permitted to be installed in those portions of the building that is not required to be of _____ construction by the applicable building code.

   (a) Class I, Division 1   (b) fire-rated   (c) occupancy-rated   (d) aboveground

19. In Class I, Division 1 and 2 locations, locknut-bushing and double-locknut types of fittings are depended on for bonding purposes.

   (a) True   (b) False

20. In Class I, Division 1 and 2 locations, receptacles and attachment plugs must be of the type providing for _____ a flexible cord and must be identified for the location.

   (a) sealing compound around   (b) quick connection to
   (c) connection to the grounding conductor of   (d) none of these

21. In Class II, Division 1 locations, motors, generators, or other rotating electric machinery must be _____.

   (a) identified for Class II, Division 1 locations
   (b) totally enclosed pipe-ventilated, and meet the temperature limitations of 502.5
   (c) general duty
   (d) a or b

22. In Class II, Division 1 locations, receptacles and attachment plugs must be of the type providing for connection to the grounding conductor of the flexible cord and must be identified _____.

    (a) as explosionproof   (b) for Class II locations   (c) with laminated tags   (d) for general duty

23. In Class III, Divisions 1 and 2, _____ used as or in conjunction with control equipment for motors, generators, and appliances must be provided with dusttight enclosures complying with the temperature limitations in 504.5.

    (a) transformers   (b) impedance coils   (c) resistors   (d) all of these

24. In dwelling units, the voltage between conductors that supply the terminals of _____ must not exceed 120V, nominal.

    (a) luminaires
    (b) cord-and-plug connected loads of 1,440 VA, nominal, or less
    (c) cord-and-plug connected loads of more than 1/4 hp
    (d) a and b

25. In dwelling units, when determining the spacing of general-use receptacles, _____ on exterior walls are not considered wall space.

    (a) fixed panels   (b) fixed glass   (c) sliding panels   (d) all of these

26. In general, branch-circuit conductors to individual appliances must not be sized _____ than required by the appliance markings or instructions.

    (a) larger   (b) smaller

27. In information technology equipment rooms, a single disconnecting means is permitted to control _____.

    (a) only the HVAC systems to the room
    (b) only the power to electronic computer/data-processing equipment
    (c) the electronic computer/data-processing equipment and the building supply
    (d) the HVAC systems to the room and power to electronic computer/data-processing equipment

28. In marinas or boatyards, the *NEC* requires a(n) _____ disconnecting means, which allows individual boats to be isolated from their supply circuit.

    (a) accessible   (b) readily accessible   (c) remote   (d) any of these

29. In one- and two-family dwellings, the grounding conductor for CATV must be as short as practicable, not to exceed _____ in length.

    (a) 5 ft   (b) 8 ft   (c) 10 ft   (d) 20 ft

30. In one- and two-family dwellings, the primary protector grounding conductor for communications systems must be as short as practicable, not to exceed _____ in length.

    (a) 5 ft   (b) 8 ft   (c) 10 ft   (d) 20 ft

31. In order for equipment and materials to receive approval _____.

    (a) the equipment and material must always be listed by UL
    (b) the authority having jurisdiction must decide on approval
    (c) the authority having jurisdiction can never approve nonlisted items
    (d) the local electrical distributor must decide on approval

32. In order to use the optional method for calculating a service to a school, the school must be equipped with _____.

   (a) cooking facilities   (b) electric space heating   (c) air-conditioning   (d) b or c

33. In walls or ceilings constructed of wood or other combustible surface material, boxes, plaster rings, extension rings, or listed extenders must _____.

   (a) be flush with the surface   (b) project from the surface
   (c) a or b   (d) be set back no more than 1/4 in.

34. Individual unit equipment for legally required standby illumination must be permanently fixed in place. Flexible cord-and-plug connection is permitted, provided the cord does not exceed _____ in length.

   (a) 3 ft   (b) 18 in.   (c) 6 ft   (d) 12 in.

35. Indoor antenna and lead-in conductors for radio and television receiving equipment must be separated by at least _____ from conductors of any electric light, power, or Class 1 circuit conductors.

   (a) 6 ft   (b) 2 in.   (c) 12 in.   (d) 18 in.

36. Insulated conductors and cables exposed to the direct rays of the sun must be _____.

   (a) covered with insulating material that is listed or listed and marked sunlight resistant
   (b) listed and marked sunlight resistant
   (c) listed for sunlight resistance
   (d) any of these

37. It is permitted to base the _____ rating of a range receptacle on a single range demand load specified in Table 220.19.

   (a) circuit   (b) voltage   (c) ampere   (d) resistance

38. Legally required standby system equipment must be suitable for _____ at its line terminals.

   (a) the maximum available fault current   (b) the maximum overload current only
   (c) the minimum fault current   (d) a one hour rating

39. Lighting outlets can be controlled by occupancy sensors equipped with a _____ that will allow the sensor to function as a wall switch.

   (a) manual override   (b) photo cell
   (c) GFCI device   (d) selenium controlled rectifier (SCR)

40. Lighting systems operating at 30V or less need not be listed for the purpose.

   (a) True   (b) False

41. Listed plenum signaling raceways and _____ cable for Class 1, Class 2, and Class 3 circuits are permitted to be installed in other spaces used for environmental air as described in 300.22(C).

   (a) Type CL2P   (b) Type CL3P   (c) a or b   (d) none of these

42. Listed spa and hot tub packaged units installed indoors, rated 20A or less, are permitted to be cord-and-plug connected.

   (a) True   (b) False

43. Locations in which combustible dust is in the air under normal operating conditions in quantities sufficient to produce explosive or ignitible mixtures are classified as _____.

    (a) Class I, Division 2   (b) Class II, Division 1   (c) Class II, Division 2   (d) Class III, Division 1

44. Luminaires and ceiling fans located over or within 5 ft, measured horizontally, from the inside walls of an indoor spa or hot tub must have a mounting height of not less than _____ above the maximum water level when GFCI protection is NOT provided.

    (a) 4.7 ft   (b) 5 ft   (c) 7 ft 6 in.   (d) 12 ft

45. Luminaires are permitted to be installed in a commercial cooking hood where specific conditions are met, including the requirement that the luminaire be identified for use within a _____ cooking hood.

    (a) nonresidential   (b) commercial   (c) multifamily   (d) all of these

46. Luminaires containing a metal halide lamp, other than a thick-glass parabolic reflector lamp (PAR), must be provided with a containment barrier that encloses the lamp, or the luminaire must be provided with a physical means that only allows the use of a(n) _____.

    (a) Type "O" lamp   (b) Type PAR lamp   (c) a or b   (d) inert gas

47. Luminaires installed in a fountain must _____

    (a) be capable of being removed from the water for relamping or normal maintenance
    (b) not be permanently embedded into the fountain structure
    (c) a and b
    (d) a or b

48. Manufactured wiring systems constructed with Type MC cable must be supported and secured at intervals not exceeding _____.

    (a) 3 ft   (b) 4 1/2 ft   (c) 6 ft   (d) none of these

49. Masts and metal structures supporting antennas must be grounded in accordance with the requirements of Article 250.

    (a) True   (b) False

50. Materials such as straps, bolts, etc., associated with the installation of RMC in a wet location are required to be _____.

    (a) weatherproof   (b) weathertight   (c) corrosion-resistant   (d) none of these

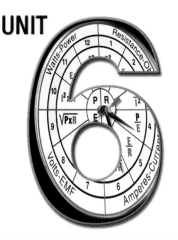

UNIT 6

Conductor Sizing and Protection Calculations

Introduction

Every conductor has a certain amount of resistance. Any time current flows through a conductor there is resistance, and heat is generated. The amount of heat produced is directly proportional to the resistance of the wire and the square of the actual current flow. In order to determine what size conductor is needed to carry a certain amount of current, the heat that will be generated must be taken into consideration. The number of conductors in the same raceway that are carrying current can have an effect on this decision, as can the ambient or surrounding temperature.

This unit explains how to evaluate all of these factors and make the proper choice in sizing electrical conductors, and how to select the proper conductor based on the temperature rating of the equipment terminals. As you can see, this can become a complicated choice, and this unit must be studied carefully to learn how to make the right conductor sizing decisions.

The amount of current that a conductor is allowed to carry must be limited to a level that will not allow destructive overheating of the conductor or of the equipment or structure it may be in contact with. In order to make sure that the amount of current on a conductor is kept within safe limits, overcurrent protection is used to open the circuit. Generally this protection is provided by installing a fuse or circuit breaker, of a size based on the conductor's ampacity, at the point where the conductor receives its supply. The general rules for overcurrent protection are covered in this unit, along with exceptions to the general rules, such as those for tap conductors and special cases such as motor circuits. Motor circuits will be covered in more depth in Unit 7.

PART A—GENERAL CONDUCTOR REQUIREMENTS

6.1 Conductor Insulation Property [Table 310.13]

Table 310.13 of the *NEC* provides information on conductor properties such as permitted use, maximum operating temperature, and other insulation details. **Figure 6–1**

The following abbreviations and explanations should be helpful in understanding Table 310.13 as well as Table 310.16.

-2   Conductor is permitted to be used at a continuous 90°C operating temperature [Table 310.13, Note 4]

F   Fixture wire (solid or 7-strand) [Table 402.3]

FF   Flexible fixture wire (19-strand) [Table 402.3]

H   75°C Insulation rating

HH   90°C Insulation rating

N   Nylon outer cover

T   Thermoplastic insulation

W   Wet or Damp

For more information about fixture wires, see Article 402, Table 402.3, and Table 402.5. For more information on flexible cords and flexible cables, see Article 400, Table 400.4, Table 400.5(A), and Table 400.5(B).

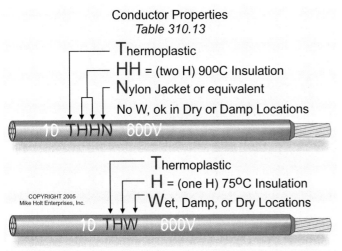

Conductor Properties
Table 310.13

Thermoplastic
HH = (two H) 90ºC Insulation
Nylon Jacket or equivalent
No W, ok in Dry or Damp Locations

10 THHN 600V

Thermoplastic
H = (one H) 75ºC Insulation
Wet, Damp, or Dry Locations

COPYRIGHT 2005
Mike Holt Enterprises, Inc.

10 THW 600V

Table 310.13 contains conductor insulation information, such as operating temperature and applications. These conductors can be used in any Chapter 3 wiring method.

Figure 6–1

▶ **Table 310.13**

TW can be described as _____. Figure 6–2

   (a) thermoplastic insulation
   (b) suitable for dry or wet locations
   (c) maximum operating temperature of 60°C
   (d) all of these

   • Answer: (d) all of these

▶ **Table 402.3**

TFFN can be described as _____.

   (a) stranded fixture wire
   (b) thermoplastic insulation with a nylon outer cover
   (c) suitable for dry and wet locations
   (d) both a and b

   • Answer: (d) both a and b

Table 310.13 Conductor Information

Type Letter	Column 2 Insulation	Column 3 Maximum Operating Temperature	Column 4 Application	Column 5 Sizes Available AWG or Kcmil	Column 6 Outer Covering
THHN	Heat-resistant thermoplastic	90°C	Dry and damp locations	14 – 1,000	Nylon jacket or equivalent
THHW	Moisture- & heat-resistant thermoplastic	75°C 90°C	Wet locations Dry and damp locations	14 – 1,000	None
THW	Moisture- & heat-resistant thermoplastic	75°C 90°C	Dry, damp, and wet locations Within electrical discharge lighting equipment *See Section 410.33*	14 – 2,000	None
THWN	Moisture- & heat-resistant thermoplastic	75°C	Dry and wet locations	14 – 1,000	Nylon jacket or equivalent
TW	Moisture-resistant thermoplastic	60°C	Dry and wet locations	14 – 2,000	None
XHHW	Moisture-resistant thermoset	90°C 75°C	Dry and damp locations Wet locations	14 – 2,000	None

Understanding Conductor Insulation Markings
Table 310.13

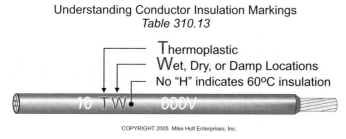

Thermoplastic
Wet, Dry, or Damp Locations
No "H" indicates 60°C insulation

COPYRIGHT 2005 Mike Holt Enterprises, Inc.

Figure 6–2

6.2 Allowable Conductor Ampacity [310.15]

The ampacity of a conductor is the current in amperes that a conductor can carry continuously without exceeding its temperature rating under specific conditions of use.

General Requirements

Tables or Engineering Supervision. There are two ways to determine conductor ampacity:

• Tables 310.16 [310.15(B)]
• Engineering formula

AUTHOR'S COMMENT: For all practical purposes, use the ampacities listed in Table 310.16.

FPN: The ampacities listed in Table 310.16 are based on temperature alone and don't take voltage drop into consideration. Voltage drop considerations are for efficiency of operation and not for safety; therefore, sizing conductors for voltage drop is not a *Code* requirement. See 210.19(A)(1) FPN No. 4 and 215.2(A)(3) FPN No. 2 for more details.

Table 310.16. Allowable Ampacities of Insulated Conductors
Based On Not More Than Three Current-Carrying Conductors and Ambient Temperature of 30°C (86°F)

Size	Temperature Rating of Conductor, See Table 310.13						Size
	60°C (40°F)	75°C (167°F)	90°C (194°F)	60°C (40°F)	75°C (167°F)	90°C (194°F)	
AWG kcmil	TW UF	THHW THW THWN XHHW Wet Location	THHW XHHW Dry Location	TW UF	THHW THW THWN XHHW Wet Location	THHN THHW XHHN Dry Location	AWG kcmil
	Copper			Aluminum/Copper-Clad Aluminum			
14*	20	20	25				12*
12*	25	25	30	20	20	25	10*
10*	30	35	40	25	30	35	8*
8	40	50	55	30	40	45	8
6	55	65	75	40	50	60	6
4	70	85	95	55	65	75	4
3	85	100	110	65	75	85	3
2	95	115	130	75	90	100	2
1	110	130	150	85	100	115	1
1/0	125	150	170	100	120	135	1/0
2/0	145	175	195	115	135	150	2/0
3/0	165	200	225	130	155	175	3/0
4/0	195	230	260	150	180	205	4/0
250	215	255	290	170	205	230	250
300	240	285	320	190	230	255	300
350	260	310	350	210	250	280	350
400	280	335	380	225	270	305	400
500	320	380	430	260	310	350	500

*See 240.4(D)

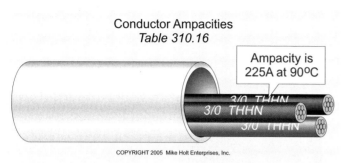

Conductor Ampacities
Table 310.16

Ampacity is 225A at 90°C

3/0 THHN
3/0 THHN
3/0 THHN

COPYRIGHT 2005 Mike Holt Enterprises, Inc.

Table 310.16 is based on an ambient temperature of 86°F and 3 current-carrying conductors in a raceway or cable.

Figure 6–3

Table Ampacity

The ampacity of a conductor is listed in Table 310.16 under the condition of no more than three current-carrying conductors bundled together in an ambient temperature of 86°F, **Figure 6–3**. The ampacity of a conductor changes if the ambient temperature is not 86°F or if more than three current-carrying conductors are bundled together.

6.3 Conductor Sizing [110.6]

Conductors are sized according to the American Wire Gage (AWG) from 40 AWG through 4/0 AWG. The smaller the number, the larger the conductor up to 1 AWG. Conductors larger than 4/0 AWG are identified according to their circular cross-sectional area in mils, such as 250,000 cmil, 300,000 cmil, 500,000 cmil, etc. The circular mil size is usually expressed in kcmil (1,000 circular mils), such as 250 kcmil, 300 kcmil, 500 kcmil, etc. **Figure 6–4**

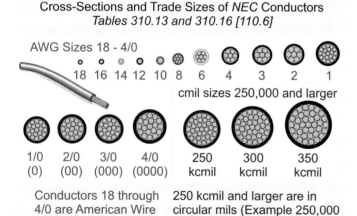

Cross-Sections and Trade Sizes of *NEC* Conductors
Tables 310.13 and 310.16 [110.6]

AWG Sizes 18 - 4/0

18 16 14 12 10 8 6 4 3 2 1

cmil sizes 250,000 and larger

1/0   2/0   3/0   4/0   250   300   350
(0)   (00)   (000) (0000) kcmil   kcmil   kcmil

Conductors 18 through 4/0 are American Wire Gage (AWG).

250 kcmil and larger are in circular mils (Example 250,000 cmil or 250 kcmil).

COPYRIGHT 2005 Mike Holt Enterprises, Inc.

Figure 6–4

Smallest Conductor Size

The smallest size conductor permitted by the *NEC* for branch circuits, feeders, or services is 14 AWG copper or 12 AWG aluminum [Table 310.5]. Some local codes require a minimum 12 AWG for commercial and industrial installations. Conductors smaller than 14 AWG are permitted for:

Class 1 remote-control circuits [725.27]
Fixture wire [402.6]
Flexible cords [400.12]
Motor control circuits [Table 430.72(B)]
Nonpower-limited fire alarm circuits [760.23]
Power-limited fire alarm circuits [760.82(B)]

6.4 Terminal Ratings [110.14(C)]

Conductors must be sized in accordance with the lowest temperature rating of any terminal, device, or conductor insulation of the circuit.

Circuits Rated 100A and Less [110.14(C)(1)(a)]

Equipment terminals rated 100A or less (and pressure connector terminals for 14 AWG through 1 AWG conductors), must have the conductor sized no smaller than the 60°C temperature rating listed in Table 310.16, unless the terminals are marked otherwise. **Figure 6–5**

AUTHOR'S COMMENT: Conductors are sized to prevent the overheating of terminals, in accordance with listing standards. For example, a 50A circuit with 60°C terminals requires the

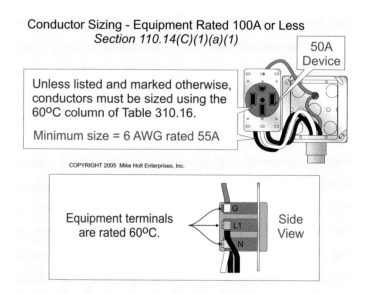

Conductor Sizing - Equipment Rated 100A or Less
Section 110.14(C)(1)(a)(1)

50A Device

Unless listed and marked otherwise, conductors must be sized using the 60°C column of Table 310.16.

Minimum size = 6 AWG rated 55A

COPYRIGHT 2005 Mike Holt Enterprises, Inc.

Equipment terminals are rated 60°C.

Side View

Figure 6–5

Conductor Sizing - Equipment Rated 100A or Less
Section 110.14(C)(1)(a)(1)

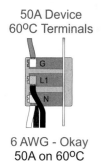
50A Device
60°C Terminals

50A Device
60°C Terminals

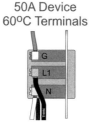
50A Device
60°C Terminals

6 AWG - Okay
50A on 60°C
wire operates
at near 60°C

8 AWG - Violation
50A on 75°C
wire operates
at near 75°C

8 AWG - Violation
50A on 90°C
wire operates
at near 90°C

COPYRIGHT 2005 Mike Holt Enterprises, Inc.

Conductors are sized to prevent the overheating
of terminals in accordance with listing standards.

Figure 6–6

Conductor Sizing - Equipment Rated 100A or Less
Section 110.14(C)(1)(a)(2) and (3)

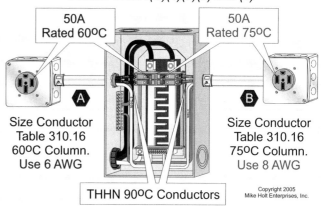

50A
Rated 60°C

50A
Rated 75°C

Size Conductor
Table 310.16
60°C Column.
Use 6 AWG

Size Conductor
Table 310.16
75°C Column.
Use 8 AWG

THHN 90°C Conductors

Copyright 2005
Mike Holt Enterprises, Inc.

If the terminals are listed and identified as suitable
for 75°C, then conductors can be sized to the 75°C
temperature column of Table 310.16.

Figure 6–7

circuit conductors to be sized not smaller than 6 AWG, in accordance with the 60°C ampacity listed in Table 310.16. However, an 8 THHN insulated conductor has a 90°C ampacity of 50A, but 8 AWG cannot be used for this circuit because the conductor's operating temperature at full-load ampacity (50A) will be near 90°C, which is well in excess of the 60°C terminal rating. **Figure 6–6**

▶ **Terminal Rated 60°C [110.14(C)(1)(a)(1)]**

What size THHN conductor is required for a 50A circuit listed for use at 60°C? **Figure 6–7A**

(a) 10 AWG   (b) 8 AWG
(c) 6 AWG   (d) any of these

• Answer: (c) 6 AWG

Conductors must be sized to the lowest temperature rating of either the equipment or the conductor. THHN insulation can be used, but the conductor size must be selected based on the 60°C terminal rating of the equipment, not the 90°C rating of the insulation. Using the 60°C column of Table 310.16, this 50A circuit requires a 6 THHN conductor (rated 55A at 60°C).

▶ **Terminal Rated 75°C [110.14(C)(1)(a)(2)]**

What size THHN conductor is required for a 50A circuit listed for use at 75°C? **Figure 6–7B**

(a) 10 AWG   (b) 8 AWG
(c) 6 AWG   (d) any of these

• Answer: (b) 8 AWG

Conductors must be sized according to the lowest temperature rating of either the equipment or the conductor. THHN insulation can be used, but the conductor size must be selected based on the 75°C terminal rating of the equipment, not the 90°C rating of the insulation. Using the 75°C column of Table 310.16, this installation will permit 8 THHN (rated 50A at 75°C) to supply the 50A circuit.

Circuits Over 100A [110.14(C)(1)(b)]

Terminals for equipment rated over 100A and pressure connector terminals for conductors larger than 1 AWG must have the conductor sized according to the 75°C temperature rating listed in Table 310.16. **Figure 6–8**

Conductor Sizing - Equipment Over 100A Circuits
Section 110.14(C)(1)(b)(1)

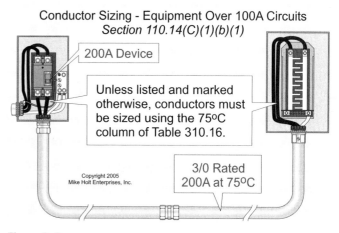

200A Device

Unless listed and marked
otherwise, conductors must
be sized using the 75°C
column of Table 310.16.

3/0 Rated
200A at 75°C

Copyright 2005
Mike Holt Enterprises, Inc.

Figure 6–8

▶ Over 100A [110.14(C)(1)(b)]

What size THHN conductor is required to supply a 225A feeder?

    (a) 1/0 AWG   (b) 2/0 AWG
    (c) 3/0 AWG   (d) 4/0 AWG

    • Answer: (d) 4/0 AWG

The conductors in this example must be sized to the lowest temperature rating of either the equipment or the conductor. THHN conductors can be used, but the conductor size must be selected according to the 75°C terminal rating of the equipment when sizing for over 100A. Using the 75°C column of Table 310.16, this will require a 4/0 THHN conductor (rated 230A at 75°C) to supply the 225A circuit. 3/0 THHN is rated 225A at 90°C, but we must size the conductor based on the 75°C terminal rating.

Minimum Conductor Size Table

When sizing conductors, the following table must always be used to determine the minimum size conductor:

Table 310.16 [110.14(C)] Terminal Size and Matching Copper Conductor

Terminal Ampacity	60°C Terminals Wire Size	75° Terminals Wire Size
15	14	14
20	12	12
30	10	10
40	8	8
50	6	8
60	4	6
70	4	4
80	3	4
90	2	3
100	1	3
110	–	2
125	–	1
150	–	1/0
200	–	3/0
225	–	4/0
250	–	250 kcmil
300	–	350 kcmil
400	–	2 – 3/0
500	–	2 – 250 kcmil

CAUTION: *When sizing conductors, we must consider conductor voltage drop, ambient temperature correction, and conductor bundle adjustment factors. These subjects are covered later in this book.*

What is the purpose of THHN if we can't use its higher ampacity?

In general, 90°C rated conductor ampacities cannot be used for sizing circuit conductors. However, THHN offers the opportunity of having a greater conductor ampacity for conductor ampacity adjustment. The higher ampacity of THHN can permit a conductor to be used without having to increase its size because of conductor ampacity adjustment. Remember, the advantage of THHN is not to permit smaller conductors, but it might prevent you from having to install a larger conductor because of ampacity adjustments.

> **AUTHOR'S COMMENT:** This is explained in detail in Part B of this unit.

6.5 Conductors in Parallel [310.4]

Parallel conductors permit a smaller cross-sectional area per ampere. This can result in a significant cost savings for circuits over 300A, Figure 6–9. The following table demonstrates the increased circular mil area required per ampere with larger conductors.

Conductor Size	Circular Mils Chapter 9, Table 8	Ampacity 75°C	Circular Mils Per Ampere
1/0 AWG	105,600 cmil	150A	704 cmil/per amp
3/0 AWG	167,600 cmil	200A	838 cmil/per amp
250 kcmil	250,000 cmil	255A	980 cmil/per amp
500 kcmil	500,000 cmil	380A	1,316 cmil/per amp
750 kcmil	750,000 cmil	475A	1,579 cmil/per amp

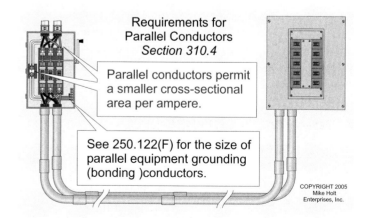

Requirements for Parallel Conductors
Section 310.4

Parallel conductors permit a smaller cross-sectional area per ampere.

See 250.122(F) for the size of parallel equipment grounding (bonding)conductors.

COPYRIGHT 2005
Mike Holt
Enterprises, Inc.

Figure 6–9

Parallel Conductors Versus Single Conductors
Section 310.4

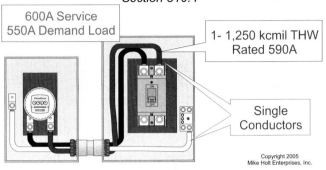

Figure 6–10

Sizing Parallel Conductors

The next two examples show the difference between single conductors and parallel conductors for a 600A service with a 550A calculated load.

▶ **Example 1: Single Conductors**

The 75°C single conductor required for a 600A service that has a calculated load of 550A is _____. Figure 6–10

(a) 500 kcmil   (b) 750 kcmil
(c) 1,000 kcmil   (d) 1,250 kcmil

• Answer: (d) 1,250 kcmil conductor, rated 590A [Table 310.16]

▶ **Example 2: Parallel Conductors**

What size 75°C parallel conductors are required in one raceway (nipple) for a 600A service? The calculated load is 550A. Figure 6–11

Parallel Conductors Versus Single Conductors
Section 310.4

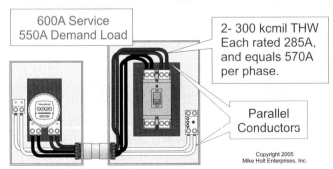

Figure 6–11

Conductors in Parallel
Equipment Grounding (Bonding) Conductor
Section 310.4 [250.122(F)(1)]

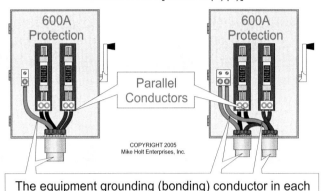

The equipment grounding (bonding) conductor in each raceway is sized to Table 250.122 based on the rating of the protection device. 600A = 1 AWG

Figure 6–12

(a) Two—300 kcmil   (b) Two—250 kcmil
(c) Two—500 kcmil   (d) Two—750 kcmil

• Answer: (a) Two—300 kcmil conductors, each rated 285A. 285A x 2 conductors = 570A [Table 310.16]

If we parallel the conductors, we can use two 300 kcmil conductors (total 600 kcmil) instead of one 1,250 kcmil conductor.

Grounding (Bonding) Conductors in Parallel [310.4]

When equipment grounding (bonding) conductors are installed with circuit conductors that are run in parallel, each raceway must have an equipment grounding (bonding) conductor sized according to the overcurrent protection device rating that protects the circuit [250.122(F)]. Figure 6–12

▶ **Sizing Grounding (Bonding) Conductors in Parallel [250.122(F)]**

What size equipment grounding (bonding) conductor is required in each of two raceways for a 400A feeder? Figure 6–13

(a) 3 AWG   (b) 2 AWG
(c) 1 AWG   (d) 1/0 AWG

• Answer: (a) 3 AWG

There must be a 3 AWG equipment grounding (bonding) conductor in each of the two raceways.

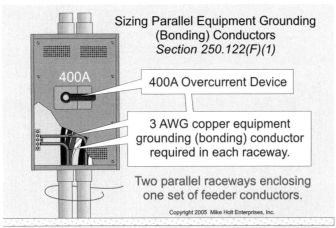

Each raceway requires an equipment grounding (bonding) conductor based on the rating of the protection device.

Figure 6–13

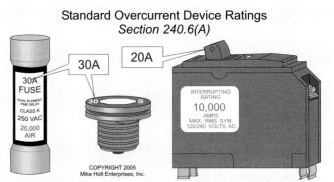

The standard ratings for fuses and inverse-time breakers include: 15, 20, 25, 30, 35, 40, 45, 50, 60, 70, 80, 90, 100, 110, 125, 150, 175, 200, 225, 250, 300, 350, 400, 450, 500, 600, 700, 800, 1000, 1200, 1600, 2000, 2500, 3000, 4000, 5000, and 6000A.

Standard fuse sizes also include 1, 3, 6, 10, and 601A.

Figure 6–14

6.6 Conductor Size—Voltage Drop [210.19(A)(1) FPN No. 4 and 215.2(A) FPN No. 2]

The *NEC* generally does not require conductors to be sized to accommodate conductor voltage drop, but 210.19(A)(1) FPN No. 4 and 215.2(A) FPN No. 2 suggest its effects should be considered.

> **AUTHOR'S COMMENT:** Voltage drop is covered in detail in Unit 8 of this book.

6.7 Overcurrent Protection [Article 240]

Overcurrent protection devices are intended to open the circuit if the current reaches a value that could result in excessive or dangerous temperature in conductors or conductor insulation. Overcurrent protection devices have two ratings, overcurrent and ampere interrupting current (AIC).

> **AUTHOR'S COMMENT:** Overcurrent protection devices are used to open the circuit to clear ground faults.

Overcurrent Rating [240.1 FPN]. Overcurrent protection for conductors and equipment is provided to open the circuit if the current reaches a value that will cause an excessive or dangerous temperature in conductors or conductor insulation. This is the actual ampere rating of the protection device, such as 15A, 20A, or 30A [240.6(A)]. **Figure 6–14**

Standard Sized Protection Devices [240.6(A)]. The *NEC* lists standard sized overcurrent protection devices: 15, 20, 25, 30, 35, 40, 45, 50, 60, 70, 80, 90, 100, 110, 125, 150, 175, 200, 225, 250, 300, 350, 400, 450, 500, 600, 700, 800, 1,000, 1,200, 1,600, 2,000, 2,500, 3,000, 4,000, 5,000, and 6,000A.

Interrupting Rating [110.9]. Overcurrent protection devices, such as circuit breakers and fuses, are intended to interrupt current at fault levels, and they must have an interrupting rating sufficient for the nominal circuit voltage and the current that is available at the line terminals of the equipment.

If the overcurrent protection device is not rated for the available fault current, it could explode while attempting to clear the fault, and/or the downstream equipment could suffer serious damage causing possible hazards to people, **Figure 6–15**. UL, ANSI, IEEE, NEMA, manufacturers, and other organizations have considerable literature on how to calculate available short-circuit current.

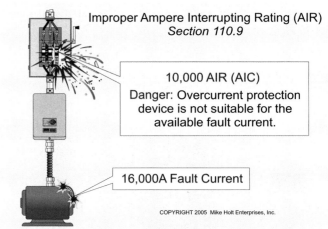

Overcurrent protection that is not properly rated for the available short-circuit and ground-fault values of the circuit could explode while attempting to clear the fault.

Figure 6–15

Interrupting Protection Rating
Section 110.9

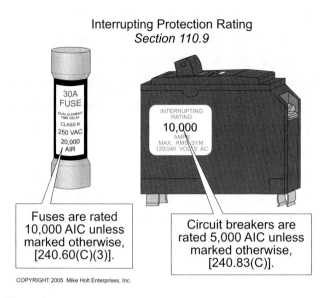

Fuses are rated 10,000 AIC unless marked otherwise, [240.60(C)(3)].

Circuit breakers are rated 5,000 AIC unless marked otherwise, [240.83(C)].

COPYRIGHT 2005 Mike Holt Enterprises, Inc.

Figure 6–16

AUTHOR'S COMMENTS:

• The minimum interruption rating for a fuse is 10,000A [240.60(C)], and for a circuit breaker is 5,000A [240.83(C)]. **Figure 6–16**

• Electrical equipment is required to have a short-circuit current rating that permits the circuit overcurrent protection device to clear short circuit or ground faults without extensive damage to the electrical components of the circuit [110.10]. **Figures 6–17 and 6–18**

Short-Circuit Current Rating
Section 110.10

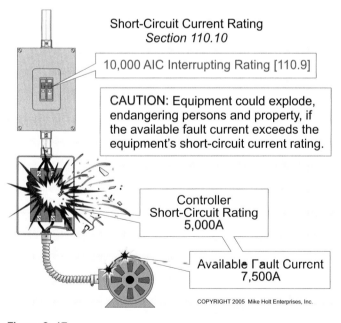

10,000 AIC Interrupting Rating [110.9]

CAUTION: Equipment could explode, endangering persons and property, if the available fault current exceeds the equipment's short-circuit current rating.

Controller Short-Circuit Rating 5,000A

Available Fault Current 7,500A

COPYRIGHT 2005 Mike Holt Enterprises, Inc.

Figure 6–17

AIC Rating Versus Short-Circuit Current Rating
Sections 110.9 and 110.10

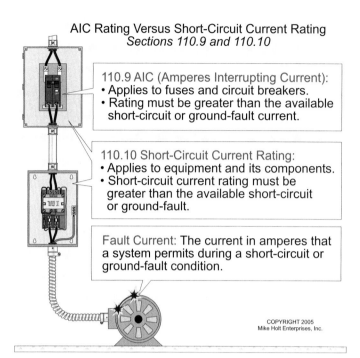

110.9 AIC (Amperes Interrupting Current):
• Applies to fuses and circuit breakers.
• Rating must be greater than the available short-circuit or ground-fault current.

110.10 Short-Circuit Current Rating:
• Applies to equipment and its components.
• Short-circuit current rating must be greater than the available short-circuit or ground-fault.

Fault Current: The current in amperes that a system permits during a short-circuit or ground-fault condition.

COPYRIGHT 2005 Mike Holt Enterprises, Inc.

Figure 6–18

Continuous Load. Overcurrent protection devices are sized no less than 125% of the continuous load, plus 100% of the noncontinuous load [210.20(A), 215.3, and 230.42(A)]. **Figure 6–19**

> **AUTHOR'S COMMENT:** Instead of saying that overcurrent devices are sized at 125% of a continuous load, it can be said that continuous loads are limited to 80% of the overcurrent device rating.

Continuous Load Limitation
Section 215.3

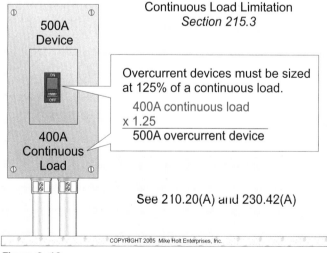

500A Device

400A Continuous Load

Overcurrent devices must be sized at 125% of a continuous load.

$$\frac{400A \text{ continuous load}}{\times 1.25} $$
500A overcurrent device

See 210.20(A) and 230.42(A)

COPYRIGHT 2005 Mike Holt Enterprises, Inc.

Figure 6–19

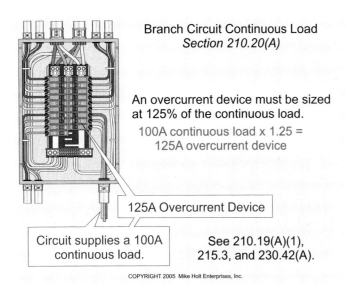

Branch Circuit Continuous Load
Section 210.20(A)

An overcurrent device must be sized at 125% of the continuous load.

100A continuous load x 1.25 = 125A overcurrent device

125A Overcurrent Device

Circuit supplies a 100A continuous load.

See 210.19(A)(1), 215.3, and 230.42(A).

COPYRIGHT 2005 Mike Holt Enterprises, Inc.

Figure 6–20

▶ **Continuous Load**

What size overcurrent protection device is required for a 100A continuous load? Figure 6–20

    (a) 150A   (b) 100A

    (c) 125A   (d) 150A

    • Answer: (c) 125A
      100A x 1.25 = 125A [240.6(A)]

6.8 Overcurrent Protection of Conductors—General Requirements [240.4]

There are many different rules for sizing and protecting conductors and equipment. It is not simply 12 AWG wire and a 20A breaker. The general rule is that conductors must be protected at the point where they receive their supply in accordance with their ampacities, as listed in Table 310.16. Other methods of protection are permitted or required as listed in subsections (A) through (G) of Section 240.4.

Next Higher Overcurrent Rating [240.4(B)]. The next higher protection device is permitted if all of the following conditions are met: Figure 6–21

• Conductors do not supply multioutlet receptacle branch circuits for portable cord-and plug connected loads.

• The ampacity of a conductor does not correspond with the standard ampere rating of a fuse or circuit breaker as listed in 240.6(A).

• The next size up breaker or fuse does not exceed 800A.

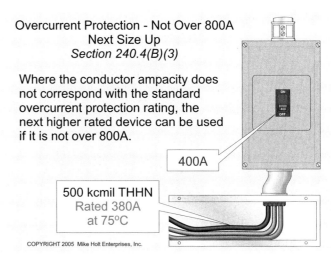

Overcurrent Protection - Not Over 800A
Next Size Up
Section 240.4(B)(3)

Where the conductor ampacity does not correspond with the standard overcurrent protection rating, the next higher rated device can be used if it is not over 800A.

400A

500 kcmil THHN
Rated 380A
at 75°C

COPYRIGHT 2005 Mike Holt Enterprises, Inc.

Figure 6–21

▶ **Overcurrent Protection of Conductors**

What size conductor is required for a 104A continuous load? Figure 6–22

    (a) 1/0 AWG   (b) 1 AWG

    (c) 2 AWG   (d) any of these

    • Answer: (b) 1 AWG

The conductor must be sized no less than 125% of the continuous load [210.19(A)(1), 215.2(A)(1)]: 104A x 1.25 = 130A. 1 THHN is rated 130A at 75°C [110.14(C)(1)(b)(1)] and can be protected by a 150A protection device.

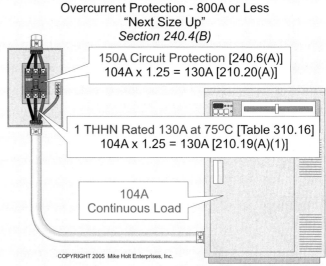

Overcurrent Protection - 800A or Less
"Next Size Up"
Section 240.4(B)

150A Circuit Protection [240.6(A)]
104A x 1.25 = 130A [210.20(A)]

1 THHN Rated 130A at 75°C [Table 310.16]
104A x 1.25 = 130A [210.19(A)(1)]

104A Continuous Load

COPYRIGHT 2005 Mike Holt Enterprises, Inc.

Where the ampacity of a conductor does not correspond with a standard ampere rating, the next size up device (maximum 800A) can be used.

Figure 6–22

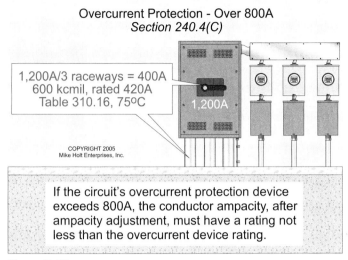

Overcurrent Protection - Over 800A
Section 240.4(C)

1,200A/3 raceways = 400A
600 kcmil, rated 420A
Table 310.16, 75°C

1,200A

COPYRIGHT 2005
Mike Holt Enterprises, Inc.

If the circuit's overcurrent protection device exceeds 800A, the conductor ampacity, after ampacity adjustment, must have a rating not less than the overcurrent device rating.

Figure 6–23

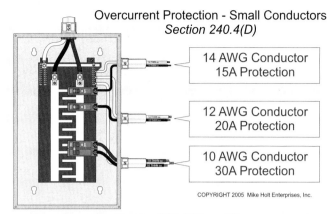

Overcurrent Protection - Small Conductors
Section 240.4(D)

14 AWG Conductor
15A Protection

12 AWG Conductor
20A Protection

10 AWG Conductor
30A Protection

COPYRIGHT 2005 Mike Holt Enterprises, Inc.

Except as permitted by 240.4(E) or (G), overcurrent protection must not exceed 15A for 14 AWG, 20A for 12 AWG, and 30A for 10 AWG copper.

Figure 6–24

Circuits with Overcurrent Protection Over 800A [240.4(C)]. If the circuit overcurrent protection device exceeds 800A, the circuit conductor ampacity must not be less than the rating of the overcurrent protection device as listed in 240.6(A).

Where the overcurrent device is over 800A, the conductors must have ampacity equal to or greater than the rating of the overcurrent device. For example, the conductors for a 1,200A feeder paralleled in three raceways must be no smaller than 600 kcmil. See Figure 6–23.

Ampere per parallel conductor = 1,200A/3 raceways

Ampere per parallel conductor = 400A minimum per raceway

Conductor size 600 kcmil rated 420A at 75C [Table 310.16 and 110.14(C)]

Total parallel ampacity = 420A x 3 conductors
Total parallel ampacity = 1,260A

Small Conductors [240.4(D)]. Unless specifically permitted in 240.4(E) or 240.4(G), overcurrent protection must not exceed 15A for 14 AWG, 20A for 12 AWG, and 30A for 10 AWG copper conductors; or 15A for 12 AWG, and 25A for 10 AWG aluminum and copper-clad aluminum conductors after ampacity correction. Figure 6–24

6.9 Overcurrent Protection of Conductors— Specific Requirements

When sizing and protecting conductors for equipment, be sure to apply the specific *NEC* requirement.

Equipment
    Air-Conditioning [440.22 and 440.32]
    Appliances [422.10 and 422.11]
    Cooking Appliances [210.19(A)(3), 210.21(B)(4), and
        Table 220.55, Note 4]
    Electric Heating Equipment [424.3]
    Fire Protective Signaling Circuits [760.23]
    Motors
        Branch Circuits [430.22 and 430.52]
        Feeders [430.24 and 430.62]
        Remote Control [430.72]
        Panelboards [408.36(A)]
        Transformers [240.21 and 450.3]

Feeders and Services
    Dwelling-Unit Feeders and Neutrals [215.2 and
        310.15(B)(6)]
    Feeder Conductors [215.2 and 215.3]
    Service Conductors [230.42 and 230.90(A)]
    Temporary Conductors [590.4]

Grounded Neutral Conductor
    Neutral Calculations [220.61]
    Grounded Service Size [250.24(C)]

Tap Conductors [240.21(B)]
    Ten feet [240.21(B)(1)]
    Twenty-five feet [240.21(B)(2)]
    One hundred feet (High Bay) [240.21(B)(4)]
    Outside Feeder [240.21(B)(5)]
    Secondary Conductors [240.21(C)]

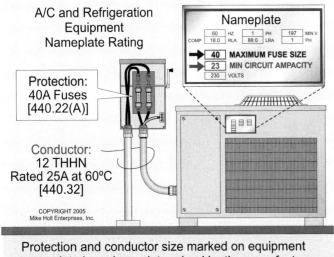

Figure 6–25

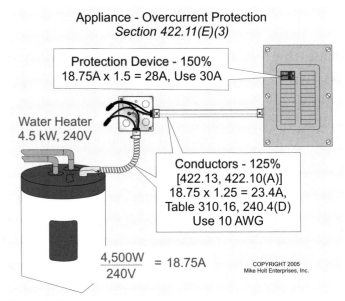

Figure 6–26

6.10 Equipment Conductor Size and Protection Examples

▶ Air-Conditioning

An air conditioner nameplate indicates the minimum circuit ampacity of 23A and maximum fuse size of 40A. What is the minimum size branch-circuit conductor and the maximum size overcurrent protection device? **Figure 6–25**

(a) 12 AWG, 60A fuse   (b) 12 AWG, 40A fuse

(c) 8 AWG, 50A fuse   (d) 10 AWG, 30A fuse

• Answer: (b) 12 AWG, 40A fuse

Conductor: Since the question did not specify 75°C terminals, the conductors must be sized based on the 60°C column of Table 310.16 [110.14(C)(1)(a)] and a 12 AWG conductor is rated 25A.

Overcurrent Protection: The protection device must not be greater than a 40A fuse, either one-time or dual-element.

AUTHOR'S COMMENT: A circuit breaker cannot be substituted where the nameplate specifically states "fuse" [110.3(B)]. Also, 12 AWG with a 40A overcurrent protection device is acceptable for this example, following the rules of Article 440 for hermetic air conditioners. [240.4(D) and 240.4(G)]

▶ Water Heater [422.11(E) and 422.13]

What size conductor and overcurrent protection device is required for a single-phase 4,500 VA, 240V water heater? **Figure 6–26** *(Note: Remember to use the single-phase formula when no phase is identified.)*

(a) 10 AWG wire with 20A protection

(b) 10 AWG wire with 25A protection

(c) 10 AWG wire with 30A protection

(d) b or c

• Answer: (d) b or c

  I = VA/E

  I = 4,500 VA/240V

  I = 18.75A

Conductor Size: The conductor is sized at 125% of the water heater rating [422.13 and 210.19(A)(1)].

Minimum conductor = 18.75A x 1.25 = 23.4A.

The conductor is sized according to the 60°C column of Table 310.16 = 12 AWG rated 25A.

However, 240.4(D) requires a maximum of 20A protection for 12 AWG copper, so to accommodate the overcurrent protection of this installation, 10 AWG is required.

Overcurrent Protection: Overcurrent protection device sized no more than 150% of appliance rating [422.11(E)(3)].

18.75A x 1.50 = 28.1A, next size up [240.4(B)] = 30A

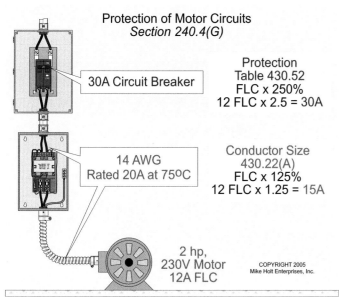

Protection of Motor Circuits
Section 240.4(G)

30A Circuit Breaker

14 AWG
Rated 20A at 75°C

Protection
Table 430.52
FLC x 250%
12 FLC x 2.5 = 30A

Conductor Size
430.22(A)
FLC x 125%
12 FLC x 1.25 = 15A

2 hp,
230V Motor
12A FLC

COPYRIGHT 2005
Mike Holt Enterprises, Inc.

Figure 6–27

▶ **Motor [240.4(G), 430.6(A), 430.22(A), and 430.52(C)(1)]**

What size branch-circuit conductor (75°C) and short-circuit protection (circuit breaker) are required for a 2 hp (12A FLC) motor rated 230V? **Figure 6–27**

    (a) 14 AWG with a 15A breaker
    (b) 12 AWG with a 20A breaker
    (c) 12 AWG with a 30A breaker
    (d) 14 AWG with a 30A breaker

    • Answer (d) 14 AWG with a 30A breaker

Conductors: Conductors are sized no less than 125% of the motor full-load current (FLC) [430.6(A), 430.22(A), and Table 430.248].

    12A x 1.25 = 15A, Table 310.16, 14 AWG is rated 20A.

Overcurrent Protection: The short-circuit protection (circuit breaker) is sized at 250% of motor full-load current.

    12A x 2.5 = 30A [240.6(A) and 430.52(C)(1)]

> **AUTHOR'S COMMENT:** The overcurrent limitations of 240.4(D) do not apply to motor circuits as stated in 240.4(G).

PART B—CONDUCTOR AMPACITY CALCULATIONS

6.11 Conductor Ampacity [310.10]

The insulation temperature rating of a conductor is limited to an operating temperature that prevents serious heat damage to the conductor's insulation. If the conductor carries excessive current, the I^2R heating within the conductor can destroy the conductor insulation. To limit elevated conductor operating temperatures, the current flow (amperes) in the conductors must be limited.

> **AUTHOR'S COMMENT:** The temperature rating of a conductor is the maximum temperature at any location along its length that the conductor can withstand over a prolonged time period without experiencing serious degradation. The main factors to consider for conductor operating temperature are ambient temperature, heat generated internally from current flow through the conductor, the rate at which heat can dissipate, and adjacent load-carrying conductors [310.10 FPN No. 1].

Allowable Ampacities

The ampacity of a conductor is the current the conductors can carry continuously under specific conditions of use [Article 100 definition]. The ampacity of a conductor is listed in Table 310.16 under the condition of no more than three current-carrying conductors bundled together in an ambient temperature of 86°F. The ampacity of a conductor changes if the ambient temperature is not 86°F, or if more than three current-carrying conductors are bundled together in any way. **Figure 6–28**

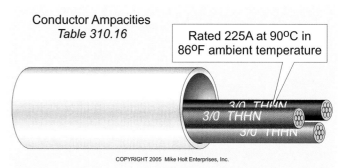

Conductor Ampacities
Table 310.16

Rated 225A at 90°C in
86°F ambient temperature

3/0 THHN
3/0 THHN
3/0 THHN

COPYRIGHT 2005 Mike Holt Enterprises, Inc.

Table 310.16 is based on an ambient temperature of 86°F and 3 current-carrying conductors in a raceway or cable.

Figure 6–28

6.12 Ambient Temperature Ampacity Correction Factor [Table 310.16]

The ampacity of a conductor as listed in Table 310.16 is based on the conductor operating at an ambient temperature of 86°F (30°C). When the ambient temperature is other than 86°F (30°C) for a prolonged period of time, the conductor ampacity listed in Table 310.16 must be corrected.

In general, 90°C rated conductor ampacities cannot be used for sizing circuit conductors. However, higher insulation temperature ratings offer the opportunity of having a greater conductor ampacity for adjustment and correction purposes. The temperature correction factors used to determine the new conductor ampacity are listed at the bottom of Table 310.16. The following formula can be used to determine the conductor's new ampacity when the ambient temperature is not 86°F (30°C). Figure 6–29

◆ **Corrected Conductor Ampacity—Ambient Temperature Correction Formula**

New Ampacity = Table 310.16 Ampacity x Ambient Temperature Correction Factor

AUTHOR'S COMMENT: When different ampacities apply to a conductor length, the higher ampacity can be used for the entire circuit if the reduced ampacity length is not in excess of 10 ft and its length does not exceed 10 percent of the length of the part of the circuit with the higher ampacity [310.15(Λ)(2) Ex]. Figure 6–30

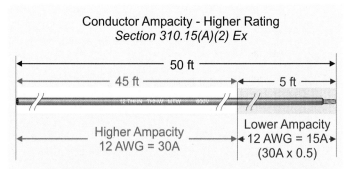

Conductor Ampacity - Higher Rating
Section 310.15(A)(2) Ex

The higher ampacity can be used if the length of the lower ampacity is not more than 10 ft, and it is not longer than 10 percent of the higher ampacity length.

COPYRIGHT 2005 Mike Holt Enterprises, Inc.

Figure 6–30

▶ **Ambient Temperature Below 86°F**

What is the ampacity of 12 THHN when installed in a walk-in cooler that has an ambient temperature of 50°F? Figure 6–31

(a) 31A   (b) 35A
(c) 30A   (d) 20A

• Answer: (a) 31A

New Ampacity = Table 310.16 Ampacity x Ambient Temperature Correction Factor

Table 310.16 ampacity for 12 THHN is 30A at 90°C.

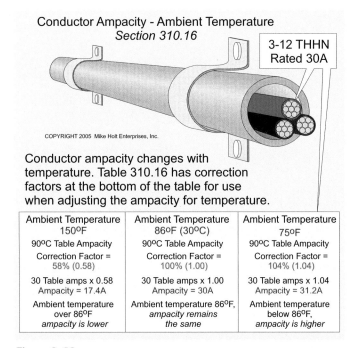

Conductor Ampacity - Ambient Temperature
Section 310.16

3-12 THHN
Rated 30A

COPYRIGHT 2005 Mike Holt Enterprises, Inc.

Conductor ampacity changes with temperature. Table 310.16 has correction factors at the bottom of the table for use when adjusting the ampacity for temperature.

Ambient Temperature 150°F	Ambient Temperature 86°F (30°C)	Ambient Temperature 75°F
90°C Table Ampacity	90°C Table Ampacity	90°C Table Ampacity
Correction Factor = 58% (0.58)	Correction Factor = 100% (1.00)	Correction Factor = 104% (1.04)
30 Table amps x 0.58 Ampacity = 17.4A	30 Table amps x 1.00 Ampacity = 30A	30 Table amps x 1.04 Ampacity = 31.2A
Ambient temperature over 86°F, *ampacity is lower*	Ambient temperature 86°F, *ampacity remains the same*	Ambient temperature below 86°F, *ampacity is higher*

Figure 6–29

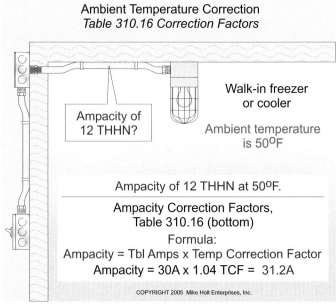

Ambient Temperature Correction
Table 310.16 Correction Factors

Walk-in freezer or cooler

Ambient temperature is 50°F

Ampacity of 12 THHN?

Ampacity of 12 THHN at 50°F.

Ampacity Correction Factors, Table 310.16 (bottom)
Formula:
Ampacity = Tbl Amps x Temp Correction Factor
Ampacity = 30A x 1.04 TCF = 31.2A

COPYRIGHT 2005 Mike Holt Enterprises, Inc.

Figure 6–31

Temperature Correction Factor for a 90°C conductor installed in an ambient temperature of 50°F is 1.04.

New Ampacity = 30A x 1.04 = 31.2A

Note: Ampacity increases when the ambient temperature is less than 86°F (30°C).

▶ **Ambient Temperature Above 86°F (30°C)**

What is the ampacity of 6 THHN when installed on a roof that has an ambient temperature of 60°C? Figure 6–32

(a) 53A   (b) 35A
(c) 75A   (d) 60A

• Answer: (a) 53A

New Ampacity = Table 310.16 Ampacity x
Ambient Temperature Correction Factor

Table 310.16 ampacity for 6 THHN is 75A at 90°C.

Temperature Correction Factor, 90°C conductor rating installed at 60°C is 0.71.

New Ampacity = 75A x 0.71 = 53.25A

Note: Ampacity decreases when the ambient temperature is more than 86°F.

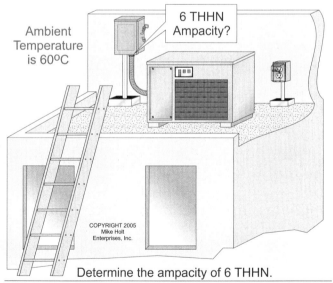

Ambient Temperature Correction
Section 310.16

Determine the ampacity of 6 THHN.

Table 310.16 ampacity = 75A
Temperature correction factor, 60°C = 0.71
New Ampacity = 75A x 0.71 = 53.25A

Figure 6–32

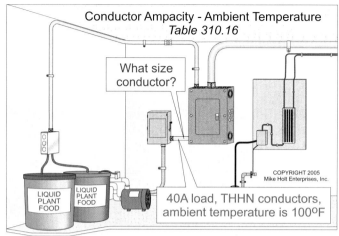

Conductor Ampacity - Ambient Temperature
Table 310.16

Determine the THHN conductor size.

New Ampacity =
Table Ampacity x Temperature Correction Factor

10 THHN, 40A x 0.91 = 36.4A, too small
8 THHN, 55A x 0.91 = 50.0A, okay
6 THHN, 75A x 0.91 = 68.3A, too large

Figure 6–33

▶ **Conductor Size**

What size THHN conductor is required to supply a 40A noncontinuous load if the conductors pass through an ambient temperature of 100°F? Figure 6–33

(a) 10 THHN   (b) 8 THHN
(c) 6 THHN   (d) any of these

• Answer: (b) 8 THHN

New Ampacity = Table 310.16 Amperes x
Ambient Temperature Correction Factor

10 THHN = 40A x 0.91 = 36.4A
8 THHN = 55A x 0.91 = 50A

Note: The conductor to the load must have an ampacity of 40A after applying the ambient temperature correction factor.

6.13 Conductor Bundling Ampacity Adjustment Factor [Table 310.15(B)(2)(a)]

When conductors are bundled together, the ability of the conductors to dissipate heat is reduced. The *NEC* requires that the ampacity of a conductor be reduced whenever four or more current-carrying conductors are bundled together, Figure 6–34. In general, 90°C rated conductor ampacities cannot be used for sizing a circuit conductor. However, higher insulation temperature rating offers the opportunity of having a greater conductor ampacity when used for ampacity adjustment.

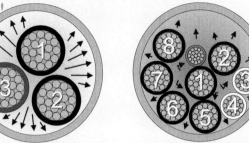

Conductor Ampacity - Table 310.16
Adjustment Factor
Table 310.15(B)(2)(a)

No Ampacity Adjustment
Three or Fewer Conductors

Ampacity Adjustment
Factor = 70%

Conductors have more surface
area for heat dissipation.

Bundled conductors
have heat held in
by other conductors.

COPYRIGHT 2005 Mike Holt Enterprises, Inc.

Figure 6–34

The ampacity adjustment factor used to determine the new ampacity is listed in Table 310.15(B)(2)(a). The following formula can be used to determine the new conductor ampacity when more than three current-carrying conductors are bundled together:

◆ **Conductor Bundling Ampacity Adjustment Formula**

New Ampacity = Table 310.16 Ampacity x
Bundled Ampacity Adjustment Factor

AUTHOR'S COMMENTS:

• Conductor bundling ampacity adjustment factors do not apply to conductors in a nipple whose length does not exceed 24 in. [310.15(B)(2)(a) Ex 3]. **Figure 6–35**

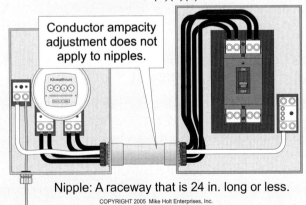

Conductor Ampacity - Table 310.16
Adjustment Factor
Table 310.15(B)(2)(a) Ex 3

Conductor ampacity
adjustment does not
apply to nipples.

Nipple: A raceway that is 24 in. long or less.

COPYRIGHT 2005 Mike Holt Enterprises, Inc.

Figure 6–35

• Not all conductors are considered current carrying. For example, an equipment grounding (bonding) conductor does not normally carry current and isn't counted as a current-carrying conductor [310.15(B)(5)]. Some grounded neutral conductors are considered current carrying and others are not, depending on the conditions described in 310.15(B)(4). Of course, all ungrounded conductors are considered current carrying. See Section 6.15 of this unit for specific information on how to determine the number of current-carrying conductors.

▶ **Conductor Ampacity**

What is the ampacity of four current-carrying 10 THHN conductors installed in a raceway or cable? **Figure 6–36**

(a) 20A (b) 24A
(c) 32A (d) none of these

• Answer: (c) 32A

New Ampacity = Table 310.16 Ampacity x
Bundled Ampacity Adjustment Factor

Table 310.16 ampacity for 10 THHN is 40A at 90°C.

Bundled adjustment factor for four current-carrying conductors is 0.8.

New Ampacity = 40A x 0.8 = 32A

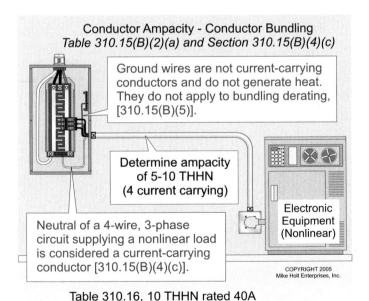

Conductor Ampacity - Conductor Bundling
Table 310.15(B)(2)(a) and Section 310.15(B)(4)(c)

Ground wires are not current-carrying
conductors and do not generate heat.
They do not apply to bundling derating,
[310.15(B)(5)].

Determine ampacity
of 5-10 THHN
(4 current carrying)

Electronic
Equipment
(Nonlinear)

Neutral of a 4-wire, 3-phase
circuit supplying a nonlinear load
is considered a current-carrying
conductor [310.15(B)(4)(c)].

COPYRIGHT 2005
Mike Holt Enterprises, Inc.

Table 310.16, 10 THHN rated 40A
Table 310.15(B)(2)(a) = 0.8 adjustment factor
40A x 0.8 = 32 ampacity

Figure 6–36

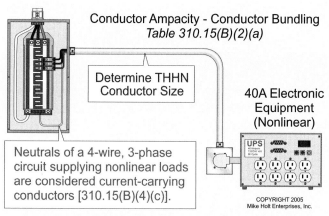

Conductor Ampacity - Conductor Bundling
Table 310.15(B)(2)(a)

Determine THHN Conductor Size

Neutrals of a 4-wire, 3-phase circuit supplying nonlinear loads are considered current-carrying conductors [310.15(B)(4)(c)].

40A Electronic Equipment (Nonlinear)

Determine conductor size to 40A noncontinuous load.

Circuit has 4 current-carrying conductors
Table 310.15(B)(2)(a) bundling adjustment factor = 0.8
Table 310.16:
10 THHN, 40A x 0.8 = 32.0A, too small
8 THHN, 55A x 0.8 = 44.0A, okay

Figure 6–37

▶ **Conductor Size**

A raceway contains four current-carrying conductors. What size conductor is required to supply a 40A noncontinuous load? Figure 6–37

(a) 10 THHN   (b) 8 THHN
(c) 6 THHN   (d) none of these

• Answer: (b) 8 THHN

The conductor must have an ampacity of 40A after applying the bundled adjustment factor.

New Ampacity = Table 310.16 Ampacity x Bundled Ampacity Adjustment Factor

10 THHN = 40A x 0.8 = 32A—too small

8 THHN = 55A x 0.8 = 44A—just right

6 THHN = 75A x 0.8 = 60A—larger than required by the *NEC*

6.14 Ambient Temperature Correction and Conductor Bundling Adjustment Factors

If the ambient temperature is other than 86°F and there are more than three current-carrying conductors bundled together, then the ampacity listed in Table 310.16 must be adjusted and corrected for both conditions. Figure 6–38

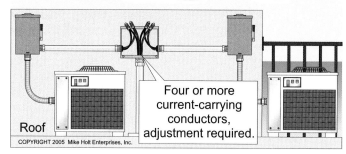

Calculating Conductor Ampacity
Temperature Correction and Bundling Adjustment
Table 310.16 and Table 310.15(B)(2)(a)

Ambient temperature is above 86°F, correction is required.

Roof

Four or more current-carrying conductors, adjustment required.

Figure 6–38

The following formula can be used to determine the new conductor ampacity when both ambient temperature correction and bundled adjustment factors apply:

New Ampacity = Table 310.16 Ampacity x Temperature Correction Factor x Bundled Adjustment Factor

▶ **Conductor Ampacity**

What is the ampacity of four current-carrying 8 THHN conductors installed in an ambient temperature of 100°F? Figure 6–39

(a) 25A   (b) 40A
(c) 55A   (d) 60A

• Answer: (b) 40A

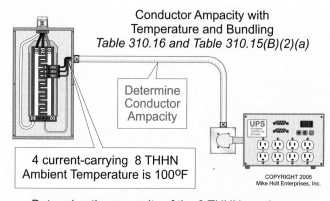

Conductor Ampacity with
Temperature and Bundling
Table 310.16 and Table 310.15(B)(2)(a)

Determine Conductor Ampacity

4 current-carrying 8 THHN
Ambient Temperature is 100°F

Determine the ampacity of the 8 THHN conductors.

Table 310.16 ampacity of 8 THHN = 55A
Table 310.16 temperature correction for 100°F = 0.91
Table 310.15(B)(2)(a) bundling, 4 current-carrying = 0.8

Figure 6–39

New Ampacity = Table 310.16 Ampacity x Temperature Factor x Bundled Adjustment Factor

Table 310.16 ampacity of 8 THHN is 55A at 90°C.

Temperature correction factor for 90°C conductor insulation at 100°F is 0.91.

Bundled adjustment factor for four conductors is 0.80.

New Ampacity = 55A x 0.91 x 0.80 = 40A

6.15 Current-Carrying Conductors

Table 310.15(B)(2)(a) adjustment factors only apply when there are more than three current-carrying conductors bundled together. Naturally, all phase conductors are considered current carrying, and the following should be helpful in determining which other conductors are considered current carrying:

Grounded Neutral Conductor—Balanced Circuits, 310.15(B)(4)(a)

The neutral conductor of a balanced 3-wire circuit, or a balanced 4-wire, three-phase wye circuit is not considered a current-carrying conductor. Figure 6–40

Grounded Neutral Conductor—Unbalanced 3-Wire Wye Circuit, 310.15(B)(4)(b)

The neutral conductor of a balanced 3-wire wye circuit of a 4-wire, three-phase wye-connected system is considered a current-carrying conductor, Figure 6–41. This can be proven with the following formula:

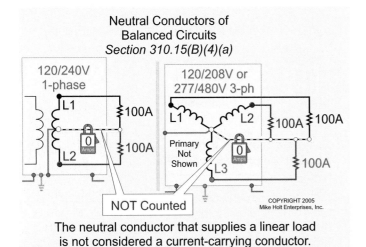

Figure 6–40

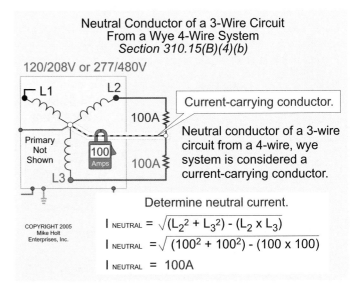

Figure 6–41

◆ **Unbalanced 3-Wire Neutral Current Formula**

$$I_{Neutral} = \sqrt{[(I_{Line1}^2 + I_{Line2}^2) - (I_{Line1} \times I_{Line2})]}$$

▶ **Grounded Neutral Conductor**

What is the neutral current for a balanced 16A, 120/208V, 3-wire, single-phase branch circuit of a 4-wire, three-phase wye-connected system that supplies fluorescent lighting? Figure 6–42

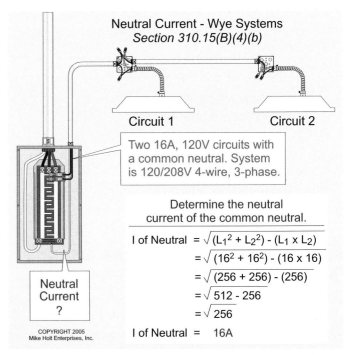

Figure 6–42

(a) 8A (b) 16A

(c) 32A (d) 40A

• Answer: (b) 16A

$$I_{Neutral} = \sqrt{[(I_{Line1}^2 + I_{Line2}^2) - (I_{Line1} \times I_{Line2})]}$$

$$I_{Neutral} = \sqrt{[(16^2 + 16^2) - (16 \times 16)]}$$

$$I_{Neutral} = \sqrt{(512 - 256)}$$

$$I_{Neutral} = \sqrt{256}$$

$$I_{Neutral} = 16A$$

Grounded Neutral Conductor—Nonlinear Loads, 310.15(B)(4)(c)

The grounded neutral conductor of a balanced 4-wire, three-phase wye circuit that is at least 50% loaded with nonlinear loads (computers, electric-discharge lighting, etc.) is considered a current-carrying conductor. Figure 6–43

> **CAUTION:** *Nonlinear loads produce harmonic currents that add on the neutral conductor, and the current on the neutral can be as much as twice the current on the ungrounded conductors.* Figure 6–44

Two-Wire Circuits

Both the grounded and ungrounded conductors of a 2-wire circuit carry current and both are considered current carrying. Figure 6–45

> **AUTHOR'S COMMENT:** The electrical trade industry typically uses the term "neutral," when referring to the white/gray wire. However, the proper term for this conductor is "grounded conductor."

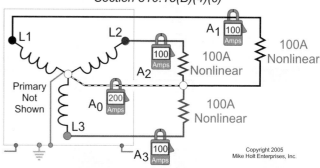

Neutral Conductor of a 4-Wire Circuit
Supplying Nonlinear Loads
Section 310.15(B)(4)(c)

Odd triplen harmonic currents from nonlinear loads add on the neutral conductor and the actual current could be almost twice the ungrounded conductor's current.

Figure 6–44

Grounded Conductor: Most electrical power supplies have one output terminal of the power supply bonded to the case of the power (system bonding jumper). The conductor that is connected to this grounded terminal is called a "grounded conductor."

Neutral Conductor: The IEEE dictionary defines a neutral conductor as the conductor with an equal potential difference between it and the other output conductors of a 3- or 4-wire system. Therefore, a neutral conductor is the white/gray wire of a 3-wire single-phase 120/240V system, of a 4-wire three-phase 120/208V, or 277/480V system. Since a neutral conductor must have equal potential between it and all ungrounded conductors in a 3- or 4-wire system, the white wire of a 2-wire circuit, and the white wire from a 4-wire three-phase 120/240V delta-connected system are not neutral conductors—they're grounded conductors.

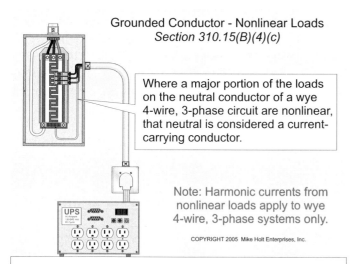

Grounded Conductor - Nonlinear Loads
Section 310.15(B)(4)(c)

Where a major portion of the loads on the neutral conductor of a wye 4-wire, 3-phase circuit are nonlinear, that neutral is considered a current-carrying conductor.

Note: Harmonic currents from nonlinear loads apply to wye 4-wire, 3-phase systems only.

COPYRIGHT 2005 Mike Holt Enterprises, Inc.

Figure 6–43

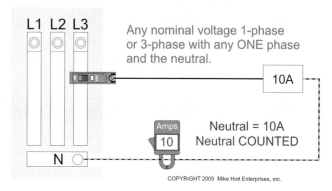

2-Wire Grounded Circuits
Section 310.15(B)(4)

Any nominal voltage 1-phase or 3-phase with any ONE phase and the neutral.

Neutral = 10A
Neutral COUNTED

COPYRIGHT 2005 Mike Holt Enterprises, Inc.

Figure 6–45

Conductor Ampacity - Grounding and Bonding Conductors
Section 310.15(B)(5)

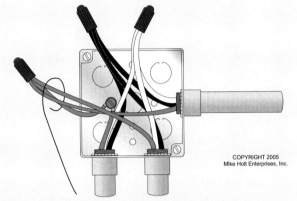

Equipment grounding and bonding conductors are not current carrying and are not counted when applying the provisions of Table 310.15(B)(2)(a).

Figure 6–46

Technically, it's improper to call a "grounded conductor" a "neutral conductor" or "neutral wire" when it's not truly a neutral conductor, but this is a long-standing industry practice. For the purpose of this textbook this conductor will be called a grounded neutral conductor. That should keep most people happy.

Grounding and Bonding Conductors, 310.15(B)(5)

Grounding and bonding conductors do not normally carry current and are not considered current carrying. **Figure 6–46**

> **AUTHOR'S COMMENT:** Grounding and bonding conductors are not counted when adjusting conductor ampacity for the effects of conductor bundling.

Conductor Ampacity - Table 310.16
Correction and Adjustment
Section 310.15(B)

This raceway contains only 3 current-carrying conductors.

Table 310.16 ampacity is based on an ambient temperature of not over 86°F and no more than 3 current-carrying conductors bundled together.

Conductor Ampacity Adjustment

Ambient Temperature	Conductor Bundling
If the ambient temperature is above 86°F, the conductor ampacity decreases.	If the number of current-carrying conductors exceeds 3, the conductor ampacity decreases.

COPYRIGHT 2005 Mike Holt Enterprises, Inc.

Figure 6–47

6.16 Conductor Sizing Summary

The ampacity of a conductor changes with changing conditions. The factors that affect conductor ampacity include: **Figure 6–47**

The allowable ampacity as listed in Table 310.16.

The ambient temperature correction factors, if the ambient temperature is not 86°F.

Conductor ampacity adjustment factors apply if four or more current-carrying conductors are bundled together.

Terminal Ratings, 110.14(C)

Equipment rated 100A or less must have the conductor sized no smaller than the 60°C column of Table 310.16 [110.14(C)(1)(a)]. Equipment rated over 100A must have the conductors sized no smaller than the 75°C column of Table 310.16 [110.14(C)(1)(b)]. However, a higher insulation temperature rating offers the opportunity of having a greater conductor ampacity for conductor ampacity adjustment.

Unit 6 Conclusion

The sizing of conductors and overcurrent protection is much more complicated than it appears on the surface. The study of this unit should have provided an insight into the numerous factors that must be taken into account in properly sizing conductors and providing for their protection.

Temperature is a key factor in the resistance of a conductor, and consequently temperature affects a conductor's current-carrying capacity. High temperature on conductors can lead to the breakdown of conductor insulation and damage to equipment terminals. Therefore, when sizing conductors, the ampacity values given in the *NEC* tables must be corrected for ambient temperatures that differ from the ambient of 86° F, on which the *Code* tables are based. A bundle of current-carrying conductors will result in an increased operating temperature, so the *NEC* also requires that an adjustment be made when bundling more than 3 current carrying conductors.

This unit also taught you that conductors must not be sized to a higher temperature column of the ampacity table than the rating of the equipment terminals allow. This means that even though you install a 90°C rated conductor such as THHN, a lower ampacity column must be used to match the terminal rating. This is a requirement that results in confusion and mistakes on exam problems, so review this part of the unit again if you're not sure of the application of 110.14(C) of the *Code*.

Overcurrent protection must be sized correctly to protect the circuit wiring and equipment from damage that can result from overheating. Common overcurrent sizing requirements as well as some of the exceptions to the general rules of Article 240 were included in this unit.

Unit 6 Calculation Practice Questions

(• Indicates that 75% or fewer of those who took this exam answered the question correctly.)

PART A—GENERAL CONDUCTOR REQUIREMENTS

6.1 Conductor Insulation Properties [Table 310.13]

1. THHN can be described as _____.

    (a) thermoplastic insulation with a nylon outer cover
    (c) having a maximum operating temperature of 90°C

    (b) suitable for dry and wet locations
    (d) a and c

6.2 Allowable Conductor Ampacity [310.15]

2. The maximum overcurrent protection device size for 14 AWG is 15A, 12 AWG is 20A, and 10 AWG is 30A. This is a general rule, but it does not apply to motors or air conditioners according to 240.4(G).

    (a) True   (b) False

6.3 Conductor Sizing [110.6]

3. Conductor sizes are expressed in American Wire Gage (AWG) from 40 AWG through 4/0 AWG. Conductors larger than _____ are expressed in circular mils.

    (a) 1/0 AWG   (b) 1 AWG   (c) 3/0 AWG   (d) 4/0 AWG

4. The smallest size conductor permitted for branch circuits, feeders, and services for residential, commercial, and industrial locations is _____.

    (a) 14 AWG copper   (b) 12 AWG aluminum   (c) 12 AWG copper   (d) a and b

6.4 Terminal Ratings [110.14(C)]

5. Equipment terminals rated 100A or less (receptacles, switches, circuit breakers, fuses, etc.) and pressure connector terminals for 14 AWG through 1 AWG conductors must have the conductor sized according to the 60°C temperature rating, as listed in Table 310.16.

    (a) True   (b) False

6. •What is the minimum size THHN conductor that is permitted to terminate on a 70A circuit breaker or fuse for a nonmotor circuit? Be sure to comply with the requirements of 110.14(C)(1).

    (a) 8 AWG   (b) 6 AWG   (c) 4 AWG   (d) none of these

7. •What size THHN conductor is required for a 70A branch circuit if the circuit breaker and equipment are listed for 75°C terminals and the noncontinuous load does not exceed 65A?

    (a) 10 AWG   (b) 8 AWG   (c) 6 AWG   (d) 4 AWG

8. Terminals for equipment rated over 100A and pressure connector terminals for conductors larger than 1 AWG must have the conductor sized according to the 75°C temperature rating, as listed in Table 310.16.

    (a) True   (b) False

9. What size THHN conductor is required for an air-conditioning unit if the nameplate requires a conductor ampacity of 34A? Terminals of all the equipment and circuit breakers are rated 75°C.

    (a) 12 AWG   (b) 10 AWG   (c) 8 AWG   (d) 14 AWG

10. What is the minimum size THHN conductor required for a 150A circuit breaker or fuse for a nonmotor circuit? Be sure to comply with the requirements of 110.14(C)(1)(b).

(a) 1/0 AWG (b) 2/0 AWG (c) 3/0 AWG (d) 4/0 AWG

11. In general, THHN (90°C) conductor ampacities cannot be used when sizing conductors. When more than three current-carrying conductors are bundled together, or if the ambient temperature is greater than 86°F, the allowable conductor ampacity must be decreased. THHN offers the opportunity of having a greater ampacity for conductor adjustment purposes, thereby permitting the same conductor to be used without having to increase the conductor size.

(a) True (b) False

12. What size conductor is required to supply a 190A noncontinuous load in a dry location? The terminals are rated 75°C.

(a) 300 kcmil (b) 4/0 AWG (c) 3/0 AWG (d) none of these

6.5 Conductors in Parallel [310.4]

13. •Phase and grounded neutral conductors sized 1 AWG and larger are permitted to be connected in parallel.

(a) True (b) False

14. To ensure that currents are evenly distributed between parallel conductors, each conductor within a parallel set must be installed in the same type of raceway (metallic or nonmetallic) and must be the same length, material, circular mils, insulation type, and must terminate in the same method.

(a) True (b) False

15. •When an electric relay (coil) is energized, the initial current can be very high which causes significant voltage drop. The reduced voltage at the coil (because of voltage drop) can cause the coil contacts to chatter (open and close like a buzzer) or not close at all. Paralleling of control wiring conductors is often necessary and permitted by the *NEC* to reduce the effects of voltage drop for long control runs.

(a) True (b) False

16. When equipment grounding conductors are installed in parallel, each raceway must have a full-size equipment grounding conductor sized according to the overcurrent protection device rating of that circuit.

(a) True (b) False

17. All parallel equipment grounding conductors are required to be a minimum 1/0 AWG.

(a) True (b) False

18. What size equipment grounding conductor is required in each raceway for an 800A, 500 kcmil feeder paralleled in two raceways?

(a) 3 AWG (b) 2 AWG (c) 1 AWG (d) 1/0 AWG

19. If an 800A service has a calculated load of 750A, what size 75°C conductors are required if the conductors are paralleled in two raceways?

(a) 4/0 AWG (b) 250 kcmil (c) 500 kcmil (d) 750 kcmil

20. •What size conductors are required for a 250A feeder paralleled in two raceways?

(a) 3 AWG (b) 2 AWG (c) 2/0 AWG (d) 1/0 AWG

6.6 Conductor Size—Voltage Drop [210.19(A)(1) FPN No. 4 and 215.2(A) FPN No. 2]

21. Generally speaking, there is no mandatory rule in the *NEC* limiting the voltage drop on conductors, but the *Code* recommends its effect be considered.

(a) True   (b) False

6.7 Overcurrent Protection [Article 240]

22. One of the purposes of conductor overcurrent protection is to protect the conductors against excessive or dangerous heat.

(a) True   (b) False

23. Overcurrent devices must be designed and rated to clear fault current and must have a short-circuit interrupting rating sufficient for the available fault levels. The minimum interruption rating for circuit breakers is _____ and _____ for fuses.

(a) 10,000A, 10,000A   (b) 5,000A, 5,000A   (c) 5,000A, 10,000A   (d) 10,000A, 5,000A

24. Which of the following is a standard size for circuit breakers and fuses?

(a) 25A   (b) 90A   (c) 350A   (d) any of these

25. Where a circuit supplies continuous loads or any combination of continuous and noncontinuous loads, the rating of the overcurrent device must not be less than the noncontinuous load plus _____ of the continuous load.

(a) 80%   (b) 100%   (c) 125%   (d) 150%

6.8 Overcurrent Protection of Conductors - General Requirements [240.4]

26. If the ampacity of a conductor does not correspond with the standard ampere rating of a fuse or circuit breaker, the next size up protection device is permitted. This applies only if the conductors supply multioutlet receptacles for portable cord-and-plug connected loads.

(a) True   (b) False

27. What size conductor (75°C) is required for a 70A breaker that supplies a 70A noncontinuous load?

(a) 8 AWG   (b) 6 AWG   (c) 4 AWG   (d) any of these

PART B—CONDUCTOR AMPACITY CALCULATIONS

6.11 Conductor Ampacity [310.10]

28. The temperature rating of a conductor is the maximum operating temperature the conductor insulation can withstand (without serious damage) over a prolonged period of time. The _____ provide guidance for adjusting conductor ampacities for different conditions.

(a) conductor allowable ampacities   (b) ambient temperature correction factors
(c) over three current-carrying conductors adjustment factors   (d) all of these

6.12 Ambient Temperature Ampacity Correction Factor [Table 310.16]

29. •The ampacities listed in Table 310.16 apply only when the ambient temperature is 40°C and there are no more than two current-carrying conductors bundled together. If the ambient temperature is not 40°C, or there are more than two current-carrying conductors in a raceway, the allowable ampacities must be adjusted to reflect the ampacity under the condition of use.

(a) True   (b) False

30. •What is the ampacity of an 8 THHN conductor when installed in a walk-in cooler if the ambient temperature is 50°F?

(a) 40A   (b) 50A   (c) 55A   (d) 57A

31. What size THHN conductor is required to feed a 16A noncontinuous load when the conductors are in an ambient temperature of 100°F? The circuit is protected with a 20A overcurrent protection device.

    (a) 14 THHN   (b) 12 THHN   (c) 10 THHN   (d) 8 THHN

6.13 Conductor Bundling Ampacity Adjustment Factor [Table 310.15(B)(2)(a)]

32. When four or more current-carrying conductors are bundled together for more than _____, the conductor allowable ampacity must be reduced according to the factors listed in Table 310.15(B)(2)(a).

    (a) 12 in.   (b) 24 in.   (c) 36 in.   (d) 48 in.

33. •What is the ampacity of four 1/0 THHN current-carrying conductors in a raceway?

    (a) 111A   (b) 136A   (c) 153A   (d) 171A

34. A raceway contains eight current-carrying conductors. What size conductor is required to feed a 21A noncontinuous lighting load? The overcurrent protection device is rated 30A.

    (a) 14 THHN   (b) 12 THHN   (c) 10 THHN   (d) any of these

6.14 Ambient Temperature Correction and Conductor Bundling Adjustment Factors

35. What is the ampacity of eight current-carrying 10 THHN conductors installed in an ambient temperature of 100°F?

    (a) 21A   (b) 25A   (c) 32A   (d) 40A

6.15 Current-Carrying Conductors

36. •The neutral conductor of a balanced 3-wire delta circuit, or 4-wire, three-phase wye circuit, is considered a current-carrying conductor for the purpose of applying the adjustment factors of Table 310.15(B)(2)(a).

    (a) True   (b) False

37. The neutral conductor of a balanced 4-wire, three-phase wye circuit that is at least 50 percent loaded with nonlinear loads (electric-discharge lighting, electronic ballasts, dimmers, controls, computers, laboratory test equipment, medical test equipment, recording studio equipment, etc.) is not considered a current-carrying conductor for the purpose of applying bundle adjustment factors.

    (a) True   (b) False

38. •The neutral conductor of a balanced 3-wire wye circuit from a 4-wire, three-phase wye system is not considered a current-carrying conductor for the purpose of applying bundle adjustment factors.

    (a) True   (b) False

6.16 Conductor Sizing Summary

39. •The ampacity of a conductor can be different along the length of the conductor. The higher calculated ampacity can be used if the length of the lower ampacity is no more than 10 ft, or no more than 10 percent of the length of the circuit conductors.

    (a) True   (b) False

40. Most terminals are rated 60°C for equipment 100A or less and 75°C for equipment terminals rated over 100A. Regardless of the conductor ampacity, conductors must be sized no smaller than the terminal temperature rating.

    (a) True   (b) False

Unit 6 Calculation Challenge Questions

(• Indicates that 75% or fewer of those who took this exam answered the question correctly.)

PART A—GENERAL CONDUCTOR REQUIREMENTS

6.7 Overcurrent Protection [240]

1. •A continuous load of 27A requires the circuit overcurrent protection device to be sized at _____.

   (a) 20A   (b) 30A   (c) 40A   (d) 35A

2. •What size overcurrent protection device is required for a 45A continuous load? The circuit is in a raceway with 14 current-carrying conductors.

   (a) 45A   (b) 50A   (c) 60A   (d) 70A

3. •A 65A continuous load requires a _____ overcurrent protection device.

   (a) 60A   (b) 70A   (c) 75A   (d) 90A

4. A department store (continuous load) feeder supplies a lighting load of 103A. The minimum size overcurrent protection device permitted for this feeder is _____.

   (a) 110A   (b) 125A   (c) 150A   (d) 175A

PART B—CONDUCTOR AMPACITY CALCULATIONS

6.12 Ambient Temperature Ampacity Correction Factor [Table 310.16]

5. A 2 TW conductor is installed in a location where the ambient temperature is expected to be 102°F. The temperature correction factor for conductor ampacity in this location is _____.

   (a) 0.96   (b) 0.88   (c) 0.82   (d) 0.71

6. •If the ambient temperature is 71°C, the minimum insulation temperature rating that a conductor must have and still have the capacity to carry current is _____.

   (a) 60°C   (b) 105°C   (c) 90°C   (d) any of these

6.13 Conductor Bundling Ampacity Adjustment Factor [Table 310.15(B)(2)(a)]

7. The ampacity of six current-carrying 4/0 XHHW aluminum conductors installed in a ground floor slab (wet location) is _____.

   (a) 135A   (b) 185A   (c) 144A   (d) 210A

6.14 Ambient Temperature Correction and Conductor Bundling Adjustment Factors

8. The ampacity of 15 current-carrying 10 RHW aluminum conductors in an ambient temperature of 75°F is _____.

   (a) 30A   (b) 22A   (c) 16A   (d) 12A

9. •A(n) _____ THHN conductor is required for a 19.7A noncontinuous load if the ambient temperature is 75°F and there are nine current-carrying conductors in the raceway.

    (a) 14   (b) 12   (c) 10   (d) 8

10. •The ampacity of nine current-carrying 10 THW conductors installed in a 20 in. long raceway is _____.

    (a) 25A   (b) 30A   (c) 35A   (d) none of these

11. •The ampacity of 10 current-carrying 6 THHW conductors installed in an 18 in. long conduit in a dry location having an ambient temperature of 39°C is _____.

    (a) 47A   (b) 68A   (c) 66A   (d) 75A

6.15 Current-Carrying Conductors

12. A raceway contains the following: one 4-wire multiwire branch circuit that supplies a balanced incandescent 120V lighting load; one 4-wire multiwire branch circuit that supplies a balanced 120V fluorescent lighting load; two conductors that supply a receptacle; and one equipment grounding conductor. The system is 120/208V, three-phase. Taking these factors into consideration, how many of these conductors are considered current carrying?

    (a) 7 conductors   (b) 8 conductors   (c) 9 conductors   (d) 11 conductors

13. •There is a total of nine 10 THW conductors in a raceway. The system voltage is 120/208V, three-phase. One conductor is an equipment grounding conductor, four conductors supply a 4-wire multiwire branch circuit for balanced electric-discharge luminaires, and the remaining conductors supply a 4-wire multiwire branch circuit for balanced incandescent luminaires. Taking all of these factors into consideration, how many of these conductors are considered current carrying?

    (a) 6 conductors   (b) 7 conductors   (c) 9 conductors   (d) 10 conductors

(• Indicates that 75% or fewer of those who took this exam answered the question correctly.)

Article 342 Intermediate Metal Conduit (Type IMC) (continued)

1. Where intermediate metal conduit enters a box, fitting, or other enclosure, _____ must be provided to protect the wire from abrasion.

    (a) a bushing   (b) duct seal   (c) electrical tape   (d) seal off fittings

Article 344 Rigid Metal Conduit (Type RMC)

Rigid metal conduit is similar to intermediate metal conduit, except the wall thickness is greater, so it has a smaller interior cross-sectional area. Rigid metal conduit is heavier than intermediate metal conduit and it's permitted to be installed in any location, just like intermediate metal conduit.

2. RMC can be installed in or under cinder fill subject to permanent moisture when protected on all sides by a layer of noncinder concrete not less than _____ thick.

    (a) 2 in.   (b) 4 in.   (c) 6 in.   (d) 18 in.

3. Aluminum fittings and enclosures can be used with _____ conduit where not subject to severe corrosive influences.

    (a) steel rigid metal   (b) aluminum rigid metal
    (c) PVC-coated rigid conduit only   (d) a and b

4. The minimum radius of a field bend on 1 1/4 in. RMC is _____.

    (a) 7 in.   (b) 8 in.   (c) 14 in.   (d) 10 in.

5. When rigid metal conduit is threaded in the field, a standard die with _____ must be used.

    (a) 3/4 in. taper per foot   (b) 1 in. taper per foot   (c) 1/16 in. taper per foot   (d) no taper

6. Straight runs of 1 in. RMC using threaded couplings may be secured at intervals not exceeding _____.

    (a) 5 ft   (b) 10 ft   (c) 12 ft   (d) 14 ft

7. Horizontal runs of RMC supported by openings through _____ at intervals not exceeding 10 ft and securely fastened within 3 ft of termination points are permitted.

    (a) walls   (b) trusses   (c) rafters   (d) framing members

8. Threadless couplings and connectors used with RMC and installed in wet locations must be _____.

    (a) listed for wet locations   (b) listed for damp location   (c) nonabsorbent   (d) weatherproof

9. Where rigid metal conduit enters a box, fitting, or other enclosure, a bushing must be provided to protect the wire from abrasion unless the design of the box, fitting, or enclosure is such as to afford equivalent protection.

    (a) True   (b) False

10. The standard length of RMC as shipped must _____.

    (a) be in lengths of 10 ft   (b) include a coupling on each length
    (c) be threaded on each end   (d) all of these

Article 348 Flexible Metal Conduit (Type FMC)

Flexible metal conduit is a raceway of circular cross section made of a helically wound, interlocked metal strip of either steel or aluminum. It's commonly called "Greenfield" or "Flex."

11. FMC cannot be installed _____.

(a) underground   (b) embedded in poured concrete
(c) where subject to physical damage   (d) all of these

12. The largest size THHN conductor permitted in trade size 3/8 FMC is _____ AWG.

(a) 12   (b) 16   (c) 14   (d) 10

13. Bends in flexible metal conduit must be made so that the conduit is not damaged and the internal diameter of the conduit is _____. The radius of the curve to the centerline of any bend must not be less than shown in Table 2, Chapter 9 using the column for "Other Bends."

(a) larger than 3/8 in   (b) not effectively reduced   (c) increased   (d) larger than 1 in

14. All cut ends of flexible metal conduit must be trimmed or otherwise finished to remove rough edges, except where fittings _____.

(a) are the crimp-on type   (b) thread into the convolutions
(c) contain insulated throats   (d) are listed for grounding

15. Unsupported lengths of flexible metal conduit are allowed at terminals where flexibility is required but must not exceed _____.

(a) 3 ft for trade sizes 1/2 in. through 1 1/4 in   (b) 4 ft for trade sizes 1 1/2 in. through 2 in
(c) 5 ft for trade size 2 1/2 in. and larger   (d) all of these

16. In a concealed FMC installation, _____ connectors must not be used.

(a) straight   (b) angle   (c) grounding-type   (d) none of these

Article 350 Liquidtight Flexible Metal Conduit (Type LFMC)

Liquidtight flexible metal conduit is a listed raceway of circular cross section with an outer liquidtight, nonmetallic, sunlight-resistant jacket over an inner flexible metal core, with associated couplings, connectors, and fittings. It's listed for the installation of electric conductors. Liquidtight flexible metal conduit is commonly called Sealtite® or simply "liquidtight." Liquidtight flexible metal conduit is of similar construction to flexible metal conduit but has an outer thermoplastic covering.

17. The use of listed and marked LFMC is permitted for _____.

(a) direct burial where listed and marked for the purpose   (b) exposed work
(c) concealed work   (d) all of these

18. The maximum number of 14 THHN conductors permitted in trade size 3/8 LFMC with outside fittings is _____.

(a) 4   (b) 7   (c) 5   (d) 6

19. When LFMC is used as a fixed raceway, it must be secured within _____ in. on each side of the box and must be supported and secured at intervals not exceeding _____ ft.

(a) 12, 4 1/2   (b) 18, 3   (c) 12, 3   (d) 18, 4

20. Horizontal runs of liquidtight flexible metal conduit supported by openings through framing members at intervals not greater than _____ and securely fastened within 12 in. of termination points are permitted.

(a) 1.4 ft   (b) 12 in.   (c) 4 1/2 ft   (d) 6 ft

21. When LFMC is used to connect equipment requiring flexibility, a separate _____ conductor must be installed.

    (a) main bonding jumper   (b) grounded   (c) equipment grounding   (d) none of these

Article 352 Rigid Nonmetallic Conduit (Type RNC)

Rigid nonmetallic conduit is a listed nonmetallic raceway of circular cross section with integral or associated couplings, connectors, and fittings. It's listed for the installation of electrical conductors. Typically, it's constructed of polyvinyl chloride (PVC).

22. Extreme _____ may cause rigid nonmetallic conduit to become brittle, and therefore more susceptible to damage from physical contact.

    (a) sunlight   (b) corrosive conditions   (c) heat   (d) cold

23. Rigid nonmetallic conduit is permitted for exposed work in buildings _____, where not subject to physical damage and if identified for such use.

    (a) three floors and less   (b) twelve floors and less   (c) six floors and less   (d) without height limits

24. Among the uses that are NOT permitted for rigid nonmetallic conduit, RNC must not be used _____.

    (a) in hazardous (classified) locations
    (b) for the support of luminaires or other equipment
    (c) where subject to physical damage unless identified for such use
    (d) all of these

25. Bends in rigid nonmetallic conduit must be made so that the conduit is not damaged and the internal diameter of the conduit is not effectively reduced. Field bends must be made only _____.

    (a) by hand forming the bend   (b) with bending equipment identified for the purpose
    (c) with a truck exhaust pipe   (d) by use of an open flame torch

26. When installing rigid nonmetallic conduit, _____.

    (a) all cut ends must be trimmed inside and outside to remove rough edges
    (b) there must be a support within 2 ft of each box and cabinet
    (c) all joints must be made by an approved method
    (d) a and c

27. Trade Size 1 rigid nonmetallic conduit must be supported every _____, unless otherwise listed.

    (a) 2 ft   (b) 3 ft   (c) 4 ft   (d) 6 ft

28. Where rigid nonmetallic conduit enters a box, fitting, or other enclosure, a bushing or adapter must be provided to protect the wire from abrasion unless the design of the box, fitting, or enclosure is such as to afford equivalent protection.

    (a) True   (b) False

29. An equipment grounding conductor is not required in rigid nonmetallic conduit if the grounded conductor is used to ground equipment as permitted in 250.142.

    (a) True   (b) False

Article 353 High-Density Polyethylene Conduit (Type HDPE)

This article covers the use, installation, and construction specifications for high density-polyethylene (HDPE) conduit and associated fittings. It's lightweight and durable. It resists decomposition, oxidation, and hostile elements that cause damage to other materials. HDPE is mechanically and chemically resistant to a host of environmental conditions. Uses include communication, data, cable television, and general-purpose raceways.

30. High-Density Polyethylene Conduit (HDPE) can be manufactured _____.

    (a) in discrete lengths   (b) in continuous lengths from a reel
    (c) only in 20 ft. lengths   (d) either a or b

31. There is never a case where HDPE can be installed in a hazardous location.

    (a) True   (b) False

32. HDPE is not permitted where it will be subject to ambient temperatures in excess of _____.

    (a) 50°C   (b) 60°C   (c) 75°C   (d) 90°C

33. Bends made in HDPE must be made _____.

    (a) in a manner that will not damage the raceway
    (b) so as not to significantly reduce the internal diameter of the raceway
    (c) only with mechanical bending tools
    (d) a and b

34. The cut ends of HDPE must be _____ to avoid rough edges.

    (a) filed on the inside   (b) trimmed inside and outside
    (c) cut only with a hack saw   (d) all of these

35. Any joints between lengths of HDPE must be made using _____.

    (a) expansion fittings   (b) an approved method   (c) a listed method   (d) none of these

36. HDPE must be resistant to _____.

    (a) moisture   (b) corrosive chemical atmospheres
    (c) impact and crushing   (d) all of these

Article 354 Nonmetallic Underground Conduit with Conductors (Type NUCC)

Nonmetallic underground conduit with conductors is a factory assembly of conductors or cables inside a nonmetallic, smooth wall conduit with a circular cross section. It can also be supplied on reels without damage or distortion and is of sufficient strength to withstand abuse, such as impact or crushing when handled and installed, without damage to conduit or conductors.

37. NUCC and its associated fittings must be _____.

    (a) listed   (b) approved   (c) identified   (d) none of these

38. NUCC must not be used _____.

    (a) in exposed locations   (b) inside buildings
    (c) in hazardous (classified) locations   (d) all of these

39. Bends in nonmetallic underground conduit with conductors (NUCC) must be _____ so that the conduit will not be damaged and the internal diameter of the conduit will not be effectively reduced.

    (a) manually made   (b) made only with approved benders
    (c) made with rigid metal conduit bending shoes   (d) made using an open flame torch

40. In order to _____ NUCC, the conduit must be trimmed away from the conductors or cables using an approved method that will not damage the conductor or cable insulation or jacket.

(a) facilitate installing   (b) enhance the appearance of the installation of
(c) terminate   (d) provide safety to the persons installing

41. All joints between nonmetallic underground conduit with conductors (NUCC), fittings, and boxes must be made by _____.

(a) a qualified person   (b) set screw fittings   (c) an approved method   (d) exothermic welding

Article 356 Liquidtight Flexible Nonmetallic Conduit (Type LFNC)

Liquidtight flexible nonmetallic conduit is a listed raceway of circular cross section with an outer liquidtight, nonmetallic, sunlight-resistant jacket over an inner flexible core, with associated couplings, connectors, and fittings. It's listed for the installation of electric conductors. LFNC is available in three types:

- Type LFNC-A (orange). A smooth seamless inner core and cover bonded together. One or more reinforcement layers are inserted between the core and covers.
- Type LFNC-B (gray). A smooth inner surface with integral reinforcement within the conduit wall.
- Type LFNC-C (black). A corrugated internal and external surface without integral reinforcement within the conduit wall.

42. Type LFNC-B can be installed in lengths longer than _____ where secured in accordance with 356.30.

(a) 2 ft   (b) 3 ft   (c) 6 ft   (d) 10 ft

43. The number of conductors allowed in LFNC must not exceed that permitted by the percentage fill specified in _____.

(a) Chapter 9, Table 1   (b) Table 250.66   (c) Table 310.16   (d) 240.6

44. Bends in LFNC must _____ between pull points.

(a) not be made   (b) not be limited in degrees
(c) be limited to not more than 360 degrees   (d) be limited to 180 degrees

45. Where flexibility is necessary, securing LFNC is not required for lengths less than _____ at terminals.

(a) 2 ft   (b) 3 ft   (c) 4 ft   (d) 6 ft

Article 358 Electrical Metallic Tubing (Type EMT)

Electrical metallic tubing is a listed metallic tubing of circular cross section raceway listed for the installation of electrical conductors. Compared to rigid metal conduit and intermediate metal conduit, electrical metallic tubing is relatively easy to bend, cut, and ream. Because it isn't threaded, all connectors and couplings are of the threadless type.

46. When EMT is installed in wet locations, all support, bolts, straps, screws, and so forth must be _____.

(a) of corrosion-resistant materials   (b) protected against corrosion
(c) a or b   (d) nonmetallic materials only

47. The minimum and maximum size of EMT is _____, except for special installations.

(a) 5/16 and 3 in.   (b) 3/8 and 4 in.   (c) 1/2 and 3 in.   (d) 1/2 and 4 in.

48. EMT must not be threaded.

(a) True   (b) False

49. Fastening of unbroken lengths of EMT conduit can be increased to a distance of _____ from the termination point where the structural members do not readily permit fastening within 3 ft.

    (a) 10 ft   (b) 5 ft   (c) 4 ft   (d) 25 ft

50. Couplings and connectors used with EMT must be made up _____.

    (a) of metal   (b) in accordance with industry standards
    (c) tight   (d) none of these

Article 360 Flexible Metallic Tubing (Type FMT)

This article covers the use, installation, and construction specifications for Flexible Metal Tubing (FMT) and associated fittings. Which is a raceway that is circular in cross section, flexible, metallic, and liquidtight without a nonmetallic jacket.

51. The maximum size FMT permitted is _____

    (a) 3/8 in.   (b) 1/2 in.   (c) 3/4 in.   (d) 1 in.

Article 362 Electrical Nonmetallic Tubing (Type ENT)

Electrical nonmetallic tubing is a pliable, corrugated, circular raceway made of PVC. It's often called "Smurf Pipe" or "Smurf Tube," because it originally came out at the height of popularity of the children's cartoon characters "the Smurfs," and was available only in blue.

52. ENT is composed of a material that is resistant to moisture, chemical atmospheres, and is _____.

    (a) flexible   (b) flame-retardant   (c) fireproof   (d) flammable

53. When a building is supplied with a(n) _____ fire sprinkler system, ENT can be installed exposed or concealed in buildings of any height.

    (a) listed   (b) identified   (c) NFPA 13-2002 approved   (d) none of these

54. When a building is supplied with an approved fire sprinkler system, ENT is permitted to be installed above any suspended ceiling.

    (a) True   (b) False

55. ENT is not permitted in hazardous (classified) locations, except for intrinsically safe applications.

    (a) True   (b) False

56. ENT is not permitted in places of assembly unless it is encased in at least _____ of concrete.

    (a) 1 in.   (b) 2 in.   (c) 3 in.   (d) 4 in.

57. The number of conductors allowed in ENT must not exceed that permitted by the percentage fill specified in _____.

    (a) Chapter 9, Table 1   (b) Table 250.66   (c) Table 310.16   (d) 240.6

58. All cut ends of ENT must be trimmed inside and _____ to remove rough edges.

    (a) outside   (b) tapered   (c) filed   (d) beveled

59. Bushings or adapters are required at ENT terminations to protect the conductors from abrasion, unless the box, fitting, or enclosure design provides equivalent protection.

    (a) True   (b) False

60. Where equipment grounding is required by Article 250 for ENT installations, a separate equipment grounding conductor must _____.

(a) be run outside the raceway using solid copper wire
(b) be installed in the raceway
(c) be obtained using a separate driven ground rod
(d) not be required

Article 366 Auxiliary Gutters

This article covers the use, installation, and construction requirements of metal auxiliary gutters and nonmetallic auxiliary gutters and associated fittings. Auxiliary gutters are enclosures with hinged or removable covers for housing and protecting electric wires, cable, and busbars in which conductors are laid in place after the wireway has been installed as a complete system.

61. An auxiliary gutter is permitted to contain _____.

(a) conductors
(b) overcurrent devices
(c) busways
(d) none of these

62. When conductor ampacity adjustment factors of 310.15(B)(2)(a) are used, an auxiliary gutter must not contain more than _____ at any cross section. Also, conductors are not permitted to fill more than 20 percent of the cross sectional area.

(a) 25 conductors
(b) 40 current-carrying conductors
(c) 20 conductors
(d) no limit on the number of conductors

63. The maximum ampere rating of a 4 in. x 1/2 in. copper busbar that is 4 ft long and installed in an auxiliary gutter is _____.

(a) 500A
(b) 750A
(c) 650A
(d) 2,000A

64. Auxiliary gutters must be constructed and installed so that adequate _____ continuity of the complete system is secured.

(a) mechanical
(b) electrical
(c) a or b
(d) a and b

Article 368 Busways

This article covers service-entrance, feeder, and branch-circuit busways and associated fittings. Busways are a grounded metal enclosure containing factory-mounted, bare or insulated conductors, which are usually copper or aluminum bars, rods, or tubes.

65. It is permissible to extend busways vertically through dry floors if totally enclosed (unventilated) where passing through, and for a minimum distance of _____ above the floor to provide adequate protection from physical damage.

(a) 6 ft
(b) 6 1/2 ft
(c) 8 ft
(d) 10 ft

66. Busways must not be installed _____.

(a) where subject to severe physical damage
(b) outdoors or in wet or damp locations unless identified for such use
(c) in hoistways
(d) all of these

67. Busways must be securely supported, unless otherwise designed and marked as such, at intervals not to exceed _____.

(a) 10 ft
(b) 5 ft
(c) 3 ft
(d) 8 ft

68. When busway enclosures for voltage levels exceeding 600V terminate at machines cooled by flammable gas, _____ or other means must be provided to prevent accumulation of flammable gas within the bus enclosures.

(a) seal-off bushings
(b) baffles
(c) a or b
(d) none of these

Article 370 Cablebus

This article covers the use and installation requirements of cablebus and associated fittings. A cablebus is an assembly of insulated conductors with fittings and conductor terminations in a completely enclosed, ventilated protective metal housing. Cablebus is ordinarily assembled at the point of installation from the components furnished or specified by the manufacturer in accordance with instructions for the specific job.

69. The cablebus assembly is designed to carry _____ current and to withstand the magnetic forces of such current.

 (a) service   (b) load   (c) fault   (d) grounded

70. Cablebus framework that is _____ is permitted as the equipment grounding conductor for branch circuits and feeders.

 (a) bonded   (b) welded   (c) protected   (d) galvanized

71. The individual conductors in a cablebus must be supported at intervals not greater than _____ for vertical runs.

 (a) 1/2 ft   (b) 1 ft   (c) 1 1/2 ft   (d) 2 ft

72. Each section of cablebus must be marked with the manufacturer's name or trade designation and the minimum diameter, number, voltage rating, and ampacity of the conductors to be installed. Markings must be so located as to be visible after installation.

 (a) True   (b) False

Article 372 Cellular Concrete Floor Raceways

This article covers cellular concrete floor raceways, the hollow spaces in floors constructed of precast cellular concrete slabs, together with suitable metal fittings designed to provide access to the floor cells.

73. A transverse metal raceway for electrical conductors, providing access to predetermined cells of precast cellular concrete floors, which permits installation of electrical conductors from a distribution center to the floor cells, is usually known as a(n) _____.

 (a) cell   (b) header   (c) open-bottom raceway   (d) none of these

74. Connections from cellular concrete floor raceway headers to cabinets must be made by means of _____.

 (a) listed metal raceways (b) PVC raceways   (c) listed fittings   (d) a and c

75. In cellular concrete floor raceways, a grounding conductor must connect the insert receptacle to a _____.

 (a) negative ground connection provided in the raceway (b) negative ground connection provided on the header
 (c) positive ground connection provided on the header (d) grounded terminal located within the insert

Article 374 Cellular Metal Floor Raceways

This article covers the use and installation requirements for cellular metal floor raceways, which are approved as enclosures for electric conductors.

76. A _____ is defined as a single, enclosed tubular space in a cellular metal floor member, the axis of which is parallel to the axis of the metal floor member.

 (a) cellular metal floor raceway (b) cell   (c) header   (d) none of these

77. Loop wiring _____ in a cellular metal raceway.

 (a) is not permitted   (b) is not considered a splice or tap
 (c) is considered a splice or tap when used (d) none of these

78. Inserts for cellular metal floor raceways must be leveled to the floor grade and sealed against the entrance of _____.

    (a) concrete   (b) water   (c) moisture   (d) all of these

Article 376 Metal Wireways

This article covers the use, installation, and construction specifications for metal wireways and associated fittings. A metal wireway is a sheet metal trough with hinged or removable covers for housing and protecting electric wires and cable, in which conductors are placed after the wireway has been installed as a complete system.

79. Metal wireways can be installed either exposed or concealed under all conditions.

    (a) True   (b) False

80. Wireways are permitted to pass transversely through a wall _____. Access to the conductors must be maintained on both sides of the wall.

    (a) if the length passing through the wall is unbroken   (b) if the wall is not fire rated
    (c) in hazardous locations   (d) if the wall is fire rated

81. The sum of the cross-sectional areas of all contained conductors at any cross section of a metal wireway must not exceed _____.

    (a) 50 percent   (b) 20 percent   (c) 25 percent   (d) 80 percent

82. Where insulated conductors are deflected within a metallic wireway, the wireway must be sized to meet the bending requirements corresponding to one wire per terminal in Table 312.6(A).

    (a) True   (b) False

83. Wireways must be supported where run horizontally at each end and at intervals not to exceed _____, or for individual lengths longer than _____ at each end or joint, unless listed for other support intervals.

    (a) 5 ft   (b) 10 ft   (c) 3 ft   (d) 6 ft

84. Splices and taps are permitted within a metal wireway provided they are accessible. The conductors, including splices and taps, must not fill the wireway to more than _____ percent of its area at that point.

    (a) 25   (b) 80   (c) 125   (d) 75

85. In addition to the wiring space requirement in 376.56(A), the power distribution block must be installed in a metal wireway not smaller than that specified _____.

    (a) by the wireway manufacturer   (b) by the manufacturer of the power distribution block
    (c) both a and b   (d) either a or b

86. Extensions from wireways by raceway or cable wiring methods are not permitted.

    (a) True   (b) False

Article 378 Nonmetallic Wireways

A nonmetallic wireway is a flame-retardant trough with hinged or removable covers for housing and protecting electric wires and cable, in which conductors are placed after the wireway has been installed as a complete system.

87. Nonmetallic wireways can pass transversely through a wall _____.

    (a) if the length through the wall is unbroken   (b) if the wall is not fire rated
    (c) in hazardous locations   (d) if the wall is fire rated

88.   The derating factors in 310.15(B)(2)(a) apply to a nonmetallic wireway.

       (a) True   (b) False

89.   Nonmetallic wireways must be supported where run horizontally at each end and at intervals not to exceed _____ and at each end
       or joint, unless listed for other support intervals.

       (a) 5 ft   (b) 10 ft   (c) 3 ft   (d) 6 ft

90.   Expansion fittings for nonmetallic wireways must be provided to compensate for thermal expansion and contraction, where the
       length change is expected to be _____ or greater in a straight run.

       (a) 1/4 in.   (b) 1/2 in.   (c) 6 in.   (d) 1/16 in.

91.   Where equipment grounding is required by Article 250 for nonmetallic wireway installations, a separate equipment grounding
       conductor must _____.

       (a) be run outside the raceway using solid copper wire   (b) be installed in the raceway
       (c) be obtained using a separate driven ground rod   (d) not be required

Article 380 Multioutlet Assemblies

A multioutlet assembly is a surface, flush, or freestanding raceway designed to hold conductors and receptacles. It's assembled in the
field or at the factory.

92.   A multioutlet assembly cannot be installed _____.

       (a) in concealed locations   (b) where subject to severe physical damage
       (c) where subject to corrosive vapors   (d) all of these

Article 382 Nonmetallic Extensions

This article covers the use, installation, and construction specifications for nonmetallic extensions. A nonmetallic extension is an
assembly of two insulated conductors within a nonmetallic jacket or an extruded thermoplastic covering. The classification includes
surface extensions intended for mounting directly on the surface of walls or ceilings.

93.   Nonmetallic surface extensions are permitted in _____ when occupied for residential or office purposes.

       (a) buildings not over three stories high   (b) buildings over four stories high
       (c) all buildings   (d) none of these

94.   Each run of nonmetallic extension must terminate in a fitting that covers the _____.

       (a) device   (b) box   (c) end of the extension   (d) end of the assembly

Article 384 Strut-Type Channel Raceways

A strut-type channel raceway is a metallic raceway intended to be mounted to the surface or suspended with associated accessories, in
which conductors are placed after the raceway has been installed as a complete system.

95.   A strut-type channel raceway can be installed _____.

       (a) where exposed   (b) as a power pole
       (c) unbroken through walls, partitions, and floors   (d) all of these

96. The ampacity adjustment factors of 310.15(B)(2)(a) do not apply to conductors installed in strut-type channel raceways where _____.

    (a) the cross-sectional area of the raceway is at least 4 sq in.
    (b) the number of current-carrying conductors do not exceed 30
    (c) the sum of the cross-sectional areas of all contained conductors does not exceed 20 percent of the interior cross-sectional area of the strut-type channel raceways
    (d) all of these

97. Splices and taps are permitted within a strut-type channel raceway provided they are accessible. The conductors, including splices and taps, must not fill the raceway to more than _____ percent of its area at that point.

    (a) 25   (b) 80   (c) 125   (d) 75

Article 386 Surface Metal Raceways

A surface metal raceway is a metallic raceway intended to be mounted to the surface with associated accessories, in which conductors are placed after the raceway has been installed as a complete system.

98. It is permissible to run unbroken lengths of surface metal raceways through dry _____.

    (a) walls   (b) partitions   (c) floors   (d) all of these

99. In general, the voltage limitation between conductors in a surface metal raceway must not exceed _____ unless the metal has a thickness of not less than 0.040 in., nominal.

    (a) 300V   (b) 150V   (c) 600V   (d) 1,000V

100. •The maximum number of conductors permitted in any surface raceway must be _____.

    (a) no more than 30 percent of the inside diameter   (b) no greater than the number for which it was designed
    (c) no more than 75 percent of the cross-sectional area   (d) that which is permitted in the Table 312.6(A)

(• Indicates that 75% or fewer of those who took this exam answered the question correctly.)

1. RMC can be installed in concrete, in direct contact with the earth, or in areas subject to severe corrosive influences when protected by _____ and judged suitable for the condition.

   (a) ceramic   (b) corrosion protection   (c) backfill   (d) a natural barrier

2. •A cablebus system must include approved fittings for dead ends.

   (a) True   (b) False

3. •LFMC smaller than _____ must not be used, except as permitted in 348.20(A).

   (a) 3/8 in.   (b) 1/2 in.   (c) 1 1/2 in.   (d) 1 1/4 in.

4. A junction box used with a cellular metal floor raceway must be _____.

   (a) level with the floor grade   (b) sealed against the entrance of water or concrete
   (c) metal and electrically continuous with the raceway   (d) all of these

5. A multioutlet assembly can be installed in _____.

   (a) dry locations   (b) wet locations   (c) a and b   (d) none of these

6. A run of EMT between outlet boxes must not exceed _____ offsets close to the box.

   (a) 360° plus   (b) 360° total including   (c) four quarter bends plus   (d) 180° total including

7. A strut-type channel raceway cannot be installed _____.

   (a) in concealed locations   (b) where subject to corrosive vapors if protected solely by enamel
   (c) a or b   (d) none of these

8. All joints between lengths of ENT, and between ENT and couplings, fittings, and boxes must be made by _____.

   (a) a qualified person   (b) set screw fittings   (c) an approved method   (d) exothermic welding

9. Bends in flexible metal conduit must _____ between pull points.

   (a) not be made   (b) not be limited in degrees
   (c) be limited to not more than 360 degrees   (d) be limited to 180 degrees

10. Bends in LFNC must be made so that the conduit will not be damaged and the internal diameter of the conduit will not be effectively reduced. Bends are permitted to be made only _____.

    (a) manually without auxiliary equipment   (b) with bending equipment identified for the purpose
    (c) with any kind of conduit bending tool that will work   (d) by use of an open flame torch

11. Bends in nonmetallic underground conduit with conductors (NUCC) must _____ between termination points.

    (a) not be made   (b) not be limited in degrees
    (c) be limited to not more than 360 degrees   (d) be limited to 180 degrees

12. Bends in rigid nonmetallic conduit must _____ between pull points.

    (a) not be made
    (b) not be limited in degrees
    (c) be limited to not more than 360 degrees
    (d) be limited to 180 degrees

13. Bends made in HDPE must not exceed _____ degrees between pull points.

    (a) 180
    (b) 270
    (c) 360
    (d) 480

14. Busway runs with nominal voltage levels exceeding 600V, having sections located both inside and outside of buildings, must have a _____ at the building wall to prevent interchange of air between indoor and outdoor sections.

    (a) waterproof rating
    (b) vapor seal
    (c) fire seal
    (d) b and c

15. Cablebus is not permitted for _____.

    (a) a service
    (b) branch circuits
    (c) exposed work
    (d) concealed work through walls and floors except as allowed by 370.6.

16. Conductors, including splices and taps, must not fill the auxiliary gutter to more than _____ percent of its cross-sectional area.

    (a) 20
    (b) 40
    (c) 60
    (d) 75

17. Each length of RMC must be clearly and durably identified every _____.

    (a) 3 ft
    (b) 5 ft
    (c) 10 ft
    (d) none of these

18. ENT is permitted for direct earth burial when used with fittings listed for this purpose.

    (a) True
    (b) False

19. Expansion fittings for rigid nonmetallic conduit must be provided to compensate for thermal expansion and contraction when the length change in a straight run between securely mounted boxes, cabinets, elbows, or other conduit terminations is expected to be _____ or greater.

    (a) 1/4 in.
    (b) 1/2 in.
    (c) 1 in.
    (d) none of these

20. FMC can be installed exposed or concealed where not subject to physical damage.

    (a) True
    (b) False

21. HDPE is not permitted to be installed _____.

    (a) where exposed
    (b) within a building
    (c) for conductors operating at a temperature above the rating of the raceway
    (d) all of these

22. Horizontal runs of EMT supported by openings through framing members at intervals not greater than _____, and securely fastened within 3 ft of termination points, are permitted.

    (a) 1.4 ft
    (b) 12 in.
    (c) 4 1/2 ft
    (d) 10 ft

23. Horizontal runs of flexible metal conduit supported by openings through framing members at intervals not greater than _____ and securely fastened within 12 in. of termination points are permitted.

    (a) 1.4 ft
    (b) 12 in.
    (c) 4 1/2 ft
    (d) 6 ft

24. In a building without a fire sprinkler system, ENT is permitted to be installed above a suspended ceiling if the suspended ceiling provides a thermal barrier having at least a _____-minute finish rating as identified in listings of fire-rated assemblies.

    (a) 5   (b) 10   (c) 15   (d) none of these

25. In electrical nonmetallic tubing, the maximum number of bends between pull points cannot exceed _____ degrees, including any offsets.

    (a) 320   (b) 270   (c) 360   (d) unlimited

26. Liquidtight flexible metal conduit is not required to be fastened when used for tap conductors to luminaires up to _____ in length.

    (a) 4 1/2 ft   (b) 18 in.   (c) 6 ft   (d) no limit on length

27. Nonmetallic extensions must be secured in place by approved means at intervals not exceeding _____

    (a) 6 in.   (b) 8 in.   (c) 10 in.   (d) 16 in.

28. NUCC must be capable of being supplied on reels without damage or _____, and must be of sufficient strength to withstand abuse, such as impact or crushing in handling and during installation, without damage to conduit or conductors.

    (a) distortion   (b) breakage   (c) shattering   (d) all of these

29. Power distribution blocks installed in metal wireways must _____.

    (a) allow for sufficient wire-bending space at terminals   (b) not have exposed live parts after installation
    (c) either a or b   (d) both a and b

30. Rigid nonmetallic conduit and fittings must be composed of suitable nonmetallic material that is resistant to moisture and chemical atmospheres. For use above ground it must have additional characteristics including _____.

    (a) flame retardance   (b) resistance to low temperatures and sunlight effects
    (c) resistance to distortion from heat   (d) all of these

31. Rigid nonmetallic conduit can be used to support nonmetallic conduit bodies not larger than the largest raceway, but the conduit bodies must not contain devices, luminaires, or other equipment.

    (a) True   (b) False

32. Strut-type channel raceway enclosures must have a means for connecting an equipment grounding conductor. The raceway is permitted as an equipment grounding conductor in accordance with 250.118(14).

    (a) True   (b) False

33. The adjustment factors of 310.15(B)(2)(a), (Notes to Ampacity Tables of 0 through 2,000V), do not apply to conductors installed in surface metal raceways where _____.

    (a) the cross-sectional area exceeds 4 sq in.
    (b) the current-carrying conductors do not exceed 30 in number
    (c) the total cross-sectional area of all conductors does not exceed 20 percent of the interior cross-sectional area of the raceway
    (d) all of these

34. The derating factors in 310.15(B)(2)(a) must be applied to a metal wireway only where the number of current-carrying conductors in the wireway exceeds _____.

    (a) 30   (b) 20   (c) 80   (d) 3

35. The header on a cellular concrete floor raceway must be installed _____ to the cells.

    (a) in a straight line   (b) at right angles   (c) a and b   (d) none of these

36. The minimum radius for a field bend of 1 in. rigid metal conduit is _____, when using a one-shot bender.

    (a) 10 1/2 in.   (b) 11 1/2 in.   (c) 5 3/4 in.   (d) 9 1/2 in.

37. The sum of the cross-sectional areas of all contained conductors at any cross section of a nonmetallic wireway must not exceed _____.

    (a) 50 percent   (b) 20 percent   (c) 25 percent   (d) 80 percent

38. The use of NUCC is permitted _____.

    (a) for direct-burial underground installations   (b) to be encased or embedded in concrete
    (c) in cinder fill   (d) all of these

39. Trade Size 2 RMC must typically be supported every _____.

    (a) 10 ft   (b) 12 ft   (c) 14 ft   (d) 15 ft

40. Vertical runs of metal wireways must be securely supported at intervals not exceeding _____ and must not have more than one joint between supports.

    (a) 5 ft   (b) 20 ft   (c) 10 ft   (d) 15 ft

41. When a vertical busway penetrates the floor (in other than industrial establishments), a minimum 4 in.-high curb must be installed around the busway floor opening to prevent liquids from entering the vertical busway. The curb must be installed within _____ of the floor opening for the busway and electrical equipment must be located so that liquids retained by the 4 in. curb will not damage equipment.

    (a) 12 in.   (b) 6 in.   (c) 12 ft   (d) 6 ft

42. When an auxiliary gutter is used to supplement wiring space at meter centers, distribution centers, switchboards, and similar points, it is not allowed to extend a distance greater than _____ beyond the equipment that it supplements.

    (a) 50 ft   (b) 30 ft   (c) 10 ft   (d) 25 ft

43. When an outlet is _____ from a cellular concrete floor raceway, the sections of circuit conductors supplying the outlet must be removed from the raceway.

    (a) discontinued   (b) abandoned   (c) removed   (d) any of these

44. When LFNC is used to connect equipment requiring flexibility, a separate _____ must be installed.

    (a) equipment grounding conductor   (b) expansion fitting
    (c) flexible nonmetallic connector   (d) none of these

45. When threadless couplings and connectors used in the installation of RMC are buried in masonry or concrete, they must be of the _____ type.

    (a) raintight   (b) wet and damp location   (c) nonabsorbent   (d) concrete-tight

46.   Where trade size 3/8 FMT has a fixed bend for installation purposes and is not flexed for service, the minimum radius measured to the inside of the bend must not be less than _____

(a) 8 in.   (b) 12 1/2 in.   (c) 3 1/2 in.   (d) 4 in.

47.   Where equipment grounding is required for an installation of HDPE, a separate equipment grounding conductor must be _____.

(a) an insulated copper conductor   (b) installed within the conduit
(c) stranded bare copper wire   (d) a solid bare copper wire

48.   Where flexibility _____ liquidtight flexible metal conduit is permitted to be used as an equipment grounding conductor when installed in accordance with 250.118(6).

(a) is required   (b) is not required   (c) either a or d   (d) is optional

49.   Where run vertically, nonmetallic wireways must be securely supported at intervals not exceeding _____, with no more than one joint between supports.

(a) 5 ft   (b) 10 ft   (c) 4 ft   (d) 6 ft

50.   Wireways are permitted for _____.

(a) exposed work   (b) concealed work   (c) wet locations if listed for the purpose   (d) a and c

(• Indicates that 75% or fewer of those who took this exam answered the question correctly.)

1. Metal conduit and metal piping within _____ of the inside walls of the pool that are not separated from the pool by a permanent barrier are required to be bonded.

    (a) 4 ft   (b) 5 ft   (c) 8 ft   (d) 10 ft

2. Metal enclosures and raceways for service conductors and equipment must be _____.

    (a) isolated   (b) insulated   (c) grounded   (d) gray

3. Metal equipment racks and enclosures for permanent audio system installations must be grounded.

    (a) True   (b) False

4. Metal multioutlet assemblies can pass through a dry partition, provided no receptacle is concealed in the partition and the cover of the exposed portion of the system can be removed.

    (a) True   (b) False

5. Metal poles used to support luminaires must be bonded to a(n) _____.

    (a) grounding electrode   (b) grounded conductor
    (c) equipment grounding conductor (d) any of these

6. Metal surface type enclosures in damp or wet locations must be mounted so there is at least _____ airspace between the enclosure and the wall or supporting surface.

    (a) 1/16 in.   (b) 1 1/4 in.   (c) 1/4 in.   (d) 6 in.

7. Metal surfaces that are within 5 ft of the inside walls of an indoor spa or hot tub, and not separated from the indoor spa or hot tub area by a permanent barrier, are not required to be bonded.

    (a) True   (b) False

8. Metal wireways are sheet metal troughs with _____ for housing and protecting electric wires and cable.

    (a) removable covers (b) hinged covers (c) a or b   (d) none of these

9. Mobile home service equipment must be located adjacent to the mobile home and not mounted in or on the mobile home. The service equipment must be located in sight from but not more than _____ from the exterior wall of the mobile home it serves.

    (a) 15 ft   (b) 20 ft   (c) 30 ft   (d) none of these

10. Motor control circuits must be arranged so that they will be disconnected from all sources of supply when the disconnecting means is in the open position. Where separate devices are used for the motor and control circuit, they must be located immediately adjacent to each other.

    (a) True   (b) False

11. Motor overload protection is not required where _____.

    (a) conductors are oversized by 125 percent   (b) conductors are part of a limited-energy circuit
    (c) it might introduce additional or increased hazards   (d) short-circuit protection is provided

12. Multiwire branch circuits that supply power to the wired partitions of office furnishings for _____ must be provided with a means to simultaneously disconnect all ungrounded conductors where the branch circuit originates.

    (a) fixed-type partitions   (b) free-standing type partitions
    (c) both a and b   (d) none of these

13. NFPA 70E, Standard for Electrical Safety in the Workplace provides information to help determine the electrical safety training requirements expected of a "qualified person."

    (a) True   (b) False

14. No tap conductor can supply another tap conductor.

    (a) True   (b) False

15. No wiring of any type can be installed in ducts used to transport _____.

    (a) dust   (b) flammable vapors   (c) loose stock   (d) all of these

16. Nonferrous raceways, cable trays, cablebus, auxiliary gutters, cable armor, boxes, cable sheathing, cabinets, elbows, couplings, nipples, fittings, supports, and support hardware _____ must be provided with supplementary corrosion protection.

    (a) embedded or encased in concrete   (b) in direct contact with the earth
    (c) likely to become energized   (d) a or b

17. Nonmetallic raceways of all types may be installed within the raised floor area of an information technology equipment room.

    (a) True   (b) False

18. Nonmetallic wireways are permitted for _____.

    (a) exposed work   (b) concealed work   (c) wet locations if listed for the purpose   (d) a and c

19. NUCC larger than _____ must not be used.

    (a) 1 in.   (b) 2 in.   (c) 3 in.   (d) 4 in.

20. On a three-phase, 4-wire, delta-connected service where the midpoint of one phase winding is grounded, the service conductor having the higher-phase voltage-to-ground must be durably and permanently marked by an outer finish that is _____ in color, or by other effective means, at each termination or junction point.

    (a) orange   (b) red   (c) blue   (d) any of these

21. On the load side of the service disconnecting means, the _____ circuit conductor is permitted to ground meter enclosures if all meter enclosures are located near the service disconnecting means and no service ground-fault protection is installed.

    (a) grounding   (b) bonding   (c) grounded   (d) phase

22. One receptacle outlet must be installed at each island or peninsular countertop space with a long dimension of 2 ft or greater, and a short dimension of 12 in. or greater. When breaks occur in countertop spaces for appliances, sinks, etc., there is never a need for more than one receptacle outlet.

    (a) True   (b) False

23. Only wiring, raceways, and cables used directly in connection with the elevator must be inside the hoistway and the machine room.

    (a) True   (b) False

24. Openings in cabinets, cutout boxes, and meter socket enclosures through which conductors enter must be _____.

    (a) adequately closed   (b) made using concentric knockouts only
    (c) centered in the cabinet wall   (d) identified

25. Optical fiber cable not terminated at equipment and not identified for future use with a tag are considered abandoned.

    (a) True   (b) False

26. Optical fiber cables are not required to be listed and marked where the length of the cable within the building, measured from its point of entrance, does not exceed _____ and the cable enters the building from the outside and is terminated in an enclosure.

    (a) 25 ft   (b) 30 ft   (c) 50 ft   (d) 100 ft

27. Optical fiber cables installed _____ on the surface of ceilings and sidewalls must be supported by the building structure in such a manner that the cable will not be damaged by normal building use.

    (a) exposed   (b) concealed   (c) hidden   (d) a and b

28. Optical fiber cables utilized for fire alarm circuits must be installed in accordance with Article 770.

    (a) True   (b) False

29. Optical fibers are permitted in the same cable, and conductive and nonconductive optical fiber cables are permitted in the same cable tray, enclosure, or raceway with conductors of power-limited fire alarm circuits in compliance with Article 760.

    (a) True   (b) False

30. Optional standby system wiring is permitted to occupy the same raceways, cables, boxes, and cabinets with other general wiring.

    (a) True   (b) False

31. Outlet boxes can be secured to suspended-ceiling framing members by mechanical means such as _____, or other means identified for the suspended-ceiling framing member(s).

    (a) bolts   (b) screws   (c) rivets   (d) all of these

32. Overcurrent protection devices for emergency power systems _____ all supply-side overcurrent protective devices.

    (a) must be selectively coordinated with   (b) are allowed to be selectively coordinated with
    (c) must be the same amperage as   (d) must be a larger amperage than

33. Overcurrent protection devices for legally required power systems _____ all supply-side overcurrent protective devices.

    (a) must be selectively coordinated with   (b) are allowed to be selectively coordinated with
    (c) must be the same amperage as   (d) must be a higher amperage than

34. Overhead conductors must have a minimum of _____ vertical clearance from final grade over residential property and driveways, as well as those commercial areas not subject to truck traffic where the voltage is limited to 300 volts-to-ground.

    (a) 10 ft   (b) 12 ft   (c) 15 ft   (d) 18 ft

35. Overhead conductors over a swimming pool must meet the clearance requirements of Article 680. Where a minimum clearance from the water level is given, it is taken from the _____ water level of the specified body of water.

    (a) average   (b) maximum   (c) minimum   (d) nominal

36. Overhead service conductors can be supported to hardwood trees.

    (a) True   (b) False

37. Panelboards supplied by a three-phase, 4-wire, delta-connected system must have that phase with the higher voltage-to-ground (high-leg) connected to the _____ phase.

    (a) A   (b) B   (c) C   (d) any of these

38. Pendant luminaires installed in Class I, Division 1 locations must be suspended by and supplied through threaded conduit stems, and threaded joints must be provided with set screws or other means to prevent loosening. Stems _____.

    (a) must not be longer than 12 in.
    (b) over 12 in. must be provided with lateral bracing
    (c) must be provided with a fitting or flexible connector approved for the Class I, Division 1 location
    (d) any of these

39. Pendant luminaires installed in Class II, Division 1 locations must be suspended by threaded conduit stems, by chains with approved fittings, or by other approved means. Stems _____.

    (a) must not be longer than 12 in.
    (b) if over 12 in., must be provided with lateral bracing
    (c) must be provided with a fitting or flexible connector listed for the location
    (d) any of these

40. Plug fuses of the Edison-base type must be used _____.

    (a) where overfusing is necessary   (b) only as replacement in existing installations
    (c) as a replacement for Type S fuses   (d) only for 50A and above

41. Plug-in-type circuit breakers that are back-fed (to supply a panelboard) must be _____ by an additional fastener that requires more than a pull to release.

    (a) grounded   (b) secured in place   (c) shunt tripped   (d) none of these

42. Portable distribution or terminal boxes installed outdoors at carnivals, circuses, or fairs must be weatherproof and mounted so the bottom of the enclosure is not less than _____ above the ground.

    (a) 6 in.   (b) 2 ft   (c) 6 ft 6 in.   (d) 5 ft 6 in.

43. Power distribution blocks installed in metal wireways must be listed.

    (a) True   (b) False

44. Power for sensitive electronic equipment, called "Technical Power" is a separately derived single-phase, 3-wire system with _____ volts to a grounded conductor on each of two ungrounded conductors. The line-to-line voltage is _____.

    (a) 30, 60   (b) 60, 120   (c) 120, 120   (d) none of these

45. Power-limited fire alarm (PLFA) cables can be supported by strapping, taping, or attaching to the exterior of a conduit or raceway.

    (a) True   (b) False

46. Raceways or cable trays containing electric conductors must not contain any pipe, tube, or equal method of routing for steam, water, air, gas, drainage, or any service other than _____.

    (a) allowed by the authority having jurisdiction
    (b) electrical
    (c) pneumatic
    (d) designed by the engineer

47. Raceways, cable trays, cable bus, auxiliary gutters, cable armor, boxes, cable sheathing, cabinets, elbows, couplings, fittings, supports, and support hardware must be of materials suitable for _____.

    (a) corrosive locations
    (b) wet locations
    (c) the environment in which they are to be installed
    (d) none of these

48. Receptacle outlet(s) for a _____ must be GFCI protected.

    (a) self-contained spa or hot tub
    (b) packaged spa or hot tub equipment assembly
    (c) field-assembled spa or hot tub with a heater load of 50A or less
    (d) all of these

49. Receptacle outlets can be installed below the countertop surface in dwelling units when necessary for the physically impaired, or if there is no means available to mount a receptacle above an island or peninsular countertop.

    (a) True
    (b) False

50. Receptacles and cord connectors having grounding terminals must have those terminals effectively _____.

    (a) grounded
    (b) bonded
    (c) labeled
    (d) listed

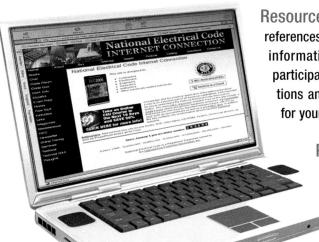

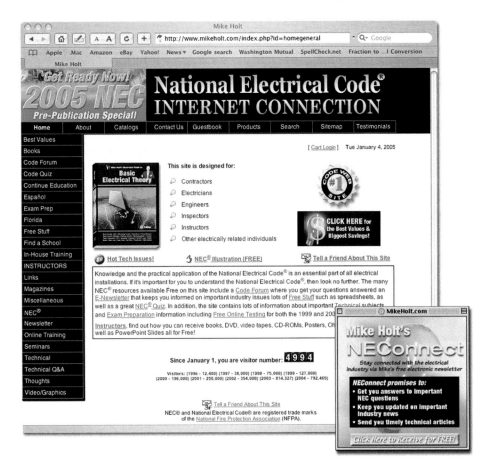

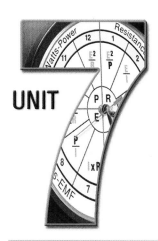

UNIT 7

Motor Calculations

Introduction

Motor circuits have special requirements that affect how the overcurrent protection is sized and installed. Motors will typically draw about six times as much current at start-up as they draw during normal operation. Article 430 provides guidance on how to properly protect the motor from overcurrent and still avoid nuisance tripping of the fuse or circuit breaker protecting the motor.

The *Code* definition of "Overcurrent" is made up of three factors; short circuits, ground faults, and overloads. For motors, the function of overcurrent protection is divided into two components. The short-circuit and ground-fault protection of a motor is usually provided by a fuse or circuit breaker which is sized large enough to let the motor start while providing short-circuit and ground-fault protection, but too large to provide overload protection. Overload protection is provided to protect the motor and wiring at a value close to the actual running current of the motor, but with sufficient time delay to allow the motor to start. This protection is often provided by the "heaters" which are overload sensing devices of a magnetic starter.

Article 430 spells out the minimum sizing of conductors for motor branch circuits and feeders as well. When conductors and short-circuit ground-fault protection are sized based on Article 430, the fuse or circuit breaker may appear to be much larger than it should be for the conductors selected. Make sure everything is sized correctly based on Article 430, then don't be concerned. The overcurrent protection rules of Article 240 do not apply to motors, so often an installation may not "look right," even though it complies with Article 430 requirements.

Careful study of this unit will help in understanding the requirements of Article 430 that might sometimes be confusing.

7.1 Single Motor Conductors [430.22(A)]

Branch-circuit conductors to a single motor must have an ampacity of not less than 125 percent of the motor's full-load current (FLC) as listed in Tables 430.247 through 430.250 [430.6(A)(1)], Figure 7–1. When selecting motor current from one of these tables, note that the last sentence above each table allows us to use the ampacity columns for a range of system voltages without any adjustment. The actual conductor size must be selected from Table 310.16 according to the terminal temperature rating (60°C or 75°C) of the equipment [110.14(C)].

AUTHOR'S COMMENT: 110.14(C)(1)(a) tells us that terminals are rated 60°C for equipment rated 100A or less unless marked 75°C. In real life, most terminals are now rated 75°C, so in this Unit, we will assume all motors are rated 75°C unless specified 60°C. For exam purposes, read the problem carefully to be certain you know what terminal rating the exam question specifies. If unspecified, use the rules of 110.14(C).

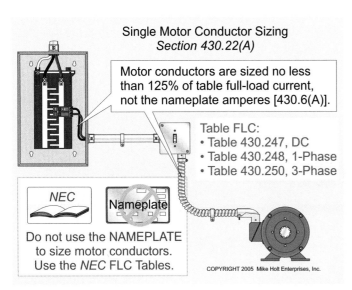

Figure 7–1

▶ **Motor Branch-Circuit Conductors**

What size conductor is required for a 2 hp, 230V, single-phase motor? Figure 7–2

(a) 14 AWG   (b) 12 AWG

(c) 10 AWG   (d) 8 AWG

• Answer: (a) 14 AWG

Motor FLC – Table 430.248:
2 hp, 230V, single-phase FLC = 12A

The conductor is sized no less than 125% of motor FLC:
12A x 1.25 = 15A, Table 310.16, 14 AWG rated 20A at 75°C

Note: The minimum size conductor permitted for building wiring is 14 AWG [310.5]; however, some local codes and many industrial facilities have requirements that 12 AWG be used as the smallest branch-circuit conductor.

7.2 Motor Overcurrent Protection

Motors and their associated equipment must be protected against overcurrent (overload, short circuit, or ground fault) [Article 100], Figure 7–3 Due to the special characteristics of induction motors, overcurrent protection is generally accomplished by having the overload protection separated from the short-circuit and ground-fault protection device, Figure 7–4 Article 430, Part III contains the requirements for motor overload protection and Part IV of Article 430 contains the requirements for motor short-circuit and ground-fault protection.

Overload Protection

Overload is the condition where current exceeds the equipment ampere rating, which can result in equipment damage due to dangerous overheating [Article 100]. Overload protection devices, sometimes called heaters, are intended to protect the motor, the motor control equipment, and the branch-circuit conductors from excessive heating due to motor overload [430.31].

Overload protection is not intended to protect against short circuits or ground-fault currents. Figure 7–5

If overload protection is to be accomplished by using fuses, a fuse must be installed to protect each ungrounded conductor [430.36 and 430.55].

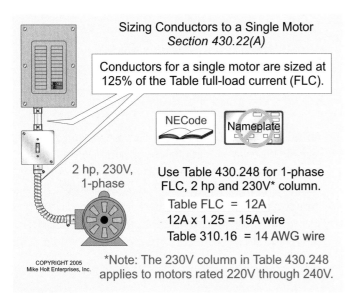

Figure 7–2

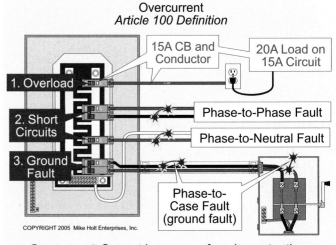

Overcurrent: Current in excess of equipment rating caused from an overload, short circuit, or ground fault.

Figure 7–3

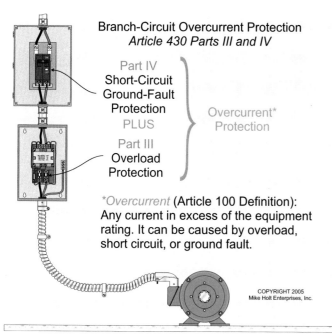

Branch-Circuit Overcurrent Protection
Article 430 Parts III and IV

Part IV
Short-Circuit
Ground-Fault
Protection
PLUS

Overcurrent*
Protection

Part III
Overload
Protection

Overcurrent (Article 100 Definition):
Any current in excess of the equipment
rating. It can be caused by overload,
short circuit, or ground fault.

COPYRIGHT 2005
Mike Holt Enterprises, Inc.

Figure 7–4

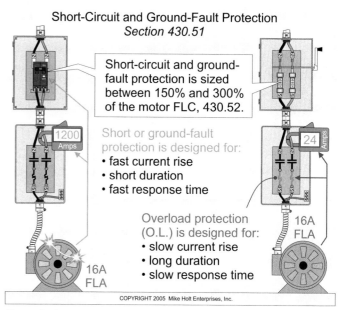

Short-Circuit and Ground-Fault Protection
Section 430.51

Short-circuit and ground-
fault protection is sized
between 150% and 300%
of the motor FLC, 430.52.

1200
Amps

Short or ground-fault
protection is designed for:
• fast current rise
• short duration
• fast response time

24
Amps

Overload protection
(O.L.) is designed for:
• slow current rise
• long duration
• slow response time

16A
FLA

16A
FLA

COPYRIGHT 2005 Mike Holt Enterprises, Inc.

Figure 7–6

Short-Circuit and Ground-Fault Protection

Branch-circuit short-circuit and ground-fault protection devices are intended to protect the motor, the motor control apparatus, and the conductors against short circuits or ground faults, but they are not intended to protect against an overload [430.51]. Figure 7–6

AUTHOR'S COMMENT: The short-circuit and ground-fault protection device required for motor circuits is not the type required for personnel [210.8], feeders [215.9 and 240.13], services [230.95], or temporary wiring for receptacles [590.6].

7.3 Overload Protection [430.6(2) and 430.32(A)]

In addition to short-circuit and ground-fault protection, motors must be protected against overload. Generally, the motor overload device is part of the motor starter; however, a separate overload device like a dual-element fuse can be used [430.55]. Motors rated more than 1 hp without integral thermal protection, and motors 1 hp or less (automatically started) [430.32(B)], must have an overload device sized in response to the motor nameplate current rating [430.6(A)(2)]. The overload device must be sized no larger than required by 430.32.

Service Factor

Motors with a nameplate service factor (SF) rating of 1.15 or more must have their overload protection device sized no more than 125 percent of the motor nameplate current rating [430.6(A)(2)].

Types of Overload
Section 430.31

Overloads protect the motor, conductor, and associated equipment from excessive heat due to motor overloads. They are not intended to protect against short circuits and ground faults.

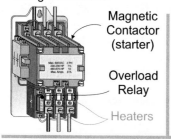

Magnetic
Contactor
(starter)

Overload
Relay

Heaters

Electronic

Settings are done with
dip switches using a
binary code, or an
adjustable setting dial.

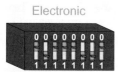

Fuses can provide overload protection
as well as short-circuit and ground fault
protection [430.55].

COPYRIGHT 2005 Mike Holt Enterprises, Inc.

Figure 7–5

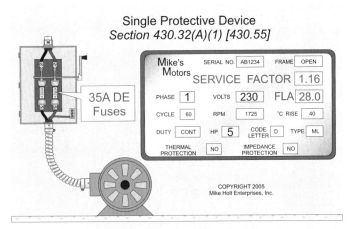

Single Protective Device
Section 430.32(A)(1) [430.55]

35A DE Fuses

COPYRIGHT 2005
Mike Holt Enterprises, Inc.

5 hp, 230V, SF 1.16, 28A nameplate.

Dual element (DE) fuse [430.32(A)(1)]
Nameplate value [430.6(A)(2)]
Service factor of 1.16, use 125%
28 FLA x 1.25 = 35A [240.6(A)]

Figure 7–7

▶ Service Factor

If a dual-element fuse is used for overload protection, what size fuse is required for a 5 hp, 230V, single-phase motor, with a service factor of 1.16, if the motor nameplate current rating is 28A? Figure 7–7

(a) 25A   (b) 30A
(c) 35A   (d) 40A

• Answer: (c) 35A

Overload protection is sized to the motor nameplate current rating [430.6(A), 430.32(A)(1), and 430.55].

28A x 1.25 = 35A [240.6(A)]

Temperature Rise

Motors with a nameplate temperature rise rating not over 40°C must have the overload protection device sized no more than 125 percent of the motor nameplate current rating.

▶ Temperature Rise

If a dual-element fuse is used for the overload protection, what size fuse is required for a 50 hp, 460V, three-phase motor, with a temperature rise of 39°C, and a motor nameplate current rating of 60A (FLA)? Figure 7–8

(a) 40A   (b) 50A
(c) 60A   (d) 70A

• Answer: (d) 70A

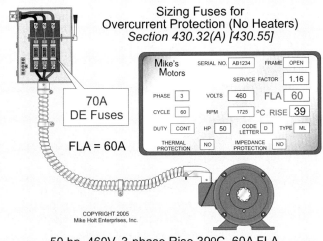

Sizing Fuses for
Overcurrent Protection (No Heaters)
Section 430.32(A) [430.55]

70A DE Fuses

FLA = 60A

COPYRIGHT 2005
Mike Holt Enterprises, Inc.

50 hp, 460V, 3-phase Rise 39ºC, 60A FLA.

Dual element (DE) fuse [430.32(A)(1)]
Nameplate (FLA) value to be used.
Temperature Rise 39ºC, use 125%
60A nameplate x 1.25 = 75A
Next size down* = 70A DE Fuses [240.6(A)]

*The next size up rule does not apply when fuses are used for overload protection.

Figure 7–8

Overloads are sized according to the motor nameplate current rating, not the motor FLC rating from the *Code* book tables.

60A x 1.25 = 75A, 70A [240.6(A) and 430.32(A)(1)]

All Other Motors

Motors that do not have a service factor rating of 1.15 and up, or a temperature rise rating of 40°C and less, must have the overload protection device sized at not more than 115 percent of the motor nameplate ampere rating.

A motor has a nameplate that specifies the following: service factor is 1.12; temperature rise is 41°C, nameplate current rating of 25A. What amperage size alloy-type overload device should be used as protection? Figure 7–9

(a) 33.75A   (b) 31.25A
(c) 28.75A   (d) 25A

• Answer: (c) 28.75A

Since 1.12 is less than 1.15 for the service factor, and 41°C is over 40°C, the overload protection is sized based on 115% of the motor nameplate ampere rating.

25A x 1.15 = 28.75A overload device

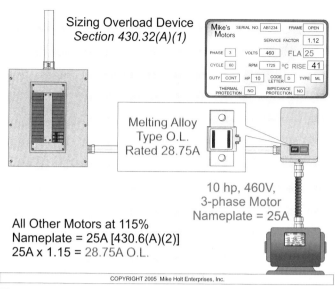

Sizing Overload Device
Section 430.32(A)(1)

Melting Alloy
Type O.L.
Rated 28.75A

10 hp, 460V,
3-phase Motor
Nameplate = 25A

All Other Motors at 115%
Nameplate = 25A [430.6(A)(2)]
25A x 1.15 = 28.75A O.L.

COPYRIGHT 2005 Mike Holt Enterprises, Inc.

Figure 7–9

7.4 Branch-Circuit Short-Circuit Ground-Fault Protection [430.51]

NEC Table 430.52			
	Percent of FLC Tables 430.247, 248, and 250		
Type of Motor	One-Time Fuse	Dual-Element Fuse	IT Circuit Breaker
Direct-Current and Wound-Rotor Motors	150	150	150
All Other Motors	300	175	250

In addition to overload protection, each motor and its accessories require short-circuit and ground-fault protection. Section 430.52(C)(1) requires the motor branch-circuit short-circuit and ground-fault protection (except torque motors) to be sized no greater than the percentages listed in Table 430.52. When the short-circuit ground-fault protection device value determined from Table 430.52 does not correspond with the standard rating or setting of overcurrent protection devices as listed in 240.6(A), the next higher protection device size may be used [430.52(C)(1) Ex 1], Figure 7–11 To determine the percentage from Table 430.52 to be used to size the motor branch-circuit short-circuit ground-fault protection device, the following steps should be helpful:

AUTHOR'S COMMENT: A service factor of 1.15 means that the motor is designed to operate at 115 percent of its rated horsepower continuously, Figure 7–10A A temperature rise of 40ºC means that the motor is designed to operate so that it will not heat up more than 40ºC above its rating. Figure 7–10B

Number of Overloads [430.37]

An overload protection device must be installed in each ungrounded conductor according to the requirements of Table 430.37. If fuses are used for overload protection, a fuse must be installed in each ungrounded conductor [430.36].

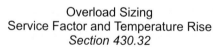

Overload Sizing
Service Factor and Temperature Rise
Section 430.32

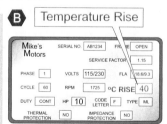

A service factor of 1.15 means that the motor is designed to operate at 115 percent of its rated horsepower continuously.

Temperature rise 40ºC means that the motor is designed to operate so that it will not heat up more than 40ºC above its rating.

COPYRIGHT 2005 Mike Holt Enterprises, Inc.

Figure 7–10

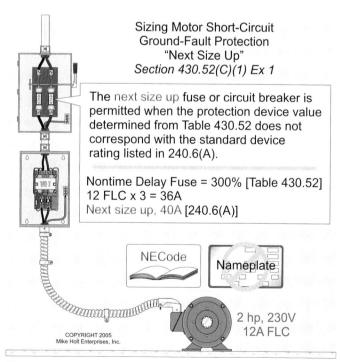

Sizing Motor Short-Circuit
Ground-Fault Protection
"Next Size Up"
Section 430.52(C)(1) Ex 1

The next size up fuse or circuit breaker is permitted when the protection device value determined from Table 430.52 does not correspond with the standard device rating listed in 240.6(A).

Nontime Delay Fuse = 300% [Table 430.52]
12 FLC x 3 = 36A
Next size up, 40A [240.6(A)]

NECode

Nameplate

2 hp, 230V
12A FLC

COPYRIGHT 2005
Mike Holt Enterprises, Inc.

Figure 7–11

Step 1: Locate the motor type in Table 430.52

Step 2: Select the percentage from Table 430.52 according to the type of protection device, such as nontime delay (one-time) fuse, dual-element fuse, or inverse-time circuit breaker.

Step 3: Where the protection device rating determined by Table 430.52 does not correspond with the standard size or rating of fuses or circuit breakers listed in 240.6(A), use of the next higher standard size or rating is permitted [430.52(C)(1) Ex 1].

▶ **Branch Circuit**

Which of the following statements are true?

(a) The branch-circuit short-circuit protection (nontime delay fuse) for a 3 hp, 115V, single-phase motor must not exceed 110A.

(b) The branch-circuit short-circuit protection (dual-element fuse) for a 5 hp, 230V, single-phase, motor must not exceed 50A.

(c) The branch-circuit short-circuit protection (inverse-time breaker) for a 25 hp, 460V, three-phase synchronous motor must not exceed 70A.

(d) all of these

• Answer: (d) all of these

Short-circuit and ground-fault protection, 430.52(C)(1) Ex 1 and Table 430.52:

Table 430.248: 34A x 3.00 = 102A, next size up permitted, 110A

Table 430.248: 28A x 1.75 = 49A, next size up permitted, 50A

Table 430.250: 26A x 2.50 = 65A, next size up permitted, 70A

WARNING: *Conductors are sized at 125% of the motor FLC [430.22(A)], overloads are sized from 115% to 125% of the motor nameplate current rating [430.32(A)(1)], and the short-circuit ground-fault protection device is sized from 150% to 300% of the motor FLC [Table 430.52]. There is no relationship between the branch-circuit conductor ampacity (125%) and the short-circuit ground-fault protection device (150% up to 300%).* Figure 7–12

▶ **Branch Circuit**

Which of the following statements are true for a 5 hp, 230V motor that has a nameplate current rating of 26A? Figure 7–13

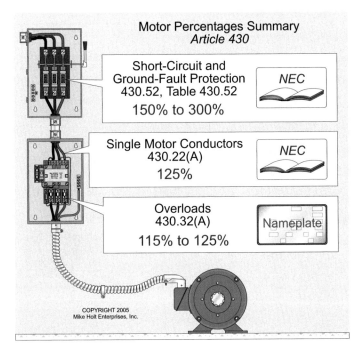

Figure 7–12

(a) The branch-circuit conductors can be 10 AWG.

(b) Overload protection is 29.9A.

(c) Short-circuit and ground-fault protection is permitted to be a 70A circuit breaker.

(d) all of these

• Answer: (d) all of these

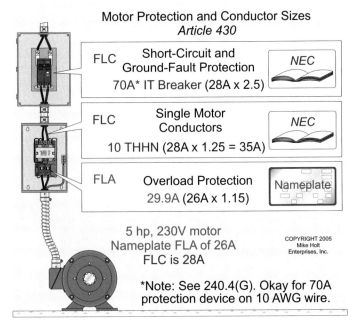

Figure 7–13

Conductor Size [430.22(A) and 430.6(A)(1)].
Table 430.248, FLC = 16A

28A x 1.25 = 35A, 10 AWG at 75°C, Table 310.16

Overload Protection Size [430.32(A)(1)]

26A (nameplate) x 1.15 = 29.9A

Short-Circuit and Ground-Fault Protection [240.6(A),
430.52(C)(1), and Table 430.52]

Use an inverse-time circuit breaker if a fuse is not
specified, Table 430.52 = 250%

28A x 2.50 = 70A circuit breaker

This bothers many electrical people, but the 10 THHN conductors and motor are protected against overcurrent by the 26A overload protection device and against short circuit and ground fault by the 70A protection device. The small conductor overcurrent protection rule of 240.4(D) does not apply to motors [240.4(G)].

7.5 Feeder Conductor Size [430.24]

Conductors that supply several motors must have an ampacity of not less than:

(1) 125% of the highest-rated motor FLC [430.17], plus

(2) The sum of the FLCs of the other motors (on the same line) [430.6(A)].

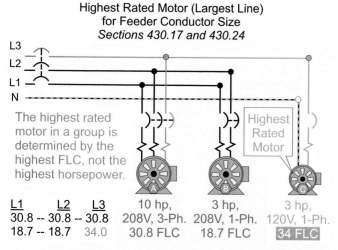

Highest Rated Motor (Largest Line)
for Feeder Conductor Size
Sections 430.17 and 430.24

The highest rated motor in a group is determined by the highest FLC, not the highest horsepower.

L1	L2	L3	10 hp,	3 hp,	3 hp,
30.8	30.8	30.8	208V, 3-Ph.	208V, 1-Ph.	120V, 1-Ph.
18.7	18.7	34.0	30.8 FLC	18.7 FLC	34 FLC

Highest rated motor is the 120V motor at 34 FLC.
The other motor(s) in the group (phase) is the 10 hp,
3-phase motor as indicated by the shaded area.

COPYRIGHT 2005 Mike Holt Enterprises, Inc.

Figure 7–14

AUTHOR'S COMMENT: The highest-rated motor is based on the motor with the highest full-load current [430.17]. The "other motors in the group" (on the same line) is determined by balancing the motors' FLCs on the feeder being sized, then selecting the line that has the highest-rated motor on it. Figure 7–14

▶ Feeder Conductor Size

What size feeder conductor is required for two motors; a 5 hp, 230V (FLC = 28A), single-phase and a 3 hp, 230V (FLC = 17A), single-phase? The terminals are rated for 75°C. Figure 7–15

(a) 40A   (b) 60A
(c) 76A   (d) 52A

• Answer: (d) 52A
(28A x 1.25) + 17A = 52A

Note: A 6 AWG conductor at 75°C is rated for 65A [Table 310.16].

7.6 Feeder Protection [430.61]

Motor feeder conductors must have protection against short circuits and ground faults but not against overload.

The feeder must be provided with a protective device having a rating or setting not greater than the largest rating or setting of

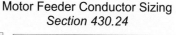

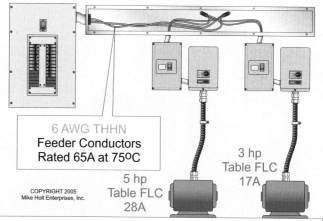

Motor Feeder Conductor Sizing
Section 430.24

6 AWG THHN
Feeder Conductors
Rated 65A at 75ºC

COPYRIGHT 2005
Mike Holt Enterprises, Inc.

5 hp
Table FLC
28A

3 hp
Table FLC
17A

Motor feeder conductors must be sized not less
than 125% of the largest motor FLC plus the sum
of the FLCs of the other motors on the same phase.

Largest FLC is 28A
(28 FLC x 1.25) + 17 FLC = 52A
Table 310.16, use 6 AWG

Figure 7–15

the branch-circuit short-circuit and ground-fault protective device, plus the sum of the full-load currents of the other motors of the group [430.62(A)].

▶ Feeder Protection

What size feeder protection (inverse-time breaker) is required for a 5 hp, 230V, single-phase motor and a 3 hp, 230V, single-phase motor? The terminals are rated for 75°C. Figure 7–16

(a) 30A breaker   (b) 40A breaker
(c) 50A breaker   (d) 80A breaker

• Answer: (d) 80A breaker

Motor FLC [Table 430.248]
5 hp motor FLC = 28A
3 hp motor FLC = 17A

Branch-Circuit Protection [240.6(A), 430.52(C)(1), and Table 430.52]
5 hp: 28A x 2.5 = 70A
3 hp: 17A x 2.5 = 42.5A, next size up, 45A

Feeder Protection [430.62]
Not greater than 70A protection, plus 17A = 87A, next size down, 80A

AUTHOR'S COMMENT: There is no exception to permit the next size up motor feeder protection device. Always round down to the next size device listed in 240.6(A).

7.7 Highest-Rated Motor [430.17]

When selecting the feeder conductors or the feeder short-circuit ground-fault protection device, the highest-rated motor must be the highest-rated motor FLC (not the highest-rated horsepower) [430.17].

▶ Highest-Rated Motor

Which is the highest-rated motor of the following? Figure 7–17

(a) 10 hp, 208V, three-phase   (b) 3 hp, 208V, single-phase
(c) 3 hp, 115V, single-phase   (d) any of these

• Answer: (c) 3 hp, 115V, single-phase
10 hp = 30.8A [Table 430.250]
3 hp, 208V = 18.75A [Table 430.248]
3 hp, 120V = 34.0A [Table 430.248]

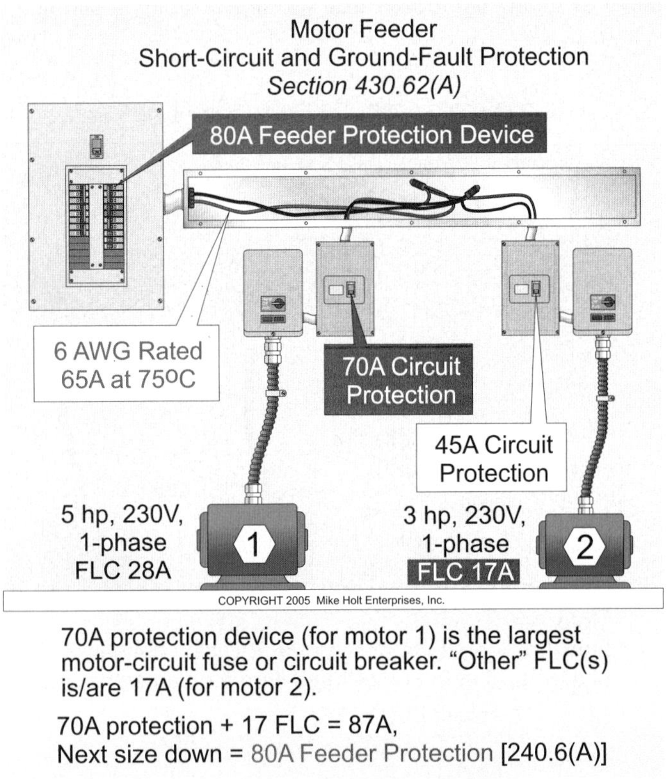

Motor Feeder
Short-Circuit and Ground-Fault Protection
Section 430.62(A)

80A Feeder Protection Device

6 AWG Rated 65A at 75°C

70A Circuit Protection

45A Circuit Protection

5 hp, 230V, 1-phase
FLC 28A ①

3 hp, 230V, 1-phase ②
FLC 17A

COPYRIGHT 2005 Mike Holt Enterprises, Inc.

70A protection device (for motor 1) is the largest motor-circuit fuse or circuit breaker. "Other" FLC(s) is/are 17A (for motor 2).

70A protection + 17 FLC = 87A,
Next size down = 80A Feeder Protection [240.6(A)]

Figure 7–16

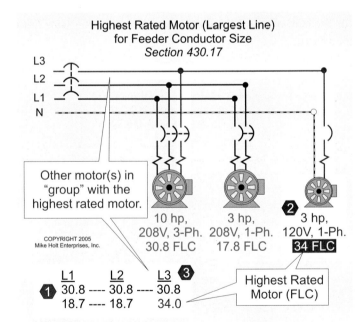

Highest Rated Motor (Largest Line)
for Feeder Conductor Size
Section 430.17

Other motor(s) in "group" with the highest rated motor.

COPYRIGHT 2005
Mike Holt Enterprises, Inc.

10 hp, 208V, 3-Ph. 30.8 FLC
3 hp, 208V, 1-Ph. 17.8 FLC
3 hp, 120V, 1-Ph. **34 FLC** ②

Highest Rated Motor (FLC)

L1	L2	L3 ③
① 30.8 ---- 30.8 ----		30.8
18.7 ---- 18.7		34.0

1. Balance the FLC of all the motors between the ungrounded conductors (L1, L2, and L3).
2. Determine the highest rated motor [430.17].
3. Select the ungrounded conductor that has the highest rated motor to determine other motors in the group.

Figure 7–17

7.8 Motor Calculations Steps

Table 7–1 can be used to calculate branch circuits and feeders for two or more motors. It may also be helpful to draw out the motor circuits and balance the motors on L1 and L2 for single-phase or L1, L2, and L3 for three-phase. See Figures 7-17 and 7-18.

▶ Motor Calculation Steps Example

Given: One 10 hp, 208V, three-phase motor and three 1 hp, 115V, single-phase motors. Determine the branch-circuit conductor (75°C) and short-circuit ground-fault protection device (inverse-time breaker) for all motors, then determine the feeder conductor and protection size. Figure 7–18 See Table 7–2.

7.9 Motor Calculation Review

▶ Branch Circuit

Size the branch-circuit conductors and the short-circuit ground-fault protection device for a 5 hp, 230V, single-phase motor. The motor nameplate full-load amperes are 26A and dual-element fuses are to be used for short-circuit and ground-fault protection. Figure 7–19

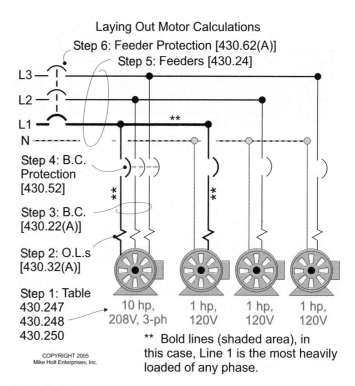

Laying Out Motor Calculations
Step 6: Feeder Protection [430.62(A)]
Step 5: Feeders [430.24]

Step 4: B.C. Protection [430.52]

Step 3: B.C. [430.22(A)]

Step 2: O.L.s [430.32(A)]

Step 1: Table 430.247 430.248 430.250

10 hp, 208V, 3-ph   1 hp, 120V   1 hp, 120V   1 hp, 120V

COPYRIGHT 2005
Mike Holt Enterprises, Inc.

** Bold lines (shaded area), in this case, Line 1 is the most heavily loaded of any phase.

Figure 7–18

Table 7–1			
Steps & *NEC* Rules	M1	M2	M3
Step 1: **Motor FLC** Tables 430.247, 248 and 250	_____ FLC	_____ FLC	_____ FLC
Step 2: **Overload Protection** Standard 430.32(A)(1)	____ x 1. ____ = ____	____ x 1. ____ = ____	____ x 1. ____ = ____
Step 3: **Single Motor Conductors** 430.22(A) and Table 310.16	_____ x 1.25 = _____	_____ x 1.25 = _____	_____ x 1.25 = _____
Step 4: **Branch-Circuit Protection** 240.6(A), 430.52(C) and Table 430.52	_____ x _____ = _____ Next Size Up	_____ x _____ = _____ Next Size Up	_____ x _____ = _____ Next Size Up
Step 5: **Feeder Conductor** 430.24 and Table 310.16	_____ x 1.25 + _____ + _____ + _____ = _____ Table 310.16, Use _____ (75°C unless specified otherwise)		
Step 6: **Feeder Protection** 240.6(A), 430.62, and Table 430.52	_____ + _____ + _____ + _____ = _____ Next Size Down		

Table 7–2		
	M1	**M2, M3, and M4**
Step 1: **Motor FLC** Tables 430.247, 248, or 250	Table 430.250 30.8 FLC	Table 430.248 16 FLC
Step 2: **Overload Protection** Nameplate 430.32(A)(1)	No Nameplate, Use FLC 30.8A x 1.15 = 35.4A	No Nameplate, Use FLC 16A x 1.15 = 18.4A
Step 3: **Single Motor Conductors 125 Percent of FLC** 110.14(C), 430.22(A), and Table 310.16	30.8A x 1.25 = 38.5A Table 310.16, 8 AWG 75°C	16A × 1.25 = 20A Table 310.16, 14 AWG 75°C
Step 4: **Branch-Circuit Protection** FLC x Table 430.52 percent 240.6(A) and 430.52(C)	30.8A x 2.5 = 77A Next size up 240.6(A) = 80A	16A x 2.5 = 40A 240.6(A) = 40A
Step 5: **Feeder Conductor** FLC x 125 percent + FLCs of other motors 430.24 and Table 310.16	(30.8A x 1.25) + 16A = 54.5A Table 310.16, Use 6 THHN, rated 65A 75°C	
Step 6: **Feeder Protection** Largest branch protection + FLCs of other motors 240.6(A), 430.62(A), and Table 430.52	Inverse-Time Breaker 80A + 16A = 96A, next size down, 90A	

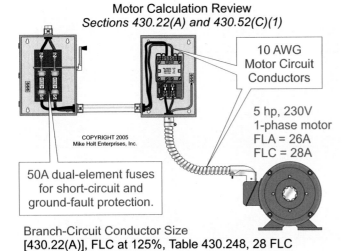

Motor Calculation Review
Sections 430.22(A) and 430.52(C)(1)

10 AWG
Motor Circuit
Conductors

5 hp, 230V
1-phase motor
FLA = 26A
FLC = 28A

COPYRIGHT 2005
Mike Holt Enterprises, Inc.

50A dual-element fuses
for short-circuit and
ground-fault protection.

Branch-Circuit Conductor Size
[430.22(A)], FLC at 125%, Table 430.248, 28 FLC
28 FLC x 1.25 = 35A
Table 310.16 = 10 AWG rated 35A at 75°C

DE Fuse Size, [430.52(C)(1)]
Use FLC, not FLA (nameplate), Table 430.52, 175%
28 FLC x 1.75 = 49A
240.6(A) = 50A DE Fuses

Figure 7–19

Branch-Circuit Conductors [430.22(A)]

Branch-circuit conductors to a single motor must have an ampacity of not less than 125% of the motor FLC as listed in Tables 430.247 through 430.250 [430.6(A)].

5 hp, 230V FLC = 28A [Table 430.248]

28A x 125% = 35A

Table 310.16, 75°C terminals: The conductor must be a 10 AWG, rated 35A.

Branch-Circuit Short-Circuit Protection [430.52(C)(1)]

The branch-circuit short-circuit and ground-fault protection device protects the motor, the motor control apparatus, and the conductors against overcurrent due to short circuits or ground faults, but not against overloads [430.51]. The branch-circuit short-circuit and ground-fault protection devices are sized by considering the type of motor and the type of protection device and applying the percent of motor FLC listed in Table 430.52. When the protection device values determined from Table

430.52 do not correspond with the standard rating of overcurrent protection devices as listed in 240.6(A), the next higher overcurrent protection device can be installed [430.52(C)(1) Ex No. 1].

28A x 175% = 50A dual-element fuse [240.6(A)]

See Example No. D8 in Annex D of the *NEC*.

▶ Feeder

Size the feeder conductor (THHN) and protection device (inverse-time breakers 75°C terminal rating) for the following motors: Three 1 hp, 115V, single-phase motors; three 5 hp, 208V, single-phase motors; and one wound-rotor 15 hp, 208V, three-phase motor.

In order to determine the feeder conductor size, the highest-rated motor must be determined as well as all the other motors in the same group. To determine the feeder protection size, the largest branch-circuit ground-fault and short-circuit protection device must be determined. Figure 7–20 shows how this example can be drawn out and how to balance the motors on L1, L2, and L3 of the feeder.

Branch-circuit short-circuit protection [240.6(A), 430.52(C)(1), and Table 430.52]

15 hp 208V, three-phase FLC= 46.2A

Protection = 46.2A x 150% (wound-rotor) = 69A: Next size up = 70A

5 hp 208V, single-phase FLC = 30.8A

Protection = 30.8A x 250% = 77A: Next size up = 80A

1 hp 120V, single-phase FLC = 16A

Protection = 16A x 250% = 40A

Feeder Conductor [430.24]

Conductors that supply several motors must have an ampacity of not less than 125% of the highest-rated motor FLC [430.17], plus the sum of the other motor FLCs [430.6(A)]. Figure 7–21

(46.2A x 1.25) + 30.8A + 30.8A + 16A = 135A

Table 310.16, 110.14(C)(1), 1/0 AWG, rated 150A at 75° C.

Note: When sizing the feeder conductor, be sure to only include the motors that are on the same line. For that reason, only four motors are used in this calculation.

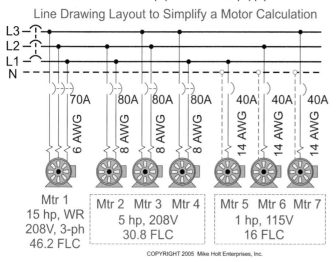

Motor Circuit Review
Sections 430.22(A) and 430.52(C)(1)
Line Drawing Layout to Simplify a Motor Calculation

Single Motor Circuits [430.22(A)]:
125% of Table FLC, 110.14, 75°C conductors.

Figure 7–20

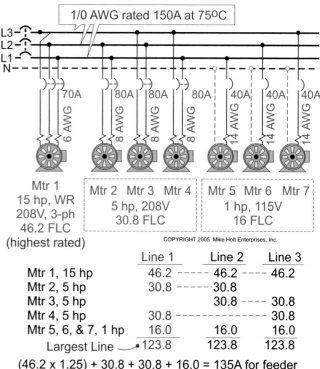

Feeder Conductor Review
Section 430.24
1/0 AWG rated 150A at 75°C

COPYRIGHT 2005 Mike Holt Enterprises, Inc.

	Line 1	Line 2	Line 3
Mtr 1, 15 hp	46.2	46.2	46.2
Mtr 2, 5 hp	30.8	30.8	
Mtr 3, 5 hp		30.8	30.8
Mtr 4, 5 hp	30.8		30.8
Mtr 5, 6, & 7, 1 hp	16.0	16.0	16.0
Largest Line	123.8	123.8	123.8

(46.2 x 1.25) + 30.8 + 30.8 + 16.0 = 135A for feeder
Table 310.16, 1/0 AWG rated 150A at 75°C

Figure 7–21

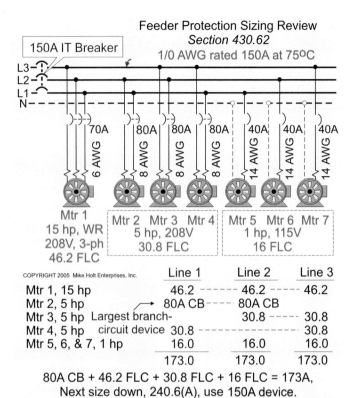

Feeder Protection Sizing Review
Section 430.62
1/0 AWG rated 150A at 75ºC

COPYRIGHT 2005 Mike Holt Enterprises, Inc.

	Line 1	Line 2	Line 3
Mtr 1, 15 hp	46.2	46.2	46.2
Mtr 2, 5 hp	80A CB	80A CB	
Mtr 3, 5 hp Largest branch-		30.8	30.8
Mtr 4, 5 hp circuit device	30.8		30.8
Mtr 5, 6, & 7, 1 hp	16.0	16.0	16.0
	173.0	173.0	173.0

80A CB + 46.2 FLC + 30.8 FLC + 16 FLC = 173A,
Next size down, 240.6(A), use 150A device.

Figure 7–22

Feeder Protection [430.62]

Feeder conductors must be protected against short circuits and ground faults by devices sized not greater than the maximum branch-circuit short-circuit ground-fault protection device [430.52(C)(1)], plus the sum of the FLCs of the other motors on the same line. Figure 7–22

80A + 46.2A +30.8 + 16A = 173A

Next size down, 150A circuit breaker [240.6(A)]. See Example D8 in Annex D of the *NEC*.

Note: When sizing the feeder protection, be sure to only include the motors that are on the same line. For that reason, only four motors are used in this calculation.

7.10 Motor VA Calculations

The measure of mechanical output of a motor is horsepower. Horsepower can be converted to watts by multiplying the horsepower rating by 746 watts per horsepower. Since this is a measure of a motor's output, don't confuse it with the input power required by a motor.

What is the output VA for a dual voltage, 1 hp motor, rated 115/230V?

(a) 746W   (b) 1,840W

(c)1000W   (d) none of these

• Answer: (a) 746W
746W x 1 hp = 746W Output power

The input VA of a motor is determined by multiplying the motor volts by the motor amperes. To determine the motor VA rating, the following formulas can be used:

◆ **Motor Single-Phase VA Formula**
Motor Single-Phase VA =
Motor Volt Rating x Motor Ampere Rating

◆ **Motor Three-Phase VA Formula**
Motor Three-Phase VA =
Motor Volt Rating x Motor Ampere Rating x 1.732

▶ **Motor VA—Single-Phase**

What is the input VA for a dual voltage, 1 hp motor, rated 115/230V? Figure 7–23

(a) 1,840 VA at 115V   (b) 1,840 VA at 230V

(c) a and b   (d) none of these

• Answer: (c) a and b
Motor VA = Volts x FLC
Table 430.248, 115V FLC = 16A, 230V FLC = 8A

VA at 230V = 230V x 8A
VA at 230V = 1,840 VA
VA at 115V = 115V x 16A
VA at 115V = 1,840 VA

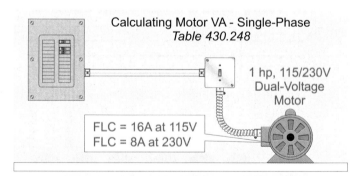

Calculating Motor VA - Single-Phase
Table 430.248

1 hp, 115/230V
Dual-Voltage
Motor

FLC = 16A at 115V
FLC = 8A at 230V

Determine the VA (volt-amperes) of the motor.

Formula: VA = Volts x Amperes   Copyright 2005
Mike Holt Enterprises, Inc.

VA connected 115V
Volts = 115V, Amps = 16A
VA = 115V x 16A
VA = 1,840 VA

VA connected 230V
Volts = 230V, Amps = 8A
VA = 230V x 8A
VA = 1,840 VA

Figure 7–23

Note: Many people believe that a 230V motor consumes less power than a 115V motor (I thought that), but both motors consume the same amount of power.

▶ Motor VA—Three-Phase

What is the input VA for a 5 hp, 230V, three-phase motor? Figure 7–24

    (a) 6,055 VA   (b) 3,730 VA

    (c) 6,440 VA   (d) 8,050 VA

• Answer: (a) 6,055 VA, Table 430.250

Motor three-phase VA = Volts x FLC x 1.732

Table 430.250, FLC = 15.2A

Motor VA = 230V x 15.2A x 1.732

Motor VA = 6,055 VA

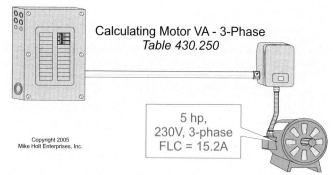

Calculating Motor VA - 3-Phase
Table 430.250

Copyright 2005
Mike Holt Enterprises, Inc.

5 hp,
230V, 3-phase
FLC = 15.2A

Determine the VA (volt-amperes) of the motor.

Formula: VA (3-phase) = Volts x Amperes x √3

Volts = 230V,   Amperes = 15.2A,   √3 = 1.732

VA (3-ph) = 230V x 15.2A x 1.732 = 6,055 VA

Figure 7–24

Unit 7 Conclusion

Article 430 can be intimidating and confusing because there are provisions for motor circuits that differ from the general *NEC* rules. This unit explained that the overload protection for motors is treated separately from short-circuit and ground-fault protection. Motor circuits must accommodate increased starting current and still provide satisfactory running protection. For this reason, the overcurrent protection rules you learned in Article 240 do not apply to motor circuits. Article 430 contains the rules that are used to size protection as well as conductors for motor branch circuits and feeders.

A common mistake made in motor circuits is the use of the motor nameplate current for calculations that should be made using the full-load current from the Article 430 tables. The nameplate full-load amperes is only used for overload protection; Tables 430.248, 430.249, and 430.250 are used for sizing conductors, short-circuit and ground-fault protection, and disconnect switches. Review the material in this unit regarding 430.6(A) if this is not clear to you.

Be sure you understand the differences between motor branch circuits and feeders, and how to apply the requirements of Article 430 to size the conductors and short-circuit and ground-fault protection for each.

(• Indicates that 75% or fewer of those who took this exam answered the question correctly.)

Introduction

1. When sizing conductors, Table 240.4(G) allows Article 430 to be used for sizing the overcurrent protection of motors.

    (a) True   (b) False

7.1 Single Motor Conductors [430.22(A)]

2. What size THHN conductor is required for a 5 hp, 230V, single-phase motor? The terminals are rated 75°C.

    (a) 14 AWG   (b) 12 AWG   (c) 10 AWG   (d) 8 AWG

7.2 Motor Overcurrent Protection

3. Motors and their associated equipment must be protected against overcurrent (overload, short circuit, or ground fault), but because of the special characteristics of induction motors, overcurrent protection is generally accomplished by having the overload protection separate from the short-circuit and ground-fault protection.

    (a) True   (b) False

4. •Which parts of Article 430 contain the requirements for motor overcurrent protection?

    (a) Motor and Branch-Circuit Overload Protection—Part III
    (b) Motor Branch-Circuit Short-Circuit and Ground-Fault Protection—Part IV
    (c) a and b
    (d) none of these

5. •Overload is the condition where current is greater than the equipment ampacity rating, resulting in equipment damage due to dangerous overheating [Article 100]. Overload protection devices, sometimes called heaters, are intended to protect the _____ from dangerous overheating.

    (a) motor   (b) motor control equipment   (c) branch-circuit conductors   (d) all of these

6. The branch-circuit short-circuit and ground-fault protection device is intended to protect the motor, the motor control apparatus, and the conductors against overcurrent due to _____.

    (a) short circuits   (b) ground faults   (c) overloads   (d) a and b

7.3 Overload Protection [430.6(2) and 430.32(A)]

7. •The *NEC* requires motor overload protection devices to be sized according to the motor full-load current rating as listed in Tables 430.247, 430.248, or 430.250.

    (a) True   (b) False

8. If the motor overload protection relay sized according to 430.32 is not capable of carrying the motor starting and running current, a larger overload can be used if sized according to the requirements of 430.32(C).

    (a) True   (b) False

9. Motors with a nameplate service factor (SF) rating of 1.15 or more must have the overload protection device sized at no more than _____ percent of the motor nameplate current rating.

    (a) 100   (b) 115   (c) 125   (d) 135

10. Motors with a nameplate temperature rise rating not over 40°C must have the overload protection device sized at no more than _____ percent of the motor nameplate current rating.

    (a) 100   (b) 115   (c) 125   (d) 135

11. Motors that have a service factor rating of 1.10 must have the overload protection device sized at not more than _____ percent of the motor nameplate ampere rating.

    (a) 100   (b) 115   (c) 125   (d) 135

12. If a dual-element fuse is used for overload protection, what size fuse is required for a 5 hp, 208V, three-phase motor with a service factor of 1.16 and a motor nameplate current rating of 16A (FLA)?

    (a) 20A   (b) 25A   (c) 30A   (d) 35A

13. If a dual-element fuse is used for overload protection, what size fuse is required for a 30 hp, 460V, three-phase synchronous motor, with a temperature rise of 39°C?

    (a) 20A   (c) 30A   (b) 25A   (d) 40A

7.4 Branch-Circuit Short-Circuit Ground-Fault Protection [430.51]

14. In addition to overload protection, each motor and its accessories require short-circuit and ground-fault protection according to 430.52. When sizing the branch-circuit protection device, which of the following factors must be considered?

    (a) The motor type, such as induction, synchronous, wound-rotor, single-phase ac, three-phase ac, etc.
    (b) The motor full load current from the *Code* book tables must be used.
    (c) The type of protection device to be used; nontime delay fuse, dual-element fuse, or inverse-time breaker.
    (d) all of these

15. The *NEC* requires motor branch-circuit short-circuit and ground-fault protection to be sized not greater than the percentages listed in Table 430.52. When the short-circuit ground-fault protection device value determined from Table 430.52 does not correspond with the standard rating of overcurrent protection devices as listed in 240.6(A), the next _____ device size is permitted to be used.

    (a) smaller   (b) larger   (c) a or b   (d) none of these

16. To determine the percentage of the motor FLC from Table 430.52 that is to be used to size the motor branch-circuit short-circuit and ground-fault protection device, which of the following steps should be used?

    (a) Locate the motor type on Table 430.52, such as dc, wound rotor, single phase, or poly phase ac. motors.
    (b) Select the percentage from Table 430.52 according to the type of protection device, such as nontime delay fuse, dual-element fuse or inverse-time circuit breaker.
    (c) After making the necessary calculations, round up to the next standard size overcurrent device.
    (d) all of these

17. Where the next size up time delay (dual-element) fuse is not sufficient for the starting current of the motor, the rating of the fuse is permitted to be increased, but must in no case exceed _____ of the motor full-load current.

    (a) 125%   (b) 150%   (c) 175%   (d) 225%

18. Conductors are sized at _____ of the motor full-load current [430.22(A)], overloads from _____, and the motor short-circuit, ground-fault protection device (inverse-time circuit breaker) is sized up to _____ of the motor full-load current.

    (a) 125%, 115%, 250%   (b) 100%, 125%, 150%   (c) 125%, 125%, 125%   (d) 100%, 100%, 100%

19. Which of the following statements are true for a 10 hp, 208V, three-phase motor with a nameplate current of 29A?

    (a) The branch-circuit conductors can be 8 THHN.
    (b) Overload protection is 33A.
    (c) Short-circuit and ground-fault protection can be an 80A circuit breaker.
    (d) all of these

7.5 Feeder Conductor Size [430.24]

20. Feeder conductors that supply several motors must have an ampacity of not less than _____.

    (a) 125% of the highest-rated motor's FLC
    (b) the sum of the full-load currents of the other motors on the same phase
    (c) a or b
    (d) a and b

7.6 Feeder Protection [430.61]

21. Motor feeder conductors (sized according to 430.24) must have a feeder protection device to protect against short circuits and ground faults (not overloads), sized not greater than the _____.

    (a) largest branch-circuit short-circuit ground-fault protection device [430.52] of any motor of the group
    (b) sum of the full-load currents of the other motors on the same phase
    (c) a or b
    (d) a and b

22. •Which of the following statements about a 30 hp, 460V, three-phase synchronous motor and a 10 hp 460V, three-phase motor are true?

    (a) The 30 hp motor has 8 THHN with an 80A breaker.
    (b) The 10 hp motor has 14 THHN with a 35A breaker.
    (c) The feeder conductors must be 6 THHN with a 90A breaker.
    (d) all of these

7.7 Highest-Rated Motor [430.17]

23. When selecting the feeder conductors and short-circuit ground-fault protection device, the highest-rated motor must be the highest-rated _____.

    (a) horsepower   (b) full-load current   (c) nameplate current   (d) any of these

24. •Which is the highest-rated FLC of the following?

    (a) 25 hp, synchronous, three-phase, 460V   (b) 20 hp, three-phase, 460V
    (c) 15 hp, three-phase, 460V   (d) 3 hp, 120V

7.10 Motor VA Calculations

25. What is the VA input of a dual voltage 5 hp, three-phase motor rated 460/230V?

    (a) 3,027 VA at 460V   (b) 6,055 VA at 230V   (c) 6,055 VA at 460V   (d) b and c

26. What is the input VA of a 3 hp, 208V, single-phase motor?

    (a) 3,890 VA   (b) 6,440 VA   (c) 6,720 VA   (d) none of these

(• Indicates that 75% or fewer of those who took this exam answered the question correctly.)

7.1 Single Motor Conductors [430.22(A)]

1. •The branch-circuit conductors of a 5 hp, 230V motor with a nameplate rating of 25A must have an ampacity of not less than _____. *Note: The motor is used for intermittent duty and, due to the nature of the apparatus it drives, it cannot run for more than five minutes at any one time.*

   (a) 33A   (b) 37A   (c) 21A   (d) 23A

7.3 Overload Protection [430.6(2) and 430.32(A)]

2. The standard overload protection device for a 2 hp, 115V motor that has a full-load current rating of 24A and a nameplate rating of 21.5A must not exceed _____.

   (a) 20.6A   (b) 24.7A   (c) 29.9A   (d) 33.8A

3. •The maximum overload protective device relay for a 2 hp, 115V motor with a nameplate rating of 22A is _____. The service factor is 1.2.

   (a) 30.8A   (b) 33.8A   (c) 33.6A   (d) 22.6A

7.4 Branch-Circuit Short-Circuit Ground-Fault Protection [430.51]

4. A 2 hp, 120V motor requires a _____ branch-circuit short-circuit protection device. *Note: Use an inverse-time breaker for protection.*

   (a) 20A   (b) 30A   (c) 40A   (d) 60A

5. •The branch-circuit short-circuit and ground-fault protection device for a 10 hp, 230V, single-phase motor must not exceed _____. *Note: Use an inverse-time breaker for protection.*

   (a) 125A   (b) 50A   (c) 75A   (d) 80A

6. The branch-circuit short-circuit and ground-fault protection (circuit breaker) for a 125 hp, 240V, dc motor is _____.

   (a) 400A   (b) 600A   (c) 700A   (d) 800A

7.5 Feeder Conductor Size [430.24]

7. •The motor feeder conductor size for three 15 hp, 208V, three-phase motors; three 3 hp, 208V, single-phase motors; and three 1 hp, 120V, single-phase motors will be _____.

   (a) 2/0 AWG   (b) 3/0 AWG   (c) 4/0 AWG   (d) 250 kcmil

7.6 Feeder Protection [430.61]

8. •There are three motors; one 5 hp, 230V, single-phase motor with a service factor of 1.2, and two 1 1/2 hp, 120V, single-phase motors. Using an inverse-time breaker, the 3-wire feeder conductor protection device after balancing all three motors will be _____.

    (a) 60A　　　　　　(b) 70A　　　　　　(c) 80A　　　　　　(d) 90A

9. •If an inverse-time breaker is used for the feeder short-circuit protection, what size protection is required for the following 460V, three-phase motors?
    　(1) Motor 1 = 40 hp 52 FLC
    　(2) Motor 2 = 20 hp 27 FLC
    　(3) Motor 3 = 10 hp 14 FLC
    　(4) Motor 4 = 5 hp 7.6 FLC

    (a) 225A　　　　　　(b) 200A　　　　　　(c) 125A　　　　　　(d) 175A

10. •If dual-element fuses are used to protect a 3-wire, 115/230V feeder conductor for twenty-two 1/2 hp, 115V, single-phase motors, the fuse size selected should not be greater than _____.

    (a) 125A　　　　　　(b) 90A　　　　　　(c) 100A　　　　　　(d) 110A

11. •The feeder protection for one 25 hp, 208V, three-phase motor, and three 3 hp, 120V, single-phase motors will be _____ after balancing. *Note: Use inverse-time breakers.*

    (a) 225A　　　　　　(b) 200A　　　　　　(c) 300A　　　　　　(d) 250A

(• Indicates that 75% or fewer of those who took this exam answered the question correctly.)

Article 386 Surface Metal Raceways (continued)

1. The conductors, including splices and taps, in a metal surface raceway having a removable cover must not fill the raceway to more than _____ percent of its cross-sectional area at that point.

    (a) 75   (b) 40   (c) 38   (d) 53

2. Where combination surface metal raceways are used for both signaling and for lighting and power circuits, the different systems must be run in separate compartments identified by _____ of the interior finish.

    (a) stamping   (b) imprinting   (c) color-coding   (d) any of these

Article 388 Surface Nonmetallic Raceways

A surface nonmetallic raceway is intended to be surface mounted with associated accessories. Conductors are placed after the raceway has been installed as a complete system.

3. •The use of surface nonmetallic raceways is permitted _____.

    (a) in dry locations   (b) where concealed   (c) in hoistways   (d) all of these

4. The maximum number of conductors permitted in any surface raceway must be _____.

    (a) no more than 30 percent of the inside diameter   (b) no greater than the number for which it was designed
    (c) no more than 75 percent of the cross-sectional area   (d) that which is permitted in Table 312.6(A)

5. Where combination surface nonmetallic raceways are used for both signaling conductors and for lighting and power circuits, the different systems must be run in separate compartments identified by _____ of the interior finish.

    (a) stamping   (b) imprinting   (c) color-coding   (d) any of these

Article 390 Underfloor Raceways

This article covers the use and installation requirements for underfloor raceways.

6. The combined area of all conductors installed at any point of an underfloor raceway must not exceed _____ percent of the internal cross-sectional area.

    (a) 75   (b) 60   (c) 40   (d) 0

7. When an outlet from an underfloor raceway is discontinued, the circuit conductors supplying the outlet _____.

    (a) may be spliced   (b) may be reinsulated   (c) may be cut and capped off   (d) must be removed from
    the raceway

8. Inserts set in fiber underfloor raceways after the floor is laid must be _____ into the raceway.

    (a) taped   (b) glued   (c) screwed   (d) mechanically secured

Article 392 Cable Trays

A cable tray system is a unit or assembly of units or sections with associated fittings that form a structural system used to securely fasten or support cables and raceways. A cable tray isn't a raceway, but a support system for raceways, cables, and enclosures.

9. Cable trays can be used as a support system for _____.

    (a) services, feeders, and branch circuits (b) communications circuits
    (c) control and signaling circuits (d) all of these

10. Where exposed to direct rays of the sun, insulated conductors and jacketed cables must be _____ as being sunlight resistant.

    (a) listed   (b) approved   (c) identified   (d) none of these

11. Nonmetallic cable trays are permitted in corrosive areas and in areas requiring voltage isolation.

    (a) True   (b) False

12. Cable trays must _____.

    (a) include fittings for changes in direction and elevation
    (b) have side rails or equivalent structural members
    (c) be made of corrosion-resistant material or protected from corrosion as required by 300.6
    (d) all of these

13. Each run of cable tray must be _____ before the installation of cables.

    (a) tested for 25 ohms resistance (b) insulated
    (c) completed (d) all of these

14. Cable trays can extend through partitions and walls or vertically through platforms and floors where the installation is made in accordance with the fire seal requirements of 300.21.

    (a) True   (b) False

15. In industrial facilities where conditions of maintenance and supervision ensure that only qualified persons will service the installation, cable tray systems can be used to support _____.

    (a) raceways   (b) cables   (c) boxes and conduit bodies   (d) all of these

16. Steel or aluminum cable tray systems can be used as an equipment grounding conductor provided the cable tray sections and fittings are identified for _____ purposes, among other requirements.

    (a) grounding   (b) special   (c) industrial   (d) all

17. Steel cable trays must not be used as equipment grounding conductors for circuits with ground-fault protection above _____.

    (a) 200A   (b) 300A   (c) 600A   (d) 800A

18. Cable _____ made and insulated by approved methods can be located within a cable tray provided they are accessible, and do not project above the side rails.

    (a) connections   (b) jumpers   (c) splices   (d) conductors

19.   Where single conductor cables comprising each phase or grounded conductor of a circuit are connected in parallel in a cable tray, the conductors must be installed _____ , to prevent current unbalance in the paralleled conductors due to inductive reactance.

(a) in groups consisting of not more than three conductors per phase or neutral
(b) in groups consisting of not more than one conductor per phase or neutral
(c) as individual conductors securely bound to the cable tray
(d) in separate groups

Article 394 Concealed Knob-and-Tube Wiring

This article covers the use, installation, and construction specifications of concealed knob-and-tube wiring, which is a wiring method using knobs, tubes, and flexible nonmetallic tubing for the protection and support of single insulated conductors.

20.   Concealed knob-and-tube wiring can be used in commercial garages, theaters and similar locations, motion picture studios, hazardous (classified) locations or in the hollow spaces of walls, ceilings and attics where such spaces are insulated by loose, rolled or foamed-in-place insulating material that envelops the conductors.

(a) True   (b) False

21.   Supports for concealed knob-and-tube wiring must be installed within _____ in. of each side of each tap or splice and at intervals not exceeding _____ ft.

(a) 3, 2 1/2   (b) 2, 3 1/2   (c) 6, 4 1/2   (d) 4, 6 1/2

Article 396 Messenger Supported Wiring

This article covers the use, installation, and construction specifications for messenger supported wiring.

22.   An exposed wiring support system using a messenger wire to support insulated conductors is known as _____.

(a) open wiring   (b) messenger-supported wiring
(c) field wiring   (d) none of these

23.   The conductors supported by messenger is permitted to come into contact with the messenger supports or any structural members, walls, or pipes.

(a) True   (b) False

Article 398 Open Wiring on Insulators

This article covers the use, installation, and construction specifications of open wiring on insulators, which is an exposed wiring method using cleats, knobs, tubes, and flexible tubing for the protection and support of single insulated conductors run in or on buildings.

24.   Open wiring on insulators is a(n) _____ wiring method using cleats, knobs, tubes, and flexible tubing for the protection and support of single insulated conductors run in or on buildings and not concealed by the building structure.

(a) temporary   (b) acceptable   (c) enclosed   (d) exposed

25.   •Open wiring on insulators within _____ from the floor are considered exposed to physical damage.

(a) 4 ft   (b) 2 ft   (c) 7 ft   (d) none of these

26.   A conductor used for open wiring that must penetrate a wall, floor, or other framing member must be carried through a _____.

(a) separate sleeve or tube   (b) weatherproof tube   (c) tube of absorbent material   (d) grounded metallic tube

27. Conductors smaller than 8 AWG for open wiring on insulators must be supported within _____ of a tap or splice.

    (a) 6 in.   (b) 8 in.   (c) 10 in.   (d) 12 in.

28. When screws are used to mount knobs for the support of open wiring on insulators, they must be of a length sufficient to penetrate the wood to a depth equal to at least _____ the height of the knob and the full thickness of the cleat.

    (a) one-eighth   (b) one-quarter   (c) one-third   (d) one-half

CHAPTER 4 EQUIPMENT FOR GENERAL USE
Article 400 Flexible Cords and Cables

This article covers the general requirements, applications, and construction specifications for flexible cords and flexible cables.

29. HPD cord is permitted for _____ usage.

    (a) normal   (b) hard   (c) extra-hard   (d) all of these

30. The allowable ampacity of flexible cords and cables is found in _____.

    (a) Table 310.16   (b) Table 400.5(A) and (B)   (c) Chapter 9, Table 1   (d) Table 430.52

31. Conductors within flexible cords and cables must not be associated together in such a way (with respect to the kind of circuit, the wiring method used, or the number of conductors) that the _____ temperature of the conductors is exceeded.

    (a) operating   (b) governing   (c) ambient   (d) limiting

32. Flexible cords and cables can be used for _____.

    (a) wiring of luminaires
    (b) connection of portable lamps or appliances
    (c) connection of utilization equipment to facilitate frequent interchange
    (d) all of these

33. Unless specifically permitted in 400.7, flexible cords and cables must not be used where _____.

    (a) run through holes in walls, ceilings, or floors   (b) run through doorways, windows, or similar openings
    (c) attached to building surfaces   (d) all of these

34. Repair of hard-service cord having conductors _____ AWG and larger is permitted if conductors are spliced in accordance with 110.14(B) and the completed splice retains the insulation, outer sheath properties, and usage characteristics of the cord being spliced.

    (a) 16   (b) 15   (c) 14   (d) 12

35. Flexible cords and cables must be protected by _____ where passing through holes in covers, outlet boxes, or similar enclosures.

    (a) bushings   (b) fittings   (c) a or b   (d) none of these

36. One conductor of flexible cords intended to be used as a(n) _____ conductor must have a continuous marker readily distinguishing it from the other conductor or conductors.

    (a) grounded neutral (b) equipment grounding (c) ungrounded   (d) all of these

37. A flexible cord conductor intended to be used as a(n) _____ conductor must have a continuous identifying marker readily distinguishing it from the other conductor or conductors.

    (a) ungrounded   (b) equipment grounding (c) service   (d) high-leg

Article 402 Fixture Wires

This article covers the general requirements and construction specifications for fixture wires.

38. The smallest size fixture wire permitted in the *NEC* is _____ AWG.

    (a) 22   (b) 20   (c) 18   (d) 16

39. Fixture wires are used to connect luminaires to the _____ conductors supplying the luminaires.

    (a) service   (b) branch-circuit   (c) feeder   (d) none of these

40. Fixture wires cannot be used for branch-circuit wiring.

    (a) True   (b) False

41. Three-way and four-way switches must be wired so that all switching is done only in the _____ circuit conductor.

    (a) ungrounded   (b) grounded   (c) equipment ground (d) neutral

42. Switches or circuit breakers must not disconnect the grounded conductor of a circuit unless the switch or circuit breaker _____.

    (a) can be opened and closed by hand levers only
    (b) simultaneously disconnects all conductors of the circuit
    (c) opens the grounded conductor before it disconnects the ungrounded conductors
    (d) none of these

Article 404 Switches

The requirements of Article 404 apply to switches of all types. These include snap (toggle) switches, dimmers, fan switches, knife switches, circuit breakers used as switches, and automatic switches such as time clocks, timers, and switches and circuit breakers used for disconnecting means.

43. Switches or circuit breakers in a wet location or outside of a building must be enclosed in a _____ enclosure or cabinet that complies with 312.2(A).

    (a) weatherproof   (b) rainproof   (c) watertight   (d) raintight

44. Single-throw knife switches must be installed so that gravity will tend to close the switch.

    (a) True   (b) False

45. All switches and circuit breakers used as switches must be installed so that they may be operated from a readily accessible place. They must be installed so that the center of the grip of the operating handle of the switch or circuit breaker, when in its highest position, is not more than 6 ft 7 in. above the floor or working platform.

    (a) True   (b) False

46. Snap switches must not be grouped or ganged in enclosures with other _____ if the voltage between adjacent devices exceeds 300V, unless barriers are permanently installed between adjacent devices.

    (a) snap switches   (b) receptacles   (c) similar devices (d) all of these

47. All snap switches, including dimmer and similar control switches, must be effectively grounded so that they can provide a means to ground metal faceplates, whether or not a metal faceplate is installed.

    (a) True   (b) False

48. A faceplate for a flush-mounted snap switch must not be less than _____ thick when made of a nonferrous metal.

(a) 0.03 in.   (b) 0.04 in.   (c) 0.003 in.   (d) 0.004 in.

49. A hand-operable circuit breaker equipped with a _____, or a power-operated circuit breaker capable of being opened by hand in the event of a power failure, is permitted to serve as a switch if it has the required number of poles.

(a) lever   (b) handle   (c) shunt trip   (d) a or b

50. Nonmetallic enclosures for switches and circuit breakers must be installed with a wiring method that provides or includes _____.

(a) a grounded conductor   (b) an equipment ground   (c) an inductive balance   (d) none of these

51. Alternating current general-use snap switches, suitable only for use on ac circuits, can control _____.

(a) resistive and inductive loads that do not exceed the ampere and voltage rating of the switch
(b) tungsten-filament lamp loads that do not exceed the ampere rating of the switch at 120V
(c) motor loads that do not exceed 80 percent of the ampere and voltage rating of the switch
(d) all of these

52. Snap switches rated _____ or less directly connected to aluminum conductors must be listed and marked CO/ALR.

(a) 15A   (b) 20A   (c) 25A   (d) 30A

53. Switches must be marked with _____.

(a) current   (b) voltage
(c) maximum horsepower, if horsepower rated   (d) all of these

54. A fused switch must not have fuses _____ except as permitted in 240.8.

(a) in series   (b) in parallel   (c) less than 100A   (d) over 15A

Article 406 Receptacles, Cord Connectors, and Attachment Plugs (Caps)

This article covers the rating, type, and installation of receptacles, cord connectors, and attachment plugs (cord caps).

55. Receptacles rated 20A or less and designed for the direct connection of aluminum conductors must be marked _____.

(a) aluminum rated   (b) alum 20a   (c) CO/ALR   (d) al wire

56. Isolated ground receptacles installed in nonmetallic boxes must be covered with a nonmetallic faceplate because a metal faceplate cannot be connected to the circuit equipment grounding conductor.

(a) True   (b) False

57. When replacing a receptacle, and the grounding means exists in the receptacle enclosure, or a grounding conductor is installed in accordance with 250.130(C), _____-type receptacles must be used.

(a) isolated ground   (b) grounding   (c) GFCI   (d) two-wire

58. •When replacing a nongrounding type receptacle in a bedroom of a dwelling unit where no grounding means exists in the receptacle enclosure, you must use a _____.

(a) nongrounding receptacle   (b) grounding receptacle   (c) GFCI-type receptacle   (d) a or c

59. Receptacles mounted in boxes set back of the wall surface must be installed so that the mounting _____ of the receptacle is/are held rigidly at the surface of the wall.

(a) screws or nails   (b) yoke or strap   (c) face plate   (d) none of these

60. Receptacles mounted to and supported by a cover must be secured by more than one screw unless listed and identified for securing by a single screw.

(a) True   (b) False

61. Metal faceplates for receptacles must be grounded.

(a) True   (b) False

62. Attachment plugs and cord connectors must be listed for the purpose and marked with the _____.

(a) manufacturer's name or identification   (b) voltage rating
(c) amperage rating   (d) all of these

63. Attachment plugs must be installed so that their prongs, blades, or pins are not energized unless inserted into an energized receptacle. No receptacle can be installed so as to require an energized attachment plug as its _____.

(a) load   (b) source of supply   (c) protective device   (d) none of these

64. A receptacle is considered to be in a location protected from the weather when located under roofed open porches, canopies, marquees, and the like, where it will not be subjected to _____.

(a) spray from a hose   (b) a direct lightning hit
(c) beating rain or water runoff   (d) falling or wind-blown debris

65. An outdoor receptacle in a location protected from the weather, or another damp location, must be installed in an enclosure that is weatherproof when the receptacle is _____.

(a) covered   (b) enclosed   (c) protected   (d) none of these

66. _____, 125 and 250V receptacles installed in a wet location must have an enclosure that is weatherproof whether or not the attachment plug cap is inserted.

(a) 15A   (b) 20A   (c) a and b   (d) none of these

67. An enclosure that is weatherproof, only when no attachment plug is connected, can be used for receptacles in a wet location other than outdoors when the receptacle is used for _____ while attended.

(a) portable equipment (b) portable tools   (c) fixed equipment   (d) a and b

68. A receptacle installed in an outlet box flush-mounted on a finished surface in a damp or wet location must be made weatherproof by means of a weatherproof faceplate assembly that provides a _____ connection between the plate and the finished surface.

(a) sealed   (b) weathertight   (c) sealed and protected   (d) watertight

Article 408 Switchboards and Panelboards

This article covers specific requirements for switchboards, panelboards, and distribution boards that control light and power circuits.

69. Conductors and busbars on a switchboard, panelboard, or control board must be located so as to be free from _____ and must be held firmly in place.

(a) obstructions   (b) physical damage   (c) a and b   (d) none of these

70. Each switchboard or panelboard used as service equipment must be provided with a main bonding jumper within the panelboard, or one of the sections of the switchboard, for connecting the grounded service conductor on its _____ side to the switchboard or panelboard frame.

    (a) load   (b) supply   (c) phase   (d) high-leg

71. The purpose or use of panelboard circuits and circuit _____ must be legibly identified on a circuit directory located on the face or inside of the doors of a panelboard, and at each switch on a switchboard.

    (a) manufacturers   (b) conductors   (c) feeders   (d) modifications

72. Noninsulated busbars must have a minimum space of _____ between the bottom of enclosure and busbar or other obstructions.

    (a) 6 in.   (b) 8 in.   (c) 10 in.   (d) 12 in.

73. Switchboards must be placed so as to reduce to a minimum the probability of communicating _____ to adjacent combustible materials.

    (a) sparks   (b) backfeed   (c) fire   (d) all of these

74. An insulated conductor used within a switchboard must be _____.

    (a) listed   (b) flame-retardant
    (c) rated for the highest voltage it may contact   (d) all of these

75. To qualify as a lighting and appliance branch-circuit panelboard, the number of circuits rated at 30A or less and having a neutral conductor must be _____ of the total.

    (a) more than 10 percent   (b) 10 percent   (c) 20 percent   (d) 40 percent

76. A lighting and appliance branch-circuit panelboard must be provided with physical means to prevent the installation of more _____ devices than that number for which the panelboard was designed, rated, and approved.

    (a) overcurrent   (b) equipment   (c) circuit breaker   (d) all of these

77. A lighting and appliance branch-circuit panelboard is not required to be individually protected if the panelboard _____ conductor has protection not greater than the panelboard rating.

    (a) grounded neutral   (b) feeder   (c) branch circuit   (d) none of these

78. When a lighting and appliance branch-circuit panelboard is supplied from a transformer, the overcurrent protection must be located _____.

    (a) on the secondary side of the transformer   (b) on the primary side of the transformer
    (c) none is required   (d) either a or b

79. When equipment grounding conductors are installed in panelboards, a _____ is required for the proper termination of the equipment grounding conductors.

    (a) grounded conductor   (b) terminator strip   (c) grounding terminal bar   (d) none of these

80. Pilot lights, instruments, potential transformers, current transformers, and other switchboard devices with potential coils must be supplied by a circuit that is protected by overcurrent devices rated _____.

    (a) 15A or more   (b) 15A or less   (c) 20A or less   (d) 10A or less

Article 410 Luminaires, Lampholders, and Lamps

Article 410 contains the requirements for luminaires, lampholders, and lamps. Because of the many types and applications of luminaires, manufacturer's instructions are very important and helpful for proper installation. UL produces a pamphlet called the *Luminaire Marking Guide*, which provides information for properly installing common types of incandescent, fluorescent, and high-intensity discharge (HID) luminaires.

81. Article 410 covers luminaires, lampholders, pendants, and _____, and the wiring and equipment forming part of such products and lighting installations.

    (a) decorative lighting products
    (b) lighting accessories for temporary seasonal and holiday use
    (c) portable flexible lighting products
    (d) all of these

82. A luminaire marked "Suitable for Damp Locations" _____ be used in a wet location.

    (a) can   (b) cannot

83. No part of cord-connected luminaires, hanging luminaires, track lighting, pendants, or paddle fans may be located within a zone measured 3 ft horizontally and _____ vertically from the top of the bathtub rim or shower stall threshold.

    (a) 4 ft   (b) 6 ft   (c) 8 ft   (d) none of these

84. Luminaires using a _____ lamp, that are subject to physical damage and installed in playing and spectator seating areas of indoor sports, mixed-use, or all-purpose facilities, must be of the type that protects the lamp with a glass or plastic lens. Such luminaires are permitted to have an additional guard.

    (a) mercury vapor   (b) metal halide   (c) fluorescent   (d) a or b

85. Unless an individual switch is provided for each luminaire located over combustible material, lampholders must be located at least _____ above the floor, or must be located or guarded so that the lamps cannot be readily removed or damaged.

    (a) 3 ft   (b) 6 ft   (c) 8 ft   (d) 10 ft

86. Incandescent luminaires that have open lamps, and pendant-type luminaires, can be installed in clothes closets where proper clearance is maintained from combustible products.

    (a) True   (b) False

87. In clothes closets, recessed incandescent luminaires with a completely enclosed lamp are permitted to be installed in the wall or on the ceiling, provided there is a minimum clearance of _____ between the luminaire and the nearest point of a storage space.

    (a) 3 in.   (b) 6 in.   (c) 9 in.   (d) 12 in.

88. Electric-discharge luminaires supported independently of the outlet box must be connected to the branch circuit through _____.

    (a) raceways   (b) Type MC, AC, MI, NM, or NMC cable
    (c) flexible cords   (d) a, b, or c

89. The maximum weight of a luminaire that can be supported by the screw-shell of a lampholder is

    (a) 2 lbs   (b) 6 lbs   (c) 3 lbs   (d) 50 lbs

90. Metal or nonmetallic poles over 20 ft in height above grade that support luminaires must meet which of the following requirements? _____.

    (a) They must have an accessible handhole (sized 2 x 4 in.) with a raintight cover
    (b) The grounding terminal must be accessible from the handhole
    (c) a and b
    (d) none of these

91. Luminaires attached to the framing of a suspended-ceiling must be secured to the framing member(s) by mechanical means such as bolts, screws, or rivets. Clips _____ and identified for use with the type of ceiling-framing member(s) and luminaires are also permitted.

    (a) marked   (b) labeled   (c) identified   (d) listed

92. Exposed conductive parts of luminaires must be _____.

    (a) grounded   (b) painted   (c) removed   (d) a and b

93. Luminaires must be wired with conductors having insulation suitable for the environmental conditions and _____ to which the conductors will be subjected.

    (a) temperature   (b) voltage   (c) current   (d) all of these

94. Splices and taps must not be located within luminaire (fixture) _____.

    (a) arms or stems   (b) bases or screw-shells   (c) a and b   (d) a or b

95. _____ conductors must be used for wiring on luminaire (fixture) chains and on other movable or flexible parts.

    (a) Solid   (b) Covered   (c) Insulated   (d) Stranded

96. Luminaires that require adjustment or aiming after installation can be cord-connected without an attachment plug.

    (a) True   (b) False

97. The flexible cord used to connect a luminaire may be terminated _____.

    (a) in a grounding-type attachment plug cap
    (b) as a part of a listed assembly incorporating a manufactured wiring system connector
    (c) as a part of a listed luminaire assembly with a strain relief and canopy
    (d) all of these

98. Branch-circuit conductors within _____ of a ballast must have an insulation temperature rating not lower than 90°C (194°F) unless supplying a luminaire that is listed and marked as suitable for a different insulation temperature.

    (a) 1 in.   (b) 3 in.   (c) 6 in.   (d) none of these

99. Tubing used as arms or stems on luminaires and provided with cut threads must have a wall thickness not less than _____

    (a) 0.020 in.   (b) 0.025 in.   (c) 0.040 in.   (d) 0.015 in.

100. Edison-base screw-shell lampholders are designed to hold lamps and to hold screw-in receptacle adapters.

    (a) True   (b) False

(• Indicates that 75% or fewer of those who took this exam answered the question correctly.)

1. Surface metal raceway enclosures providing a transition from other wiring methods must have a means for connecting a(n) _____.

    (a) grounded conductor   (b) ungrounded conductor
    (c) equipment grounding conductor   (d) all of these

2. •The intent of Article 392 is to limit the use of cable trays to industrial establishments only.

    (a) True   (b) False

3. 18 AWG TFFN has an ampacity of _____.

    (a) 14A   (b) 10A   (c) 8A   (d) 6A

4. A 3-conductor 16 AWG, SJE cable (one conductor is used for grounding) has a maximum ampacity of _____ for each conductor.

    (a) 13A   (b) 12A   (c) 15A   (d) 8A

5. A receptacle is considered to be in a location protected from the weather (damp location) where _____.

    (a) located under a roofed open porch   (b) not subjected to beating rain or water runoff
    (c) a or b   (d) a and b

6. A receptacle must not be installed within, or directly over, a bathtub or shower space.

    (a) True   (b) False

7. A snap switch without a grounding connection is allowed for replacement purposes only where the wiring method does not include an equipment ground and must be _____.

    (a) provided with a faceplate of nonconducting, noncombustible material
    (b) protected by a ground-fault circuit interrupter
    (c) a or b
    (d) none of these

8. A space of _____ or more must be provided between the top of any switchboard and any combustible ceiling.

    (a) 12 in.   (b) 18 in.   (c) 2 ft   (d) 3 ft

9. A switching device with a marked "OFF" position must completely disconnect all _____ conductors of the load it controls.

    (a) grounded   (b) ungrounded   (c) grounding   (d) all of these

10. AC or DC general-use snap switches, suitable for use on either ac or dc circuits, may be used for control of inductive loads not exceeding _____ percent of the ampere rating of the switch at the applied voltage.

    (a) 75   (b) 90   (c) 100   (d) 50

11. Barriers must be placed in all service switchboards such that no uninsulated, ungrounded service _____ or service terminal is exposed to inadvertent contact by persons or maintenance equipment while servicing load terminations.

    (a) busbar   (b) conductors   (c) cables   (d) none of these

12. Cable tray systems must not be used _____.

    (a) in hoistways   (b) where subject to severe physical damage
    (c) in hazardous locations   (d) a and b

13. Conduits and raceways, including end fittings, must not rise more than _____ above the bottom of a switchboard enclosure.

    (a) 3 in.   (b) 4 in.   (c) 5 in.   (d) 6 in.

14. Coves for luminaires must have adequate space and must be located so that the lamps and equipment can be properly installed and _____.

    (a) maintained   (b) protected from physical damage
    (c) tested   (d) inspected

15. Each _____ conductor must terminate within the panelboard at an individual terminal that is not also used for another conductor.

    (a) grounded   (b) ungrounded   (c) grounding   (d) all of these

16. Fixture wires are permitted for installation in luminaires and in similar equipment where enclosed or protected and not subject to _____ in use, or for connecting luminaires to the branch-circuit conductors supplying the luminaires.

    (a) bending or twisting   (b) knotting   (c) stretching or straining   (d) none of these

17. Fixture wires used as pendant conductors for incandescent luminaires with intermediate or candelabra-base lampholders must not be smaller than _____ AWG.

    (a) 22   (b) 18   (c) 16   (d) 14

18. Flat-top underfloor raceways over 4 in. but not over 8 in. wide with a minimum of 1 in. spacing between raceways must be covered with concrete to a depth of not less than 1 in. Raceways spaced less than 1 in. apart must be covered with concrete to a depth of _____

    (a) 1 in.   (b) 4 in.   (c) 1 1/2 in.   (d) 2 in.

19. Flexible cords and cables must not be concealed behind building _____, or run through doorways, windows, or similar openings.

    (a) structural ceilings   (b) suspended or dropped ceilings
    (c) floors or walls   (d) all of these

20. For raceways terminating at the tray, a(n) _____ cable tray clamp or adapter must be used to securely fasten the raceway to the cable tray system.

    (a) listed   (b) approved   (c) identified   (d) none of these

21. Handholes in metal or nonmetallic poles supporting luminaires are not required for poles _____ or less in height above finished grade, if the pole is provided with a hinged base and the grounding terminal is accessible within the hinged base.

    (a) 8 ft   (b) 18 ft   (c) 20 ft   (d) none of these

22. In industrial establishments where conditions of maintenance and supervision ensure that only qualified persons service the installation, flexible cords and cables are permitted to be installed in aboveground raceways that are no longer than _____, to protect the flexible cord or cable from physical damage.

    (a) 25 ft   (b) 50 ft   (c) 100 ft   (d) no limit

23. It is permissible to run unbroken lengths of surface nonmetallic raceways through dry _____.

    (a) walls   (b) partitions   (c) floors   (d) all of these

24. Luminaires designed for end-to-end connection to form a continuous assembly, or luminaires connected together by recognized wiring methods, are permitted to contain the conductors of a 2-wire branch circuit, or one _____ branch circuit, supplying the connected luminaires and need not be listed as a raceway.

    (a) small-appliance   (b) appliance   (c) multiwire   (d) industrial

25. Luminaires located in bathtub and shower zones must be listed for damp locations, or listed for wet locations where _____.

    (a) below 7 ft in. height   (b) below 6 ft 7 in. in height   (c) subject to shower spray   (d) not GFCI protected

26. Luminaires, lampholders, and receptacles must have no live parts normally exposed to contact. But cleat-type lampholders located at least _____ above the floor are permitted to have exposed terminals.

    (a) 3 ft   (b) 6 ft   (c) 8 ft   (d) none of these

27. Metal enclosures for switches or circuit breakers must be _____ as specified in Article 250.

    (a) ventilated   (b) dustproof   (c) grounded   (d) sealed

28. Not counting the main breaker, the maximum number of overcurrent devices that can be installed in any one cabinet of a lighting and appliance branch-circuit panelboard is _____.

    (a) 12   (b) 42   (c) 6   (d) none of these

29. One of the requirements that must be met to use steel or aluminum cable tray systems as equipment grounding conductors, is that the cable tray sections and fittings have been _____ marked to show the cross-sectional area of metal in channel cable trays, or cable trays of one-piece construction and total cross sectional area of both side rails for ladder or trough cable trays.

    (a) legibly   (b) durably   (c) a or b   (d) a and b

30. Panelboards equipped with snap switches rated at 30A or less must have overcurrent protection not exceeding _____.

    (a) 30A   (b) 50A   (c) 100A   (d) 200A

31. Portable lamps must be wired with _____ recognized by 400.4, and have an attachment plug of the polarized or grounding type.

    (a) flexible cable   (b) flexible cord
    (c) nonmetallic flexible cable   (d) nonmetallic flexible cord

32. Receptacle faceplate covers made of insulating material must be noncombustible and not less than _____ in thickness.

    (a) 0.10 in.   (b) 0.04 in.   (c) 0.01 in.   (d) 0.22 in.

33. Receptacles incorporating an isolated grounding connection intended for the reduction of electrical noise must be identified by _____ on the face of the receptacle.

    (a) an orange triangle   (b) a green triangle
    (c) a completely orange device   (d) the engraved word "ISOLATED"

34. Receptacles mounted in boxes flush with the wall surface or projecting beyond it must be installed so that the mounting yoke or strap of the receptacle is _____.

    (a) held rigidly against the box or box cover   (b) mounted behind the wall surface
    (c) held rigidly at the finished surface   (d) none of these

35. Receptacles, cord connectors, and attachment plugs must be constructed so that the receptacles or cord connectors do not accept an attachment plug with a different _____ or current rating than that for which the device is intended.

    (a) voltage rating   (b) amperage interrupting capacity
    (c) temperature rating   (d) all of these

36. Supports for cable trays must be provided in accordance with _____.

    (a) installation instructions   (b) the *NEC*   (c) a or b   (d) none of these

37. Switches and circuit breakers used as switches can be mounted _____ if they are installed adjacent to motors, appliances, or other equipment that they supply and are accessible by portable means.

    (a) never more than 6 ft 7 in.   (b) higher than the standard maximum of 6 ft 7 in.
    (c) only in the mechanical equipment room   (d) up to 8 ft high

38. Switches must not be installed within wet locations in tub or shower spaces unless installed as part of a listed tub or shower assembly.

    (a) True   (b) False

39. The messenger must be supported at dead ends and at intermediate locations so as to eliminate _____ on the conductors.

    (a) static   (b) magnetism   (c) tension   (d) induction

40. The *NEC* requires a lighting outlet in clothes closets.

    (a) True   (b) False

41. TPT and TST cords are permitted in lengths not exceeding _____ when attached directly, or by means of a special type of plug, to a portable appliance rated 50W or less.

    (a) 8 ft   (b) 10 ft   (c) 15 ft   (d) none of these

42. Trees can to be used to support outdoor luminaires.

    (a) True   (b) False

43. Underfloor raceways must be laid so that a straight line from the center of one _____ to the center of the next _____ will coincide with the centerline of the raceway system.

    (a) termination point   (b) junction box   (c) receptacle   (d) panelboard

44. When grouping conductors of three-way and four-way switch loops in the same raceway to avoid inductive heating according to 300.20(A), it is not necessary to include a grounded conductor in every switch loop.

    (a) True   (b) False

45. When nails are used to mount knobs for the support of open wiring on insulators, they must not be smaller than _____-penny.

    (a) six   (b) eight   (c) ten   (d) none of these

46. When replacing receptacles in locations that would require GFCI protection under the current *Code,*_____ receptacles must be installed.

    (a) two wire   (b) isolated ground   (c) GFCI-protected   (d) grounding

47. Where a solid-bottom cable tray having a usable inside depth of 6 in. or less contains multiconductor control and/or signal cables only, the sum of the cross-sectional areas of all cables at any cross-section must not exceed _____ percent of the interior cross-sectional area of the cable tray.

    (a) 25   (b) 30   (c) 35   (d) 40

48. Where open conductors cross ceiling joists and wall studs, and are exposed to physical damage, they must be protected by a substantial running board. Running boards must extend at least _____ in. outside the conductors, but not more than _____ in., and the protecting sides must be at least 2 in. high and at least 1 in., nominal, in thickness.

    (a) 1/2, 1   (b) 1/2, 2   (c) 1, 2 1/2   (d) 1, 2

49. Where solid knobs are used, conductors must be securely tied to them by _____ equivalent to that of the conductor.

    (a) tie wires having insulation   (b) wires having an AWG   (c) nonconductive material   (d) none of these

50. Wiring on fixture chains and other movable parts must be _____.

    (a) rated for 110°C   (b) stranded   (c) hard-usage rated   (d) none of these

(• Indicates that 75% or fewer of those who took this exam answered the question correctly.)

1. Receptacles and cord connectors must be rated not less than _____ at 125V, or at 250V and must be of a type not suitable for use as lampholders.

   (a) 30A   (b) 20A   (c) 15A   (d) 10A

2. Receptacles connected to circuits having different voltages, frequencies, or types of current (ac or dc) on the _____ must be of such design that the attachment plugs used on these circuits are not interchangeable.

   (a) building   (b) interior   (c) same premises   (d) exterior

3. Receptacles in countertops and similar work surfaces in dwelling units must not be installed _____.

   (a) in the sides of cabinets   (b) in a face-up position   (c) on GFCI circuits   (d) on the kitchen small-appliance circuit

4. Receptacles installed behind a bed in the guest rooms in hotels and motels must be located so as to prevent the bed from contacting an attachment plug, or the receptacle must be provided with a suitable guard.

   (a) True   (b) False

5. Receptacles installed outdoors, in a location protected from the weather or other damp locations, must be in an enclosure that is _____ when the receptacle is covered.

   (a) raintight   (b) weatherproof   (c) rainproof   (d) weathertight

6. Recessed incandescent luminaires must have _____ protection and must be identified as thermally protected.

   (a) physical   (b) corrosion   (c) thermal   (d) all of these

7. Rigid metal conduit that is directly buried outdoors must have at least _____ of cover.

   (a) 6 in.   (b) 12 in.   (c) 18 in.   (d) 24 in.

8. Rigid nonmetallic conduit and fittings can be used in areas of dairies, laundries, canneries, or other wet locations and in locations where walls are frequently washed. However, the entire conduit system including boxes and _____ must be installed and equipped to prevent water from entering the conduit.

   (a) luminaires   (b) fittings   (c) supports   (d) all of these

9. Rigid nonmetallic conduit must be securely fastened within _____ of each box.

   (a) 6 in.   (b) 24 in.   (c) 12 in.   (d) 36 in.

10. Running threads must not be used on rigid metal conduit for connection at _____.

    (a) boxes   (b) cabinets   (c) couplings   (d) meter sockets

11. Running threads of IMC must not be used on conduit for connection at couplings.

    (a) True   (b) False

12. Seals in a Class II hazardous (classified) location are required to be explosionproof.

   (a) True   (b) False

13. Separately-installed pressure connectors must be used with conductors at the _____ not exceeding the ampacity at the listed and identified temperature rating of the connector.

   (a) voltages   (b) temperatures   (c) listings   (d) ampacities

14. Service conductors only originate from the service point and terminate at the service equipment (disconnect).

   (a) True   (b) False

15. Service conductors that are not encased in concrete and that are buried 18 in. or more below grade must have their location identified by a warning ribbon placed in the trench at least _____ above the underground installation.

   (a) 6 in.   (b) 12 in.   (c) 18 in.   (d) none of these

16. Service raceways threaded into metal service equipment such as bosses (hubs) are considered to be effectively _____ to the service metal enclosure.

   (a) attached   (b) bonded   (c) grounded   (d) none of these

17. Short sections of metal enclosures or raceways used to provide support or protection of _____ from physical damage are not required to be grounded.

   (a) conduit   (b) 600V feeders   (c) cable assemblies   (d) none of these

18. Short sections of raceways used for _____ are not required to be installed complete between outlet, junction, or splicing points.

   (a) meter to service enclosure connection   (b) protection of cables from physical damage
   (c) nipples   (d) separately derived systems

19. Signaling, alarm, remote-control, and local loudspeaker communications systems are not required to comply with Article 503 when installed in Class III, Division 1 and 2 locations.

   (a) True   (b) False

20. Signs and outline lighting systems must be installed so that adjacent combustible materials are not subjected to temperatures in excess of _____.

   (a) 90°C   (b) 60°C   (c) 75°C   (d) 40°C

21. Signs or outline lighting systems operated by electronic or electromechanical controllers located external to the sign or outline lighting system are permitted to have a disconnecting means that disconnects all ungrounded supply conductors located _____ when capable of being locked in the open position.

   (a) within sight of the controller   (b) in the same enclosure with the controller
   (c) a or b   (d) none of these

22. Since Class 3 control circuits permit higher allowable levels of voltage and current than do Class 2 control circuits, additional _____ are specified to provide protection against the electric shock hazard that could be encountered.

   (a) circuits   (b) safeguards   (c) conditions   (d) requirements

23. Single conductors as specified in Table 310.13 are only permitted when installed as part of a recognized wiring method of Chapter _____ of the *NEC*.

    (a) 4   (b) 3   (c) 2   (d) 9

24. Single-pole breakers utilizing approved handle ties cannot be used for the required disconnecting means for gasoline dispensing equipment.

    (a) True   (b) False

25. Snap switches installed in recessed boxes must have the _____ seated against the finished wall surface.

    (a) mounting yoke   (b) body   (c) toggle   (d) all of these

26. Snap switches must not be grouped or ganged in enclosures unless they can be arranged so that the voltage between adjacent devices does not exceed _____, or unless they are installed in enclosures equipped with permanently installed barriers between adjacent devices.

    (a) 100V   (b) 200V   (c) 300V   (d) 400V

27. Splices and taps are permitted within a nonmetallic wireway provided they are accessible. The conductors, including splices and taps, must not fill the wireway to more than _____ percent of its area at that point.

    (a) 25   (b) 80   (c) 125   (d) 75

28. Supplementary overcurrent devices used in luminaires or appliances are not required to be readily accessible.

    (a) True   (b) False

29. Surface metal raceways and their fittings must be so designed that the sections can be _____.

    (a) electrically coupled together   (b) mechanically coupled together
    (c) installed without subjecting the wires to abrasion   (d) all of these

30. Surface metal raceways must be secured and supported at intervals _____.

    (a) in accordance with the manufacturer's installation instructions
    (b) appropriate for the building design
    (c) not exceeding 8 ft
    (d) not exceeding 4 ft

31. Surface metal raceways must not be used _____.

    (a) where subject to severe physical damage   (b) where subject to corrosive vapors
    (c) in hoistways   (d) all of these

32. Surface mounted enclosures (boxes) must be _____ the building surface.

    (a) rigidly and securely fastened to
    (b) supported by cables that protrude from
    (c) supported by cable entries from the top and allowed to rest against
    (d) none of these

33. Surface-mounted fluorescent luminaires in clothes closets can be installed on the wall above the door, or on the ceiling, provided there is a minimum clearance of _____ between the luminaire and the nearest point of a storage space.

    (a) 3 in.   (b) 6 in.   (c) 9 in.   (d) 12 in.

34. Switch or circuit-breaker enclosures can be used as a junction box or raceway for conductors feeding through splices or taps, when installed in accordance with 312.8.

    (a) True   (b) False

35. Switchboards, panelboards, industrial control panels, meter socket enclosures, and motor control centers that are in other than dwelling occupancies and are likely to require examination, adjustment, servicing, or maintenance while _____ must be field marked to warn qualified persons of potential electric arc flash hazards.

    (a) being installed   (b) energized   (c) de-energized   (d) in fault condition

36. Switches must be located at least _____, measured horizontally, from the inside walls of an indoor spa or hot tub.

    (a) 4.7 ft   (b) 5 ft   (c) 7 ft 6 in.   (d) 12 ft

37. Switching devices must be at least 5 ft horizontally from the inside walls of a pool unless the switch is listed as being acceptable for use within 5 ft. An example of a switch that meets this requirement would be a pneumatic switch listed for this purpose.

    (a) True   (b) False

38. Table 430.91 provides the basis for selecting enclosures for use in specific locations other than _____.

    (a) agricultural buildings   (b) hazardous locations   (c) recreational vehicle parks   (d) assembly occupancies

39. Temporary electrical power and lighting installations are permitted for a period not to exceed 90 days for _____ decorative lighting and similar purposes.

    (a) Christmas   (b) New Year's   (c) July 4th   (d) holiday

40. The _____ of a circuit must be so selected and coordinated as to permit the circuit protective devices to clear a fault without extensive damage to the electrical components of the circuit.

    (a) overcurrent protective devices   (b) total circuit impedance
    (c) component short-circuit current ratings   (d) all of these

41. The _____ of alcohol-based windshield washer fluid does not cause the areas used for service and repair operations in connection with self-propelled vehicles to be classified as hazardous.

    (a) storage   (b) handling
    (c) dispensing into motor vehicles   (d) any of these

42. The _____ pool bonding conductor must be connected to the equipotential bonding grid either by exothermic welding or by pressure connectors that are labeled as being suitable for the purpose.

    (a) 8 AWG   (b) insulated or bare   (c) copper   (d) all of these

43. The alternate power source (generator, UPS, etc.) of an emergency system can supply emergency, legally required standby, and optional standby system loads where automatic selective load pickup and load shedding is provided as needed to ensure adequate power for all of these purposes equally.

    (a) True   (b) False

44. The ampacity adjustment factors of Table 310.15(B)(2)(a) do not apply to AC or MC cable without an overall outer jacket, if which of the following conditions are met?

   (a) Each cable has not more than three current-carrying conductors.
   (b) The conductors are 12 AWG copper.
   (c) No more than 20 current-carrying conductors are bundled or stacked.
   (d) all of these

45. The ampacity for the supply conductors for a resistance welder with a duty cycle of 15 percent and a primary current of 21A is _____.

   (a) 9.45A   (b) 8.19A   (c) 6.72A   (d) 5.67A

46. The ampacity of a conductor can be different along the length of the conductor. The higher ampacity is permitted to be used beyond the point of transition for a distance no more than _____ ft or no more than _____ percent of the circuit length figured at the higher ampacity, whichever is less.

   (a) 10, 20   (b) 20, 10   (c) 10, 10   (d) 15, 15

47. The ampacity of the supply conductors to an individual electric welder must not be less than the effective current value on the rating plate.

   (a) True   (b) False

48. The antenna mast and antenna discharge unit grounding conductor must be guarded from physical damage.

   (a) True   (b) False

49. The bonding jumper used to bond the metal water piping system to the service must be sized in accordance with _____.

   (a) Table 250.66   (b) Table 250.122   (c) Table 310.16   (d) Table 310.15(B)(6)

50. The *Code* covers underground installations in mines and self-propelled mobile surface mining machinery and its attendant electrical trailing cable.

   (a) True   (b) False

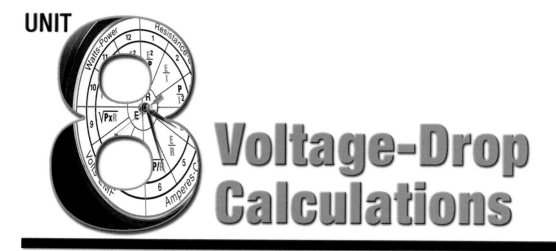

UNIT 8

Voltage-Drop Calculations

Introduction

When electrical current flows through a conductor, there is a certain amount of voltage drop in the conductor due to its inherent resistance. This is just another example of Ohm's Law at work. The results of voltage drop, however, are not useful work. One of the effects of high voltage drop is a large amount of heat given off by the conductors. This is wasted power that must be paid for on the utility bill. This wasted power heats up any other conductors in the same raceway or in close proximity. This results in inefficiency at the least, and overheated circuit conductors that can result in damage as a worst-case scenario.

Excessive voltage drop can also result in delivering a voltage to the circuit load that is less than the rated voltage of the equipment. In some cases this may not be of serious consequence, but for circuits such as sensitive electronic equipment, it is very likely to be critical. The manufacturer's nameplate and installation information should be consulted to determine the acceptable voltage limitations of any particular piece of equipment.

The amount of voltage drop encountered in a particular circuit is directly proportional to the amount of current flow in the circuit and directly proportional to the resistance of the circuit, just as predicted by Ohm's Law. The resistance of the circuit is determined by the material of the conductor (copper or aluminum, for instance), the cross-sectional area of the conductor, and the length of the conductor.

In this unit, we will show you how to find all the information necessary to make an accurate voltage-drop calculation for either single-phase or three-phase circuits. This will be helpful in designing practical circuits as well as in preparing for an exam.

PART A—CONDUCTOR RESISTANCE CALCULATIONS

8.1 Conductor Resistance

Metals intended to carry electric current are called conductors or wires, and by their nature, they oppose the flow of electrons. Conductors can be solid or stranded, and they can be made from copper, aluminum, silver, or even gold. The conductor's opposition to the flow of current depends on the conductor material (copper or aluminum), its cross-sectional area (wire size), its length, and its operating temperature.

Material

Silver is the best conductor because it has the lowest resistance, but its high cost limits its use to special applications. Aluminum is often used when weight or costs are important considerations, but copper is the most common type of metal used for electrical conductors. Gold does not tarnish so it is used mostly for plating terminals (electroplating) for some electronic equipment. Figure 8–1

Cross-Sectional Area

The cross-sectional area of a conductor is the conductor's surface area expressed in circular mils (cmils), Figure 8-2. The

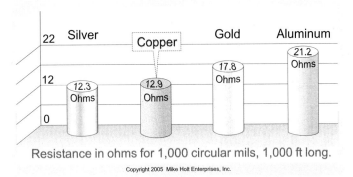

Resistance of Conductor Material at 75°C

Resistance in ohms for 1,000 circular mils, 1,000 ft long.

Copyright 2005 Mike Holt Enterprises, Inc.

Figure 8–1

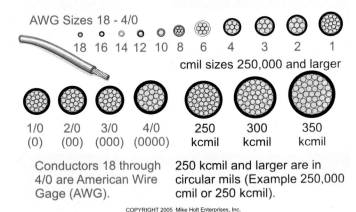

Cross-Sections and Trade Sizes of *NEC* Conductors
Tables 310.13 and 310.16 [110.6]

AWG Sizes 18 - 4/0

cmil sizes 250,000 and larger

Conductors 18 through 4/0 are American Wire Gage (AWG).

250 kcmil and larger are in circular mils (Example 250,000 cmil or 250 kcmil).

COPYRIGHT 2005 Mike Holt Enterprises, Inc.

Figure 8–3

greater the conductor cross-sectional area (the larger the conductor), the greater the number of available electron paths and the lower the conductor resistance. Conductors are sized according to the American Wire Gage (AWG), which ranges from 40 AWG to 4/0 AWG. Conductors larger than 4/0 are identified in circular mils such as 250,000 cmil, 500,000 cmil, etc. Figure 8-3

Conductor resistance varies inversely with the conductor's diameter; that is, the smaller the wire size, the greater the resistance, and the larger the wire size, the lower the resistance. Figure 8–4

"Resistance" is the total opposition to current flow in a dc circuit, measured in ohms. "Impedance" is the total opposition to current flow in an ac circuit, measured in ohms.

Conductor Length

The resistance of a conductor is directly proportional to its length. Table 8–1 provides examples of conductor resistance and

circular mils area for conductor lengths of 1,000 ft. Longer or shorter lengths will naturally result in different conductor resistances.

Temperature

The resistance of a conductor changes with changing temperature; this is called temperature coefficient. Temperature coefficient describes the effect that temperature has on the resistance of a conductor. Positive temperature coefficient indicates that as the temperature rises, the conductor resistance will also rise. Examples of conductors that have a positive temperature coefficient are silver, copper, gold, and aluminum conductors. Negative temperature coefficient means that as the temperature increases, the conductor resistance decreases.

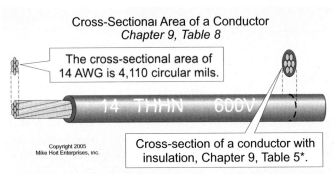

Cross-Sectional Area of a Conductor
Chapter 9, Table 8

The cross-sectional area of 14 AWG is 4,110 circular mils.

Copyright 2005
Mike Holt Enterprises, Inc.

Cross-section of a conductor with insulation, Chapter 9, Table 5*.

The cross-sectional area of a conductor is the conductor's surface area expressed in circular mils [Chapter 9, Table 8]

*Note: Chapter 9, Table 5 contains the cross-sectional area of conductors with insulation. The actual conductor within the insulation is in circular mils or AWG [110.6].

Figure 8–2

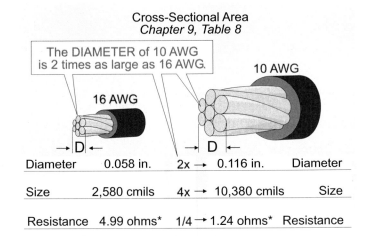

Cross-Sectional Area
Chapter 9, Table 8

The DIAMETER of 10 AWG is 2 times as large as 16 AWG.

10 AWG

16 AWG

Diameter	0.058 in.	2x → 0.116 in.	Diameter
Size	2,580 cmils	4x → 10,380 cmils	Size
Resistance	4.99 ohms*	1/4 → 1.24 ohms*	Resistance

*Note: Resistance per 1,000 ft from Chapter 9, Table 8.

COPYRIGHT 2005 Mike Holt Enterprises, Inc.

Figure 8–4

Table 8–1 Conductor Properties, *NEC* Chapter 9, Table 8			
Conductor Size American Wire Gage	Conductor Resistance Per 1,000 Feet at 75°C	Conductor Diameter Inches	Conductor Area Circular Mils
14 AWG	3.140 ohms (stranded)	0.073	4,110
12 AWG	1.980 ohms (stranded)	0.092	6,530
10 AWG	1.240 ohms (stranded)	0.116	10,380
8 AWG	0.778 ohms (stranded)	0.146	16,510
6 AWG	0.491 ohms (stranded)	0.184	26,240

The conductor resistances listed in the *NEC* Chapter 9, Tables 8 and 9, are based on an operating temperature of 75°C. A three-degree change in temperature results in a one percent change in conductor resistance for both copper and aluminum conductors. The formula to determine the change in conductor resistance with changing temperature is listed at the bottom of Table 8. For example, the resistance of copper at 90°C is about five percent more than at 75°C.

8.2 Conductor Resistance—Direct-Current Circuits [Chapter 9, Table 8]

The *NEC* lists the resistance and area in circular mils for both dc and ac circuit conductors. Direct-current circuit conductor resistances are listed in Chapter 9, Table 8, and alternating-current circuit conductor resistances are listed in Chapter 9, Table 9. The tables include both solid and stranded conductors. Stranded conductors will be used in this textbook unless specified otherwise.

The dc conductor resistances listed in Chapter 9, Table 8 apply to conductor lengths of 1,000 ft. The following formula can be used to determine the conductor resistance for conductor lengths other than 1,000 ft:

◆ **DC Conductor Resistance Formula**
DC Conductor Resistance =
(Conductor Resistance Ohms/1000 ft) x Conductor Length

▶ **Conductor Resistance Copper**

What is the dc resistance of 420 ft of 6 AWG copper? **Figure 8–5**

(a) 0.49 ohms   (b) 0.29 ohms
(c) 0.72 ohms   (d) 0.21 ohms

• Answer: (d) 0.21 ohms

The dc resistance of 6 AWG copper 1,000 ft long is 0.491 ohms, Chapter 9, Table 8.

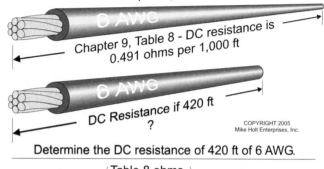

Direct Current Resistance
Chapter 9, Table 8

Chapter 9, Table 8 - DC resistance is 0.491 ohms per 1,000 ft

DC Resistance if 420 ft ?

COPYRIGHT 2005
Mike Holt Enterprises, Inc.

Determine the DC resistance of 420 ft of 6 AWG.

$$\text{DC Resistance} = \left(\frac{\text{Table 8 ohms}}{1,000 \text{ ft}} \right) \times \text{Number of ft}$$

$$\text{DC Resistance} = \left(\frac{0.491 \text{ ohms}}{1,000 \text{ ft}} \right) \times 420 \text{ ft} = 0.206 \text{ ohms}$$

Note: Dividing the table ohms by 1,000 ft determines "Ohms Per Foot."

Figure 8–5

The dc resistance of 420 ft is: (0.491 ohms/1,000 ft) x 420 ft = 0.206 ohms, rounded to 0.21

▶ **Conductor Resistance Aluminum**

What is the resistance of 1,490 ft of 3 AWG aluminum?

(a) 0.60 ohms   (b) 0.29 ohms
(c) 0.72 ohms   (d) 0.21 ohms

• Answer: (a) 0.60 ohms

The resistance of 3 AWG aluminum 1,000 ft long is 0.403 ohms, Chapter 9, Table 8.

The resistance of 1,490 ft is: (0.403 ohms/1,000 ft) x 1,490 ft = 0.60 ohms

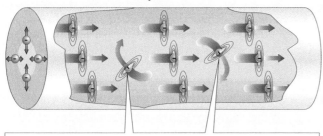

Eddy Currents

Eddy Currents are stray currents that consume power and oppose current flow. They are produced by the expanding and collapsing magnetic field of alternating current circuits.

Copyright 2005 Mike Holt Enterprises, Inc.

Figure 8–6

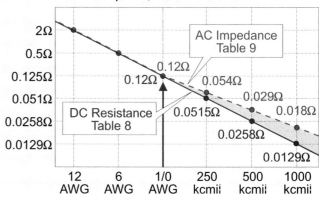

AC Impedance Versus DC Resistance
Chapter 9, Tables 8 and 9

The differences in ac impedance and dc resistance are very small for conductor sizes 1/0 AWG and smaller.

COPYRIGHT 2005 Mike Holt Enterprises, Inc.

Figure 8–8

8.3 Conductor Impedance—Alternating-Current Circuits

In dc circuits, the only property that opposes the flow of electrons is resistance. In ac circuits, the expanding and collapsing magnetic field within the conductor induces an electromotive force that opposes the flow of ac. This opposition to the flow of ac is called inductive reactance.

In addition, ac flowing through a conductor generates small, erratic, independent currents called eddy currents. **Figure 8-6** Eddy currents are greatest in the center of the conductors and repel the flowing electrons toward the conductor surface; this is known as skin effect. **Figure 8-7**

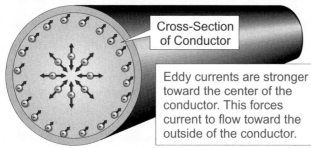

Skin Effect of Alternating Current
Chapter 9, Table 8

Cross-Section of Conductor

Eddy currents are stronger toward the center of the conductor. This forces current to flow toward the outside of the conductor.

Skin effect is directly proportional to frequency. 60 hertz is the standard frequency in the United States and does not create a significant skin effect when stranded wire is used.

Copyright 2005 Mike Holt Enterprises, Inc.

Figure 8–7

Because of skin effect, the effective cross-sectional area of an ac conductor is reduced, which results in an increased opposition to current flow. The total opposition to the movement of electrons in an ac circuit (resistance and inductive reactance) is called impedance.

8.4 Alternating-Current Impedance as Compared to Direct-Current Resistance

The opposition to current flow (impedance) is greater for ac circuits as compared to the resistance of dc circuits because of inductive reactance, eddy currents, and skin effect in addition to the resistance of the conductor. **Table 8–2** provides some comparisons between ac impedance and dc resistance. Note that for conductors smaller than 1/0 AWG, the two values are essentially equal. **Figure 8-8**

Table 8–2 shows the larger conductor sizes, and the percentage by which the impedance of an ac circuit increases over dc resistance as the conductor size increases.

8.5 Impedance [Chapter 9, Table 9]

An alternating-current conductor's opposition to current flow (resistance and reactance) is listed in Chapter 9, Table 9 of the *NEC*. The total opposition to current flow in an ac circuit is called impedance and depends on the conductor material (copper or aluminum) and on the magnetic property of the raceway or cable in which they are installed.

Table 8–2			
COPPER – Alternating-Current Impedance versus Direct-Current Resistance at 75°C			
Conductor Size	AC Impedance Chapter 9, Table 9	DC Resistance Chapter 9, Table 8	AC impedance greater than dc resistance by %
250,000	0.054 ohms per 1,000 ft	0.0515 ohms per 1,000 ft	4.85%
500,000	0.029 ohms per 1,000 ft	0.0258 ohms per 1,000 ft	12.40%
1,000,000	0.018 ohms per 1,000 ft	0.0129 ohms per 1,000 ft	39.50%
ALUMINUM – Alternating-Current Impedance versus Direct-Current Resistance at 75°C			
Conductor Size	AC Impedance Chapter 9, Table 9	DC Resistance Chapter 9, Table 8	AC impedance greater than dc resistance by %
250,000	0.086 ohms per 1,000 ft	0.0847 ohms per 1,000 ft	1.5%
500,000	0.045 ohms per 1,000 ft	0.0424 ohms per 1,000 ft	6.13%
1,000,000	0.025 ohms per 1,000 ft	0.0212 ohms per 1,000 ft	17.92%

The first row of Chapter 9, Table 9 shows "Ohms to Neutral per Kilometer" and directly under that it reads "Ohms to Neutral per 1,000 Feet." For example, the ac resistance (impedance) for 2 AWG in PVC is 0.62 ohms per kilometer and 0.19 ohms per 1,000 ft. For the purpose of this textbook, we will only be using the "Ohms to Neutral per 1,000 Feet" for all calculations.

▶ **Alternating-Current Ohms-to-Neutral Impedance Per 1,000 Ft**

What is the ac ohms-to-neutral impedance of a 250,000 cmil conductor that is 1,000 ft long in each of the following situations?

Copper conductor in nonmetallic raceway	0.052 ohms
Copper conductor in aluminum raceway	0.057 ohms
Copper conductor in steel raceway	0.054 ohms
Aluminum conductor in nonmetallic raceway	0.085 ohms
Aluminum conductor in aluminum raceway	0.090 ohms
Aluminum conductor in steel raceway	0.086 ohms

Alternating-Current Conductor Impedance Formula

The following formula can be used to determine conductor impedance:

◆ **Alternating-Current Impedance Formula**
Alternating-Current Impedance = (Conductor Ohms-to-Neutral Impedance/ 1,000 ft) x Conductor Length

▶ **Ohms-to-Neutral Impedance**

What is the ac ohms-to-neutral impedance of 420 ft of 2/0 AWG copper installed in a steel raceway? **Figure 8-9**

(a) 0.069 ohms (b) 0.042 ohms
(c) 0.072 ohms (d) 0.021 ohms

• Answer: (b) 0.042 ohms

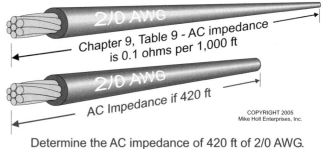

Alternating Current Impedance
Chapter 9, Table 9

Determine the AC impedance of 420 ft of 2/0 AWG.

AC Impedance = (Table 9 Ohms / 1,000 ft) x Number of ft

AC Impedance = (0.1 Ohm / 1,000 ft) x 420 ft = 0.042 Ohms

Note: Dividing the table ohms by 1,000 ft determines "Ohms Per Foot."

Figure 8–9

The ohms-to-neutral impedance of 2/0 AWG copper is 0.1 ohms per 1,000 ft, Chapter 9, Table 9.

The ohms-to-neutral impedance of 420 ft of 2/0 AWG is: (0.1 ohms/1,000 ft) x 420 ft = 0.042 ohms

What is the ac ohms-to-neutral impedance of 169 ft of 500 kcmil aluminum conductors installed in an aluminum conduit?

(a) 0.0049 ohms   (b) 0.0029 ohms
(c) 0.0081 ohms   (d) 0.0021 ohms

• Answer: (c) 0.0081 ohms

The ohms-to-neutral impedance of 500 kcmil installed in an aluminum conduit is 0.048 ohms per 1,000 ft.

Ohms-to-neutral impedance of 169 ft of 500 kcmil in an aluminum conduit: (0.048 ohms/1,000 ft) x 169 ft = 0.0081 ohms

Converting Copper to Aluminum or Aluminum to Copper

When determining the replacement conductor for copper or aluminum in an ac circuit, the following steps should be helpful:

Step 1: Determine the ohms-to-neutral impedance of the existing conductor using Chapter 9, Table 9 for 1,000 ft for ac circuits or Chapter 9, Table 8 for dc circuits

Step 2: Using Chapter 9, Table 9, locate a replacement conductor that has an ohms-to-neutral impedance of not more than the existing conductors.

Step 3: Verify that the replacement conductor has an ampacity sufficient for the load [Table 310.16].

▶ Aluminum to Copper

A 240V, 100A, single-phase load is wired with 2/0 AWG aluminum conductors in a steel raceway. What size copper wires can be used to replace the aluminum wires and not have a greater voltage drop? If the resistance of the copper conductors is equal to or less than the resistance of the existing aluminum conductors, the voltage drop will be the same or less. *Note: The wire selected must have an ampacity of at least 100A.* Figure 8-10

(a) 1/0 AWG   (b) 1 AWG
(c) 2 AWG   (d) 3 AWG

• Answer: (b) 1 AWG copper

The ohms-to-neutral impedance of 2/0 AWG aluminum (steel raceway) is 0.16 ohms per 1,000 ft.

The ohms-to-neutral impedance of 1 AWG copper (steel raceway) is 0.16 ohms per 1,000 ft (ampacity of 130A at 75°C).

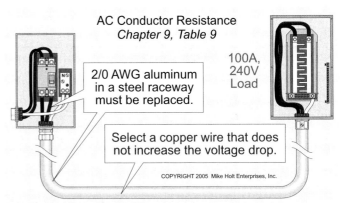

AC Conductor Resistance
Chapter 9, Table 9

2/0 AWG aluminum in a steel raceway must be replaced.

100A, 240V Load

Select a copper wire that does not increase the voltage drop.

COPYRIGHT 2005 Mike Holt Enterprises, Inc.

Replace the wire without increasing the voltage drop.

Calculation not required. Use Chapter 9, Table 9 to find a copper resistance equal to or slightly more than aluminum.

2/0 AWG aluminum, steel raceway = 0.16 ohms per 1,000 ft
Closest copper in a steel raceway = 1 AWG = 0.16 ohms per 1,000 ft

Table 310.16, 1 AWG rated 130A at 75°C is okay for 100A load and will not increase voltage drop.

Figure 8–10

Determining the Resistance of Parallel Conductors

The total resistance of a parallel circuit is always less than the smallest resistor. The equal resistors' formula can be used to determine the resistance total of parallel conductors:

◆ Resistance Total Formula
Resistance Total =
Resistance of One Conductor*/Number of Parallel Conductors

*Resistance according to Chapter 9, Table 8 or Impedance Chapter 9, Table 9 of the *NEC*, assuming 1,000 ft unless specified otherwise.

▶ DC Resistance of Parallel Conductors

What is the dc resistance for two 500 kcmil conductors in parallel? Figure 8-11

(a) 0.0129 ohms   (b) 0.0258 ohms
(c) 0.0518 ohms   (d) 0.0347 ohms

• Answer: (a) 0.0129 ohms
Resistance Total = Resistance of One Conductor/Number of Parallel Conductors [Chapter 9, Table 8]

Resistance Total = 0.0258 ohms/2 conductors
Resistance Total = 0.0129 ohms

Note: The resistance of 1,000 kcmil in Chapter 9, Table 8, is 0.0129 ohms.

Direct Current Resistance of Parallel Conductors
Chapter 9, Table 8

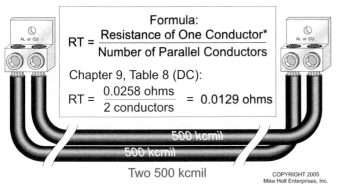

Formula:

$$RT = \frac{\text{Resistance of One Conductor*}}{\text{Number of Parallel Conductors}}$$

Chapter 9, Table 8 (DC):

$$RT = \frac{0.0258 \text{ ohms}}{2 \text{ conductors}} = 0.0129 \text{ ohms}$$

500 kcmil
500 kcmil

Two 500 kcmil

COPYRIGHT 2005
Mike Holt Enterprises, Inc.

*NOTE: Since the length of the conductors
is not specified, assume 1,000 ft.

Figure 8–11

Voltage-Drop Considerations
Section 210.19(A)(1) FPN 4

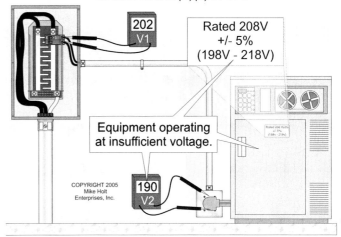

202
V1

Rated 208V
+/- 5%
(198V - 218V)

Equipment operating
at insufficient voltage.

COPYRIGHT 2005
Mike Holt
Enterprises, Inc.

190
V2

Figure 8–12

PART B—VOLTAGE-DROP CALCULATIONS

8.6 Voltage-Drop Considerations

The voltage drop of a circuit is in direct proportion to the conductor's resistance and the magnitude (size) of the current. The longer the conductor, the greater the conductor resistance, the greater the conductor voltage drop; or the greater the current, the greater the conductor voltage drop.

▶ **Ohm's Law Method for Calculating Voltage Drop—Single-Phase Only**

$$VD = I \times R$$

VD = Conductor voltage drop expressed in volts.

I = The load in amperes at 100%, not at 125%, for motors or continuous loads.

R* = Conductor Resistance, Chapter 9, Table 8 for dc or Chapter 9, Table 9 for ac.

*For conductors 1/0 AWG and smaller, the difference in resistance between dc and ac circuits is so little that it can be ignored. In addition, you can ignore the small difference in resistance between stranded and solid wires.

AUTHOR'S COMMENT: Undervoltage for inductive loads can cause overheating, inefficiency, and a shorter life span for electrical equipment. This is especially true in such solid-state equipment as TVs, data-processing equipment (computers for example), and similar equipment. When a conductor resistance causes the voltage to drop below an acceptable point, the conductor size should be increased. **Figure 8-12**

8.7 *NEC* Voltage-Drop Recommendations

Contrary to many beliefs, the *NEC* generally does not require conductors to be increased in size to accommodate voltage drop. However, it does recommend that we consider the effects of conductor voltage drop when sizing conductors.

See some of these recommendations in 210.19(A)(1) FPN No. 4, 215.2(A) FPN No. 2, and 310.15(A)(1) FPN No. 1. Be aware that Fine Print Notes in the *NEC* are recommendations, not requirements [90.5(C)]. There may be other standards beside the *NEC* that specify voltage-drop requirements on a specific project. The *Code* recommends that the maximum combined voltage drop for both the feeder and branch circuit should not exceed five percent, and the maximum on the feeder or branch circuit should not exceed three percent. **Figure 8-13**

▶ *NEC* Voltage-Drop Recommendation

What is the minimum *NEC* recommended operating volts for a 115V rated load that is connected to a 120V source? **Figure 8-14**

(a) 120V (b) 115V
(c) 114V (d) 116V

• Answer: (c) 114V

The maximum conductor voltage drop recommended for both the feeder and branch circuit is five percent of the voltage source (120V). The total conductor voltage drop (feeder and branch circuit) should not exceed 120V x 0.05 = 6V. The operating voltage at the load is calculated by subtracting the conductor's voltage drop from the voltage source: 120V – 6V = 114V.

NEC Recommendations
Sections 210.19(A)(1) FPN 4 and 215.2(A) FPN 2

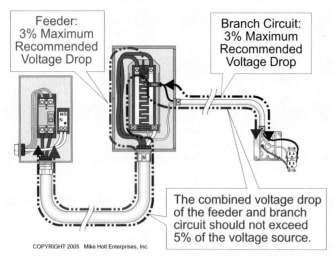

Figure 8–13

8.8 Determining Circuit Conductors' Voltage Drop

When the circuit conductors have already been installed, the voltage drop of the conductors can be determined by the Ohm's Law method or by the formula method:

◆ **Ohm's Law Method – Single-Phase Only**
$VD = I \times R$

NEC Recommendations
Sections 210.19(A)(1) FPN 4 and 215.2(A) FPN 2

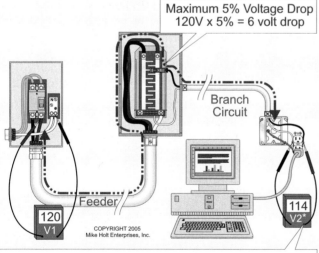

*Minimum Recommended Operating Voltage:
Operating Voltage = Voltage Source - Voltage Drop
Operating Voltage = 120V - 6 Volt Drop = 114V at Load

Figure 8–14

VD = Conductor voltage drop expressed in volts.

I = The load in amperes at 100%, not at 125%, for motors or continuous loads.

R* = Conductor Resistance, Chapter 9, Table 8 for dc resistance or Chapter 9, Table 9 for ac impedance.

*For conductors 1/0 AWG and smaller, the difference in resistance between dc and ac circuits is so little that it can be ignored. In addition, you can ignore the small difference in resistance between stranded and solid wires.

AUTHOR'S COMMENT: Conductor resistance is based on the total length of both circuit conductors.

▶ **Voltage Drop 120V**

What is the voltage drop of two 12 AWG conductors that supply a 16A, 120V single-phase load located 100 ft from the power supply? **Figure 8-15**

(a) 3.2V   (b) 6.4V
(c) 9.6V   (d) 12.8V

• Answer: (b) 6.4V
$VD = I \times R$

$I = 16A$

R = 2 ohms per 1,000 ft, Chapter 9, Table 9
R = (2 ohms per 1000 ft/1000 ft) x 200 ft
R = 0.40 ohms

$VD = I \times R$
VD = 16A x 0.40 ohms
VD = 6.4V

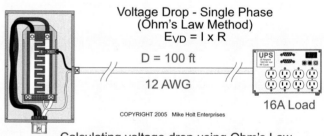

Calculating voltage drop using Ohm's Law.

Ohm's Law: $E_{VD} = I \times R$

Chapter 9, Table 9:
Resistance of 12 AWG = 2 ohms per 1,000 ft
Number of ft: 100 ft x 2 conductors = 200 ft

Resistance $= \left(\dfrac{2 \text{ ohms}}{1,000 \text{ ft}} \right) \times 200 \text{ ft} = 0.4 \text{ ohms}$

$E_{VD} = I \times R = 16A \times 0.4 \text{ ohms} = 6.4V$

Figure 8–15

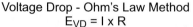

Voltage Drop - Ohm's Law Method
$$E_{VD} = I \times R$$

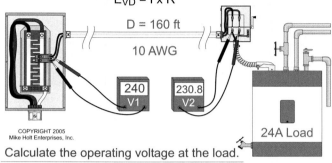

D = 160 ft

10 AWG

240 V1

230.8 V2

24A Load

COPYRIGHT 2005
Mike Holt Enterprises, Inc.

Calculate the operating voltage at the load.

Ohm's Law: $E_{VD} = I \times R$

Chapter 9, Table 9: R of 10 AWG = 1.2 ohms per 1,000 ft
Number of ft: 160 ft x 2 conductors = 320 ft

$$\text{Resistance} = \left(\frac{1.2 \text{ ohms}}{1,000 \text{ ft}} \right) \times 320 \text{ ft} = 0.384 \text{ ohms}$$

$$E_{VD} = I \times R, \quad 24A \times 0.384 \text{ ohms} = 9.22V$$

$$V2 = 240V \text{ source} - 9.22 \text{ volts dropped} = 230.8V$$

Figure 8–16

▶ **Voltage Drop 240V**

A 240V, 24A, single-phase load is located 160 ft from the panel-board and is wired with 10 AWG. What is the voltage drop of the circuit conductors? **Figure 8-16**

    (a) 4.53V   (b) 9.22V   (c) 3.64V   (d) 5.54V

  • Answer: (b) 9.22V
  $VD = I \times R$

  I = 24A

  R = 1.2 ohms per 1,000 ft, Chapter 9, Table 9
  R = (1.2 ohms per 1000 ft/1000 ft) x 320 ft
  R = 0.384 ohms

  $VD = I \times R$
  $VD = 24A \times 0.384$ ohms
  $VD = 9.216$ V

Voltage Drop Using the Formula Method

In addition to the Ohm's Law method, the following formula can be used to determine the conductor voltage drop:

◆ **Single-Phase Circuit Voltage Drop**
$$VD = (2 \times K \times Q \times I \times D)/Cmil$$

◆ **Three-Phase Circuit Voltage Drop**
$$VD = (1.732 \times K \times Q \times I \times D)/Cmil$$

VD = Volts Dropped: The voltage drop of the circuit expressed in volts. The *NEC* recommends a maximum 3% voltage drop for either the branch circuit or feeder.

K = Direct-Current Constant: This constant K represents the dc resistance for a 1,000 circular mils conductor that is 1,000 ft long, at an operating temperature of 75°C. The constant K value is 12.9 ohms for copper and 21.2 ohms for aluminum.

Q = Alternating-Current Adjustment Factor: For ac circuits with conductors 2/0 AWG and larger, the dc resistance constant K must be adjusted for the effects of self-induction (eddy currents). The "Q" adjustment factor is calculated by dividing the ac ohms-to-neutral impedance listed in Chapter 9, Table 9 by the dc resistance listed in Chapter 9, Table 8 in the *NEC*. For all practical exam purposes, this resistance adjustment factor can be ignored because exams rarely include ac voltage-drop questions with conductors larger than 1/0 AWG.

I = Amperes: The load in amperes at 100% (not at 125% for motors or continuous loads).

D = Distance: The distance the load is from the power supply. Do not use length of wire for this formula.

Cmil = Circular Mils: The circular mils of the circuit conductor as listed in *NEC* Chapter 9, Table 8.

▶ **Voltage Drop—Single-Phase**

A 24A, 240V load is located 160 ft from a panelboard and is wired with 10 AWG. What is the approximate voltage drop of the branch-circuit conductors? **Figure 8-17**

    (a) 4.25V   (b) 9.5V   (c) 3%   (d) 5%

  • Answer: (b) 9.5V
  $VD = (2 \times K \times I \times D)/Cmil$

  K = 12.9V, copper

  I = 24A

  D = 160 ft

  Cmil = 10,380 cmil, (10AWG) Chapter 9, Table 8

  $VD = (2 \times K \times I \times D)/Cmil$
  $VD = (2 \times 12.9 \text{ ohms} \times 24A \times 160 \text{ ft})/10,380 \text{ cmil}$
  $VD = 9.54V$

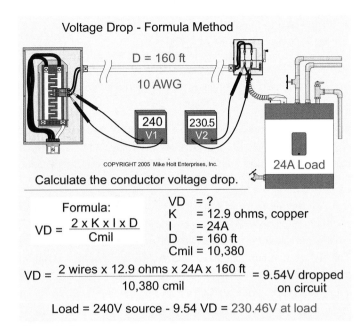

Voltage Drop - Formula Method

D = 160 ft

10 AWG

240 V1   230.5 V2

COPYRIGHT 2005 Mike Holt Enterprises, Inc.

24A Load

Calculate the conductor voltage drop.

Formula:
$$VD = \frac{2 \times K \times I \times D}{Cmil}$$

VD = ?
K = 12.9 ohms, copper
I = 24A
D = 160 ft
Cmil = 10,380

$$VD = \frac{2 \text{ wires} \times 12.9 \text{ ohms} \times 24A \times 160 \text{ ft}}{10,380 \text{ cmil}} = 9.54V \text{ dropped on circuit}$$

Load = 240V source - 9.54 VD = 230.46V at load

Figure 8–17

▶ **Voltage Drop—Three-Phase**

A 36 kVA, three-phase load rated 208V is located 80 ft from the panelboard and is wired with 1 AWG aluminum. What is the approximate voltage drop of the feeder circuit conductors? **Figure 8-18**

(a) 3.5V   (b) 7V   (c) 3%   (d) 5%

• Answer: (a) 3.5V

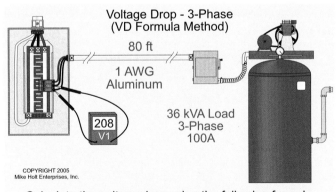

Voltage Drop - 3-Phase
(VD Formula Method)

80 ft

1 AWG
Aluminum

208 V1

36 kVA Load
3-Phase
100A

COPYRIGHT 2005
Mike Holt Enterprises, Inc.

Calculate the voltage drop using the following formula.

Formula
$$VD = \frac{\sqrt{3} \times K \times I \times D}{Cmil}$$

√3 = 1.732
K = 21.2 ohms, aluminum
I = 100A
D = 80 ft
Cmil = 83,690

$$VD = \frac{1.732 \times 21.2 \text{ ohms} \times 100A \times 80 \text{ ft}}{83,690 \text{ cmil}} = 3.5V$$

Figure 8–18

$$VD = (1.732 \times K \times I \times D)/Cmil$$

K = 21.2 ohms, aluminum

I = VA/(E × 1.732)
I = 36,000 VA/(208V × 1.732)
I = 100A

D = 80 ft

Cmil = 83,690, (1 AWG) Chapter 9, Table 8

$$VD = (1.732 \times 21.2 \text{ ohms} \times 100A \times 80 \text{ ft})/83,690 \text{ cmil}$$
$$VD = 3.51V$$

8.9 Sizing Conductors to Prevent Excessive Voltage Drop

The size of a conductor (actually its resistance) affects voltage drop. If we want to decrease the voltage drop of a circuit, we can increase the cross-sectional area of the conductor (reduce its resistance). When sizing conductors to prevent excessive voltage drop, use the following formulas:

◆ **Single-Phase Circuit Voltage Drop**
Cmil = (2 × K × I × D)/VD

◆ **Three-Phase Circuit Voltage Drop**
Cmil = (1.732 × K × I × D)/VD

▶ **Size Conductor—Single-Phase**

A 5 hp motor is located 90 ft from a 120/240V, single-phase panelboard. What size conductor should be used to limit the voltage drop to no more than 3 percent if the motor nameplate indicates 26A at 230V? The terminals are rated for 75°C. **Figure 8-19**

(a) 10 AWG   (b) 8 AWG
(c) 6 AWG   (d) 4 AWG

• Answer: (a) 10 AWG
Cmil = (2 × K × I × D)/VD

K = 12.9 ohms, copper

I = 26A at 230V

D = 90 ft

VD = 240V × 0.03
VD = 7.2V

Cmil = (2 × 12.9 ohms × 26A × 90 ft)/7.2V
Cmil = 8,385 cmil, (10 AWG), Chapter 9, Table 8

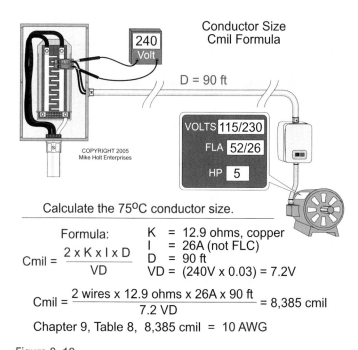

Conductor Size
Cmil Formula

D = 90 ft

VOLTS 115/230
FLA 52/26
HP 5

Calculate the 75°C conductor size.

Formula:
$$Cmil = \frac{2 \times K \times I \times D}{VD}$$

K = 12.9 ohms, copper
I = 26A (not FLC)
D = 90 ft
VD = (240V x 0.03) = 7.2V

$$Cmil = \frac{2 \text{ wires} \times 12.9 \text{ ohms} \times 26A \times 90 \text{ ft}}{7.2 \text{ VD}} = 8,385 \text{ cmil}$$

Chapter 9, Table 8, 8,385 cmil = 10 AWG

Figure 8–19

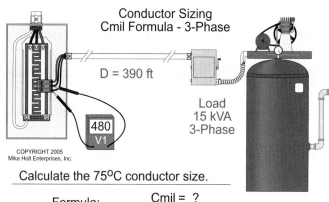

Conductor Sizing
Cmil Formula - 3-Phase

D = 390 ft

Load
15 kVA
3-Phase

480
V1

Calculate the 75°C conductor size.

Formula:
$$Cmil = \frac{\sqrt{3} \times K \times I \times D}{\text{Allowable VD}}$$

Cmil = ?
√3 = 1.732
K = 12.9 ohms, copper
I = 18A
D = 390 ft
VD = (480V x 0.03) = 14.4V

$$Cmil = \frac{1.732 \times 12.9 \text{ ohms} \times 18A \times 390 \text{ ft}}{14.4 \text{ VD}} = 10,892 \text{ cmil}$$

Chapter 9, Table 8, 10,892 cmil = 8 AWG

Figure 8–20

Note: 430.22(A) requires that the motor conductors be sized not less than 125% of the motor FLCs as listed in Table 430.248. The motor FLC is 26A so the conductor must be sized at: 26A x 1.25 = 32.5A. The 10 THHN required for voltage drop is rated for 35A at 75°C according to 110.14(C) and Table 310.16.

▶ **Size Conductor—Three-Phase**

A 15 kVA, three-phase load rated 480V is located 390 ft from the panelboard. What size conductor is required to prevent the voltage drop from exceeding three percent? **Figure 8-20**

(a) 10 AWG　　　　　　　(b) 8 AWG
(c) 6 AWG　　　　　　　(d) 4 AWG

• Answer: (b) 8 AWG
Cmil = (1.732 x K x I x D)/VD

K = 12.9 ohms, copper

I = VA/(E x 1.732)
I = 15,000 VA/(480V x 1.732)
I = 18A

D = 390 ft

VD = 480V x 0.03 = 14.4V

Cmil = (1.732 x 12.9 ohms x 18A x 390 ft)/14.4V
Cmil = 10,892 cmil, (8 AWG), Chapter 9, Table 8

8.10 Limiting Conductor Length to Minimize Voltage Drop

Limiting the length of the conductors can also reduce voltage drop. The following formulas can be used to help determine the maximum conductor length to limit the voltage drop to *NEC* recommendations:

◆ **Single-Phase Circuit Voltage Drop**
D = (Cmil x VD)/(2 x K x I)

◆ **Three-Phase Circuit Voltage Drop**
D = (Cmil x VD)/(1.732 x K x I)

▶ **Distance—Single-Phase**

What is the maximum distance a 240V, single-phase, 10 kVA load can be located from the panelboard so the voltage drop does not exceed three percent? The load is wired with 8 AWG. **Figure 8-21**

(a) 55 ft　　　(b) 110 ft　　　(c) 165 ft　　　(d) 220 ft

• Answer: (b) 110 ft
D = (Cmil x VD)/(2 x K x I)

Cmil − 16,510 (8 AWG), Chapter 9, Table 8

VD = 240V x 0.03
VD = 7.2V

K = 12.9 ohms, copper

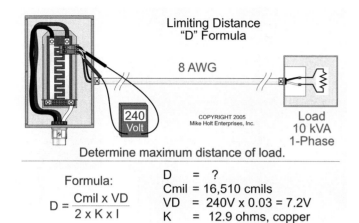

Limiting Distance
"D" Formula

8 AWG

240 Volt

COPYRIGHT 2005
Mike Holt Enterprises, Inc.

Load
10 kVA
1-Phase

Determine maximum distance of load.

Formula:

$$D = \frac{Cmil \times VD}{2 \times K \times I}$$

D = ?
Cmil = 16,510 cmils
VD = 240V × 0.03 = 7.2V
K = 12.9 ohms, copper
I = 10,000 VA/240V = 42A

$$D = \frac{16,510 \text{ cmil} \times 7.2 \text{ VD}}{2 \text{ wires} \times 12.9 \text{ ohms} \times 42A} = 110 \text{ ft}$$

Figure 8–21

$I = VA/E$
$I = 10,000VA/240V$
$I = 42A$

$D = (16,500 \text{ cmil} \times 7.2V)/(2 \times 12.9 \text{ ohms} \times 42A)$
$D = 110 \text{ ft}$

▶ **Distance—Three-Phase**

What is the maximum distance a 37.5 kVA, 480V, three-phase, transformer, wired with 6 AWG, can be located from the panelboard so the voltage drop does not exceed three percent? Figure 8-22

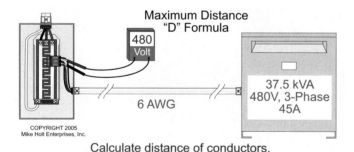

Maximum Distance
"D" Formula

480 Volt

6 AWG

37.5 kVA
480V, 3-Phase
45A

COPYRIGHT 2005
Mike Holt Enterprises, Inc.

Calculate distance of conductors.

Formula:

$$D = \frac{Cmil \times VD}{\sqrt{3} \times K \times I}$$

D = ?
Cmil = 26,240 cmils
VD = 480V × 0.03 = 14.4V
√3 = 1.732
K = 12.9 ohms, copper
I = 45A

$$D = \frac{26,240 \text{ cmil} \times 14.4VD}{1.732 \times 12.9 \text{ ohms} \times 45A} = 376 \text{ ft}$$

Figure 8–22

(a) 275 ft　　(b) 325 ft　　(c) 375 ft　　(d) 425 ft

• Answer: (c) 375 ft
$D = (Cmil \times VD)/(1.732 \times K \times I)$

Cmil = 26,240, (6 AWG), Chapter 9, Table 8

VD = 480V × 0.03
VD = 14.4V

K = 12.9 ohms, copper

$I = VA/(V \times 1.732)$
$I = 37,500 \text{ VA}/(480V \times 1.732)$
$I = 45A$

$D = (26,240 \text{ cmil} \times 14.4V)/(1.732 \times 12.9 \text{ ohms} \times 45A)$
$D = 376 \text{ ft}$

8.11 Limiting Current to Limit Voltage Drop

Sometimes the only method of limiting the circuit voltage drop is to limit the load on the conductors. The following formulas can be used to determine the maximum load:

◆ **Single-Phase Circuit Voltage Drop**
$I = (Cmil \times VD)/(2 \times K \times D)$

◆ **Three-Phase Circuit Voltage Drop**
$I = (Cmil \times VD)/(1.732 \times K \times D)$

▶ **Maximum Load—Single-Phase**

An existing installation contains 1/0 AWG aluminum conductors in a nonmetallic raceway to a panelboard located 220 ft from a 240V single-phase power source. What is the maximum load that can be placed on the panelboard so the *NEC* recommendation for voltage drop is not exceeded? Figure 8-23

(a) 51A　　(b) 82A　　(c) 94A　　(d) 115A

• Answer: (b) 82A
$I = (Cmil \times VD)/(2 \times K \times D)$

Cmil = 105,600 (1/0 AWG), Chapter 9, Table 8

VD = 240V × 0.03
VD = 7.2V

K = 21.2 ohms, aluminum

D = 220 ft

$I = (105,600 \text{ cmil} \times 7.2V)/ 2 \times 21.2 \text{ ohms} \times 220 \text{ ft})$
$I = 81.5A$

Note: The maximum load permitted on 1/0 AWG aluminum at 75°C terminals is 120A [Table 310.16].

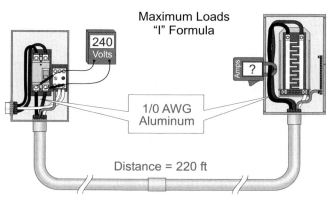

Maximum Loads "I" Formula

Distance = 220 ft

Calculate the maximum load on the conductor.

Formula:

$I = \dfrac{Cmil \times VD}{2 \times K \times D}$

COPYRIGHT 2005 Mike Holt Enterprises, Inc.

I = ?
Cmil = 105,600, Chapter 9, Table 8
VD = 240V x 0.03 = 7.2V
K = 21.2 ohms, aluminum
D = 220 ft

$I = \dfrac{105,600 \text{ cmil} \times 7.2 \text{ VD}}{2 \text{ wires} \times 21.2 \text{ ohms} \times 220 \text{ ft}} = 81.5A$

Check: Table 310.16, 1/0 AWG AL rated 120A at 75°C will carry the 81.5A.

Figure 8–23

▶ **Maximum Load—Three-Phase**

An existing installation contains 1 AWG conductors in an aluminum raceway to a panelboard located 300 ft from a 240/480V, three-phase power source. What is the maximum load the conductors can carry and comply with *NEC* requirements, as well as the *NEC* recommendation for voltage drop? **Figure 8-24**

(a) 130A   (b) 190A   (c) 210A   (d) 240A

• Answer: (a) 130A

$I = (Cmil \times VD)/(1.732 \times K \times D)$

Cmil = 83,690 (1 AWG), Chapter 9, Table 8

VD = 480V x 0.03

VD = 14.4V

K = 12.9 ohms, copper

D = 300 ft

I = (83,690 cmils x 14.4V)/(1.732 x 12.9 x 300 ft)
I = 179.8A

Note: The maximum load of 180A will limit the voltage drop to no more than 3%. When working this type of problem, do not lose sight of other Code requirements. Table 310.16 must also be consulted for the maximum ampacity permitted on 1 AWG at 75°C, which is 130A, so 130A is the working limit for this circuit [110.14(C) and Table 310.16].

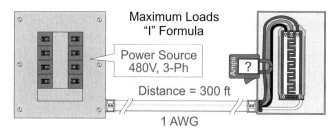

Maximum Loads "I" Formula

Power Source 480V, 3-Ph

Distance = 300 ft

1 AWG

Calculate the maximum load on the conductor.

Formula:

$I = \dfrac{Cmil \times VD}{\sqrt{3} \times K \times D}$

COPYRIGHT 2005 Mike Holt Enterprises, Inc.

I = ?
Cmil = 83,690, Chapter 9, Table 8
VD = 480V x 0.03 = 14.4V
√3 = 1.732
K = 12.9 ohms, copper
D = 300 ft

$I = \dfrac{83,690 \text{ cmil} \times 14.4 \text{ VD}}{1.732 \times 12.9 \text{ ohms} \times 300 \text{ ft}} = 179.8A$

Check: Table 310.16, 75°C, 1 AWG is limited to 130A. The maximum recommended voltage drop is not exceeded, but Table 310.16 requirements are violated.

Figure 8–24

8.12 Extending Circuits

If you want to extend an existing circuit and you want to limit the voltage drop, follow these steps:

Step 1: Determine the voltage drop of the existing conductors using the appropriate formula.
Single-phase VD = (2 x K x I x D)/Cmil
or
Three-phase VD = (1.732 x K x I x D)/Cmil

Step 2: Determine the voltage drop permitted for the extension by subtracting the voltage drop of the existing conductors from the permitted voltage drop.

Step 3: Determine the extended conductor size using the appropriate formula.
Single-phase Cmil = (2 x K x I x D)/VD
or
Three-phase Cmil= (1.732 x K x I x D)/VD

▶ **Extending Circuits**

An existing junction box is located 55 ft from the panelboard and contains 4 THW aluminum conductors. This circuit is to be extended 65 ft and supply a 50A, 240V load. What size copper conductors must be used for the extension? **Figure 8-25**

(a) 8 AWG   (b) 6 AWG
(c) 4 AWG   (d) 5 AWG

• Answer: (b) 6 AWG

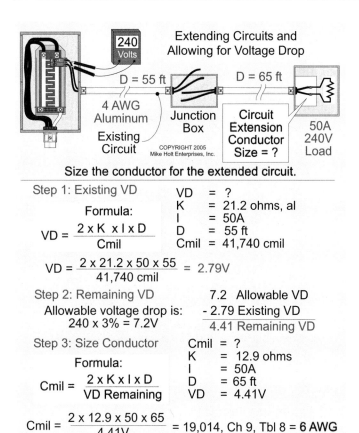

Extending Circuits and Allowing for Voltage Drop

D = 55 ft   D = 65 ft

240 Volts

4 AWG Aluminum
Existing Circuit

Junction Box

Circuit Extension Conductor Size = ?

50A 240V Load

COPYRIGHT 2005
Mike Holt Enterprises, Inc.

Size the conductor for the extended circuit.

Step 1: Existing VD

Formula:

$$VD = \frac{2 \times K \times I \times D}{Cmil}$$

VD = ?
K = 21.2 ohms, al
I = 50A
D = 55 ft
Cmil = 41,740 cmil

$$VD = \frac{2 \times 21.2 \times 50 \times 55}{41,740 \text{ cmil}} = 2.79V$$

Step 2: Remaining VD

Allowable voltage drop is:
240 x 3% = 7.2V

7.2   Allowable VD
- 2.79 Existing VD
―――――――――――
4.41 Remaining VD

Step 3: Size Conductor

Formula:

$$Cmil = \frac{2 \times K \times I \times D}{VD \text{ Remaining}}$$

Cmil = ?
K = 12.9 ohms
I = 50A
D = 65 ft
VD = 4.41V

$$Cmil = \frac{2 \times 12.9 \times 50 \times 65}{4.41V} = 19,014, \text{ Ch 9, Tbl 8} = \mathbf{6\ AWG}$$

Figure 8–25

Step 1: Determine the voltage drop of the existing conductors:

VD = (2 x K x I x D)/Cmil
K = 21.2V, aluminum
I = 50A
D = 55 ft
Cmil = 4 AWG (41,740 circular mils),
        Chapter 9, Table 8
VD = (2 x 21.2 ohms x 50A x 55 ft)/41,740 cmils
VD = 2.79V

Step 2: Determine the voltage drop permitted for the extension by subtracting the voltage drop of the existing conductors from the total recommended voltage drop.

Total recommended voltage drop =
    240V x 0.03 = 7.2V
Voltage drop recommended for the extension =
    7.2V - 2.79V = 4.41V

Step 3: Determine the extended conductor size.

Cmil = (2 x K x I x D)/VD
K = 12.9 ohms, copper
I = 50A
D = 65 ft
VD = 4.41V

Cmil = (2 x 12.9 x 50A x 65 ft)/4.41V
Cmil = 19,014, 6 AWG, Chapter 9, Table 8

Unit 8 Conclusion

This unit explained that voltage drop results anytime there is current flowing through a resistor. Every conductor has resistance (opposes the flow of electrons), which is determined by factors such as the conductor material, cross-sectional area, length, and operating temperature. Excessive voltage drop results in power losses and possibly under-operating voltage for electrical equipment.

The *Code* provides specific voltage-drop requirements in some special cases, such as for fire pumps, but does not generally require conductors to be sized to limit conductor voltage drop. Manufacturer's instructions may require a minimum operating voltage, which means that voltage drop must be considered. In this unit, you learned how to correctly size conductors in order to stay within the *NEC* recommendations for voltage drop.

Transpositions of voltage-drop formulas were reviewed in this unit so that you will be able to select the proper formula to solve for various unknowns. You now have the tools needed to properly install circuits for proper equipment operation.

If you are not yet fully comfortable with voltage-drop calculations, go back and review this unit carefully and see how each voltage-drop formula relates to Ohm's Law. It all can be traced back to the basics.

(• Indicates that 75% or fewer of those who took this exam answered the question correctly.)

PART A—CONDUCTOR RESISTANCE CALCULATIONS

8.1 Conductor Resistance

1. The larger the cross-sectional area of a conductor, the _____ the number of paths for electrons, which lowers the resistance of the conductor.

    (a) greater   (b) fewer

2. Conductor resistance is determined by the _____.

    (a) material type   (b) cross-sectional area   (c) conductor length   (d) all of these

3. _____ is the best conductor, better than gold, but the high cost limits its use to special applications, such as fuse elements and some switch contacts.

    (a) Silver   (b) Copper   (c) Aluminum   (d) none of these

4. _____ conductors are often used when weight or cost are important considerations.

    (a) Silver   (b) Copper   (c) Aluminum   (d) none of these

5. •Conductor cross-sectional area is expressed in AWG or _____.

    (a) sq in.   (b) mils   (c) circular mils   (d) none of these

6. The resistance of a conductor is directly proportional to its length.

    (a) True   (b) False

7. The resistance of a conductor changes with temperature. Temperature coefficient describes the effect that temperature has on the resistance of a conductor. Conductors with a _____ temperature coefficient have an increase in resistance with an increase in temperature.

    (a) positive   (b) negative   (c) neutral   (d) none of these

8.2 Conductor Resistance—Direct-Current Circuits [Chapter 9, Table 8]

8. The *National Electrical Code* lists the resistance and area in circular mils for both dc and ac conductors. DC conductor resistances are listed in Chapter 9, Table _____ and ac conductor resistances are listed in Chapter 9, Table _____.

    (a) 1, 5   (b) 3, 4   (c) 9, 8   (d) 8, 9

9. What is the dc resistance of 400 ft of a 6 AWG copper conductor?

    (a) 0.20 ohms   (b) 0.30 ohms   (c) 0.40 ohms   (d) 0.50 ohms

10. What is the dc resistance of 200 ft of a 1 AWG copper conductor?

    (a) 0.0308 ohms   (b) 0.0311 ohms   (c) 0.0423 ohms   (d) 0.0564 ohms

11. What is the dc resistance of 1,000 ft of a 3 AWG aluminum conductor?

    (a) 0.231 ohms   (b) 0.313 ohms   (c) 0.422 ohms   (d) 0.403 ohms

12. What is the dc resistance of 800 ft of a 1/0 AWG aluminum conductor?

    (a) 0.23 ohms   (b) 0.16 ohms   (c) 0.08 ohms   (d) 0.56 ohms

13. What is the dc resistance of 100 ft of a 1 AWG copper conductor?

    (a) 0.233 ohms   (b) 0.162 ohms   (c) 0.0154 ohms   (d) 0.561 ohms

14. What is the dc resistance of 500 ft of a 3 AWG aluminum conductor?

    (a) 0.2331 ohms   (b) 0.1614 ohms   (c) 0.0231 ohms   (d) 0.2015 ohms

8.3 Conductor Impedance—Alternating-Current Circuits

15. The intensity of the magnetic field is dependent on the intensity of ac. The greater the current flow, the greater the overall magnetic field.

    (a) True   (b) False

16. In ac circuits, the expanding and collapsing magnetic field within the conductor induces an electromotive force that opposes the flow of ac. This opposition to the flow of ac is called inductive reactance.

    (a) True   (b) False

17. _____ currents are small independent currents that are produced as a result of the expanding and collapsing magnetic field. They flow erratically within the conductor opposing current flow and consuming power.

    (a) Lenz   (b) Ohm's   (c) Eddy   (d) Kirchoff's

18. The expanding and collapsing magnetic field induces a counter voltage within the conductors, which repels the flowing electrons towards the conductor surface. This is known as _____ effect.

    (a) inductive   (b) skin   (c) surface   (d) watt

8.4 Alternating-Current Impedance as Compared to Direct-Current Resistance

19. The opposition to current flow is greater for ac circuits than for dc circuits because of _____.

    (a) eddy currents   (b) skin effect   (c) inductive reactance   (d) all of these

8.5 Impedance [Chapter 9, Table 9]

20. The ac conductor resistances listed in Chapter 9, Table 9 of the *NEC* are different for copper and aluminum and for nonmagnetic and magnetic raceways.

    (a) True   (b) False

21. What is the ac ohms-to-neutral resistance for 300 ft of a 2/0 AWG copper conductor?

    (a) 0.03 ohms   (b) 0.04 ohms   (c) 0.05 ohms   (d) 0.06 ohms

22. What is the ac ohms-to-neutral resistance for 1,000 ft of a 500 kcmil copper conductor installed in an aluminum raceway?

    (a) 0.032 ohms   (b) 0.027 ohms   (c) 0.029 ohms   (d) 0.030 ohms

23. What is the ac ohms-to-neutral resistance for 100 ft of a 3 AWG copper conductor?

(a) 0.012 ohms   (b) 0.025 ohms   (c) 0.33 ohms   (d) 0.43 ohms

24. What is the ac ohms-to-neutral resistance of 400 ft of a 500 kcmil copper conductor installed in PVC (RNC) conduit?

(a) 0.0108 ohms   (b) 0.0204 ohms   (c) 0.0333 ohms   (d) 0.0431 ohms

25. A 2-wire circuit supplies a 36A load that is located 100 ft from the panelboard. The load is wired with 1 THHN aluminum in PVC conduit. What is the total ac ohms-to-neutral resistance of the circuit conductors?

(a) 0.05 ohms   (b) 0.25 ohms   (c) 0.50 ohms   (d) 0.62 ohms

26. What size copper conductors in a steel raceway can be used to replace 1/0 AWG aluminum that supplies a 110A load? *Note: We do not want to increase the circuit voltage drop.*

(a) 3 AWG   (b) 2 AWG   (c) 1 AWG   (d) 1/0 AWG

27. What is the dc resistance in ohms for three 300 kcmil conductors in a parallel run that is 1,000 ft in length?

(a) 0.014 ohms   (b) 0.026 ohms   (c) 0.052 ohms   (d) 0.047 ohms

28. •What is the ac ohms-to-neutral resistance for three 1/0 THHN aluminum conductors run in parallel for 1,000 ft?

(a) 0.114 ohms   (b) 0.231 ohms   (c) 0.413 ohms   (d) 0.067 ohms

PART B—VOLTAGE-DROP CALCULATIONS

8.6 Voltage-Drop Considerations

29. Because of the great demand for electricity, utilities sometimes are forced to reduce their output voltage. In addition, the utility and customer transformers, services, feeders, and branch-circuit conductors oppose the flow of current. The opposition to current flow results in voltage drop. All circuits have voltage drop, simply because all conductors have resistance.

(a) True   (b) False

30. When sizing conductors for feeders and branch circuits, the *NEC* _____ that we take voltage drop into consideration.

(a) assumes   (b) suggests   (c) requires   (d) demands

31. •_____ equipment such as motors and electromagnetic ballasts can overheat at reduced voltage. This results in reduced equipment operating life and inconvenience to the customer.

(a) Inductive   (b) Electronic   (c) Resistive   (d) all of these

32. •_____ equipment such as computers, laser printers, copy machines, etc., can suddenly power down because of reduced voltage, resulting in data losses.

(a) Inductive   (b) Electronic   (c) Resistive   (d) all of these

33. When a conductor resistance causes the voltage to be dropped below an acceptable point, the conductor size should be increased.

(a) True   (b) False

34. •What is the power consumed by a 4.5 kW, 230V water heater operating at 200V?

(a) 2,700W   (b) 3,400W   (c) 4,500W   (d) 5,500W

35. How can conductor voltage drop be reduced?

    (a) Reduce the conductor resistance.   (b) Increase the conductor size.
    (c) Decrease the conductor length.   (d) all of these

8.7 *NEC* Voltage-Drop Recommendations

36. If the branch-circuit supply voltage is 208V, the maximum recommended voltage drop of the circuit should not be more than _____.

    (a) 3.6V   (b) 6.24V   (c) 6.9V   (d) 7.2V

37. If the feeder supply voltage is 240V, the maximum recommended voltage drop of the feeder should not be more than _____.

    (a) 3.6V   (b) 6.24V   (c) 6.9V   (d) 7.2V

8.8 Determining Circuit Conductors' Voltage Drop

38. What is the voltage drop of two 12 THHN conductors supplying a 12A continuous load? *Note: The continuous load is located 100 ft from the power supply.*

    (a) 3.2V   (b) 4.76V   (c) 4V   (d) 12.8V

39. A 240V, 24A, single-phase load is located 160 ft from the panelboard. The load is wired with 10 THHN. What is the approximate voltage drop of the branch-circuit conductors?

    (a) 4.25V   (b) 9.5V   (c) 3.2V   (d) 5.9V

40. A 208V, 36 kVA, three-phase load is located 100 ft from the panelboard and is wired with 1 THHN aluminum. What is the approximate voltage drop of the circuit conductors?

    (a) 3.5V   (b) 5V   (c) 3V   (d) 4.4V

8.9 Sizing Conductors to Prevent Excessive Voltage Drop

41. A single-phase, 5 hp motor is located 110 ft from a panelboard. The nameplate indicates that the voltage is 115/230 and the FLA is 52/26A. What size conductor is required if the motor windings are connected in parallel and operate at 115V? *Note: Apply the NEC recommended voltage-drop limits.*

    (a) 10 THHN   (b) 8 THHN   (c) 6 THHN   (d) 3 THHN

42. •A single-phase, 5 hp motor is located 110 ft from a panelboard. The nameplate indicates that the voltage is 115/230 and the FLA is 52/26A. What size conductor is required if the motor windings are connected in series and operate at 230V? *Note: Apply the NEC recommended voltage-drop limits.*

    (a) 10 THHN   (b) 8 THHN   (c) 6 THHN   (d) 4 THHN

43. A 480V, 15 kW, three-phase load is located 300 ft from the panelboard. What size copper conductor is required to prevent the voltage drop from exceeding 3 percent?

    (a) 10 THHN   (b) 8 THHN   (c) 6 THHN   (d) 4 THHN

8.10 Limiting Conductor Length to Minimize Voltage Drop

44.   What is the approximate distance that a 240V, 7.5 kVA, single-phase load can be located from the panelboard so the voltage drop does not exceed 3 percent? The load is wired with 8 THHN copper.

(a) 55 ft   (b) 110 ft   (c) 145 ft   (d) 220 ft

45.   What is the approximate distance a 460V, 37.5 kVA, three-phase transformer, wired with 6 THHN copper can be located from the panelboard so the voltage drop does not exceed 3 percent?

(a) 250 ft   (b) 300 ft   (c) 345 ft   (d) 400 ft

8.11 Limiting Current to Limit Voltage Drop

46.   An existing installation consists of 1/0 THHN copper conductors in a nonmetallic raceway to a panelboard located 200 ft from a 240V, single-phase power source. What is the maximum load that can be placed on the panelboard so that the *NEC* recommendations for voltage drop are not exceeded?

(a) 94A   (b) 109A   (c) 71A   (d) 147A

47.   An existing installation contains 2 THHN aluminum conductors in an aluminum raceway to a panelboard located 350 ft from a 460/230V, three-phase power source. What is the maximum load the conductors can carry without exceeding the *NEC* recommendation for voltage drop?

(a) 71A   (b) 85A   (c) 64A   (d) 49A

8.12 Extending Circuits

48.   An existing junction box is located 65 ft from the panelboard and contains 4 THHN aluminum conductors. What size copper conductor can be used to extend this circuit 85 ft and supply a 50A, 208V load? *Note: Apply the* NEC *recommended voltage-drop limits.*

(a) 8 THHN   (b) 6 THHN   (c) 4 THHN   (d) 10 THHN

49.   What is the circuit voltage if the conductor voltage drop is 3.3V? *Note: Assume 3 percent voltage drop.*

(a) 110V   (b) 115V   (c) 120V   (d) none of these

Unit 8 Calculation Challenge Questions

PART A—CONDUCTOR RESISTANCE CALCULATIONS

8.1 Conductor Resistance

1. The resistance of a conductor is affected by temperature change. This is called the _____.

    (a) temperature correction factor   (b) temperature coefficient
    (c) ambient temperature factor   (d) none of these

8.3 Conductor Impedance—Alternating-Current Circuits

2. The total opposition to current flow in an ac circuit is expressed in ohms and is called _____.

    (a) impedance   (b) conductance   (c) reluctance   (d) resistance

8.5 Impedance [Chapter 9, Table 9]

3. A 240V, 40A, single-phase load is located 150 ft from an existing junction box. The junction box is located 50 ft from the panelboard and is wired with 4 THHN aluminum wire. The total resistance of the two 4 AWG conductors from the panelboard to the junction box is approximately _____.

    (a) 0.03 ohms   (b) 0.09 ohms   (c) 0.05 ohms   (d) 0.04 ohms

4. A load is located 100 ft from a 230V power supply and is wired with 4 THHN aluminum conductors. What size copper conductor can be used to replace the aluminum conductors and not increase the conductor voltage drop?

    (a) 6 AWG   (b) 8 AWG   (c) 1/0 AWG   (d) 2 AWG

PART B—VOLTAGE-DROP CALCULATIONS

8.7 *NEC* Voltage-Drop Recommendations

5. A 40A, 240V rated, single-phase load is wired 150 ft from a junction box and the junction box is located 50 ft from a panelboard (for a total of 200 ft). If the voltage at the panelboard is 240V, what is the minimum voltage recommended by the *NEC* at the 40A load?

    (a) 228.2V   (b) 232.8V   (c) 236.2V   (d) 117.7V

8.8 Determining Circuit Conductors' Voltage Drop

6. What is the voltage drop of two 4 AWG aluminum conductors that supply a 5 hp, 208V, single-phase motor that has a nameplate rating of 55A? The motor is located 95 ft from the power supply.

    (a) 3.25V   (b) 5.31V   (c) 6.24V   (d) 7.26V

8.9 Sizing Conductors to Prevent Excessive Voltage Drop

7. A 240V, 40A, single-phase load is located 150 ft from an existing junction box. The junction box is located 50 ft from the panelboard. When the 40A load is on, the voltage at the junction box is calculated to be 236V. The *NEC* recommends the voltage drop for this branch circuit not exceed 3 percent of the 240V source (7.2V). What size copper conductor can be installed from the junction box to the load and still meet the *NEC* recommendations?

    (a) 3 AWG   (b) 1 AWG   (c) 1/0 AWG   (d) 6 AWG

8.10 Limiting Conductor Length to Minimize Voltage Drop

8. How far can a 230V, 50A, three-phase load be located from the panel if it is fed with 3 THHN and still meet the *NEC* recommendations for voltage drop?

    (a) 275 ft   (b) 300 ft   (c) 325 ft   (d) 350 ft

8.11 Limiting Current to Limit Voltage Drop

9. Two 8 THHN copper conductors supply a 120V load that is located 225 ft from the panelboard. What is the maximum load in amperes that can be applied to these conductors without exceeding the *NEC* recommendation on conductor voltage drop?

    (a) 0A   (b) 5A   (c) 10A   (d) 15A

Miscellaneous Voltage-Drop Questions

10. An 8 ohm resistor is connected to a 120V power supply. Using a voltmeter, 112V are measured across the resistor. What is the current of the 8 ohm resistor in amperes?

    (a) 14A   (b) 13A   (c) 15A   (d) 19A

11. A 480V, single-phase feeder carries 400A and has a 7.2 voltage drop. What is the total resistance of the conductors in this circuit?

    (a) 0.1880 ohms   (b) 0.1108 ohms   (c) 0.0190 ohms   (d) 0.0180 ohms

12. An 8 ohm resistor operates at 112V and is connected to a 115V power supply. The voltage drop of this circuit is _____ percent of the voltage source.

    (a) 2.6   (b) 2.3   (c) 3.5   (d) 3.3

(• Indicates that 75% or fewer of those who took this exam answered the question correctly.)

Article 410 Luminaires, Lampholders, and Lamps (continued)

1. Switched lampholders must be of such construction that the switching mechanism interrupts the electrical connection to the _____.

    (a) lampholder   (b) center contact   (c) branch circuit   (d) screw shell only

2. A recessed incandescent luminaire (fixture) must be installed so that adjacent combustible material will not be subjected to temperatures in excess of _____°C.

    (a) 75   (b) 90   (c) 125   (d) 150

3. A recessed luminaire (fixture) that is not identified for contact with insulation must have all recessed parts spaced not less than _____ from combustible materials, except for points of support and the trim finishing off the opening in the ceiling or wall.

    (a) 1/4 in.   (b) 1/2 in.   (c) 1 1/4 in.   (d) 6 in.

4. Thermal insulation must not be installed above a recessed luminaire or within _____ of the recessed luminaire's enclosure, wiring compartment, or ballast unless it is a Type IC luminaire.

    (a) 6 in.   (b) 12 in.   (c) 3 in.   (d) 1/2 in.

5. The raceway or cable for tap conductors to recessed luminaires must have a minimum length of _____

    (a) 6 in.   (b) 12 in.   (c) 18 in.   (d) 24 in.

6. Ballasts for fluorescent or electric-discharge lighting installed indoors must have _____ protection.

    (a) AFCI   (b) supplementary   (c) integral thermal   (d) none of these

7. In indoor locations, other than dwellings and associated accessory structures, fluorescent luminaires that utilize double-ended lamps and contain ballast(s) that can be serviced or re-ballasted in place must have a disconnecting means, to disconnect simultaneously all conductors of the ballast, including the _____ conductor if any. The disconnecting means must be accessible to qualified persons. This requirement will become effective January 1, 2008

    (a) high leg   (b) grounded neutral   (c) equipment ground   (d) b and c

8. Auxiliary equipment not installed as part of a luminaire (lighting fixture) assembly must be enclosed in accessible, permanently installed _____.

    (a) nonmetallic cabinets   (b) enclosures   (c) metal cabinets   (d) all of these

9. Electric-discharge luminaires having an open-circuit voltage exceeding _____ must not be installed in or on dwelling occupancies.

    (a) 120V   (b) 250V   (c) 600V   (d) 1,000V

10. Lighting track is a manufactured assembly designed to support and _____ luminaires that are capable of being readily repositioned on the track.

    (a) connect   (b) protect   (c) energize   (d) all of these

11. Track lighting must not be installed _____.

(a) where subject to physical damage   (b) in wet or damp locations
(c) a and b   (d) none of these

12. Lighting track must not be installed within the zone measured 3 ft horizontally and _____ vertically from the top of the bathtub rim.

(a) 2 ft   (b) 3 ft   (c) 4 ft   (d) 8 ft

13. Lighting track must be securely mounted so each fastening will be suitable to support the maximum weight of _____.

(a) 35 lbs   (b) 50 lbs
(c) luminaires that can be installed   (d) none of these

14. Decorative lighting and similar accessories used for holiday lighting and similar purposes in accordance with 590.3(B) must be _____.

(a) approved   (b) listed   (c) arc-fault protected   (d) all of these

Article 411 Lighting Systems Operating at 30V or Less

This article covers lighting systems and their associated components operating at 30V or less.

15. Lighting systems operating at 30V or less are allowed to be concealed or extended through a building wall without regard to the wiring method used.

(a) True   (b) False

16. Lighting systems operating at 30V or less must not be installed within 10 ft of pools, spas, fountains, or similar locations except as permitted by Article 680.

(a) True   (b) False

Article 422 Appliances

Article 422 covers electric appliances used in any occupancy.

17. Individual circuits for nonmotor-operated appliances that are continuously loaded must have the branch-circuit rating sized no less than _____ percent of the appliance marked ampere rating.

(a) 150   (b) 100   (c) 125   (d) 80

18. Infrared lamps for industrial heating appliances must have overcurrent protection not exceeding _____.

(a) 30A   (b) 40A   (c) 50A   (d) 60A

19. Central heating equipment, other than fixed electric space-heating equipment, must be supplied by a(n) _____ branch circuit.

(a) multiwire   (b) individual
(c) multipurpose   (d) small-appliance branch circuit

20. A waste disposal can be cord-and-plug connected, but the cord must not be less than 18 in. or more than _____ in length and must be protected from physical damage.

(a) 30 in.   (b) 36 in.   (c) 42 in.   (d) 48 in.

21. Range hoods are permitted to be cord-and-plug connected with a flexible cord identified as suitable for use on range hoods in the manufacturer's instructions when necessary conditions are met, including: _____.

    (a) The cord must not be less than 18 in. in length
    (b) The cord must be no longer than 36 in. in length
    (c) The receptacle must be supplied by an individual branch circuit
    (d) all of these

22. The maximum allowable hp rating of a permanently connected appliance, when the branch-circuit overcurrent protection device is used as the appliance disconnecting means, is _____ or 300 VA.

    (a) 1/8 hp   (b) 1/4 hp   (c) 1/2 hp   (d) 3/4 hp

23. For cord-and-plug connected appliances, an accessible separable connector or _____ plug and receptacle is permitted to serve as the disconnecting means.

    (a) a labeled   (b) an accessible   (c) a metal enclosed   (d) none of these

24. Appliances that have a unit switch with a marked _____ setting that disconnects all the ungrounded conductors is permitted to serve as the disconnecting means for the appliance, where other means of disconnection are also provided in accordance with 422.34.

    (a) "on"   (b) "off"   (c) "on/off"   (d) all of these

25. Electrically heated smoothing irons must be equipped with an identified _____ means.

    (a) disconnecting   (b) temperature-limiting   (c) current-limiting   (d) none of these

26. Cord-and-plug connected vending machines manufactured or remanufactured on or after January 1, 2005 must include a ground-fault circuit interrupter as an integral part of the attachment plug or in the power-supply cord within 12 in. of the attachment plug. Cord-and-plug connected vending machines not incorporating integral GFCI protection must _____.

    (a) be remanufactured
    (b) be disabled
    (c) be connected to a GFCI-protected outlet
    (d) be connected to an AFCI-protected circuit

Article 424 Fixed Electric Space-Heating Equipment

This article covers fixed electrical equipment used for space heating. For the purpose of this article, heating equipment includes heating cable, unit heaters, boilers, central systems, and other fixed electric space-heating equipment. This article does not apply to process heating and room air-conditioning.

27. Fixed electric space-heating equipment is considered a(n) _____ load.

    (a) noncontinuous   (b) intermittent   (c) continuous   (d) none of these

28. Fixed electric space-heating equipment requiring supply conductors with insulation rated over _____ must be clearly and permanently marked.

    (a) 75°C   (b) 60°C   (c) 90°C   (d) all of these

29. Means must be provided to disconnect the _____ of all fixed electric space-heating equipment from all ungrounded conductors.

    (a) heater
    (b) motor controller(s)
    (c) supplementary overcurrent protective device(s)
    (d) all of these

30. A unit switch with a marked "off" position that is part of a fixed space heater, and disconnects all ungrounded conductors, is permitted as the disconnecting means required by Article 424 for one-family dwellings.

   (a) True   (b) False

31. •Electric space-heating appliances employing resistance-type heating elements rated more than _____ must have the heating elements subdivided.

   (a) 60A   (b) 50A   (c) 48A   (d) 35A

32. On space-heating cables, blue leads indicate a cable rated for use on a circuit voltage of _____, nominal.

   (a) 120V   (b) 240V   (c) 208V   (d) 277V

33. Electric space-heating cables must not extend beyond the room or area in which they _____.

   (a) provide heat   (b) originate   (c) terminate   (d) are connected

34. The minimum clearance between an electric space-heating cable and an outlet box used for surface luminaires must not be less than _____

   (a) 8 in.   (b) 14 in.   (c) 18 in.   (d) 6 in.

35. Duct heater controller equipment must have a disconnecting means installed within _____ the controller.

   (a) 25 ft of   (b) sight from   (c) the side of   (d) none of these

36. A boiler employing resistance-type immersion heating elements contained in an ASME-rated and stamped vessel, and rated at more than 120A, must have the heating elements subdivided into loads not exceeding _____.

   (a) 70A   (b) 100A   (c) 120A   (d) 150A

37. Electrode-type boilers, which are designed so that in normal operation there is no change in state of the heat transfer medium, must be equipped with a temperature-sensitive _____.

   (a) protective device   (b) limiting means   (c) shut-off device   (d) all of these

Article 426 Fixed Outdoor Electric Deicing and Snow-Melting Equipment

The requirements of this article shall apply to electrically energized heating systems and the installation of these systems.

38. Examples of snow-melting resistance heaters include _____.

   (a) tubular heaters and strip heaters   (b) heating panels
   (c) heating cables or heating tape   (d) all of these

39. Embedded deicing and snow-melting cables, units, and panels must not be installed where they bridge _____, unless provision is made for expansion and contraction.

   (a) roads   (b) water spans   (c) runways   (d) expansion joints

40. An impedance heating system that is operating at a(n) _____ greater than 30, but not more than 80, must be grounded at a designated point(s).

   (a) voltage   (b) amperage   (c) wattage   (d) temperature

Article 427 Fixed Electric Heating Equipment for Pipelines and Vessels

The requirements of this article shall apply to electrically energized heating systems and the installation of these systems used with pipelines or vessels or both.

41. Pipeline resistance heating elements include heating _____.

    (a) blankets   (b) tape   (c) cables   (d) all of these

42. External surfaces of pipeline and vessel heating equipment that operates at temperatures exceeding _____ must be physically guarded, isolated, or thermally insulated to protect against contact by personnel in the area.

    (a) 110°F   (b) 120°F   (c) 130°F   (d) 140°F

43. For a skin-effect heating installation complying with Article 427, the provisions of 300.20 must apply to the installation of a single conductor in a ferromagnetic envelope (metal enclosure).

    (a) True   (b) False

Article 430 Motors, Motor Circuits, and Controllers

This article contains the specific requirements for conductor sizing, overcurrent protection, control circuit conductors, motor controllers, and disconnecting means. The installation requirements for motor control centers are covered in Article 430, Part VIII.

44. The motor _____ current as listed in Tables 430.247 through 430.250 must be used for sizing motor circuit conductors and short-circuit, ground-fault protection devices.

    (a) nameplate   (b) full-load   (c) power factor   (d) service factor

45. Motor controllers and terminals of control circuit devices are required to be connected with copper conductors unless identified for use with a different type of conductor.

    (a) True   (b) False

46. Where motors are provided with terminal housings, the housings must be of _____ and of substantial construction.

    (a) steel   (b) iron   (c) metal   (d) copper

47. Motors must be located so that adequate _____ is provided and so that maintenance, such as lubrication of bearings and replacing of brushes, can be readily accomplished.

    (a) space   (b) ventilation   (c) protection   (d) all of these

48. In determining the highest-rated motor for purposes of 430.24, the highest-rated motor must be based on the rated full-load current as selected _____.

    (a) from the motor nameplate   (b) from tables 430.247, 430.248, 430.249, and 430.250
    (c) from taking the horsepower times 746 watts   (d) using the largest horsepower motor

49. Conductors supplying several motors must not be sized smaller than _____ of the full-load current rating of the highest-rated motor plus the sum of the full-load current ratings of all other motors in the group as determined by 430.6(A), plus the ampacity for any other loads.

    (a) 80 percent   (b) 100 percent   (c) 125 percent   (d) 150 percent

50. Overload devices are intended to protect motors, motor control apparatus, and motor branch-circuit conductors against _____.

(a) excessive heating due to motor overloads   (b) excessive heating due to failure to start
(c) short circuits and ground faults   (d) a and b

51. An overload device used to protect continuous-duty motors (rated more than 1 hp) must be selected to trip, or be rated, at no more than _____ percent of the motor nameplate full-load current rating for motors with a marked service factor of 1.15 or greater.

(a) 110   (b) 115   (c) 120   (d) 125

52. When an overload relay, selected in accordance with 430.32(A)(1) and (B)(1), is not sufficient to start the motor or carry the load, higher-size sensing elements or incremental settings are permitted to be used as long as the trip current does not exceed _____ percent of the motor full-load current rating when the motor is marked with a service factor of 1.12.

(a) 100   (b) 110   (c) 120   (d) 130

53. Motor overload protection must not be shunted or cut out during the starting period if the motor is _____.

(a) not automatically started   (b) automatically started   (c) manually started   (d) none of these

54. The minimum number of overload unit(s) required for a three-phase ac motor is/are _____.

(a) one   (b) two   (c) three   (d) any of these

55. A motor _____ device that can restart a motor automatically after overload tripping must not be installed if automatic restarting of the motor can result in injury to persons.

(a) short-circuit   (b) ground-fault   (c) overcurrent   (d) overload

56. The motor branch-circuit short-circuit and ground-fault protective device must be capable of carrying the _____ current of the motor.

(a) varying   (b) starting   (c) running   (d) continuous

57. Where the motor short-circuit and ground-fault protection devices determined by Table 430.52 do not correspond to the standard sizes or ratings, a higher size may be used that does not exceed the next higher standard ampere rating.

(a) True   (b) False

58. •A feeder must have a protective device with a rating or setting _____ branch-circuit short-circuit and ground-fault protective device for any motor in the group, plus the sum of the full-load currents of the other motors of the group.

(a) not greater than the largest rating or setting of the   (b) 125 percent of the largest rating of any
(c) equal to the largest rating of any   (d) none of these

59. Overcurrent protection for motor control circuits must not exceed 400 percent if the conductor does not extend beyond the motor control equipment enclosure.

(a) True   (b) False

60. Motor control circuit transformers, with a primary current rating of less than 2A, can have the primary protection device set at no more than _____ percent of the rated primary current rating.

(a) 150   (b) 200   (c) 400   (d) 500

61. If the control circuit transformer is located in the controller enclosure, the transformer must be connected to the _____ side of the control circuit disconnect.

   (a) line   (b) load   (c) adjacent   (d) none of these

62. The motor controller must have horsepower ratings at the application voltage not _____ the horsepower rating of the motor.

   (a) lower than   (b) higher than   (c) equal to   (d) none of these

63. For stationary motors of 2 horsepower or less and 300V or less on ac circuits, the controller is permitted to be an ac-rated general-use snap switch where the motor full-load current rating is not more than _____ percent of the rating of the switch.

   (a) 80   (b) 50   (c) 75   (d) 125

64. Each motor must be provided with an individual controller.

   (a) True   (b) False

65. A disconnecting means is required to disconnect the _____ from all ungrounded supply conductors.

   (a) motor   (b) motor or controller   (c) controller   (d) motor and controller

66. The motor disconnecting means is not required to be in sight from the motor and the driven machinery location, provided _____.

   (a) the controller disconnecting means is capable of being individually locked in the open position
   (b) the provisions for locking are permanently installed on, or at, the switch or circuit breaker used as the controller disconnecting means
   (c) locating the motor disconnecting means within sight of the motor is impractical or introduces additional or increased hazards to people or property
   (d) all of these

67. The motor disconnecting means must _____ whether it is in the open (off) or closed (on) position.

   (a) plainly indicate   (b) provide current   (c) be in the upper position   (d) none of these

68. The motor disconnecting means can be a _____.

   (a) circuit breaker   (b) motor-circuit switch rated in horsepower
   (c) molded-case switch   (d) any of these

69. A branch-circuit overcurrent protection device such as a plug fuse may serve as the disconnecting means for a stationary motor of 1/8 hp or less.

   (a) True   (b) False

70. The disconnecting means for a 50 hp, 460V, three-phase induction motor (FLC 65A) must have an ampere rating of not less than _____.

   (a) 126   (b) 75   (c) 91   (d) 63

71. An oil switch is permitted to be used as both the controller and disconnecting means on a circuit whose rating _____ or 100A.

   (a) does not exceed 300V   (b) exceeds 600V   (c) does not exceed 600V   (d) none of these

Article 440 Air-Conditioning and Refrigerating Equipment

This article applies to electrically driven air-conditioning and refrigeration equipment with a motorized hermetic refrigerant compressor. The requirements in this article are in addition to, or amend, the requirements in Article 430 and other articles.

72. Article 440 applies to electric motor-driven air-conditioning and refrigerating equipment that has a hermetic refrigerant motor-compressor.

    (a) True   (b) False

73. Equipment such as _____ are considered appliances, and the provisions of Article 422 are applicable in addition to Article 440.

    (a) room air conditioners   (b) household refrigerators and freezers
    (c) drinking water coolers and beverage dispensers   (d) all of these

74. For cord-connected equipment such as _____, a separable connector or an attachment plug and receptacle is permitted to serve as the disconnecting means.

    (a) room air conditioners   (b) household refrigerators and freezers
    (c) drinking water coolers and beverage dispensers   (d) all of these

75. Disconnecting means must be located within sight from and readily accessible from the air-conditioning or refrigerating equipment. The disconnecting means is permitted to be installed _____ the air-conditioning or refrigerating equipment, but not on panels that are designed to allow access to the air-conditioning or refrigeration equipment.

    (a) on   (b) within   (c) a or b   (d) none of these

76. The rating of the branch-circuit short-circuit and ground-fault protection device for an individual motor-compressor must not exceed _____ percent of the rated-load current or branch-circuit selection current, whichever is greater, if the protection device will carry the starting current of the motor.

    (a) 100   (b) 125   (c) 175   (d) none of these

77. Conductors supplying more than one motor-compressor must have an ampacity not less than the sum of the rated load or branch-circuit current ratings, whichever is larger, of all the motor-compressors plus the full-load currents of any other motors, plus _____ percent of the highest motor or motor-compressor rating in the group.

    (a) 80   (b) 50   (c) 25   (d) 100

78. The rating of the attachment plug and receptacle must not exceed _____ at 250V for a cord-and-plug connected air conditioner.

    (a) 15A   (b) 20A   (c) 30A   (d) 40A

79. An attachment plug and receptacle is permitted to serve as the disconnecting means for a single-phase room air conditioner rated 250V or less if _____.

    (a) manual controls on the air conditioner are readily accessible within 6 ft of the floor
    (b) an approved operable switch is installed in a readily-accessible location within sight of the air conditioner
    (c) a pushbutton kill switch is installed at the entrance to the room
    (d) a or c

Article 445 Generators

This article contains the electrical installation requirements for generators, such as where they can be installed, nameplate markings, conductor ampacity, and disconnecting means.

80. Each generator must be provided with a _____ listing the manufacturer's name, the rated frequency, power factor, number of phases (if of alternating current), and the rating in kilowatts or kilovolt-amperes.

    (a) list   (b) faceplate   (c) nameplate   (d) sticker

81. The ampacity of ungrounded (phase) conductors from the generator terminals to the first overcurrent protection devices must not be less than _____ percent of the nameplate rating of the generator.

(a) 75   (b) 115   (c) 125   (d) 140

Article 450 Transformers and Transformer Vaults

This article covers the installation of all transformers.

82. According to Article 450, a transformer rated 600V, nominal, or less, and whose primary current rating is 9A or more, is protected against overcurrent only when _____.

(a) an individual overcurrent device on the primary side is set at not more than 125 percent of the rated primary current of the transformer
(b) a secondary overcurrent device is set at not more than 125 percent of the rated secondary current of the transformer, and a primary overcurrent device is set at not more than 250 percent of the rated primary current of the transformer
(c) a or b
(d) none of these

83. What size "primary only" overcurrent protection is required for a 600 volt, 45 kVA transformer that has a primary current rating of 54A?

(a) 70   (b) 80   (c) 90   (d) 100

84. A secondary tie of a transformer is a circuit operating at _____ nominal, or less, between phases that connects two power sources or power-supply points.

(a) 600V   (b) 1,000V   (c) 12,000V   (d) 35,000V

85. Each transformer must be provided with a nameplate listing the name of the manufacturer, rated kilovolt-amperes, frequency, primary and secondary voltage, impedance of transformers _____ and larger, required clearances for transformers with ventilating openings, and the amount and kind of insulating liquid where used.

(a) 112 kVA   (b) 25 kVA   (c) 33 kVA   (d) 50 kVA

86. Indoor transformers of greater than _____ rating must be installed in a transformer room of fire-resistant construction.

(a) 35,000 kVA   (b) 87 1/2 kVA   (c) 112 1/2 kVA   (d) 75 kVA

87. Indoor transformers rated over 35,000V, and insulated with nonflammable dielectric fluid, must be installed in a vault furnished with a _____.

(a) liquid confinement area
(b) pressure-relief vent
(c) means for absorbing or venting any gases generated by arcing
(d) all of these

88. The walls and roofs of transformer vaults must be constructed of materials that have adequate structural strength for the conditions with a minimum fire resistance of _____ hour(s).

(a) 1   (b) 2   (c) 3   (d) 4

89. Personnel doors for transformer vaults must _____ and be equipped with panic bars, pressure plates, or other devices that are normally latched but open under simple pressure.

(a) be clearly identified   (b) swing out   (c) a and b   (d) a or b

90. For phase converters serving variable loads, the ampacity of the single-phase supply conductors must not be less than _____ percent of the single-phase input full-load amperes listed on the phase converter nameplate.

    (a) 75   (b) 100   (c) 125   (d) 150

91. The phase converter disconnecting means must be _____ and located in sight from the phase converter.

    (a) protected from physical damage   (b) readily accessible
    (c) easily visible   (d) clearly identified

Article 460 Capacitors

This article covers the installation of capacitors, including those in hazardous (classified) locations as modified by Articles 501 through 503.

92. Capacitors must be _____ so that persons cannot come into accidental contact or bring conducting materials into accidental contact with exposed energized parts, terminals, or buses associated with them.

    (a) enclosed   (b) located   (c) guarded   (d) any of these

93. The ampacity of capacitor circuit conductors must not be less than _____ percent of the rated current of the capacitor.

    (a) 100   (b) 115   (c) 125   (d) 135

94. A separate overcurrent device is not required for a capacitor connected on the load side of a motor overload protective device.

    (a) True   (b) False

95. A separate disconnecting means is required where a capacitor is connected on the load side of a motor controller.

    (a) True   (b) False

96. Where a motor installation includes a capacitor connected on the load side of the motor overload device, the effect of a capacitor must be disregarded in determining the motor circuit conductor size in accordance with 430.22.

    (a) True   (b) False

Article 470 Resistors and Reactors

This article covers the installation of separate resistors and reactors on electric circuits.

97. For installations of resistors and reactors, a thermal barrier is required if the space between them and any combustible material is less than _____

    (a) 2 in.   (b) 3 in.   (c) 6 in.   (d) 12 in.

Article 480 Storage Batteries

The provisions of this article shall apply to all stationary installations of storage batteries.

98. Nominal Battery Voltage: The voltage computed on the basis of _____ per cell for the lead-acid type and _____ per cell for the alkali type.

    (a) 6V, 12V   (b) 12V, 24V   (c) 2V, 1.2V   (d) 1.2V, 2V

99. Provisions must be made for sufficient diffusion and ventilation of the gases from the storage battery to prevent the accumulation of a(n) _____ mixture.

    (a) corrosive   (b) explosive   (c) toxic   (d) all of these

CHAPTER 5 SPECIAL OCCUPANCIES

Article 500 Hazardous (Classified) Locations

A hazardous (classified) location is an area where the possibility of fire or explosion exists because of the presence of flammable gases or vapors, combustible dusts, or ignitible fibers or flyings. The three components necessary to create a fire or explosion are fuel, oxygen, and a source of ignition.

100. Portable battery-operated devices such as cordless drills, cell phones, etc., must be listed for use in a hazardous (classified) location and the equipment must comply with the requirements of Chapter 5. This is because battery-operated devices can produce enough energy in a hazardous (classified) location to ignite a fire or cause an explosion.

    (a) True   (b) False

(• Indicates that 75% or fewer of those who took this exam answered the question correctly.)

1. A 1,000W incandescent lamp requires a _____ base.

   (a) mogul   (b) standard   (c) medium   (d) copper

2. •A _____ must be located in sight from the motor location and the driven machinery location.

   (a) controller   (b) protection device   (c) disconnecting means   (d) all of these

3. •Exposed live parts of motors and controllers operating at _____ or more between terminals must be guarded against accidental contact by enclosure or by location.

   (a) 24V   (b) 50V   (c) 150V   (d) 60V

4. A disconnecting means that serves a hermetic refrigerant motor-compressor must be selected on the basis of the nameplate rated-load current or branch-circuit selection current, whichever is greater. It must have an ampere rating of at least _____ percent of the nameplate rated-load current or branch-circuit selection current, whichever is greater.

   (a) 125   (b) 80   (c) 100   (d) 115

5. A heating panel is a complete assembly provided with a junction box or length of flexible conduit for connection to a(n) _____.

   (a) wiring system   (b) service   (c) branch circuit   (d) approved conductor

6. A hermetic motor-compressor controller must have a _____ current rating not less than the respective nameplate rating(s) on the compressor.

   (a) continuous-duty full-load   (b) locked-rotor   (c) a or b   (d) a and b

7. A motor can be provided with combined overcurrent protection using a single protective device to provide branch-circuit _____ where the rating of the device provides the necessary overload protection specified in 430.32.

   (a) short-circuit protection   (b) ground-fault protection   (c) motor-overload protection   (d) all of these

8. A storage-type water heater having a capacity of _____ gallons or less is considered a continuous load.

   (a) 60   (b) 75   (c) 90   (d) 120

9. A Type IC recessed luminaire, which is identified for contact with insulation, is permitted to be in contact with _____.

   (a) combustible material at recessed parts
   (b) points of support
   (c) portions passing through or finishing off the opening in the building structure
   (d) all of these

10. All transformers and transformer vaults must be readily accessible to qualified personnel for inspection and maintenance, except that _____.

    (a) dry-type transformers 600V, nominal, or less, located in the open on walls, columns, or structures, are not required to be readily accessible
    (b) dry-type transformers rated not more than 50 kVA and not over 600V are permitted to be installed in hollow spaces of buildings not permanently closed in by structure as long as requirements are met concerning ventilation and separation from combustible materials
    (c) a or b
    (d) none of these

11. An infrared heating lamp used in a medium-base lampholder must be rated _____ or less.

    (a) 150W   (b) 300W   (c) 600W   (d) 750W

12. An overcurrent device must be provided in each ungrounded conductor for each capacitor bank. The rating or setting of the overcurrent device must be _____.

    (a) 20A   (b) as low as practicable
    (c) 400% of conductor ampacity   (d) 100A

13. Capacitors containing more than _____ of flammable liquid must be enclosed in vaults or outdoor fenced enclosures.

    (a) 10 gallons   (b) 5 gallons   (c) 3 gallons   (d) 11 gallons

14. Ceiling-suspended (paddle) fans must be supported independently of an outlet box or by outlet boxes or outlet box systems _____ for the application and installed in accordance with 314.27(D).

    (a) satisfactory   (b) approved   (c) strong enough   (d) identified

15. Each vented cell of a battery must be equipped with _____ that is/are designed to prevent destruction of the cell due to ignition of gases within the cell by an external spark or flame under normal operating conditions.

    (a) pressure relief (b) a flame arrester (c) fluid level indicators (d) none of these

16. Electric space-heating cables must be furnished complete with factory-assembled nonheating leads that are at least _____ in length.

    (a) 6 in.   (b) 18 in.   (c) 3 ft   (d) 7 ft

17. Electric space-heating cables must not be installed over cabinets whose clearance from the ceiling is less than the minimum _____ dimension of the cabinet to the nearest cabinet edge that is open to the room or area.

    (a) horizontal   (b) vertical   (c) overall   (d) depth

18. Exposed elements of impedance heating systems must be physically guarded, isolated, or thermally insulated with a _____ jacket to protect against contact by personnel in the area.

    (a) corrosion-resistant (b) waterproof   (c) weatherproof   (d) flame-retardant

19. Feeder tap conductors supplying motor circuits, with an ampacity of at least one-third that of the feeder, must not exceed _____ in length.

    (a) 10 ft   (b) 15 ft   (c) 20 ft   (d) 25 ft

20. Fixed electric heating equipment for pipelines and vessels is considered to be a(n) _____ load.

    (a) noncontinuous   (b) insignificant   (c) continuous   (d) proprietary

21. For cord-and-plug connected household electric ranges, an attachment plug and receptacle connection at the rear base of the range, if it is _____ is allowed to serve as the disconnecting means.

    (a) less than 40A
    (c) GFCI protected
    (b) a flush-mounted receptacle
    (d) accessible by removal of a drawer

22. For general motor applications, the motor branch-circuit short-circuit and ground-fault protection device must be sized based on the _____ amperes.

    (a) motor nameplate   (b) NEMA standard   (c) *NEC* Table   (d) Factory Mutual

23. If a protective device rating is marked on an appliance, the branch-circuit overcurrent protection device rating must not be greater than _____ percent of the protective device rating marked on the appliance.

    (a) 100   (b) 50   (c) 80   (d) 115

24. If a(n) _____ shutdown is necessary to reduce hazards to persons, the overload sensing devices are permitted to be connected to a supervised alarm instead of causing immediate interruption of the motor circuit.

    (a) emergency   (b) normal   (c) orderly   (d) none of these

25. If the disconnect is not within sight of the fixed electric space heater which includes a motor rated over 1/8 hp (without supplementary overcurrent protection devices), it must be capable of being _____.

    (a) locked
    (c) locked in the open position
    (b) locked in the closed position
    (d) within sight

26. Incandescent luminaires must be marked to indicate the maximum allowable _____ of lamps.

    (a) voltage   (b) amperage   (c) rating   (d) wattage

27. Lighting systems operating at 30V or less are allowed to be concealed or extended through a building wall using _____.

    (a) any of the wiring methods specified in Chapter 3
    (b) wiring supplied by a listed class 2 power source installed in accordance with 725.52
    (c) both a and b
    (d) metal raceways only

28. Lighting track is a manufactured assembly and its length may not be altered by the addition or subtraction of sections of track.

    (a) True   (b) False

29. Lighting track must have two supports for a single section of _____ or shorter in length and each individual section of not more than 4 ft attached to it must have one additional support.

    (a) 4 ft   (b) 6 ft   (c) 10 ft   (d) 2 ft

30. Lighting track must not be installed less than _____ above the finished floor except where protected from physical damage or track operating at less than 30V RMS, open-circuit voltage.

    (a) 4 ft   (b) 5 ft   (c) 5 1/2 ft   (d) 6 ft

31. Motor control circuit conductors that extend beyond the motor control equipment enclosure are required to have short-circuit and ground-fault protection sized not greater than _____ percent of the conductor ampacity as listed in Table 430.72(B) for 60°C conductors.

    (a) 100   (b) 150   (c) 300   (d) 500

32. Open motors having commutators or collector rings must be located or protected so that sparks cannot reach adjacent combustible material. This must not prohibit the installation of these motors _____.

    (a) on wooden floors   (b) over combustible fiber
    (c) under combustible material   (d) none of these

33. Permanently installed electric baseboard heaters equipped with factory-installed receptacle outlets are permitted to be used as the outlets required by 210.50(B).

    (a) True   (b) False

34. Resistors and reactors rated over 600V must be isolated by _____ to protect personnel from accidental contact with energized parts.

    (a) an enclosure   (b) elevation   (c) a or b   (d) a and b

35. Short-circuit and ground-fault protection for an individual motor compressor must not exceed _____ percent of the motor-compressor rated-load current or branch-circuit protection current, whichever is greater.

    (a) 80   (b) 125   (c) 175   (d) 250

36. Surface-mounted luminaires with a ballast must have a minimum clearance of _____ from combustible low-density cellulose fiberboard, unless the fixture is marked "Suitable for Surface Mounting on Combustible Low-Density Cellulose Fiberboard."

    (a) 1/2 in.   (b) 1 in.   (c) 1 1/2 in.   (d) 2 in.

37. The _____ for a hermetic refrigerant motor-compressor is the current resulting when the motor-compressor is operated at the rated load, rated voltage, and rated frequency of the equipment it serves.

    (a) full-load current   (b) nameplate rating   (c) selection current   (d) rated-load current

38. The branch-circuit protective device is permitted to serve as the controller for a stationary motor rated at _____ or less that is normally left running and cannot be damaged by overload or failure to start.

    (a) 1/8 hp   (b) 1/4 hp   (c) 3/8 hp   (d) 1/2 hp

39. The controller is required to open all conductors to the motor.

    (a) True   (b) False

40. The disconnecting means for a torque motor must have an ampere rating of at least _____ percent of the motor nameplate current.

    (a) 100   (b) 115   (c) 125   (d) 175

41. The ultimate trip current of a thermally-protected motor with a full-load current not exceeding 9A must not exceed _____ percent of the motor full-load current as listed in Tables 430.248, 430.249, and 430.250.

    (a) 140   (b) 156   (c) 170   (d) none of these

42. Torque requirements for motor control circuit device terminals must be a minimum of _____ lbs-inch (unless otherwise identified) for screw-type pressure terminals used for 14 AWG and smaller copper conductors.

    (a) 7   (b) 9   (c) 10   (d) 15

43. Transformer vaults must be located where they can be ventilated to the outside air without using flues or ducts, wherever such an arrangement is _____.

    (a) permitted   (b) practicable   (c) required   (d) all of these

44. Unless two restrictive conditions exist, a generator must be equipped with one or more disconnecting means to disconnect the generator, its protective devices, and all control apparatus entirely from the circuits supplied by the generator.

    (a) True   (b) False

45. When fuses are used for motor overload protection, a fuse must be inserted in each ungrounded conductor and also in the grounded conductor if the supply system is _____ with one conductor grounded.

    (a) 2-wire, three-phase dc (b) 2-wire, three-phase ac (c) 3-wire, three-phase dc (d) 3-wire, three-phase ac

46. When installing duct heaters, sufficient clearance must be maintained to permit replacement and adjustment of controls and heating elements.

    (a) True   (b) False

47. When supplying a room air conditioner rated 120V, the length of the flexible supply cord must not exceed _____

    (a) 4 ft   (b) 6 ft   (c) 8 ft   (d) 10 ft

48. Where a motor installation includes a capacitor connected on the load side of the motor overload device, the rating or setting of the motor overload device must be based on the improved power factor of the motor circuit.

    (a) True   (b) False

49. Where more than one motor disconnecting means is provided in the same motor branch circuit, only one of the disconnecting means is required to be readily accessible.

    (a) True   (b) False

50. Where practicable, transformer vaults containing more than _____ total kVA transformer capacity must be provided with a drain or other means that will carry off any accumulation of oil or water in the vault, unless local conditions make this impracticable.

    (a) 100   (b) 150   (c) 200   (d) 250

(• Indicates that 75% or fewer of those who took this exam answered the question correctly.)

1. The *Code* prohibits damage to the internal parts of electrical equipment by foreign material such as paint, plaster, cleaners, etc. Precautions must be taken to provide protection from the detrimental effects of paint, plaster, cleaners, etc. on internal parts such as _____.

   (a) busbars   (b) wiring terminals   (c) insulators   (d) all of these

2. The conductors for the TVSS cannot be any longer than _____, and unnecessary bends should be avoided.

   (a) 6 in.   (b) 12 in.   (c) 18 in.   (d) none of these

3. The conductors, including splices and taps, in a nonmetallic surface raceway having a removable cover, must not fill the raceway to more than _____ percent of its cross-sectional area at that point.

   (a) 75   (b) 40   (c) 38   (d) 53

4. The connection between the grounded circuit conductor and the equipment grounding conductor at a separately derived system is the _____.

   (a) main bonding jumper   (b) system bonding jumper   (c) circuit bonding jumper   (d) equipment bonding jumper

5. The continuity of the grounding conductor system used to reduce electrical shock hazards at carnivals, fairs, and similar locations must be verified each time the portable electrical equipment is connected.

   (a) True   (b) False

6. The cord for a dishwasher and trash compactor must not be longer than _____ measured from the back of the appliance.

   (a) 2 ft   (b) 4 ft   (c) 6 ft   (d) 8 ft

7. The cross-sectional area of trade size 1 IMC is approximately _____

   (a) 1.22 sq in.   (b) 0.62 sq in.   (c) 0.96 sq in.   (d) 2.13 sq in.

8. The cross-sectional area of the conductors permitted in a sealing fitting must not exceed _____ percent of the cross-sectional area of rigid metal conduit of the same trade size unless the seal is specifically listed for a higher percentage of conductor fill.

   (a) 25   (b) 50   (c) 100   (d) 125

9. The dedicated space above a panelboard extends to a dropped or suspended ceiling, which is considered a structural ceiling.

   (a) True   (b) False

10. The demand factors of Table 220.56 apply to space heating, ventilating, or air-conditioning equipment.

    (a) True   (b) False

11. The dimension of working clearance for access to live parts operating at 300V, nominal-to-ground, where there are exposed live parts on both sides of the workspace is _____ according to Table 110.26(A)(1).

    (a) 3 ft   (b) 3 1/2 ft   (c) 4 ft   (d) 4 1/2 ft

12. The disconnecting means for air-conditioning and refrigerating equipment must be _____ from the air-conditioning or refrigerating equipment.

    (a) readily accessible   (b) within sight   (c) a or b   (d) a and b

13. The disconnecting means for the controller and motor must open all ungrounded supply conductors and must be designed so that no pole can be operated independently.

    (a) True   (b) False

14. The disconnecting means is not required to be located at the building or structure where documented safe switching procedures are established and maintained, and where the installation is monitored by _____ persons.

    (a) maintenance   (b) management   (c) service   (d) qualified

15. The electrical datum plane (in land areas subject to tidal fluctuation) is a horizontal plane _____ above the highest high tide under normal circumstances.

    (a) 1 ft   (b) 2 ft   (c) 3 ft   (d) none of these

16. The environment of a wiring method under the eaves of a house having a roofed open porch would be considered a _____ location.

    (a) dry   (b) damp   (c) wet   (d) moist

17. The feeder and service conductors for motors must be computed in accordance with Article _____.

    (a) 450   (b) 240   (c) 430   (d) 100

18. The feeder demand load for nine 12 kW ranges is _____.

    (a) 13,000W   (b) 14,700W   (c) 24,000W   (d) 16,000W

19. The grounding conductor for a CATV system must be connected to the nearest accessible location included on the list in 820.100(B)(2) when the building _____.

    (a) has a grounding means   (b) is without a grounding means
    (c) has an emergency transfer switch   (d) is wired using a metallic cable or raceway system

20. The highest current at rated voltage that a device is intended to interrupt under standard test conditions is the _____.

    (a) interrupting rating   (b) manufacturer's rating   (c) interrupting capacity   (d) GFCI rating

21. The insulation rating of ungrounded conductors in Type NM cable must be _____.

    (a) 60°C   (b) 75°C   (c) 90°C   (d) any of these

22. The intentional electrical connection of one system terminal to ground without the insertion of any resistor or impedance device is _____.

    (a) grounded   (b) solidly grounded   (c) effectively grounded   (d) grounding conductor

23. The localization of an overcurrent condition to restrict outages to the circuit or equipment affected, accomplished by the choice of overcurrent-protective devices is called _____.

    (a) overcurrent protection   (b) interrupting capacity   (c) selective coordination   (d) overload protection

24. The location of the disconnecting means for an elevator must be _____ to qualified persons.

    (a) accessible   (b) readily accessible
    (c) disclosed only   (d) accessible only with a key

25. The maximum length of an unprotected feeder tap conductor in a high-bay manufacturing building over 35 ft high is _____.

    (a) 15 ft   (b) 20 ft   (c) 50 ft   (d) 100 ft

26. The maximum rating or setting of an inverse-time breaker used as the motor branch-circuit short-circuit and ground-fault protective device for a single-phase motor is _____ percent of the full-load current given in Table 430.248.

    (a) 125   (b) 175   (c) 250   (d) 300

27. The metal water-pipe system of a building or structure is not required to be bonded to the separately derived system neutral terminal where the metal frame of the building or structure is used as the grounding electrode for the separately derived system and is bonded to the metal water piping in the area served by the separately derived system.

    (a) True   (b) False

28. The minimum distance that an outlet box containing tap supply conductors can be placed from a recessed luminaire (fixture) is _____.

    (a) 1 ft   (b) 2 ft   (c) 3 ft   (d) 4 ft

29. The minimum headroom of working spaces about motor control centers must be _____.

    (a) 3 ft   (b) 5 ft   (c) 6 ft   (d) 6 1/2 ft

30. The *NEC* requires that electrical work be installed _____.

    (a) in a neat and workmanlike manner   (b) under the supervision of a qualified person
    (c) completed before being inspected   (d) all of these

31. The number of conductors allowed in rigid nonmetallic conduit must not exceed that permitted by the percentage fill specified in _____.

    (a) Chapter 9, Table 1   (b) Table 250.66   (c) Table 310.16   (d) 240.6

32. The number of fixture wires in a single conduit or tubing must not exceed that permitted by the percentage fill specified in _____.

    (a) Chapter 9, Table 1   (b) Table 250.66   (c) Table 310.16   (d) 240.6

33. The number of nonpower-limited fire alarm (NPLFA) conductors in a raceway is not required to be in accordance with the fill requirements contained in 300.17.

    (a) True   (b) False

34. The parallel conductors in each phase or grounded conductor must _____.

    (a) be the same length and conductor material   (b) have the same circular mil area and insulation type
    (c) be terminated in the same manner   (d) all of these

35. The patient care area is any portion of a health care facility where patients are intended to be _____.

(a) examined   (b) treated   (c) registered   (d) a or b

36. The power source for a Class 2 circuit must be _____.

(a) a listed Class 2 or 3 transformer
(b) a listed Class 2 or 3 power supply
(c) other listed equipment marked to identify the Class 2 or Class 3 power source
(d) any of these

37. The power source for a nonpower-limited fire alarm (NPLFA) circuit must not operate at more than _____.

(a) 600V   (b) 300V   (c) 20A   (d) 120V

38. The power source for a power-limited fire alarm (PLFA) circuit is allowed to be supplied through a ground-fault circuit interrupter or an arc-fault circuit interrupter.

(a) True   (b) False

39. The rating or setting of an overcurrent protection device for a 16.3A single nonmotor-operated appliance must not exceed _____.

(a) 15A   (b) 35A   (c) 25A   (d) 45A

40. The requirement for maintaining a 3 ft vertical clearance from the edge of the roof does not apply to the final conductor span where the conductors are attached to _____.

(a) a building pole   (b) the side of a building   (c) an antenna   (d) the base of a building

41. The rules of _____, as applicable, apply to air-conditioning and refrigerating equipment that do not incorporate a hermetic refrigerant motor-compressor.

(a) Article 422   (b) Article 424   (c) Article 430   (d) all of these

42. The scope of Article 285 applies to devices such as cord-and-plug connected TVSS units or receptacles or appliances that have integral TVSS protection.

(a) True   (b) False

43. The screw shell of a luminaire or lampholder must be connected to the _____

(a) grounded conductor   (b) ungrounded conductor
(c) equipment grounding conductor   (d) forming shell terminal

44. The size of the grounded conductor for a feeder must not be smaller than specified in _____.

(a) Table 250.122   (b) Table 250.66   (c) Table 310.16   (d) Table 430.52

45. The size of the grounding electrode conductor for a building or structure supplied by a feeder cannot be smaller than that identified in _____ based on the largest ungrounded supply conductor.

(a) 250.66   (b) 250.122   (c) Table 310.16   (d) not specified

46. The small-appliance branch circuits can supply the _____ as well as the kitchen.

(a) dining room   (b) refrigerator   (c) breakfast room   (d) all of these

47. The total rating of a cord-and-plug connected room air conditioner, connected to the same branch circuit which supplies lighting units, other appliances, or general-use receptacles, must not exceed _____ percent of the branch-circuit rating.

    (a) 80   (b) 70   (c) 50   (d) 40

48. The upper end of the rod electrode must be _____ ground level unless the aboveground end and the grounding electrode conductor attachment are protected against physical damage.

    (a) above   (b) flush with   (c) below   (d) b or c

49. The use of listed and marked LFNC is permitted for _____.

    (a) direct burial where listed and marked for the purpose   (b) exposed work
    (c) concealed work   (d) all of these

50. The voltage at the line terminals of a fire-pump motor controller must not drop more than _____ percent below the controller's normal rated voltage under motor-starting conditions.

    (a) 5   (b) 10   (c) 15   (d) any of these

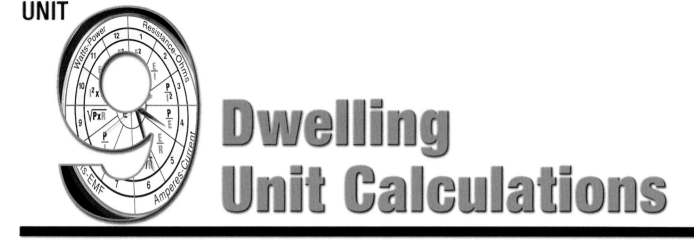

UNIT 9

Dwelling Unit Calculations

Introduction

The *Code* defines "Service Point" as the point where the serving utility connects to the wiring of the premises. Up to this point, the utility company is responsible for the electrical installation, and is not required to follow the *NEC*. After the service point, the responsibility is transferred to the owner of the property and the electrician hired by the owner to make the installation, who must follow the *Code* requirements.

Sizing the service is not simply a matter of adding up all of the loads or all of the circuit breaker sizes. The *NEC* recognizes that not all loads will be used simultaneously under normal living conditions, and so there are a number of "demand factors" that come into play in sizing an electrical service. For this reason, it is important to be familiar with all of the requirements of Article 220 so the proper demand factors will be applied to a given installation. There are numerous tables and requirements to follow, but take them one at a time and you will be able to complete these calculations.

Unit 9 focuses on sizing the service for a one-family dwelling unit. The *Code* provides for the use of either a standard or an optional method of calculation. Both methods are included in this unit and you should be familiar with both for exam purposes. A good grasp of the material in this unit is important as a basis for the following units which will address multifamily dwellings and commercial calculations, so be sure to study the examples and complete the questions in this unit to solidify your understanding.

PART A—GENERAL REQUIREMENTS

9.1 General Requirements

Article 220 provides the requirements for residential branch circuits, feeders, and service calculations [220.1]. Other important articles include Branch Circuits—210, Feeders—215, Services—230, Overcurrent Protection—240, Wiring Methods—300, Conductors—310, Appliances—422, Electric Space-Heating Equipment—424, Motors—430, and Air-Conditioning—440 [220.1].

9.2 Voltages [220.5(A)]

Unless other voltages are specified, branch-circuit, feeder, and service loads must be calculated using nominal system voltage, such as 120, 120/240, 120/208, 240, 347, 277/480, 480, 347/600, or 600. For single-family dwelling unit calculations, the nominal voltage is typically 120/240V. Figure 9–1

AUTHOR'S COMMENTS

- A nominal value is assigned to a circuit for the purpose of conveniently designating its voltage class. The actual voltage at which a circuit operates can vary from the nominal within a range that permits satisfactory operation of equipment [100].

- Motor VA is based on motor table [430.248 and 430.250] voltage and current values, such as 115V, 230V, or 460V – not 120V, 240V, or 480V.

9.3 Fraction of an Ampere [220.5(B)]

Where calculations result in a fraction of 0.50A or less, such fractions can be dropped.

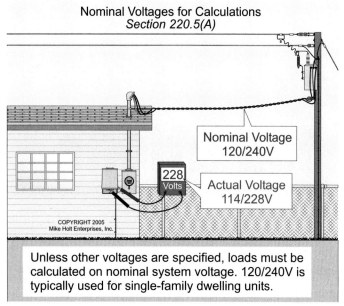

Nominal Voltages for Calculations
Section 220.5(A)

Nominal Voltage
120/240V

Actual Voltage
114/228V

228 Volts

Unless other voltages are specified, loads must be calculated on nominal system voltage. 120/240V is typically used for single-family dwelling units.

Figure 9–1

AUTHOR'S COMMENT: When do you round—after each calculation, or at the final calculation? The *NEC* isn't specific on this issue, but I guess it all depends on the answer you want to see!

▶ **Rounding**

According to 424.3(B), the branch-circuit conductors and overcurrent protection device for electric space-heating equipment must be sized no less than 125 percent of the total load. What size conductor is required to supply a 9 kVA (37.5A), 240V single-phase fixed space heater with a 3A blower motor if equipment terminals are rated 75°C. **Figure 9–2**

    (a) 10 AWG   (b) 8 AWG
    (c) 6 AWG   (d) 4 AWG

    • Answer: (c) 6 AWG

    Step 1: Determine the total load
                 I = VA/E
                 I = 9,000 VA/240V
                 I = 37.5A

    Step 2: The conductor is sized at 125% of the load.

                 Conductor Size = (37.5A + 3A) x 1.25
                 Conductor Size = 50.63A, round up to 51A

                 If we rounded down, then 8 AWG rated 50A at 75°C could be used, but since we have to round up, 6 AWG rated 65A at 75°C is required.

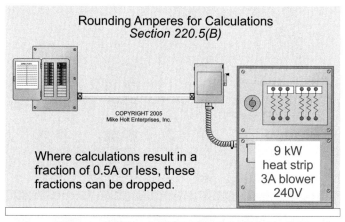

Rounding Amperes for Calculations
Section 220.5(B)

Where calculations result in a fraction of 0.5A or less, these fractions can be dropped.

9 kW
heat strip
3A blower
240V

40.5A x 125% = 50.63A, Round up to 51A
Table 310.16, 6 AWG rated 65A at 75°C

Figure 9–2

9.4 Small-Appliance Circuits [210.11(C)(1)]

A minimum of two, 20A small-appliance branch circuits are required for receptacle outlets in the kitchen, dining room, breakfast room, pantry, or similar dining areas [220.11(C)(1)]. In general, receptacles from other areas or lighting outlets cannot be connected to these 20A small-appliance branch circuits [210.52(B)(2) Exceptions]. **Figure 9–3**

Feeder and Service

When sizing the feeder or service, each dwelling unit must have a minimum of two 20A small-appliance branch circuits with a feeder load of 1,500 VA for each circuit [220.52(A)].

Other Related Code Sections

15 or 20A receptacles can be used on 20A circuits [210.21(B)(3)].

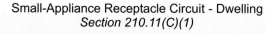

Small-Appliance Receptacle Circuit - Dwelling
Section 210.11(C)(1)

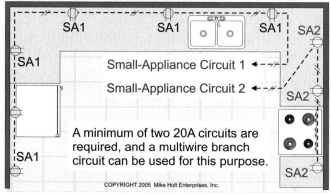

SA1   SA1   SA1   SA2

SA1

Small-Appliance Circuit 1

Small-Appliance Circuit 2

SA2

A minimum of two 20A circuits are required, and a multiwire branch circuit can be used for this purpose.

SA1

SA2

Figure 9–3

Receptacle outlets required for kitchen countertops [210.52(C)].

Areas supplied by the small-appliance circuits [210.52(B)(1)].

AUTHOR'S COMMENT: 210.52(B)(1) states that the refrigerator outlet is part of a small-appliance circuit. The refrigerator outlet is also permitted to be on an individual 15 or 20A branch circuit [210.52(B)(1) Ex 1].

9.5 Cooking Equipment—Branch Circuit [Table 220.55, Note 4]

To determine the branch-circuit calculated load for household ranges and cooking equipment, we are allowed to apply the provisions of Table 220.55, Note 4. The branch-circuit calculated load for one range may be calculated according to the demand factors listed in Table 220.55, but a minimum 40A circuit is required for ranges rated 8.75 kVA and larger [210.19(A)(3)].

▶ **Less Than 12 kVA, Column C**

What is the branch-circuit calculated load (in amperes) for one 9 kVA range? **Figure 9–4**

(a) 21A   (b) 27A
(c) 38A   (d) 33A

• Answer: (d) 33A

The calculated load for one range in Table 220.55 Column C is 8 kVA.

This can be converted to amperes by dividing the power by the voltage:

$I = VA/E$
$I = (8 \text{ kVA} \times 1,000)/240V*$
$I = 33A$

*Assume 120/240V, single-phase for all calculations unless the question gives a specific voltage and system [220.5(A)].

▶ **More than 12 kVA, Table 220.55 Note 1**

What is the branch-circuit load for one 14 kVA range? **Figure 9–5**

(a) 33A   (b) 37A   (c) 50A   (d) 58A

• Answer: (b) 37A

Step 1: Since the range exceeds 12 kVA, follow Note 1 of Table 220.55. The first step is to determine the calculated load as listed in Column C of Table 220.55 for one unit = 8 kVA.

Step 2: We must increase the Column C value (8 kVA) by 5% for each kVA that the range exceeds 12 kVA. In this case, 14 kVA exceeds 12 kVA by 2 kVA. This results in an increase of the Column C value (8 kVA) by 10%, 8 kVA x 1.1 = 8.8 kVA or 8,800W.

Step 3: Convert the calculated load to amperes.
$I = VA/E$
$I = 6,000 \text{ VA}/240V$
$I = 36.7A$

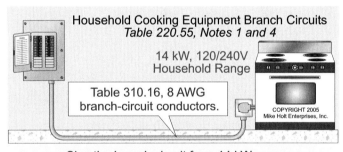

Household Cooking Equipment Branch Circuits
Table 220.55, Notes 1 and 4

14 kW, 120/240V
Household Range

Table 310.16, 8 AWG
branch-circuit conductors.

COPYRIGHT 2005
Mike Holt Enterprises, Inc.

Size the branch circuit for a 14 kW range.

Branch-Circuit Conductor: Table 220.55, Note 4; use Note 1
Step 1: Column C, one unit = 8 kW demand.
Step 2: Increase Column C answer by 5% for each kW over 12 kW.
    14 kW - 12 kW = 2 kW over 12 kW
    2 kW x 5% = 10% increase in Column C answer
    8 kW x 1.10 = 8.8 kW demand
Step 3: Convert the demand load into amperes.
    P – 8.8 kW x 1,000 – 8,800W
    E = 240V
    $I = \dfrac{P}{E} = \dfrac{8,800W}{240V} = 37A$

Figure 9–5

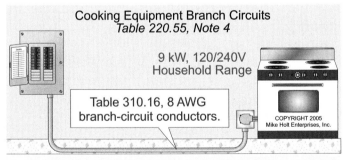

Cooking Equipment Branch Circuits
Table 220.55, Note 4

9 kW, 120/240V
Household Range

Table 310.16, 8 AWG
branch-circuit conductors.

COPYRIGHT 2005
Mike Holt Enterprises, Inc.

Size the branch circuit for the 9 kW range.

Branch-Circuit Conductor Size, Table 220.55, Note 4
Column C = 8 kW demand

$$I = \frac{P}{E} = \frac{8,000W}{240V} = 33A$$

Table 310.16 = 8 AWG Conductor

Figure 9–4

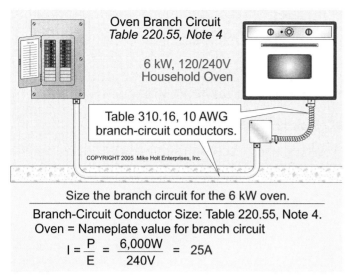

Figure 9–6

One Counter-Mounted Cooking Unit or One Oven

What is the branch-circuit load for one 6 kVA wall-mounted oven? Figure 9–6

    (a) 15A   (b) 20A   (c) 25A   (d) 30A

• Answer: (c) 25A

P = 6 kVA nameplate value
E = 240V (assumed)

$I = VA/E$
I = 6,000 VA/240V
I = 25A

The branch-circuit load of one wall-mounted oven or one counter-mounted cooking unit must be the nameplate rating of the oven or cooking unit [Table 220.55, Note 4].

AUTHOR'S COMMENT: Article 100 defines "Demand Factor" as the ratio of the maximum demand of a system, or part of a system, to the total connected load of that part of the system.

One Counter-Mounted Cooking Unit and Up To Two Ovens [Table 220.55, Note 4]

To calculate the load for one counter-mounted cooking unit (cooktop) and up to two wall-mounted ovens, complete the following steps:

Step 1: Add the nameplate ratings of the cooking appliances and treat this total as one range.

Step 2: Determine the kVA load for one unit from Table 220.55, Column C.

Step 3: If the total nameplate rating exceeds 12 kVA, increase Column C (8 kVA) 5% for each kVA, or major fraction (0.50 kVA), that the combined rating exceeds 12 kVA.

Cooktop and One Oven

What is the branch-circuit load for one 6 kVA counter-mounted cooking unit and one 3 kVA wall-mounted oven? Figure 9–7

    (a) 25A   (b) 38A   (c) 33A   (d) 42A

• Answer: (c) 33A

Step 1: Total connected load: 6 kVA + 3 kVA = 9 kVA

Step 2: kVA load for one range, Column C of Table 220.55: 8 kVA

Step 3: Convert the calculated load to amperes:
$I = VA/E$
I = 8,000 VA/240V
I = 33.3A

Cooktop and Two Ovens

What is the branch-circuit load for one 6 kVA counter-mounted cooking unit (cooktop) and two 4 kVA wall-mounted ovens? Figure 9–8

    (a) 22A   (b) 27A   (c) 33A   (d) 37A

• Answer: (d) 37A

Step 1: The total connected load:
6 kVA + 4 kVA + 4 kVA = 14 kVA

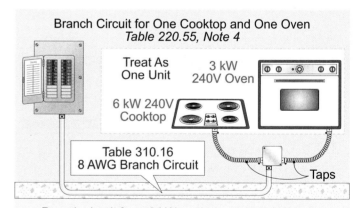

Branch circuit for a 6 kW cooktop and a 3 kW oven.

Branch-Circuit Conductor Size: Table 220.55, Note 4
Add all the nameplate ratings, 6 kW + 3 kW = 9 kW
Treat as one unit, Table 220.55, Column C, 8 kW demand

$$I = \frac{P}{E} = \frac{8,000W}{240V} = 33A$$

COPYRIGHT 2005
Mike Holt Enterprises, Inc.

Figure 9–7

Branch Circuit for Two Ovens and One Cooktop
Table 220.55, Note 4

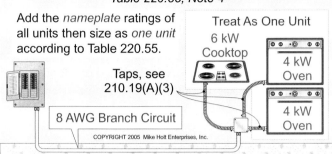

Add the *nameplate* ratings of all units then size as *one unit* according to Table 220.55.

Treat As One Unit
6 kW Cooktop
4 kW Oven
4 kW Oven

Taps, see 210.19(A)(3)

8 AWG Branch Circuit

COPYRIGHT 2005 Mike Holt Enterprises, Inc.

Branch circuit for a 6 kW cooktop and two 4 kW ovens.

Step 1: Total nameplate of all three units,
6 kW + 4 kW + 4 kW = 14 kW

Step 2: Treat as one 14 kW range. Column C for one unit is 8 kW. Increase Column C answer (8 kW) by 5% for every kW over 12 kW; 14 kW - 12 kW = 2 kW = 10%, 8 kW x 1.10 = 8.8 kW

I = P/E = 8,800W/240V = 37A

Figure 9–8

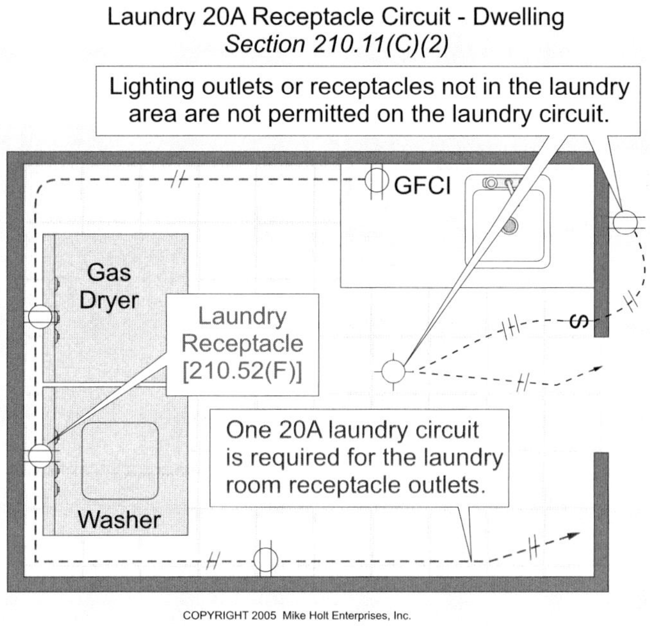

Laundry 20A Receptacle Circuit - Dwelling
Section 210.11(C)(2)

Lighting outlets or receptacles not in the laundry area are not permitted on the laundry circuit.

GFCI

Gas Dryer

Laundry Receptacle [210.52(F)]

One 20A laundry circuit is required for the laundry room receptacle outlets.

Washer

COPYRIGHT 2005 Mike Holt Enterprises, Inc.

Figure 9–9

Step 2: Demand load for one range, Column C of Table 220.55: 8 kVA

Step 3: Since the total (14 kVA) exceeds 12 kVA, we must increase Column C (8 kVA) 5% for each kVA that the total exceeds 12 kVA.

14 kVA exceeds 12 kVA by 2 kVA, which results in a 10% increase of the Column C value.

8 kVA x 1.1 = 8.8 kVA

Step 4: Convert the calculated load to amperes:
I = VA/E
I = 8,800 VA/240V
I = 36.7A

9.6 Laundry Receptacle(s) Circuit [210.11(C)(2)]

One 20A branch circuit for the laundry receptacle outlet (or outlets) is required and this laundry circuit cannot serve any other outlet such as the laundry room lights [210.52(F) and 210.11(C)(2)]. The *NEC* does not require a separate circuit for the washing machine, but does require a separate circuit for the laundry room receptacle or receptacles. Figure 9–9

Feeder and Service Calculations

Each dwelling unit must have a feeder/service calculated load consisting of 1,500 VA for the 20A laundry receptacle circuit [220.52(B)].

Other Related *Code* Rules

A laundry area receptacle outlet must be within 6 ft of a washing machine [210.50(C)].

A laundry area receptacle outlet is required [210.52(F)].

When a laundry area receptacle outlet is within 6 ft of the outside edge of a laundry sink, it must be GFCI protected [210.8(A)(7)].

9.7 Lighting and Receptacles

General Lighting Calculated Load [220.12]

The *NEC* requires a minimum 3 VA per sq ft for the general lighting and general-use receptacles for the purpose of determining branch circuits and feeder/service calculations. The dimensions for determining the area must be computed from the outside dimensions of the building and must not include open porches, garages, or spaces not adaptable for future use. Figure 9–10

> **AUTHOR'S COMMENT:** The 3 VA per sq ft rule for general lighting includes all 15 and 20A general-use receptacles, but it does not include the small-appliance or laundry circuit receptacles. See 220.14(J) for details.

▶ General Lighting Load [Table 220.12]

What is the general lighting and receptacle load for a 2,000 sq ft dwelling unit that has 34 convenience receptacles and 12 luminaires rated 100W each? Figure 9–11

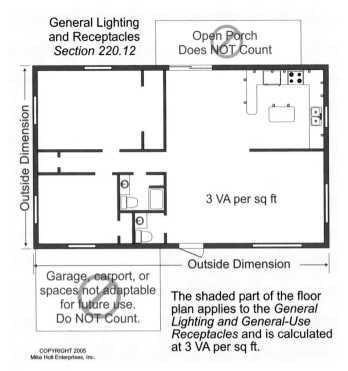

General Lighting and Receptacles *Section 220.12*

Open Porch Does NOT Count

Outside Dimension

3 VA per sq ft

Outside Dimension

Garage, carport, or spaces not adaptable for future use. Do NOT Count.

The shaded part of the floor plan applies to the *General Lighting and General-Use Receptacles* and is calculated at 3 VA per sq ft.

COPYRIGHT 2005
Mike Holt Enterprises, Inc.

Figure 9–10

(a) 2,100 VA (b) 4,200 VA
(c) 6,000 VA (d) 8,400 VA

• Answer: (c) 6,000 VA
2,000 sq ft x 3 VA = 6,000 VA

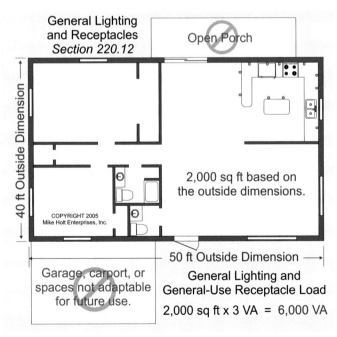

General Lighting and Receptacles *Section 220.12*

Open Porch

40 ft Outside Dimension

2,000 sq ft based on the outside dimensions.

COPYRIGHT 2005
Mike Holt Enterprises, Inc.

50 ft Outside Dimension

Garage, carport, or spaces not adaptable for future use.

General Lighting and General-Use Receptacle Load
2,000 sq ft x 3 VA = 6,000 VA

Figure 9–11

Note: No additional load is required for general-use receptacles and lighting outlets. See 220.14(J).

Number of Circuits Required [Annex D, Example D1(a)]

The number of branch circuits required for general lighting and receptacles must be determined from the general lighting load and the rating of the circuits [210.11(A)]. To determine the number of branch circuits for general lighting and receptacles, follow these steps:

Step 1: Determine the general lighting VA load:
Living Area Square Footage x 3 VA.

Step 2: Determine the general lighting ampere load:
I = VA/E

Step 3: Determine the number of branch circuits:
General Lighting Amperes (Step 2)/Circuit Amperes

▶ **Number of 15 Ampere Circuits**

How many 15A circuits are required for a 2,100 sq ft dwelling unit? **Figure 9–12**

(a) 2 circuits (b) 3 circuits (c) 4 circuits (d) 5 circuits

• Answer: (c) 4 circuits

Step 1: General Lighting VA = 2,100 sq ft x 3 VA
General Lighting VA = 6,300 VA

Step 2: General Lighting Amperes:
$I = VA/E$
$I = 6,300 \text{ VA}/120\text{V}^*$
$I = 52.5\text{A}$

*Use 120V, single-phase unless specified otherwise.

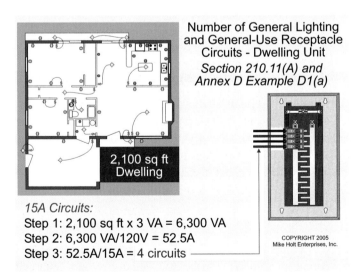

Number of General Lighting and General-Use Receptacle Circuits - Dwelling Unit
Section 210.11(A) and Annex D Example D1(a)

2,100 sq ft Dwelling

15A Circuits:
Step 1: 2,100 sq ft x 3 VA = 6,300 VA
Step 2: 6,300 VA/120V = 52.5A
Step 3: 52.5A/15A = 4 circuits

COPYRIGHT 2005
Mike Holt Enterprises, Inc.

Figure 9–12

Step 3: Determine the number of circuits:
Number of Circuits =
General Lighting Amperes/Circuit Amperes
Number of Circuits = 53A/15A
Number of Circuits = 3.53 or 4 circuits

▶ **Number of 20A Circuits**

How many 20A circuits are required for a 2,100 sq ft dwelling unit?

(a) 2 circuits   (b) 3 circuits
(c) 4 circuits   (d) 5 circuits

• Answer: (b) 3 circuits

Step 1: General Lighting VA =
2,100 sq ft x 3 VA = 6,300 VA

Step 2: General Lighting Amperes:
I = VA/E
I = 6,300 VA/120V
I = 52.5A

Step 3: Determine the number of circuits:
Number of Circuits =
General Lighting Amperes/Circuit Amperes
Number of Circuits = 53A/20A
Number of Circuits = 2.6 or 3 circuits

PART B—STANDARD METHOD— FEEDER/SERVICE LOAD CALCULATIONS

9.8 Dwelling Unit Feeder/Service Load Calculations (Article 220, Part III)

The following steps can be used to determine the feeder or service size for a dwelling unit using the standard method contained in Article 220, Part III:

Step 1: General Lighting and Receptacles, Small-Appliance, and Laundry Circuits [Table 220.42]

The *NEC* recognizes that the general lighting and receptacle, small-appliance, and laundry circuits will not all be on, or loaded, at the same time and permits a demand factor to be applied to the total connected load [220.52]. To determine the feeder calculated load for these loads, use the following steps:

Step a: Total Connected Load. Determine the total connected load for: (1) general lighting and receptacles (3 VA per

sq ft), (2) two small-appliance circuits each at 1,500 VA, and (3) one laundry circuit at 1,500 VA.

Step b: Demand Factor. Apply the Table 220.42 demand factors to the total connected load.

Step c: First 3,000 VA at 100% demand. Remaining VA at 35% demand.

Step 2: Air-Conditioning versus Heat

Because the air-conditioning and heating loads are not on at the same time, it is permissible to omit the smaller of the two loads [220.60]. The air-conditioning load is calculated at 100% and the fixed electric heating load is calculated at 100% [220.51].

Step 3: Appliances [220.53]

A 75% demand factor is permitted to be applied when four or more appliances are fastened in place, such as a dishwasher, waste disposal, trash compactor, water heater, etc., and are on the same feeder. This does not apply to space-heating equipment [220.51], clothes dryers [220.54], cooking appliances [220.55], or air-conditioning equipment.

Step 4: Clothes Dryer [220.54]

The feeder or service load for electric clothes dryers located in a dwelling unit must not be less than 5,000W or the nameplate rating if greater than 5,000W. A feeder or service dryer load is not required if the dwelling unit does not contain an electric dryer!

Step 5: Cooking Equipment [220.55]

Household cooking appliances rated over 1 3/4 kVA can have the feeder and service calculated according to the demand factors of Table 220.55 including Notes 1, 2, and 3.

Step 6: Feeder and Service Conductor Size

Step a: 400 Amperes and Less. For 3-wire, 120/240V, single-phase systems, the ungrounded and grounded neutral conductor for feeders or services can be sized using Table 310.15(B)(6) for individual dwellings. Use Table 310.16 for all other systems. The grounded neutral conductor is sized to the maximum unbalanced load using Table 310.16 [220.61].

Step b: Over 400 Amperes. The ungrounded and grounded neutral conductors are sized according to Table 310.16.

9.9 Dwelling Unit Feeder/Service Calculations Examples

Step 1: General Lighting and Receptacle, Small Appliance, and Laundry Demand [Table 220.42]

The demand factors in Table 220.42 apply to the 3 VA per sq ft for general-lighting and general-use receptacles [Table 220.12], small-appliance circuits [220.52(A)], and laundry circuit [220.52(B)].

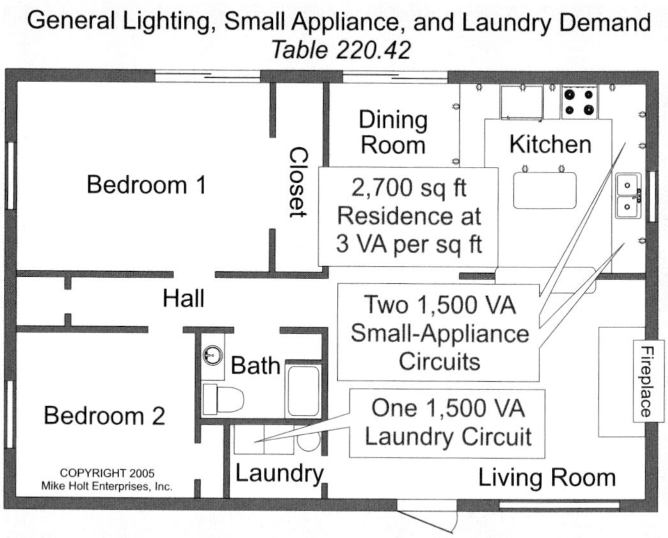

**General Lighting, Small Appliance, and Laundry Demand
Table 220.42**

Bedroom 1

Closet

Dining Room

Kitchen

2,700 sq ft Residence at 3 VA per sq ft

Hall

Two 1,500 VA Small-Appliance Circuits

Bath

Bedroom 2

One 1,500 VA Laundry Circuit

COPYRIGHT 2005
Mike Holt Enterprises, Inc.

Laundry

Fireplace

Living Room

Figure 9–13

▶ **General Lighting and Receptacle Example 1**

What is the general lighting and receptacle, small appliance, and laundry feeder/service calculated load for a 2,700 sq ft dwelling unit? Figure 9–13

    (a) 8,100 VA   (b) 12,600 VA   (c) 2,700 VA   (d) 6,360 VA

• Answer: (d) 6,360 VA

General Lighting/Receptacles (2,700 sq ft x 3 VA) [220.12]	8,100 VA		
Small-Appliance Circuits (1,500 VA x 2)	3,000 VA		
Laundry Circuit (1,500 VA x 1)	+ 1,500 VA		
Total Connected Load	12,600 VA		
First 3,000 VA at 100% [Table 220.42]	−3,000 VA	x 1.00 =	3,000 VA
Remainder at 35%	9,600 VA	x 0.35 =	+ 3,360 VA
Calculated Load			6,360 VA

▶ **General Lighting and Receptacle Example 2**

What is the general lighting and receptacle, small appliance, and laundry feeder/service calculated load for a 6,540 sq ft dwelling unit?

    (a) 8,100 VA   (b) 12,600 VA   (c) 2,700 VA   (d) 10,392 VA

• Answer: (d) 10,392 VA

General Lighting/Receptacles (6,540 sq ft x 3 VA) [220.12]	19,620 VA		
Small-Appliance Circuits (1,500 VA x 2)	3,000 VA		
Laundry Circuit (1,500 VA x 1)	+ 1,500 VA		
Total Connected Load	24,120 VA		
First 3,000 VA at 100% [Table220.42]	−3,000 VA	x 1.00 =	3,000 VA
Remainder at 35%	21,120 VA	x 0.35 =	+ 7,392 VA
Calculated Load			10,392 VA

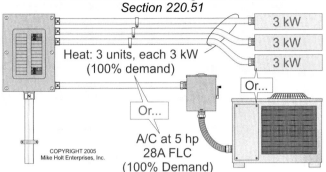

Heat Versus Air-Conditioning - Service Loads
Section 220.51

3 kW

3 kW

3 kW

Heat: 3 units, each 3 kW
(100% demand)

Or...

Or...

A/C at 5 hp
28A FLC
(100% Demand)

COPYRIGHT 2005
Mike Holt Enterprises, Inc.

Determine the service or feeder demand of heat and A/C.

Heat and A/C are not used at the same time,
see 220.60. Omit smaller.

A/C at 100% = 230V x 28A = 6,440 VA (omit A/C)
Heat at 100% = 3,000 VA x 3 units = 9,000W

Figure 9–14

Step 2: Air-Conditioning versus Heat [220.51]

Compare the A/C load at 100% against the heating load at 100% and omit the smaller of the two loads [220.60].

▶ **Air-Conditioning versus Heat Example 1**

What is the feeder/service calculated load for a 5 hp, 230V, A/C unit, versus three 3 kVA baseboard heaters? Figure 9–14

(a) 6,400 VA (b) 3,000W
(c) 8,050 VA (d) 9,000W

• Answer: (d) 9,000W

Omit smaller of A/C and heat [220.60]
A/C: 5 hp 230V; FLC = 28A [Table 430.248]

VA = V x A
VA = 230V x 28A
VA = 6,440 VA (omit)

Heat [220.51]: 3,000 VA x 3 units = 9,000 VA (use heat) [220.60]

▶ **Air-Conditioning versus Heat Example 2**

What is the feeder/service calculated load for a 5 hp 230V A/C unit and a 5 kVA electric space heater?

(a) 5,000 VA (b) 3,910 VA
(c) 6,440 VA (d) 10,350 VA

• Answer: (c) 6,440 VA

Omit smaller of A/C and heat [220.60]

A/C: 5 hp 230V; FLC = 28A [Table 430.248]

VA = V x A
VA = 230V x 28A
VA = 6,440 VA (use A/C) [220.61]

Heat [220.51]: 5,000 VA (omit)

Step 3: Appliance Calculated Load [220.53]

Add the nameplate ratings of all appliances fastened in place. If there are four or more appliances apply a 75 percent demand factor to determine the calculated load.

> **AUTHOR'S COMMENT:** This demand factor does not apply to motors [220.50], space-heating equipment [220.51], clothes dryers [220.54], electric ranges [220.55], or air-conditioning equipment.

▶ **Appliance Example 1**

What is the feeder/service calculated load for a waste disposal (940 VA), a dishwasher (1,250 VA), and a water heater (4,500 VA)?

(a) 5,018 VA (b) 6,690 VA
(c) 8,363 VA (d) 6,272 VA

• Answer: (b) 6,690 VA

Waste Disposal	940 VA
Dishwasher	1,250 VA
Water Heater	+ 4,500 VA
Calculated Load	6,690 VA

▶ **Appliance Example 2**

What is the feeder/service calculated load for a waste disposal (940 VA), a dishwasher (1,250 VA), a trash compactor (1,100 VA), and a water heater (4,500 VA)? Figure 9–15

(a) 7,790 VA (b) 5,843 VA
(c) 7,303 VA (d) 9,738 VA

• Answer: (b) 5,843 VA

Waste Disposal	940 VA
Dishwasher	1,250 VA
Trash Compactor	1,100 VA
Water Heater	+ 4,500 VA
Connected Load	7,790 VA

Calculated Load =
Connected Load x Demand Factor [220.53]
Calculated Load = 7,790 VA x 0.75
Calculated Load = 5,843 VA

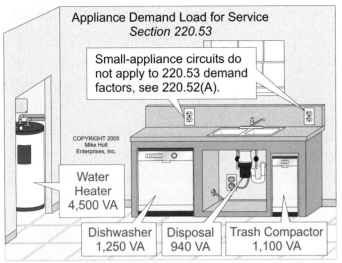

Determine the appliance calculated load.

Waste Disposer   940 VA
Dishwasher   1,250 VA
Trash Compactor   1,100 VA
Water Heater   + 4,500 VA
Total Connected   7,790 VA x 0.75 = 5,843 VA
                        Calculated Load.

Figure 9–15

Step 4: Dryer Calculated Load [220.54]

The minimum calculated load for a household electric dryer is 5,000 VA or use the nameplate rating if higher.

▶ **Dryer Example 1**

What is the feeder/service calculated load for a 4 kVA dryer?
Figure 9–16

   (a) 4,000 VA   (b) 3,000 VA
   (c) 5,000 VA   (d) 5,500 VA

   • Answer: (c) 5,000 VA
    The dryer load must not be less than 5,000 VA.

▶ **Dryer Example 2**

What is the feeder/service calculated load for a 5.5 kVA dryer?

   (a) 4,000 VA   (b) 3,000 VA
   (c) 5,000 VA   (d) 5,500 VA

   • Answer: (d) 5,500 VA
    The dryer load must not be less than the nameplate rating if greater than 5,000 VA.

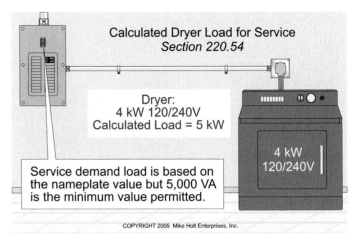

Figure 9–16

Step 5: Cooking Equipment Calculated Load [220.55]

When using Table 220.55, note the following:

   Column A applies to cooking equipment rated over 1 3/4 kVA but less than 3 1/2 kVA.

   Column B applies to cooking equipment rated 3 1/2 to 8 3/4 kVA.

   Column C applies to over 8 3/4 kVA.

These columns are used with Notes 1, 2, and 3 for determining feeder/service calculated loads.

▶ **Note 3—Over 1 3/4 and Less Than 3 1/2 kVA—Column A**

What is the feeder/service calculated load for two 3 kVA cooking appliances in a dwelling unit?

   (a) 3 kVA   (b) 4.8 kVA   (c) 4.5 kVA   (d) 3.9 kVA

   • Answer: (c) 4.5 kVA
    Feeder/Service Connected Load = 3 kVA x 2 units
    Feeder/Service Calculated Load = 6 kVA x 0.75
    Feeder/Service Calculated Load = 4.5 kVA

▶ **Note 3—Not over 8 3/4 —Column B**

What is the feeder/service calculated load for one 6 kVA cooking appliance in a dwelling unit?

   (a) 6 kVA   (b) 4.8 kVA   (c) 4.5 kVA   (d) 3.9 kVA

   • Answer: (b) 4.8 kVA
    Feeder/Service Calculated Load = 6 kVA x 0.80
    Feeder/Service Calculated Load = 4.8 kVA

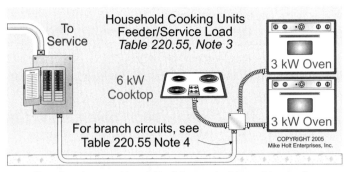

Service demand load for 3 household cooking units.

Table 220.55 Column A applies to the 3 kW ovens.
Table 220.55 Column B applies to the 6 kW cooktop.

Column A demand: (3 kW x 2 units) x 0.75 demand = 4.5 kW
Column B demand: 6 kW x 0.8 demand = <u>4.8 kW</u>
Total Service/Feeder Calculated Load   9.3 kW

Figure 9–17

▶ **Note 3—Columns A and B**

What is the feeder/service calculated load for two 3 kVA ovens and one 6 kVA cooktop in a dwelling unit? **Figure 9–17**

(a) 6 kVA   (b) 4.8 kVA   (c) 4.5 kVA   (d) 9.3 kVA

• Answer: (d) 9.3 kVA

Column A Calculated: (3 kVA x 2) x 0.75   4.5 kVA
Column B Calculated: 6 kVA x 0.80   <u>4.8 kVA</u>
Total Calculated   9.3 kVA

▶ **Column C—Not over 12 kVA**

What is the feeder/service calculated load for an 11.5 kVA range in a dwelling unit?

(a) 11.5 kVA   (b) 8 kVA
(c) 9.2 kVA   (d) 6 kVA

• Answer: (b) 8 kVA
   Table 220.55, Column C: 8 kVA

▶ **Over 12 kVA—Note 1**

What is the feeder/service calculated load for a 13.6 kVA range in a dwelling unit?

(a) 8.8 kVA   (b) 8 kVA   (c) 9.2 kVA   (d) 6 kVA

• Answer: (a) 8.8 kVA

Step a: 13.6 kVA exceeds 12 kVA by one kVA and one major fraction of a kVA (total of 2 kVA). The Column C value (8 kVA) must be increased 5% for each kVA or major fraction of a kVA (0.50 kVA

or larger) over 12 kVA [Table 220.55, Note 1]. 2 x 5% = 10% increase.

Step b: 8 kVA x 1.1 = 8.8 kVA

Step 6: Service Conductor Size [Table 310.15(B)(6)]

Dwelling Unit Feeder/Service Conductors. For individual dwelling units of one-family, two-family, and multifamily dwellings, Table 310.15(B)(6) can be used to size 3-wire single-phase 120/240V service or feeder conductors (including neutral conductors) that serve as the main power feeder. Feeder conductors are not required to have an ampacity rating greater than the service conductors [215.2(A)(3)].

AUTHOR'S COMMENT: Table 310.15(B)(6) permits a smaller feeder/service conductor size than listed in Table 310.16 for the same calculated load, but this reduced size conductor is only permitted for a 120/240V, 3-wire supplied dwelling unit up to 400A.

Grounded Neutral Conductor Sizing. Table 310.15(B)(6) can be used to size the grounded neutral conductor of a 3-wire single-phase 120/240V service or feeder that serves as the main power feeder, based on the feeder calculated load in accordance with 220.61.

AUTHOR'S COMMENT: Because the grounded neutral service conductor is required to serve as the effective ground-fault current path, it must be sized so that it can safely carry the maximum fault current likely to be imposed on it [110.10 and 250.4(A)(5)]. This is accomplished by sizing the grounded neutral conductor in accordance with Table 250.66, based on the total area of the largest ungrounded conductor [250.24(C)(1)].

▶ **Service Conductor Example 1**

What size service conductors (120/240V, single-phase) are required when the calculated load for a dwelling unit equals 195A and the maximum unbalanced neutral load is 100A? **Figure 9–18**

(a) 1/0 AWG and 6 AWG   (b) 2/0 AWG and 4 AWG
(c) 3/0 AWG and 2 AWG   (d) 4/0 AWG and 1 AWG

• Answer: (b) 2/0 AWG and 4 AWG

Service Conductor: 2/0 AWG rated 200A [Table 310.15(B)(6)]

Grounded Neutral Conductor: 4 AWG is rated 100A in accordance with Table 310.15(B)(6). In addition, 250.24(C) requires the grounded neutral conductor to be sized no smaller than 4 AWG based on 2/0 AWG service conductors in accordance with Table 250.66.

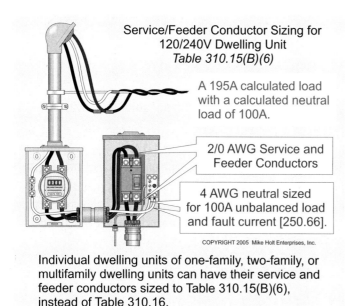

Service/Feeder Conductor Sizing for
120/240V Dwelling Unit
Table 310.15(B)(6)

A 195A calculated load with a calculated neutral load of 100A.

2/0 AWG Service and Feeder Conductors

4 AWG neutral sized for 100A unbalanced load and fault current [250.66].

COPYRIGHT 2005 Mike Holt Enterprises, Inc.

Individual dwelling units of one-family, two-family, or multifamily dwelling units can have their service and feeder conductors sized to Table 310.15(B)(6), instead of Table 310.16.

Figure 9–18

Table 310.15(B)(6) doesn't apply to 3-wire single-phase 120/208V systems, because the grounded neutral conductor in these systems carries neutral current even when the load on the phases is balanced [310.15(B)(4)(b)]. For more information on this topic, see 220.61(C)(1) in the *NEC*. Figure 9–19

AUTHOR'S COMMENT: 120/208V single-phase feeders from a 120/208V, three-phase service, are sometimes used for a single-family dwelling unit in a multifamily building.

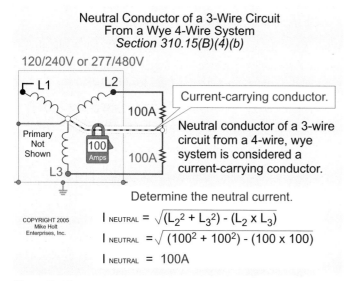

Neutral Conductor of a 3-Wire Circuit
From a Wye 4-Wire System
Section 310.15(B)(4)(b)

120/240V or 277/480V

L1   L2

Current-carrying conductor.

100A

Primary
Not
Shown

100
Amps

100A

Neutral conductor of a 3-wire circuit from a 4-wire, wye system is considered a current-carrying conductor.

L3

Determine the neutral current.

COPYRIGHT 2005
Mike Holt
Enterprises, Inc.

$$I_{NEUTRAL} = \sqrt{(L_2{}^2 + L_3{}^2) - (L_2 \times L_3)}$$
$$I_{NEUTRAL} = \sqrt{(100^2 + 100^2) - (100 \times 100)}$$
$$I_{NEUTRAL} = 100A$$

Figure 9–19

▶ **Service Conductor Example 2**

What size service conductors (120/208V, single-phase from a 120/208V, three-phase system) are required when the calculated load for a dwelling unit equals 195A and the maximum unbalanced neutral load is 100A?

(a) 1/0 AWG and 6 AWG   (b) 2/0 AWG and 4 AWG
(c) 3/0 AWG and 2 AWG   (d) 4/0 AWG and 1 AWG

• Answer: (c) 3/0 AWG and 2 AWG

Service Conductor: 3/0 AWG rated 200A [Table 310.16]

Grounded Neutral Conductor: 3 AWG is rated 100A in accordance with Table 310.16, but 250.24(C) requires the grounded neutral conductor to be sized no smaller than 2 AWG based on 3/0 AWG service conductors in accordance with Table 250.66.

PART C—OPTIONAL METHOD—FEEDER/SERVICE LOAD CALCULATIONS

9.10 Dwelling Unit Optional Feeder/Service Calculations [220.82]

Instead of sizing the dwelling unit feeder and/or service phase conductors according to the standard method (Article 220, Part III), an optional method (Article 220, Part IV) can be used [220.82]. Section 220.82 limits the use of this optional method to dwelling units served by a single 120/240V or 120/208V three-wire service, or to feeder conductors that have an ampacity of 100A or larger. The following steps can be used to determine the load:

Step 1: 220.82(B) General Loads

The calculated load must not be less than 100% for the first 10 kVA, plus 40% of the remainder of the following loads:

(1) General Lighting and Receptacles: 3 VA per sq ft

(2) Small-Appliance and Laundry Branch Circuits: 1,500 VA for each 20A small-appliance and laundry branch circuit.

(3) Appliances: The nameplate VA rating of all appliances and motors that are fastened in place (permanently connected) or located on a specific circuit.

Note: Be sure to use the range and dryer at their nameplate ratings!

Step 2: 220.82(C) Heating and Air-Conditioning Load

Include the largest of the following:

(1) 100 percent of the nameplate rating of the air-conditioning equipment.

(2) Heat Pump without Supplemental Heating: 100 percent

(3) Thermal Storage Heating: 100 percent

> **AUTHOR'S COMMENT:** Thermal storage heating is the process of heating bricks or water at night when the electric rates are lower. Then during the day, the building uses the thermally stored heat.

(4) 100 percent of the nameplate rating(s) of the heat pump compressor and 65 percent of the supplemental electric heating for central electric space-heating systems. If the heat pump compressor is prevented from operating at the same time as the supplementary heat, it can be omitted in the calculation.

(5) Space Heating (three or fewer units): 65 percent

(6) Space Heating (four or more units): 40 percent

Step 3: Size Service/Feeder Conductors [310.15(B)(6)]

400 Amperes and Less. The ungrounded conductors feeding individual dwelling units are permitted to be sized to Table 310.15(B)(6) for 120/240V, single-phase systems up to 400A. The grounded neutral conductor must be sized to carry the unbalanced load according to Table 310.15(B)(6).

Over 400 Amperes. The ungrounded and grounded neutral conductors are sized according to Table 310.16.

9.11 Dwelling Unit Optional Calculation Examples

▶ **Optional Load Calculation Example 1**

What size service conductor is required for a 1,500 sq ft dwelling unit containing the following loads?

Dishwasher	1,200 VA
Water Heater	4,500 VA
Disposal	900 VA
Dryer	4,000 VA
Cooktop	6,000 VA
Two Ovens (each)	3,000 VA
A/C	5 hp, 230V
Electric Heating (one control unit)	10 kVA

(a) 6 AWG   (b) 4 AWG (c) 3 AWG (d) 2 AWG

• Answer: (c) 3 AWG

Step 1: General Loads [220.82(B)]

General Lighting	
(1,500 sq ft x 3 VA)	4,500 VA
Small-Appliance Circuits	
(1,500 VA x 2 circuits)	3,000 VA
Laundry Circuit	1,500 VA
Appliances (nameplate)	
Dishwasher	1,200 VA
Water Heater	4,500 VA
Disposal	900 VA
Dryer	4,000 VA
Cooktop	6,000 VA
Ovens	
(3,000 VA x 2 units)	+ 6,000 VA
Connected Load	31,600 VA
First 10,000 at 100%	- 10,000 VA x 1.00 = 10,000 VA
Remainder at 40%	21,600 VA x 0.40 = + 8,640 VA
Calculated Load	18,640 VA

Step 2: Air-Conditioning versus Heat [220.82(C)]

Air-conditioning at 100% [220.82(C)(1)] versus electric space-heating at 65% [220.82(C)(5)]

Air Conditioner [Table 430.248]: 5 hp, 230V FLC = 28A [table 430.248]

230V x 28A = 6,440 VA (omit)

Electric Space Heat: 10,000 VA x 0.65 = 6,500 VA

Step 3: Service/Feeder Conductors [310.15(B)(6)]

Calculated General Loads (Step 1)	18,640 VA
Heat Calculated Load (Step 2)	+ 6,500 VA
Total Calculated Load	25,140 VA

$$I = VA/E$$
$$I = 25,140 \text{ VA}/240V$$
$$I = 105A$$

Note: The feeder/service ungrounded conductor is sized to 110A, 3 AWG [310.15(B)(6)].

▶ **Optional Load Calculation Example 2**

What size feeder/service conductor is required for a 2,330 sq ft dwelling unit that also has a 200 sq ft open porch and a 300 sq ft carport? The following loads are included in this dwelling unit:

Dishwasher	1.5 kVA
Waste Disposal	1 kVA
Trash Compactor	1.5 kVA
Water Heater	6 kVA
Range	14 kVA
Dryer	4.5 kVA
A/C (230V)	5 hp
Electric Heat (four, each)	2.5 kVA

(a) 5 AWG   (b) 4 AWG   (c) 3 AWG   (d) 2 AWG

• Answer: (d) 2 AWG

Step 1: General Loads [220.82(B)]

General Lighting	
(2,330 sq ft x 3 VA)	6,990 VA
Small-Appliance Circuits	
(1,500 VA x 2 circuits)	3,000 VA
Laundry Circuit	1,500 VA
Appliances (nameplate)	
Dishwasher	1,500 VA
Disposal	1,000 VA
Trash Compactor	1,500 VA
Water Heater	6,000 VA
Range	14,000 VA
Dryer (nameplate)	+ 4,500 VA
General Connected Load	39,990 VA
First 10,000 at 100%	− 10,000 VA x 1.00 = 10,000 VA
Remainder at 40%	29,990 VA x 0.40 = +11,996 VA
Calculated Load	21,996 VA

Step 2: Air-Conditioning versus Heat [220.82(C)]

Air-Conditioning at 100% [220.82(C)(1)] versus electric space heating at 40% for 4 or more units [220.82(C)(6)]

Air-Conditioner, 5 hp, 230V FLC = 28A [Table 430.248]:

$$VA = V \times A$$
$$VA = 230V \times 28A$$
$$VA = 6,440 \ VA$$

Electric Space Heat:
Four units x 2,500 VA = 10,000 VA
10,000 VA x 0.40 = 4,000 VA, (omit) [220.60]

Step 3: Service/Feeder Conductors [310.15(B)(6)]

General Loads (Step 1)	21,996 VA
A/C (Step 2)	+ 6,440 VA
Total Calculated Load	28,436 VA

$$I = VA/E$$
$$I = 28,436 \ VA/240V$$
$$I = 118.5A$$

125A Feeder/Service, 2 AWG ungrounded conductors [Table 310.15(B)(6)].

9.12 Neutral Calculations——General [220.61]

The feeder/service neutral load is the maximum unbalanced calculated load between the grounded neutral conductor and any ungrounded conductor as determined by Article 220, Part III.

Because phase-to-phase loads are not connected to the grounded neutral conductor, they are not considered when sizing the grounded neutral conductor.

▶ **Neutral not Over 200A**

What size 120/240V, single-phase ungrounded and grounded neutral conductors are required for a one-family dwelling unit with a calculated load of 375A, of which 175A consist of 240V loads? **Figure 9–20**

(a) Two–400 kcmil and 1–350 kcmil
(b) Two–350 kcmil and 1–350 kcmil
(c) Two–500 kcmil and 1–500 kcmil
(d) Two–400 kcmil and 1–2/0 AWG

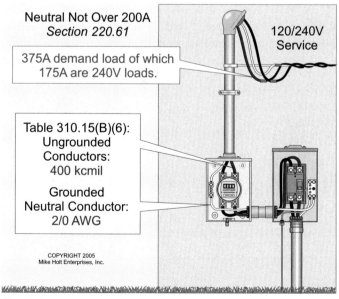

Neutral Not Over 200A
Section 220.61

375A demand load of which 175A are 240V loads.

Table 310.15(B)(6): Ungrounded Conductors: 400 kcmil

Grounded Neutral Conductor: 2/0 AWG

120/240V Service

COPYRIGHT 2005
Mike Holt Enterprises, Inc.

Figure 9–20

• Answer: (d) Two—400 kcmil and 1—2/0 AWG

The ungrounded conductor is sized at 375A (400 kcmil) according to Table 310.15(B)(6).

375A–175A (240V loads) =
200A maximum unbalanced load

The grounded neutral conductor must be sized to carry the maximum unbalanced load of 200A (120V loads only).

Grounded Neutral Conductor: 2/0 AWG is rated 200A in accordance with Table 310.15(B)(6). In addition, 250.24(C) requires the grounded neutral conductor to be sized no smaller than 2/0 AWG based on the 4/0 AWG service conductors in accordance with Table 250.66.

Cooking Appliance Feeder/Service Neutral Load [220.61(B)(1)]

The feeder/service cooking appliance neutral load for household cooking appliances, such as electric ranges, wall-mounted ovens, or counter-mounted cooking units is calculated at 70% of the calculated load as determined by 220.55.

▶ **Range Neutral**

What is the neutral load (in amperes) for one 14 kVA range?

(a) 16A   (b) 22.9A   (c) 25.7A   (d) 36.7A

• Answer: (c) 25.7A

Step 1:   Since the range exceeds 12 kVA, we must comply with Note 1 of Table 220.55. The first step is to determine the demand load as listed in Column C of Table 220.55 for one unit = 8 kVA.

Step 2:   We must increase the Column C value (8 kVA) by 5% for each kVA that the range exceeds 12 kVA [Table 220.55 Note 1], 14 kVA – 12 kVA = 2 kVA. This results in an increase of the Column C value (8 kVA) by 10%.

8 kVA x 1.1 = 8.8 kVA

I = VA/E
I = 8,800VA/240V
I = 36.7A

Neutral load at 70%: 36.7A x 0.70 = 25.7A

Dryer Feeder/Service Neutral Load [220.61(B)(1)]

The feeder and service dryer neutral load for electric clothes dryers is calculated at 70% of the calculated load as determined by 220.54.

▶ **Dryer Over 5 kVA**

What is the feeder/service neutral load for one 5.5 kVA dryer?

(a) 3.85 kVA   (b) 5.5 kVA
(c) 4.6 kVA   (d) none of these

• Answer: (a) 3.85 kVA
Feeder/Service Calculated Load = 5.5 kVA x 0.70
Feeder/Service Calculated Load = 3.85 kVA

See the *NEC* Annex D Examples D1(a) and D1(b) for more neutral calculations.

Unit 9 Conclusion

The branch circuit, feeder, and service calculations in Unit 9 required the understanding and application of many different demand factors. Since not all loads are in use simultaneously in a home, the service to a home is allowed to be sized not on the maximum instantaneous usage that could be possible, but on a percentage of that, based on what we call demand factors.

The *Code* doesn't explain how demand factors were derived, and it's not essential that you understand their derivation in order to apply them correctly. Be sure to work on some practice calculations so you understand how to apply the various demand factors to a dwelling unit calculation. It is important to have a good working knowledge of this before going on to the following unit on multifamily dwellings, which will build on the concepts developed in Unit 9.

The standard calculation and the optional calculation methods were both discussed in this unit. These are two distinctly different calculation methods, so be careful not to intermix them. Since you are allowed to use either of these, the question is naturally which method is better to use? On an exam, it is most likely that you will be told which method to use on a specific question, but if an exam question does not specify a method, use the standard calculation. The optional method is usually a lot faster and easier to apply, so it has a natural advantage for daily use on the job.

(• Indicates that 75% or fewer of those who took this exam answered the question correctly.)

PART A—GENERAL REQUIREMENTS

9.2 Voltages [220.5(A)]

1. Unless other voltages are specified, feeder and service loads must be computed at a nominal system voltage of _____.

    (a) 120   (b) 120/240   (c) 120/208V   (d) any of these

9.3 Fraction of an Ampere [220.5(B)]

2. Where a calculation results in a fraction of an ampere that is _____ or less, that fraction is permitted to be dropped.

    (a) 0.05   (b) 0.50   (c) 0.49   (d) 0.51

9.4 Small-Appliance Circuits [210.11(C)(1)]

3. A minimum of _____ 20A small-appliance branch circuit(s) is/are required for receptacle outlets in the kitchen, dining room, breakfast room, pantry, and similar areas.

    (a) one   (b) two   (c) three   (d) none of these

4. When sizing the feeder or service, each dwelling unit must have a minimum feeder load of _____ for the two small-appliance branch circuits.

    (a) 1,500 VA   (b) 2,000 VA   (c) 3,000 VA   (d) 4,500 VA

9.5 Cooking Equipment—Branch Circuit [Table 220.55, Note 4]

5. What is the branch-circuit calculated load (in amperes) for one 11 kW range?

    (a) 21A   (b) 27A   (c) 38A   (d) 33A

6. What is the branch-circuit calculated load (in amperes) for one 13.5 kW range?

    (a) 33A   (b) 37A   (c) 50A   (d) 58A

Wall-Mounted Oven and/or Counter-Mounted Cooking Unit

7. •What is the branch-circuit load (in amperes) for one 6 kW wall-mounted oven rated 240V, single-phase?

    (a) 15A   (b) 25A   (c) 30A   (d) 40A

8. •What is the branch-circuit load (in amperes) for one 4.8 kW counter-mounted cooking unit rated 240V, single-phase?

    (a) 15A   (b) 20A   (c) 25A   (d) 30A

9. What is the branch-circuit load (in amperes) for one 6 kW counter-mounted cooking unit and one 3 kW wall-mounted oven rated 240V, single-phase?

    (a) 25A   (b) 38A   (c) 33A   (d) 42A

10. What is the branch-circuit load (in amperes) for one 6 kW counter-mounted cooking unit and two 4 kW wall-mounted ovens rated 240V, single-phase?

(a) 22A   (b) 27A   (c) 33A   (d) 37A

9.6 Laundry Receptacle(s) Circuit [210.11(C)(2)]

11. The *NEC* does not require a separate circuit for the washing machine, but does require a separate circuit for the laundry room receptacle or receptacles, of which one can be for the washing machine.

(a) True   (b) False

12. Each dwelling unit must have a feeder load consisting of _____ for the 20A laundry circuit.

(a) 1,500 VA   (b) 2,000 VA   (c) 3,000 VA   (d) 4,500 VA

9.7 Lighting and Receptacles

13. The *NEC* requires a minimum of 3 VA for each sq ft of living space for the required general lighting and general-use receptacles for dwelling units. The dimensions for determining the area are computed from the outside of the building and do not include _____.

(a) open porches   (b) garages
(c) spaces not adaptable for future use   (d) all of these

14. The 3 VA for each sq ft of living space for general lighting includes receptacles rated 20A, but not the small-appliance or laundry circuit receptacles.

(a) True   (b) False

15. What is the general lighting load and general-use receptacle load for a 2,100 sq ft home that has 14 extra convenience receptacles and nine extra recessed luminaires rated at 100W each?

(a) 2,100 VA   (b) 4,200 VA   (c) 6,300 VA   (d) 8,400 VA

Number of Circuits Required [Annex D, Example No. D1(a)]

16. The number of branch circuits required for general lighting and receptacles must be determined from the general lighting load and the rating of the circuits.

(a) True   (b) False

17. How many 15A general lighting circuits are required for a 2,340 sq ft home?

(a) 2 circuits   (b) 3 circuits   (c) 4 circuits   (d) 5 circuits

18. How many 20A general lighting circuits are required for a 2,100 sq ft home?

(a) 2 circuits   (b) 3 circuits   (c) 4 circuits   (d) 5 circuits

19. How many 20A circuits are required for the general lighting and receptacles for a 1,500 sq ft dwelling unit?

(a) 2 circuits   (b) 3 circuits   (c) 4 circuits   (d) 5 circuits

PART B—STANDARD METHOD—FEEDER/SERVICE LOAD CALCULATIONS

9.8 Dwelling Unit Feeder/Service Load Calculations (Article 220, Part III)

20. The *NEC* recognizes that the general lighting and receptacles, and small-appliance and laundry circuits will not all be on or loaded at the same time and permits a(n) _____ to be applied to the total of these loads.

    (a) demand factor   (b) adjustment factor   (c) correction factor   (d) correction

21. Because the air-conditioning and heating loads are not on at the same time (simultaneously), it is permissible to omit the smaller of the two loads when determining the air-conditioning versus heat calculated load.

    (a) True   (b) False

22. A load demand factor of 75 percent is permitted for _____ or more appliances fastened in place such as dishwashers, waste disposals, trash compactors, water heaters, etc.

    (a) one   (b) two   (c) three   (d) four

23. The feeder or service calculated load for electric clothes dryers located in dwelling units must not be less than _____.

    (a) 5,000W   (b) the nameplate rating   (c) a or b   (d) the greater of a or b

24. •A feeder or service dryer load is required even if the dwelling unit does not contain an electric dryer.

    (a) True   (b) False

25. Household cooking appliances rated 1 3/4 kW can have the feeder and service loads calculated according to the demand factors of Table 220.55.

    (a) True   (b) False

26. Dwelling unit feeder and service ungrounded (hot) conductors are sized according to Table 310.15(B)(6) for _____.

    (a) 3-wire, single-phase, 120/240V systems up to 400A   (b) 3-wire, single-phase, 120/208V systems up to 400A
    (c) 4-wire, single-phase, 120/240V systems up to 400A   (d) none of these

27. What is the general lighting load for a 2,700 sq ft dwelling unit?

    (a) 8,100 VA   (b) 12,600 VA   (c) 2,700 VA   (d) 6,840 VA

28. What is the total connected load for general lighting and receptacles, small-appliance, and laundry circuits for a 6,540 sq ft dwelling unit?

    (a) 8,100 VA   (b) 12,600 VA   (c) 2,700 VA   (d) 24,120 VA

29. What is the feeder or service calculated load for one air conditioner (5 hp, 230 V) and three baseboard heaters (3 kW)?

    (a) 6,400 VA   (b) 3,000 VA   (c) 8,050 VA   (d) 9,000 VA

30. What is the feeder or service calculated load for an air conditioner (5 hp, 230 V) and electric space heater (10 kW)?

    (a) 10,000 VA   (b) 3,910 VA   (c) 6,440 VA   (d) 10,350 VA

31. What is the feeder or service calculated load for a waste disposal (940 VA), dishwasher (1,250 VA), and a water heater (4,500 VA)?

    (a) 5,018 VA   (b) 6,690 VA   (c) 8,363 VA   (d) 6,272 VA

32. •What is the feeder or service calculated load for a waste disposal (940 VA), dishwasher (1,250 VA), water heater (4,500 VA), and a trash compactor (1,100 VA)?

  (a) 7,790 VA   (b) 5,843 VA   (c) 7,303 VA   (d) 9,738 VA

33. What is the feeder or service calculated load for a 4 kW dryer?

  (a) 4 kW   (b) 3 kW   (c) 5 kW   (d) 6 kW

34. What is the feeder or service calculated load for a 5.5 kW dryer?

  (a) 4 kW   (b) 3 kW   (c) 5 kW   (d) 5.5 kW

35. What is the feeder or service calculated load for two 3 kW cooking appliances?

  (a) 3 kW   (b) 4.8 kW   (c) 4.5 kW   (d) 3.9 kW

36. What is the feeder or service calculated load for one 6 kW cooking appliance?

  (a) 6 kW   (b) 4.8 kW   (c) 4.5 kW   (d) 3.9 kW

37. What is the feeder or service calculated load for one 6 kW and two 3 kW cooking appliances?

  (a) 6 kW   (b) 4.8 kW   (c) 4.5 kW   (d) 9.3 kW

38. What is the feeder or service calculated load for an 11.5 kW range?

  (a) 11.5 kW   (b) 8 kW   (c) 9.2 kW   (d) 6 kW

39. What is the feeder or service calculated load for a 13.6 kW range?

  (a) 8.8 kW   (b) 8 kW   (c) 9.2 kW   (d) 6 kW

40. What size 120/240V, single-phase service or feeder THHN copper conductors are required for a dwelling unit that has a 190A service calculated load?

  (a) 1/0 AWG   (b) 2/0 AWG   (c) 3/0 AWG   (d) 4/0 AWG

41. •What is the net computed calculated load for the general lighting, small-appliance, and laundry circuits for a 1,500 sq ft dwelling unit?

  (a) 4,500 VA   (b) 9,000 VA   (c) 5,100 VA   (d) none of these

42. What is the feeder or service calculated load for an air conditioner (3 hp, 230V) with a blower (1/4 hp) and electric space heating (4 kW)?

  (a) 3,910 VA   (b) 4,577 VA   (c) 4,000 VA   (d) none of these

43. What is the feeder or service calculated load for a dwelling unit that has one water heater (4 kW) and one dishwasher (1.5 kW)?

  (a) 4 kW   (b) 5.5 kW   (c) 4.13 kW   (d) none of these

44. What is the calculated load for a 4.5 kW dryer?

  (a) 4.5 kW   (b) 5 kW   (c) 5.5 kW   (d) none of these

45. What is the calculated load for a 14 kW range?

  (a) 8 kW   (b) 8.4 kW   (c) 8.8 kW   (d) 14 kW

46. If the total calculated load is 30 kW for a 120/240V dwelling unit, what is the feeder/service copper conductor size?

    (a) 4 AWG   (b) 3/0 AWG   (c) 2 AWG   (d) 1/0 AWG

47. If a service raceway contains 2 AWG service conductors, what size copper bonding jumper is required for the service raceway?

    (a) 8 AWG   (b) 6 AWG   (c) 4 AWG   (d) 3 AWG

48. If a service contains 2 AWG conductors, what is the minimum size grounding electrode conductor required?

    (a) 8 AWG   (b) 6 AWG   (c) 4 AWG   (d) 3 AWG

PART C—OPTIONAL METHOD—FEEDER/SERVICE LOAD CALCULATIONS

9.10 Dwelling Unit Optional Feeder/Service Calculations [220.82]

49. When sizing the feeder or service conductor according to the optional method we must:

    (a) Determine the total connected load of the general lighting and receptacles, small-appliance and laundry branch circuits, and the nameplate VA rating of all appliances and motors.
    (b) Determine the calculated load by applying the following demand factors to the total connected load: First 10 kVA at 100%, remainder at 40%.
    (c) Determine the air-conditioning versus heat calculated load.
    (d) All of these.

The following information applies to question 50. A 1,500 sq ft dwelling unit contains the following loads:

Dishwasher (1.5 kVA)   Water heater (5 kW)   Waste disposal (1 kVA)   Dryer (5.5 kW)
Cooktop (6 kW)   Two ovens (each 3 kW)   A/C (3 hp, 230V)
Two separately controlled 5 kW space-heating units

50. •Use the optional method of calculation to determine what size aluminum conductors are required for the 120/240V, single-phase service.

    (a) 1 AWG AL   (b) 1/0 AWG AL   (c) 2/0 AWG AL   (d) 3/0 AWG AL

The following information applies to question 51. A dwelling unit has 2,330 sq ft of living space, in addition there is a 900 sq ft of porch, and 400 sq ft of carport (not a garage) with the following loads:

Dishwasher (1.5 kW)   Waste Disposal (1 kVA)   Trash Compactor (1.5 kVA)   Water Heater (6 kW)
Range (14 kW)   Dryer (4.5 kW)   A/C Unit (5 hp 230V)
Baseboard Heat (Four at 2.5 kW each)

51. Use the optional method to determine what size aluminum conductors are required for the 120/240V, single-phase service.

    (a) 1 AWG AL   (b) 1/0 AWG AL   (c) 2/0 AWG AL   (d) 3/0 AWG AL

9.12 Neutral Calculations—General [220.61]

52. The feeder and service neutral load is the maximum unbalanced calculated load between the grounded neutral conductor and any one ungrounded (hot) conductor as determined by Article 220. Since 240V loads cannot be connected to the neutral conductor, 240V loads are not considered for sizing the feeder neutral conductor.

    (a) True   (b) False

53. •What size single-phase, 3-wire feeder is required for a 475A calculated load of which 275A consists of 240V loads? Size the conductors based on 75°C terminals in accordance with 110.14(C)(1)(b).

(a) Two 750 kcmil and one 350 kcmil   (b) Two 500 kcmil and one 350 kcmil
(c) Two 750 kcmil and one 500 kcmil   (d) Two 750 kcmil and one 3/0 AWG

54. The feeder or service neutral load for household cooking appliances, such as electric ranges, wall-mounted ovens, or counter-mounted cooking units, is permitted to be calculated at _____ of the load as determined by 220.55.

(a) 50%   (b) 60%   (c) 70%   (d) 80%

55. What is the dwelling unit service neutral load for one 9 kW range?

(a) 5.6 kW   (b) 6.5 kW   (c) 3.5 kW   (d) 12 kW

56. The service neutral load for household electric clothes dryers is permitted to be calculated at _____ of the load as determined by 220.54.

(a) 50%   (b) 60%   (c) 70%   (d) 80%

57. What is the feeder neutral load for one 6 kW household dryer?

(a) 4.2 kW   (b) 4.7 kW   (c) 5.4 kW   (d) 6.6 kW

Unit 9 Calculation Challenge Questions

(• Indicates that 75% or fewer of those who took this exam answered the question correctly.)

PART A—GENERAL REQUIREMENTS

9.5 Cooking Equipment—Branch Circuit [Table 220.55, Note 4]

1. The branch-circuit calculated load for one 18 kW range is _____.

   (a) 12 kW   (b) 8 kW   (c) 10.4 kW   (d) 18 kW

2. A dwelling unit kitchen has the following appliances: one 9 kW cooktop and one wall-mounted oven rated 5.3 kW. The branch-circuit calculated load for these appliances is _____.

   (a) 14.3 kW   (b) 12 kW   (c) 8.8 kW   (d) 8 kW

PART B—STANDARD METHOD—FEEDER/SERVICE LOAD CALCULATIONS

9.8 Dwelling Unit Feeder/Service Load Calculations (Article 220, Part III)

3. An apartment building contains 20 units, each 840 sq ft. What is the general lighting and general-use receptacle feeder calculated load for each dwelling unit? *Note: Laundry facilities are provided on the premises for all tenants and no laundry circuit is required in each unit [210.52(F) Ex 1].*

   (a) 3,520 VA   (b) 3,882 VA   (c) 4,220 VA   (d) 6,300 VA

4. What is the calculated load for the general lighting, receptacles, small-appliance circuits, and laundry circuits for a 1,800 sq ft dwelling unit?

   (a) 5,400 VA   (b) 7,900 VA   (c) 5,415 VA   (d) 6,600 VA

5. How many 15A, 120V branch circuits are required for general-use receptacles and lighting in a 1,800 sq ft dwelling unit?

   (a) 1 circuit   (b) 2 circuits   (c) 3 circuits   (d) 4 circuits

6. How many 20A, 120V branch circuits are required for general-use receptacles and lighting in a 2,800 sq ft dwelling unit?

   (a) 2 circuits   (b) 6 circuits   (c) 7 circuits   (d) 4 circuits

Appliances [220.53]

7. A dwelling unit contains one of each of the following: washing machine (1.2 kW), water heater (4 kW), dishwasher (1.2 kW), and trash compactor (1.5 kW). The appliance calculated load added to the service is _____.

   (a) 5.9 kW   (b) 6.7 kW   (c) 7.7 kW   (d) 8.8 kW

8. •A dwelling unit contains one of each of the following: water heater (4 kW), dishwasher (1/2 hp), dryer, pool pump (3/4 hp), cooktop (6 kW), oven (6 kW), A/C (4 hp, 230V), and heat (6 kW). What is the appliance calculated load for the dwelling unit?

   (a) 6.7 kW   (b) 4 kW   (c) 9 kW   (d) 11 kW

Clothes Dryer [220.54]

9. A dwelling unit contains a 5.5 kW electric clothes dryer. What is the feeder calculated load for the dryer?

    (a) 3.38 kW   (b) 4.5 kW   (c) 5 kW   (d) 5.5 kW

Cooking Equipment [220.55]

10. The feeder load for twelve 1.75 kW cooktops is _____.

    (a) 21 kW   (b) 10.5 kW   (c) 13.5 kW   (d) 12.5 kW

11. The minimum neutral for a branch circuit to an 8 kW household range is _____. See Article 210.

    (a) 10 AWG   (b) 12 AWG   (c) 8 AWG   (d) 6 AWG

12. What is the maximum dwelling unit feeder or service calculated load for fifteen 8 kW cooking units?

    (a) 38.4 kW   (b) 33 kW   (c) 88 kW   (d) 27 kW

13. What is the feeder calculated load for five 10 kW, five 14 kW, and five 16 kW household ranges?

    (a) 70 kW   (b) 23 kW   (c) 14 kW   (d) 33 kW

14. A dwelling unit has one 6 kW cooktop and one 6 kW oven. What is the minimum feeder calculated load for the cooking appliances?

    (a) 13 kW   (b) 8.8 kW   (c) 7.8 kW   (d) 8.2 kW

15. The maximum feeder calculated load for an 8 kW range is _____.

    (a) 8.5 kW   (b) 8 kW   (c) 6.3 kW   (d) 12 kW

16. The minimum feeder calculated load for five 5 kW ranges, two 4 kW ovens, and four 7 kW cooking units is _____.

    (a) 61 kW   (b) 22 kW   (c) 19.5 kW   (d) 18 kW

17. The minimum feeder calculated load for two 3 kW wall-mounted ovens and one 6 kW cooktop is _____.

    (a) 9.3 kW   (b) 11 kW   (c) 8.4 kW   (d) 9.6 kW

9.9 Dwelling Unit Feeder/Service Calculations Examples

18. •Each unit of a duplex apartment requires a 100A main, the resulting 200A service will require _____ THHN conductors.

    (a) 1/0   (b) 2/0   (c) 3/0   (d) 4

19. After all demand factors have been taken into consideration, the calculated load for a service is a 24,221 VA, 120/240V, single-phase system. The minimum service size is _____.

    (a) 150A   (b) 175A   (c) 125A   (d) 110A

PART C—OPTIONAL METHOD—FEEDER/SERVICE LOAD CALCULATIONS

9.10 Dwelling Unit Optional Feeder/Service Calculations [220.82]

20. After all demand factors have been taken into consideration, the calculated load for a dwelling unit is 21,560 VA. The minimum service size for this residence will be _____ if the optional method of service calculations is used for a 120/240V, single-phase system. Be sure to read 220.82 carefully!

    (a) 90A   (b) 100A   (c) 110A   (d) 125A

21. Using the optional calculations method, determine the calculated load for a 6 kW electric space-heating unit and a 4 kW air-conditioning unit.

    (a) 9,000W   (b) 3,900W   (c) 4,000W   (d) 5,000W

22. The total connected load of a dwelling unit is 25 kVA, not including heat or air-conditioning. If the heat is separately controlled in five rooms (10 kW) and the air-conditioning is 6 kW, then the total service calculated load is _____ if the optional method is used.

    (a) 22 kVA   (b) 29 kVA   (c) 35 kVA   (d) 36 kVA

23. Using the optional method, determine the service for the following loads: 1,200 sq ft first floor, plus 600 sq ft on the second floor, a 200 sq ft open porch, water heater (4 kW), dishwasher (1/2 hp), clothes dryer (4 kW), A/C (5 hp), electric space heating (6 kW), pool pump (3/4 hp), oven (6 kW), and cooktop (6 kW). The service source voltage is 120/240V, single-phase.

    (a) 200A   (b) 175A   (c) 125A   (d) 110A

24. An 1,800 sq ft residence contains the following: a 4 kW water heater, five separately controlled electric space-heat units totaling 10 kW, a 10 kW heat separated in five rooms, one 1.5 kW dishwasher, one 6 kW range, one 4.5 kW dryer, two 3 kW ovens, and one 6 kW air conditioner. The 120/240V, single-phase service for the loads will be _____. The optional method of service calculations is used.

    (a) 175A   (b) 110A   (c) 125A   (d) 150A

25. A dwelling unit has 1,200 sq ft on the first floor, 600 sq ft upstairs (unfinished but adaptable for future use), a 200 sq ft open porch, and the following loads: pool pump (3/4 hp), range (13.9 kW), dishwasher (1.2 kW), water heater (4 kW), dryer (4 kW), A/C (5 hp), and electric space heating (6 kW). Using the optional calculation method, what size feeder/service conductor is required for this 120/240V, single-phase service?

    (a) 100A service with 4 AWG   (b) 110A service with 3 AWG
    (c) 125A service with 2 AWG   (d) 150A service with 1 AWG

(• Indicates that 75% or fewer of those who took this exam answered the question correctly.)

Article 500 Hazardous (Classified) Locations (continued)

1. Hazardous (classified) locations are classified based on the properties of the _____ that may be present, and the likelihood that a flammable or combustible concentration or quantity is present.

   (a) flammable vapors
   (b) flammable gases or liquids
   (c) combustible dusts or fibers
   (d) all of these

2. Class I, Division 1 locations are those in which ignitible concentrations of _____ can exist under normal operating conditions.

   (a) combustible dust
   (b) easily ignitible fibers or flyings
   (c) flammable gases or vapors
   (d) flammable liquids or gases

3. Class I, Division 2 usually includes locations where volatile flammable liquids or flammable gases or vapors are used but that, in the judgment of the authority having jurisdiction, would become hazardous only in case of an accident or of some unusual operating condition.

   (a) True
   (b) False

4. Class II locations are those that are hazardous because of the presence of _____.

   (a) combustible dust
   (b) easily ignitible fibers or flyings
   (c) flammable gases or vapors
   (d) flammable liquids or gases

5. Class III locations are those that are hazardous because of the presence of _____.

   (a) combustible dust
   (b) easily ignitible fibers or flyings
   (c) flammable gases or vapors
   (d) flammable liquids or gases

6. Locations in which easily ignitible combustible fibers are stored or handled other than in the process of manufacturing are designated as _____.

   (a) Class II, Division 2
   (b) Class III, Division 1
   (c) Class III, Division 2
   (d) nonhazardous

7. In Class _____ locations for Groups A, B, C, and D, the classification involves determinations of maximum explosion pressure and maximum safe clearance between parts of a clamped joint in an enclosure .

   (a) I
   (b) II
   (c) III
   (d) all of these

8. Electrical equipment installed in hazardous (classified) locations must be constructed for the class, division, and group. An atmosphere containing _____ is classified as Group C.

   (a) hydrogen
   (b) ethylene
   (c) propylene oxide
   (d) all of these

9. An atmosphere containing carbon black, charcoal, coal, or coke dusts that have been sensitized by other materials so they present an explosive hazard is classified as Group F.

   (a) True
   (b) False

10. For Class _____ locations, the classification of Groups E, F, and G involves the tightness of the joints of assembly and shaft openings to prevent entrance of dust in the dust-ignition proof enclosure, the blanketing effect of layers of dust on the equipment that may cause overheating, and the ignition temperature of the dust.

    (a) I   (b) II   (c) III   (d) all of these

11. Suitability of equipment for a specific purpose, environment, or application may be determined by:

    (a) Equipment listing or labeling.
    (b) Evidence of equipment evaluation from a qualified testing laboratory or inspection agency concerned with product evaluation
    (c) Evidence acceptable to the authority having jurisdiction, such as a manufacturer's self evaluation or an owner's engineering judgment.
    (d) any of these

12. All threaded conduits or fittings referred to in hazardous locations must be threaded with a _____ taper per foot.

    (a) 1/2 in.   (b) 3/4 in.   (c) 1 in.   (d) all of these

13. For listed explosionproof equipment, factory threaded entries must be made up with at least _____ threads fully engaged.

    (a) 5   (b) 4 1/2   (c) 6   (d) no minimum

Article 501 Class I Hazardous (Classified) Locations

A Class I hazardous (classified) location is an area where flammable gases or vapors may be present in quantities sufficient to produce an explosive or ignitible mixture.

14. Article 501 covers the requirements for electrical and electronic equipment and wiring for all voltages in Class I, Divisions 1 and 2 locations where fire or explosion hazards may exist due to _____.

    (a) flammable gases   (b) vapors   (c) flammable liquids   (d) any of these

15. Wiring methods permitted in Class I, Division 1 locations include _____.

    (a) threaded rigid metal or threaded intermediate metal conduit   (b) flexible fittings listed for Class I, Division 1 locations
    (c) boxes approved for Class I, Division 1 locations   (d) all of these

16. When provisions for limited flexibility are required in a Class I, Division 2 location, such as motor terminations, flexible metal conduit with listed fittings may be used.

    (a) True   (b) False

17. Sealing compound is employed with MI cable terminal fittings in Class I locations for the purpose of _____.

    (a) preventing the passage of gas or vapor
    (b) excluding moisture and other fluids from the cable insulation
    (c) limiting a possible explosion
    (d) preventing the escape of powder

18. Each conduit leaving a Class I, Division 1 location requires a seal to be located on either side of the hazardous (classified) location boundary. Unions, couplings, boxes, or fittings are permitted between the seal and the point where the conduit leaves the Division 1 location.

    (a) True   (b) False

19. Where the Class I, Division 1 boundary is beneath the ground, the sealing fitting must be installed _____. Except for listed explosionproof reducers at the conduit seal, there must be no union, coupling, box or fitting between the conduit seal and the point at which the conduit leaves the ground.

    (a) after the conduit leaves the ground
    (b) before the conduit leaves the ground
    (c) within 10 ft of where the conduit leaves the ground
    (d) none of these

20. A sealing fitting is required for each conduit run passing from a Class I, Division 2 location into an unclassified location for the purpose of minimizing the passage of gases. It must be located no more than _____ from the boundary.

    (a) 3 ft   (b) 6 ft   (c) 10 ft   (d) 20 ft

21. No seal is required if a conduit (with no unions, couplings, boxes, or fittings) passes completely through a Class I, Division 2 location if the termination points of the unbroken conduit are in unclassified locations and it has no fittings less than _____ beyond each boundary of the classified location.

    (a) 6 in.   (b) 12 in.   (c) 18 in.   (d) 24 in.

22. The minimum thickness of sealing compound in Class I, Division 1 and 2 locations must not be less than the trade size of the conduit or sealing fitting and, in no case, less than _____

    (a) 1/8 in.   (b) 1/4 in.   (c) 3/8 in.   (d) 5/8 in.

23. When MC-HL cable containing shielded cables and/or twisted-pair cables is installed in a Class I, Division 1 location, the removal of the shielding material or the separation of the twisted pairs is not required, provided the termination is accomplished by a(n) _____ means to minimize the entrance of gases or vapors and to prevent propagation of flame into the cable core.

    (a) approved   (b) listed   (c) acceptable   (d) none of these

24. In Class I, Division 1 and 2 locations where condensed vapors or liquids may collect on or come in contact with the insulation on conductors, the insulation must be of a type _____.

    (a) identified for such use
    (b) with integral drying agents
    (c) listed for contact with water
    (d) enclosed only in liquidtight flexible metal conduit

25. When flexible metal conduit or LFMC is used as permitted in Class I, Division 2 locations, it must be installed with an _____ bonding jumper installed in parallel with the raceway conduit in compliance with 250.102.

    (a) internal   (b) external   (c) a or b   (d) a and b

26. Transformers and capacitors installed in Class I, Division 1 locations containing flammable liquids must be installed in vaults.

    (a) True   (b) False

27. Meters, instruments and relays including kilowatt-hour meters, instrument transformers, resistors, rectifiers, and thermionic tubes in Class I, Division 1 locations must be installed in explosionproof enclosures or purged and pressurized enclosures.

    (a) True   (b) False

28. Switches, circuit breakers, motor controllers, and fuses including pushbuttons, relays, and similar devices in Class I, Division 1 locations must be installed in enclosures, and the enclosure(s) together with the enclosed apparatus must be identified as a complete assembly for use in Class I locations.

    (a) True   (b) False

29. In Class I, Division 2 locations, fused or unfused disconnect and isolating switches for transformers or capacitor banks that are not intended to interrupt current in normal performance are permitted to be installed in general-purpose enclosures.

    (a) True   (b) False

30. Motors, generators, or other rotating electric machinery that are identified for Class I, Division 2 locations are allowed to be used in a Class 1, Division 1 location.

    (a) True   (b) False

31. Totally enclosed motors of the type specified in 501.125(A)(2) or (A)(3) must have a device to de-energize the motor or sound an alarm if there is an increase in temperature of the motor beyond designed limits when operating in Class I, Division 1 locations.

    (a) True   (b) False

32. Luminaires installed in Class I, Division 1 locations must be protected from physical damage by a suitable _____.

    (a) warning label   (b) pendant   (c) guard or by location   (d) all of these

33. Boxes, box assemblies, or fittings used to support luminaires in Class I, Division 1 locations must be identified for Class 1 locations.

    (a) True   (b) False

34. In Class I, Division 1 and 2 locations, flexible cords are never permitted.

    (a) True   (b) False

35. In Class I, Division 1 locations, all apparatus and equipment of signaling, alarm, remote-control, and communications systems, _____, must be identified for Class I, Division 1 locations.

    (a) above 50V   (b) above 100V-to-ground   (c) regardless of voltage   (d) except under 24V

Article 502 Class II Hazardous (Classified) Locations

A Class II hazardous (classified) location is an area where combustible dust may be suspended in the air in quantities sufficient to ignite or explode.

36. Raceways permitted as a wiring method in a Class II, Division 1 hazardous (classified) location include _____.

    (a) threaded rigid metal conduit and intermediate metal conduit
    (b) rigid nonmetallic conduit
    (c) electrical metallic tubing
    (d) any of these

37. In Class II locations where combustible, electrically conductive dust is present, flexible connections can be made with _____.

    (a) flexible metal conduit   (b) AC armored cable
    (c) hard-usage cord   (d) liquidtight flexible metal conduit with listed fittings

38. Rigid metal conduit and intermediate metal conduit are not required to be threaded when used in a Class II, Division 2 location.

    (a) True   (b) False

39. In Class II, Division 1 and 2 locations, an approved method of bonding is the use of _____.

    (a) bonding jumpers with approved fittings   (b) double locknut types of contacts
    (c) locknut-bushing types of contacts   (d) any of the above are approved methods of bonding

40. In a Class II, Division 1 location, a multiwire branch circuit is allowed when using a disconnect on the circuit which opens all of the circuits simultaneously.

    (a) True   (b) False

41. In a Class II, Division 1 location where dust from magnesium, aluminum, aluminum bronze powders, or other metals of similarly hazardous characteristics may be present, fuses, switches, motor controllers, and circuit breakers must have enclosures specifically approved for such locations.

    (a) True   (b) False

42. In Class II, Division 1 locations, control transformers, solenoids, impedance coils and resistors, and any overcurrent devices or switching mechanism associated with them, must have dust-ignitionproof enclosures identified for _____.

    (a) Class I, Division 1 locations   (b) control transformer duty
    (c) general duty   (d) Class II locations

43. In Class II, Division 2 locations, motors, generators, or other rotating electric machinery must be _____.

    (a) totally enclosed nonventilated or pipe ventilated   (b) totally enclosed water-air-cooled or fan cooled
    (c) dust-ignition proof   (d) any of these

44. Luminaires installed in Class II, Division 1 locations must be protected from physical damage by a suitable _____.

    (a) warning label   (b) pendant   (c) guard or by location   (d) all of these

45. Luminaires installed in Class II, Division 2 locations must be protected from physical damage by a suitable _____.

    (a) warning label   (b) pendant   (c) guard or by location   (d) all of these

46. Flexible cords used in a Class II, Division 1 or 2 location _____.

    (a) must be listed for hard usage   (b) must be listed for extra-hard usage
    (c) are not permitted   (d) none of these

47. In Class II, Division 2 locations, receptacles and attachment plugs must be of the type providing for connection to the grounding conductor of the flexible cord and must be designed so that connection to the supply circuit cannot be made or broken _____.

    (a) while live parts are exposed   (b) except by qualified persons
    (c) unless the disconnect is open   (d) unless proper ventilation equipment is functional

Article 503 Class III Hazardous (Classified) Locations

Class III locations are hazardous due to the presence of easily ignitible fibers or flyings, but these materials aren't likely to be suspended in the air in quantities sufficient to produce ignitible mixtures. This would include materials such as cotton and rayon, which are found in textile mills and clothing manufacturing plants. It can also include establishments and industries such as woodworking plants. There are no "Group" classifications for Class III locations as there are for Class I and Class II locations.

48. Raceways permitted as a wiring method in a Class III hazardous (classified) location include _____.

    (a) rigid metal conduit and intermediate metal conduit   (b) rigid nonmetallic conduit
    (c) electrical metallic tubing   (d) any of these

49. In Class III, Division 1 and 2 locations, locknut-bushing and double-locknut types of fittings are depended on for bonding purposes.

    (a) True   (b) False

50. In Class III, Division 1 and 2 locations, switches, circuit breakers, motor controllers, and fuses, including pushbuttons, relays, and similar devices, must be provided with _____.

    (a) Class I enclosures   (b) general duty enclosures
    (c) dusttight enclosures   (d) seal-offs at each enclosure

51. In Class III, Divisions 1 and 2, motors, generators, and other rotating machinery must be _____.

    (a) totally enclosed nonventilated   (b) totally enclosed pipe ventilated
    (c) totally enclosed fan cooled   (d) any of these

52. Luminaires in a Class III location that may be exposed to physical damage must be protected by a(n) _____ guard.

    (a) plastic   (b) metal   (c) suitable   (d) explosionproof

53. In Class III, Division 1 and 2 locations, portable lighting equipment must be equipped with handles and protected with substantial guards. Lampholders must be of the unswitched type with no provisions for _____.

    (a) receiving attachment plugs   (b) grounding connections
    (c) lamp installation   (d) hooks or hangers

54. In Class III, Division 1 and 2 locations, receptacles and attachment plugs must be of the grounding type, must be designed so as to minimize the accumulation or the entry of _____, and must prevent the escape of sparks or molten particles.

    (a) gases or vapors   (b) particles of combustion   (c) fibers or flyings   (d) none of these

55. The power supply to contact conductors of a crane in a Class III location must be _____.

    (a) isolated from all other systems   (b) equipped with an acceptable ground detector
    (c) have an alarm in the case of a ground fault   (d) all of these

Article 504 Intrinsically Safe Systems

This article covers the installation of intrinsically safe apparatus, wiring, and systems for Class I, II, and III locations. An intrinsically safe circuit doesn't develop sufficient electrical energy to cause ignition of a specified gas or vapor under normal or abnormal operating conditions. An intrinsically safe system reduces the risk of ignition by electrical equipment or circuits and offers an optional wiring method in hazardous (classified) locations.

56. An assembly of interconnected intrinsically safe apparatus, associated apparatus, and interconnecting cables designed so that those parts of the system that may be used in hazardous (classified) locations are intrinsically safe circuits is a(n) _____.

    (a) intrinsically safe system   (b) safe location   (c) reclassified location   (d) associated system

57. Intrinsically safe and associated apparatus are permitted to be installed in _____.

    (a) any hazardous (classified) location for which they have been identified
    (b) Class I locations only
    (c) Class II locations only
    (d) any location that is less than 30V

58. Conductors of intrinsically safe circuits must be separated at least _____ from conductors of any nonintrinsically safe circuits within enclosures.

    (a) 6 in.   (b) 2 in.   (c) 18 in.   (d) 12 in.

59. Intrinsically safe apparatus, associated apparatus, cable shields, enclosures, and raceways (if of metal), must be grounded.

    (a) True   (b) False

60. Intrinsically safe conduit or cable runs that leave a Class I or II location must be sealed. The seal must be _____.

    (a) explosionproof or flameproof   (b) flameproof
    (c) a and b   (d) none of these

61. Color coding of _____ is permitted to be used to identify cables, conduits, cable trays, and junction boxes that contain intrinsically safe wiring.

    (a) red   (b) light blue   (c) yellow   (d) any of these

Article 505 Class I, Zone 0, 1, and 2 Locations

This article covers the requirements for the zone classification system as an alternative to the division classification system covered in Article 500 for electrical and electronic equipment and wiring for all voltages in Class I, Zone 0, Zone 1, and Zone 2 hazardous (classified) locations where fire or explosion hazards may exist due to flammable gases, vapors, or liquids.

62. Multiwire branch circuits can be used in a Class I, Zone 1, location if the ungrounded conductors are opened simultaneously.

    (a) True   (b) False

Article 511 Commercial Garages, Repair, and Storage

These occupancies include locations used for service and repair operations in connection with self-propelled vehicles (including, but not limited to, passenger automobiles, buses, trucks, and tractors) in which petroleum-based chemicals (volatile organic compounds) are used for fuel or power.

63. Article _____ contains the requirements for the wiring of occupancy locations used for service and repair operations in connection with self-propelled vehicles (including passenger automobiles, buses, trucks, tractors, etc.) in which volatile flammable liquids or gases are used for fuel or power.

    (a) 500   (b) 501   (c) 511   (d) 514

64. Parking garages used for parking or storage and where no repair work is done except for exchange of parts and routine maintenance requiring no use of electrical equipment, open flame, welding, or the use of volatile flammable liquids, are not classified as hazardous (classified) locations.

    (a) True   (b) False

65. Areas adjacent to classified locations in commercial garages where flammable vapors are not likely to be released are not classified where mechanically ventilated at a rate of _____ or more air changes per hour, designed with positive air pressure, or where effectively cut off by walls or partitions.

    (a) two   (b) four   (c) six   (d) none of these

66. Where flammable liquids having a flash point below 100°F (such as gasoline, or gaseous fuels such as natural gas or LPG) will not be transferred, such location is considered to be a(n) _____ location.

    (a) Class I, Division 1   (b) Class I, Division 2   (c) Class II, Division 1   (d) unclassified

67. For each floor area inside a commercial garage where Class I liquids are transferred, the entire area up to a level of _____ above the floor is considered to be a Class I, Division 2 location.

    (a) 6 in.   (b) 12 in.   (c) 18 in.   (d) 24 in.

68. •Any ventilated pit or depression in a commercial garage lubrication or service room where Class I liquids or gaseous fuels are transferred is classified as a _____ location.

    (a) Class I, Division 2.   (b) Class II, Division 2   (c) Class II, Division 1   (d) Class I, Division 1

69. Wiring installed in a Class 1 location of commercial garages must conform to the applicable provisions of Article 501.

    (a) True   (b) False

70. For portable lighting equipment used in commercial garages, unless the lamp and its cord are supported and arranged in such a manner that they cannot be used in the locations classified in 511.3, they must be of a type identified for _____.

    (a) hard usage   (b) Class I, Division 2 locations
    (c) Class I, Division 1 locations   (d) general duty

71. For pendants installed above Class I locations in a commercial garage, flexible cord _____.

    (a) must be suitable for the type of service   (b) must be listed for hard usage
    (c) a and b   (d) must not be used

72. In a commercial garage, over a Class I location, equipment less than _____ above the floor level that may produce arcs, sparks, or particles of hot metal, must be of the totally enclosed type or constructed so as to prevent the escape of sparks or hot metal particles.

    (a) 6 ft   (b) 10 ft   (c) 12 ft   (d) 18 ft

73. For commercial garages, seals conforming to the requirements of 501.5 and 501.5(B)(2) must be provided and apply to _____ boundaries of the defined Class I location.

    (a) vertical   (b) horizontal   (c) conduit only within the   (d) (a) and (b)

74. In commercial garages, GFCI protection for personnel must be provided on all 125V, single-phase, 15 and 20 ampere receptacles installed where _____ is (are) to be used.

    (a) electrical diagnostic equipment   (b) electrical hand tools
    (c) portable lighting equipment   (d) any of these

Article 513 Aircraft Hangars

This article applies to buildings or structures in any part of which aircraft are housed or stored containing Class I (flammable) liquids or Class II (combustible) liquids whose temperatures are above their flash points, and in which aircraft might undergo service, repairs, or alterations. It isn't necessary to classify areas where only Class II combustible liquids are used or stored below the flash point. Article 513 doesn't apply to areas used exclusively for aircraft that have never contained fuel or for unfueled aircraft.

75. The entire area of an aircraft hangar, including any adjacent and communicating areas not suitably cut off from the hangar, are classified as a Class I, Division 2 or Zone 2 location up to a level of _____ above the floor.

    (a) 6 in.   (b) 5 ft 6 in.   (c) 18 in.   (d) 12 in.

76. Stock rooms and similar areas adjacent to classified locations of aircraft hangars, but effectively isolated and adequately ventilated, are designated as _____ locations.

    (a) Class I, Division 2   (b) Class II, Division 1   (c) Class II, Division 2   (d) nonhazardous

77. Attachment plugs and receptacles in Class I locations of aircraft hangars must be _____.

(a) identified for use in Class I locations
(b) designed so that they can not be energized while the connections are being made or broken
(c) a or b
(d) none of these

78. For pendants in an aircraft hangar, not installed in Class I locations, flexible cords suitable for the type of service and identified for _____ must be used.

(a) hard usage   (b) extra-hard usage   (c) general duty   (d) a or b

79. In aircraft hangars, equipment that is less than _____ above wings and engine enclosures of aircraft and that may produce arcs, sparks, or particles of hot metal must be of the totally enclosed type or constructed so as to prevent the escape of sparks or hot metal particles.

(a) 18 in.   (b) 5 ft 6 in.   (c) 10 ft   (d) 6 ft 6 in.

80. All wiring installed in or under the aircraft hangar floor must comply with the requirements for _____ locations.

(a) Class I, Division 1   (b) Class I, Division 2   (c) Class II   (d) none of these

81. Where a circuit in a Class I location of an aircraft hangar supplies portable equipment and includes a grounded conductor as provided in Article 200, _____ and similar devices must be of the grounding type, and the grounded conductor of the flexible cord must be connected to the grounded terminal of any utilization equipment supplied.

(a) receptacles   (b) attachment plugs   (c) connectors   (d) all of these

Article 514 Motor Fuel Dispensing Facilities

This article applies to gasoline dispensing and service stations where gasoline or other volatile flammable liquids or liquefied flammable gases are transferred to fuel tanks of self-propelled vehicles. Wiring and equipment in the area of service and repair rooms of service stations must comply with the installation requirements in Article 511.

82. Article 514 contains requirements for the classification of areas where _____ is stored, handled, or dispensed from motor fuel dispensing facilities.

(a) compressed natural gas   (b) liquefied natural gas   (c) liquefied petroleum gas   (d) any of these

83. A listed sealing fitting must be _____.

(a) provided in each conduit run entering a dispenser
(b) provided in each conduit run leaving a dispenser
(c) the first fitting after the conduit emerges from the earth or concrete
(d) all of these

84. Each circuit leading to or through a dispensing pump must be provided with a switch or other acceptable means to disconnect simultaneously from the source of supply all conductors of the circuit, including the _____ conductor, if any.

(a) grounding   (b) grounded   (c) bonding   (d) all of these

85. Each circuit leading to gasoline dispensing equipment must be provided with a clearly identified and readily accessible switch or other acceptable means to disconnect all conductors of the circuit.

(a) True   (b) False

86. The emergency controls for unattended self-service stations must be located not less than _____ or more than _____ from the gasoline dispensers.

    (a) 10 ft, 25 ft   (b) 20 ft, 50 ft   (c) 20 ft, 100 ft   (d) 50 ft, 100 ft

87. In motor fuel dispensing facilities, all metal raceways, the metal armor or metallic sheath on cables, and all noncurrent-carrying metal parts of fixed portable electrical equipment _____ must be grounded as provided in Article 250.

    (a) operating at under 600V   (b) regardless of voltage   (c) over 300V   (d) under 50V

Article 515 Bulk Storage Plants

This article covers a property or portion of a property where flammable liquids are received by tank vessel, pipelines, tank car, or tank vehicle and are stored or blended in bulk for the purpose of distributing such liquids by tank vessel, pipeline, tank car, tank vehicle, portable tank, or container.

88. Aboveground bulk storage tanks are classified as _____ for the space between 5 ft and 10 ft from the open end of a vent, extending in all directions.

    (a) Class I, Division 1   (b) Class I, Division 2   (c) Class II, Division 1   (d) Class II, Division 2

Article 516 Spray Application, Dipping, and Coating Processes

This article covers the regular or frequent application of flammable liquids, combustible liquids, and combustible powders by spray operations and the application of flammable liquids, or combustible liquids at temperatures above their flashpoint, by dipping, coating, or other means.

89. Locations where flammable paints are dried, with the ventilating equipment interlocked with the electrical equipment, may be designated as a(n) _____ location by the authority having jurisdiction.

    (a) Class I, Division 2   (b) unclassified   (c) Class II, Division 2   (d) Class II, Division 1

Article 517 Health Care Facilities

This article applies to electrical wiring in health care facilities such as hospitals, nursing homes, limited-care facilities, clinics, medical and dental offices, and ambulatory care, whether permanent or movable. This article isn't intended to apply to animal veterinary facilities.

90. A hospital is a building or part thereof used for the medical, psychiatric, obstetrical, or surgical care, on a 24-hour basis, of _____ or more inpatients.

    (a) 10   (b) 100   (c) 4   (d) 2

91. A nursing home is an area used for the lodging, boarding, and nursing care, on a 24-hour basis of _____ or more persons who, because of mental or physical incapacity may be unable to provide for their own needs and safety without assistance.

    (a) 4   (b) 100   (c) 10   (d) 2

92. The patient bed location would include an inpatient sleeping bed; or the bed or procedure table used in a critical patient care area.

    (a) True   (b) False

93. Patient vicinity is the space with surfaces likely to be contacted by the patient or an attendant who can touch the patient. This encloses a space not less than 6 ft beyond the perimeter of the patient bed in its normal location and extending vertically not less than _____ above the floor.

    (a) 7 1/2 ft   (b) 5 ft 6 in.   (c) 18 in.   (d) 6 ft

94. The outer metal sheath of interlocked Type MC cable is not listed as an acceptable grounding return path. However, if it contains an insulated equipment grounding conductor 12 AWG or larger, it can be used to supply branch circuits in patient care areas of health care facilities.

    (a) True   (b) False

95. Metal faceplates for switches and receptacles are permitted to be grounded by means of the metal mounting screws securing the faceplate to a grounded outlet box or grounded wiring device in patient care areas.

    (a) True   (b) False

96. In health care facilities, receptacles with insulated grounding terminals must be identified. Such identification must be visible _____.

    (a) on rough-in inspection   (b) by removal of faceplates
    (c) after installation   (d) on the blueprints only

97. Each general care area patient bed location must be provided with a minimum of _____ receptacle(s), which can be single, duplex, or a combination with each duplex counting as 2 receptacles.

    (a) 1   (b) 6   (c) 2   (d) 4

98. In critical care areas of health care centers, each patient bed location must be provided with a minimum of _____ receptacles.

    (a) 10   (b) 6   (c) 3   (d) 4

99. The wiring for the emergency system in hospitals may be installed in flexible metal raceways and listed metal-sheathed cable assemblies for specific situations, including _____.

    (a) enclosing conductors smaller than 12 AWG only
    (b) within 50 feet of a disconnect for the branch circuit
    (c) where necessary for flexible connection to equipment
    (d) only where installed so the wiring method is exposed and accessible

100. Which one of the following functions must not be connected to the life safety branch in a hospital?

    (a) Exit signs.   (b) Elevators.
    (c) Administrative office lighting.   (d) Communications systems.

(• Indicates that 75% or fewer of those who took this exam answered the question correctly.)

1. By using ingenuity in the layout of electrical installations for hazardous (classified) locations, it is frequently possible to locate much of the equipment in less hazardous or nonhazardous locations and thus reduce the amount of special equipment required.

    (a) True   (b) False

2. A fiber optic cable assembly that contains current-carrying conductors must be installed according to the applicable requirements of Articles 500, 501, 502, and 503.

    (a) True   (b) False

3. All branch circuits serving patient care areas must be installed in a metal raceway or cable that is listed in 250.118 as an acceptable grounding return path, such as EMT or Type AC cable.

    (a) True   (b) False

4. All fixed wiring in an aircraft hangar not installed in a Class I location must be installed in _____.

    (a) metal raceways   (b) Types MI, TC, or MC cable
    (c) nonmetallic raceways   (d) a or b

5. An aboveground tank in a bulk storage plant is a Class I, Division 1 location within _____ from the open end of a vent, extending in all directions.

    (a) 12 ft   (b) 10 ft   (c) 6 ft   (d) 5 ft

6. An atmosphere classified as Group G contains combustible dusts such as flour, grain, wood, plastic, and chemicals.

    (a) True   (b) False

7. An intrinsically safe circuit is a circuit in which any spark or thermal effect is incapable of causing ignition of a mixture of flammable or combustible material in air under _____.

    (a) water   (b) prescribed test conditions   (c) supervision   (d) duress

8. Any pit or depression below a garage floor level of a lubrication or service room where Class I liquids are transferred is considered to be a Class I, Division _____ location up to floor level.

    (a) 1   (b) 2   (c) 3   (d) not classified

9. Article 514 applies to _____ and fleet vehicle motor fuel dispensing facilities.

    (a) motor fuel dispensing facilities located inside or outside   (b) marine fuel dispensing facilities
    (c) commercial gas stations for motor vehicles only   (d) both a and b

10. Battery chargers and their control equipment, and batteries being charged, are allowed to be located within any area of a commercial garage.

    (a) True   (b) False

11. Class III, Division _____ location(s) include areas where easily ignitible fibers or materials producing combustible flyings are handled, manufactured, or used.

    (a) 1   (b) 2   (c) 3   (d) all of these

12. Conductors of intrinsically safe circuits must not be placed in any _____ with conductors of any nonintrinsically safe system.

    (a) raceway   (b) cable tray   (c) cable   (d) any of these

13. Conduits trade size 1 1/2 or smaller entering an explosionproof enclosure that houses switches intended to interrupt current in the normal performance of the function are not required to be sealed, if the current-interrupting contacts are within a chamber hermetically sealed against the entrance of gases and vapors.

    (a) True   (b) False

14. Each circuit leading to or through dispensing equipment, including equipment for remote pumping systems, must be provided with a switch or other acceptable means to disconnect _____ from the source of supply all conductors of the circuit, including the grounded conductor, if any.

    (a) automatically   (b) simultaneously   (c) manually   (d) individually

15. Equipment in an area containing acetylene gas must be rated as a Class I, Group A location.

    (a) True   (b) False

16. Equipment installed in hazardous locations must be approved and must be marked to show the _____.

    (a) class
    (b) group
    (c) temperature class (T Code) or operating temperature at a 40°C ambient temperature
    (d) all of these

17. Fixed electrical equipment installed above a Class I location in a commercial garage must be _____.

    (a) well ventilated   (b) located above the level of any defined Class I location
    (c) identified for the location   (d) b or c

18. For connections to enclosures that are required to be explosionproof in Class I, Division 2 locations, _____ must be located in accordance with 501.15(A)(1) and (A)4.

    (a) mounting brackets   (b) conduit seals   (c) warning signs   (d) none of these

19. Fuel dispensing units for liquid petroleum gas are allowed to be located within a commercial garage building if the requirements of Article 514 are applied.

    (a) True   (b) False

20. In a Class I, Division 1 location, a multiwire branch circuit is allowed to be protected using single-pole breakers.

    (a) True   (b) False

21. In a Class II, Division 2 location, enclosures for fuses, switches, circuit breakers, and motor controllers, including pushbuttons, relays, and similar devices, must be _____.

    (a) dusttight   (b) raintight
    (c) rated as Class I, Division 1 explosionproof   (d) general duty

22. In aircraft hangars, metal-shell, fiber-lined lampholders must not be used for fixed incandescent lighting.

    (a) True   (b) False

23. In Class I, Division 1 locations, control transformers, impedance coils, and resistors, along with any switching mechanism associated with them, must be provided with enclosures identified for _____.

    (a) Class I, Division 1 locations   (b) control transformer duty
    (c) general duty   (d) NEMA 3

24. In Class I, Division 2 locations for alarm and communications systems, enclosures that contain switches, circuit breakers, and make-and-break contacts of pushbuttons, relays, alarm bells, and horns must be identified for Class I, Division 1 locations.

    (a) True   (b) False

25. In Class II, Division 1 locations for alarm and communications systems, _____ for bells, howlers, sirens, and other devices in which sparks or arcs may be produced must be provided with enclosures identified for a Class II location.

    (a) switches   (b) circuit breakers   (c) current-breaking contacts   (d) all of these

26. In Class II, Division 2 locations, flexible cord is allowed to serve as the supporting means for a fixture.

    (a) True   (b) False

27. In Class III, Division 1 and 2 locations, flexible cords must _____.

    (a) be listed as extra-hard usage   (b) contain a grounding conductor
    (c) terminate in an approved manner   (d) all of these

28. In hazardous (classified) locations, intrinsically safe apparatus must _____ in the hazardous (classified) location in accordance with 250.100.

    (a) be secured   (b) be bonded   (c) be painted   (d) not be used

29. ITC-HL cables, listed for use in Class I, Division 1 locations, with a gas/vaportight, continuous-corrugated, metallic sheath, an overall jacket of suitable polymeric material, and provided with termination fittings listed for the application can be installed in Class I, Division 1 _____ establishments with restricted public access.

    (a) commercial   (b) industrial   (c) institutional   (d) all of these

30. Luminaires for fixed lighting in Class III, Division 1 and 2 locations must have enclosures for lamps and lampholders that are designed to prevent the escape of _____. Each luminaire must be clearly marked to show the maximum wattage of the lamps that are permitted.

    (a) sparks   (b) burning material   (c) hot metal   (d) all of these

31. Luminaires installed in Class I, Division 1 locations must be identified as a complete assembly for the Class I, Division 1 location and must be clearly marked to indicate _____.

    (a) the maximum wattage of lamps intended   (b) the minimum conductor size
    (c) the maximum overcurrent protection allowed   (d) all of these

32. Luminaires installed in Class II, Division 1 locations must be identified for Class II locations and must be clearly marked to indicate the _____.

    (a) maximum wattage of lamps for which designed   (b) minimum conductor size
    (c) maximum overcurrent protection allowed   (d) all of these

33. Luminaires more than _____ above the floor and switches located outside the patient vicinity are not required to be grounded by an insulated equipment grounding conductor in patient care areas.

    (a) 7 1/2 ft   (b) 8 ft   (c) 10 ft   (d) 18 in.

34. Meters, instruments and relays installed in Class I, Division 2 locations can have switches, circuit breakers, and make-and-break contacts of push buttons, relays, alarm bells, and horns installed in general-purpose enclosures if current-interrupting contacts are _____.

    (a) immersed in oil   (b) enclosed within a hermetically-sealed chamber
    (c) a or b   (d) a and b

35. Raceways permitted as a wiring method in a Class II, Division 2 hazardous (classified) location include _____.

    (a) rigid metal conduit and intermediate metal conduit   (b) electrical metallic tubing
    (c) rigid nonmetallic conduit   (d) a or b

36. Receptacles located within the rooms, bathrooms, playrooms, activity rooms, and patient care areas of pediatric wards, rooms, or areas must be listed as _____.

    (a) tamper resistant   (b) isolated   (c) GFCI protected   (d) specification grade

37. The cover plates for receptacles, or the receptacles themselves, supplied from the emergency system of essential electrical systems in hospitals must have a distinctive color or marking so as to be readily identifiable.

    (a) True   (b) False

38. The emergency controls for attended self-service stations must be located no more than _____ from the gasoline dispensers.

    (a) 20 ft   (b) 50 ft   (c) 75 ft   (d) 100 ft

39. The floor area where Class 1 liquids are transferred is not classified if the enforcing agency determines that there is mechanical ventilation that provides a minimum of four air changes per hour or _____ cu ft per minute of exchanged air for each square foot of floor area (cfm/sq. ft).

    (a) 1   (b) 2   (c) 3   (d) 4

40. The *NEC* contains a section covering the sealing and drainage requirements for conduits and cables in Zone classified systems.

    (a) True   (b) False

41. The patient care area is any portion of a health care facility, including business offices, corridors, lounges, day rooms, dining rooms, or similar areas.

    (a) True   (b) False

42. The requirements of Article 511 apply to locations used for service and repair operations in connection with self-propelled vehicles such as _____, in which volatile flammable liquids or flammable gases are used for fuel or power.

    (a) buses   (b) trucks   (c) tractors   (d) all of these

43. The requirements of Article 517 (Health Care Facilities) apply to buildings or portions of buildings in which medical, _____, or surgical care is provided.

    (a) psychiatric   (b) nursing   (c) obstetrical   (d) any of these

44.   When determining a Class I, Division 2 location, _____ is a factor that must be considered in determining the classification and extent of the location.

(a) the quantity of flammable material that might escape in case of an accident
(b) the adequacy of ventilating equipment
(c) the record of the industry or business with respect to explosions or fires
(d) all of these

45.   When luminaires are installed in Class I, Division 2 locations where the surface temperature may, under normal operating conditions, reach surface temperatures exceeding 80 percent of the ignition temperature of the gas or vapor involved, _____ fixtures must be used.

(a) Class I, Division 1   (b) Class I, Division 3   (c) Class II, Division 1   (d) Class II, Division 2

46.   When seals are required for Class I locations, they must comply with the following rule(s):

(a) They must be listed for Class I locations and must be accessible.
(b) The minimum thickness of the sealing compound must not be less than the trade size of the sealing fitting and, in no case, less than 5/8 in.
(c) Splices and taps must not be made in the conduit seal.
(d) all of these

47.   When shielded cables and twisted-pair cables are installed in Class I, Division 2 locations, the removal of the shielding material or separation of the twisted pairs is not required, provided the termination is by an approved means to minimize the entrance of _____ and prevent propagation of flame into the cable core.

(a) gases   (b) vapors   (c) dust   (d) a or b

48.   Where liquidtight flexible metal conduit (LFMC) or liquidtight flexible nonmetallic conduit (LFNC) is used in a Class II location, as permitted in 502.10, it must be installed with _____.

(a) an internal bonding jumper   (b) an external bonding jumper no more than 6 ft long
(c) a or b   (d) none of these

49.   Where liquidtight flexible metal conduit (LFMC) or liquidtight flexible nonmetallic conduit (LFNC) is used in a Class III location, as permitted in 504.10, it must be installed with _____.

(a) an internal bonding jumper   (b) an external bonding jumper no more than 6 ft long
(c) a or b   (d) none of these

50.   Within the vicinity of aircraft in an aircraft hangar, the area within 5 ft horizontally from aircraft power plants or aircraft fuel tanks is classified as a Class I, Division 2 or Zone 2 location that extends upward from the floor to a level of _____ above the upper surface of wings and of engine enclosures.

(a) 18 in.   (b) 3 ft   (c) 5 ft   (d) 20 ft

(• Indicates that 75% or fewer of those who took this exam answered the question correctly.)

1. The white conductor within a cable can be used for the ungrounded (hot) conductor, but the white conductor must be permanently reidentified to indicate its use as an ungrounded (hot) conductor at each location where the conductor is visible and accessible. Identification must _____.

   (a) be by painting or other effective means   (b) be a color other than white, gray, or green
   (c) both a and b   (d) none of these

2. The wiring contained inside which of the following are required to be accessible?

   (a) Outlet boxes   (b) Junction boxes   (c) Pull boxes   (d) all of these

3. The wiring for community television antenna systems must comply with Article 810 and the distribution coaxial wiring must comply with Article 820.

   (a) True   (b) False

4. The wiring for spas and hot tubs installed outdoors, such as receptacles, switches, lighting locations, grounding and bonding, and all topics covered in Parts I and II of Article 680, must comply with the same requirements as permanently installed pools except as permitted in 680.42(A) and (B).

   (a) True   (b) False

5. The wiring method used to supply signs and outline lighting systems must terminate within _____.

   (a) a sign   (b) an outline lighting system enclosure
   (c) a suitable box, or conduit body   (d) any of these

6. Totally enclosed motors of the type specified in 501.125(A)(2) or (A)(3) must have no external surface with an operating temperature that exceeds _____ when operating in Class I, Division 1 locations.

   (a) absolute zero   (b) 80 percent of the ignition temperature of the gas or liquid involved
   (c) 100°C   (d) 40°C

7. Track lighting fittings are permitted to be equipped with general-purpose receptacles.

   (a) True   (b) False

8. Transformers and capacitors installed in Class I, Division 1 locations that do not contain flammable liquids are not required to be installed in vaults if they are approved for Class I locations.

   (a) True   (b) False

9. Transformers with ventilating openings must be installed so that the ventilating openings _____.

   (a) are a minimum 18 in. above the floor   (b) are not blocked by walls or obstructions
   (c) are aesthetically located   (d) are vented to the exterior of the building

10. Two 20A small-appliance branch circuits can supply more than one kitchen in a dwelling.

    (a) True   (b) False

11.   Two or more grounding electrodes that are effectively bonded together are considered as a single grounding electrode system in this sense.

   (a) True   (b) False

12.   Type _____ is a type of multiconductor cable permitted for use as an underground service-entrance cable.

   (a) SE   (b) NMC   (c) UF   (d) USE

13.   Type CMX communications cables that are less than 1/4 in. in diameter can be installed in _____.

   (a) one- or two-family dwellings   (b) multifamily dwellings in nonconcealed spaces
   (c) a or b   (d) none of these

14.   Type ITC cable can only be installed in industrial establishments where the conditions of maintenance and supervision ensure that only _____ will service the installation.

   (a) the authority having jurisdiction   (b) authorized persons
   (c) the general public   (d) qualified persons

15.   Type MC cable installed in accessible attics or roof spaces must comply with the same requirements as given for AC cable in 320.24. This includes the installation of _____ to protect the cable when run across the top of floor joists if the space is accessible by permanent stairs or ladders.

   (a) GFCI protection   (b) arc-fault protection   (c) rigid metal conduit   (d) guard strips

16.   Type MC cable must be supported and secured at intervals not exceeding _____.

   (a) 3 ft   (b) 6 ft   (c) 4 ft   (d) 2 ft

17.   Type NM and Type NMC cables must not be used in one- and two-family dwellings exceeding three floors above grade.

   (a) True   (b) False

18.   Type NM cable installed through, or parallel to, framing members must be protected against physical damage in accordance with 300.4. Grommets or bushings for the protection of Type NM cable as required in 300.4(B)(1) must be _____ for the purpose, and they must remain in place.

   (a) marked   (b) approved   (c) identified   (d) listed

19.   Type NM cable is allowed for wiring above a Class I location in a commercial garage.

   (a) True   (b) False

20.   Type NM cable must be secured in place within _____ of every cabinet, box, or fitting.

   (a) 6 in.   (b) 10 in.   (c) 12 in.   (d) 18 in.

21.   Type NM cable must closely follow the surface of the building finish or running boards when run exposed.

   (a) True   (b) False

22.   Type NM cable, installed within accessible ceilings for the connections to luminaires and equipment, does not need to be secured within 12 in. from the luminaire or equipment when the free length does not exceed _____.

   (a) 4 1/2 ft   (b) 2 1/2 ft   (c) 3 1/2 ft   (d) any of these

23. Type S fuses, fuseholders, and adapters are required to be designed so that _____ would be difficult.

   (a) installation (b) tampering (c) shunting (d) b or c

24. Type SE cable is permitted to be formed in a _____ and taped with self-sealing weather-resistant thermoplastic.

   (a) loop (b) circle (c) gooseneck (d) none of these

25. Type SE service-entrance cable may be used for interior wiring as long as it complies with the installation requirements of Parts I and II of Article 334, excluding 334.80.

   (a) True (b) False

26. Under the optional method for calculating a single-family dwelling, general loads beyond the initial 10 kW are assessed at a _____ percent demand factor.

   (a) 40 (b) 50 (c) 60 (d) 75

27. Underground feeder and branch circuit (Type UF) cable is allowed to be used as service-entrance cable.

   (a) True (b) False

28. Underground raceways and cable assemblies entering a handhole enclosure must extend into the enclosure, but they are not required to be _____.

   (a) bonded
   (b) insulated
   (c) mechanically connected to the handhole enclosure
   (d) below minimum cover requirements after leaving the handhole

29. Underground wiring to gasoline dispensers must be installed in _____.

   (a) threaded rigid metal conduit
   (b) threaded intermediate metal conduit
   (c) rigid nonmetallic conduit when buried under not less than 2 ft of cover
   (d) any of these

30. Unit equipment (battery packs) must be on the same branch circuit that serves the normal lighting in the area and connected _____ any local switches.

   (a) with (b) ahead of (c) after (d) none of these

31. Unless specifically permitted in 240.4(E) through 240.4(G), the overcurrent protection must not exceed _____ after any correction factors for ambient temperature and the number of conductors has been applied.

   (a) 15A for 14 AWG copper (b) 20A for 12 AWG copper (c) 30A for 10 AWG copper (d) all of these

32. Unused openings for circuit breakers and switches in switchboards and panelboards must be closed using _____ or other approved means that provide protection substantially equivalent to the wall of the enclosure.

   (a) duct seal and tape (b) identified closures (c) exothermic welding (d) sheet metal

33. Using standard load calculations, the feeder demand factor for five household clothes dryers is _____ percent.

   (a) 70 (b) 85 (c) 50 (d) 100

34. Utilities include entities that install, operate, and maintain _____.

    (a) communications systems (telephone, CATV, Internet, satellite, or data services)
    (b) electric supply systems (generation, transmission, or distribution systems)
    (c) Local Area Network wiring on premises
    (d) a or b

35. Vegetation such as trees must not be used for support of _____.

    (a) overhead conductor spans   (b) surface wiring methods   (c) luminaires   (d) electric equipment

36. Wet-niche luminaires that are not supplied by a flexible cord or flexible cable must be connected to an equipment grounding conductor that is not smaller than _____ AWG.

    (a) 10   (b) 6   (c) 8   (d) 12

37. What is the minimum size copper equipment bonding jumper required for equipment connected to a 40A circuit?

    (a) 12 AWG   (b) 14 AWG   (c) 8 AWG   (d) 10 AWG

38. When an electric-discharge luminaire is mounted directly over a concealed outlet box, which is not its sole means of support, the luminaire must provide access to the conductor wiring within the outlet box by means of suitable openings in the back of the fixture.

    (a) True   (b) False

39. When counting the number of conductors in a box, a conductor running through the box with no loop in it is counted as _____ conductor(s).

    (a) one   (b) two   (c) zero   (d) none of these

40. When ENT is installed concealed in walls, floors, and ceilings of buildings exceeding three floors above grade, a thermal barrier must be provided having a minimum _____-minute finish rating as listed for fire-rated assemblies.

    (a) 5   (b) 10   (c) 15   (d) 30

41. When equipment or devices are installed in ducts or plenum chambers used to transport environmental air, and illumination is necessary to facilitate maintenance and repair, enclosed _____-type luminaires are permitted.

    (a) screw   (b) plug   (c) gasketed   (d) neon

42. When flexible metal conduit is used to install equipment where flexibility is required, _____ must be installed.

    (a) an equipment grounding conductor   (b) an expansion fitting
    (c) flexible nonmetallic connectors   (d) a grounded conductor one size larger

43. When LFNC is installed as an exposed raceway without need of flexibility, it must be securely fastened within _____ on each side of the box and must be fastened at intervals not exceeding _____.

    (a) 12 in., 4 1/2 ft   (b) 18 in., 3 ft   (c) 12 in., 3 ft   (d) 18 in., 4 ft

44. When metal raceways and cables with metal sheaths are connected to enclosures at oversized, concentric, or eccentric knockouts for circuits over 250V-to-ground that do not contain service conductors, the electrical continuity of the raceway or metal cable sheath must be ensured by bonding similar to the requirements for service raceways.

    (a) True   (b) False

45. When rigid nonmetallic conduit extends from the pool light forming shell to a suitable junction box, an 8 AWG _____ conductor must be installed in the raceway.

    (a) solid bare   (b) solid insulated   (c) stranded insulated   (d) b or c

46. When the service disconnecting means consists of more than one switch or circuit breaker, the combined ratings of all the switches or circuit breakers used _____ than the rating required by 230.79.

    (a) must be less   (b) must not be less   (c) must be more   (d) none of these

47. When the service disconnecting means is a power-operated switch or circuit breaker, it must be able to be opened by hand in the event of a _____.

    (a) ground fault   (b) short circuit   (c) power surge   (d) power-supply failure

48. When Type AC cable is run across the top of a floor joist in an attic without permanent ladders or stairs, substantial guard strips within _____ of the scuttle hole, or attic entrance, must protect the cable.

    (a) 7 ft   (b) 6 ft   (c) 5 ft   (d) 3 ft

49. When unable to maintain the minimum required distance from the edge of a wood framing member to a bored hole for cable or nonmetallic raceway installation, the cable or raceway must be protected from penetration by screws or nails by a steel plate or bushing at least _____ and of appropriate length and width to cover the area of the wiring. A thinner plate that provides equal or better protection may be used if listed and marked.

    (a) 1/4 in. thick   (b) 1/8 in. thick   (c) 1/16 in. thick   (d) 24 gauge

50. Where a box is used as the sole support of a ceiling-suspended (paddle) fan, the box must be listed for the application and must be marked with the weight of the fan to be supported if over 35 lbs.

    (a) True   (b) False

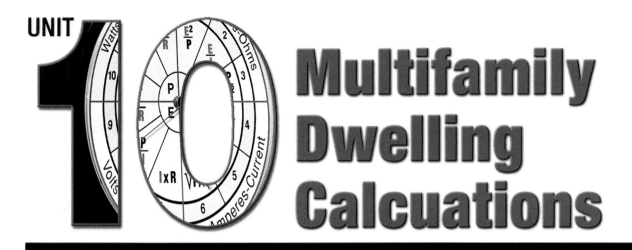

UNIT 10 Multifamily Dwelling Calcuations

Introduction

The *NEC* defines "Multifamily Dwellings" as buildings that contain three or more dwelling units. There are many similarities in the electrical requirements between multifamily and single-family dwellings, but there are differences also. The wiring method used for a single-family dwelling unit is often Type NM cable (unless local codes don't allow Type NM). Depending on several factors, such as the number of units, number of stories, the building construction type, and local building codes, a multifamily dwelling may be required to employ a wiring method of metal raceways or metallic-sheathed cable. The branch-circuit requirements of Article 210 are almost the same for each of these types of occupancies, so much of the branch-circuit design is similar.

When sizing the service or feeder conductors for a single-family dwelling in Unit 9, the use of Table 310.15(B)(6) was allowed. However, when sizing conductors for the service or feeder to a multifamily dwelling, Table 310.16 must be used instead. Table 310.15(B)(6), though, may still be used for the feeders to an individual dwelling unit within the building.

To size the electrical feeders to individual dwelling units, the requirements of Article 220 that were discussed in Unit 9 may be followed, but the main service that feeds a multifamily dwelling is based on the sum of all of the individual dwelling unit loads with the appropriate demand factors applied.

Demand factors are allowed for multifamily dwellings because diversity in usage is expected, so the maximum connected load is not likely to be in use simultaneously. Many of the principles explained in Unit 9 will still be used for multifamily dwellings here in Unit 10.

10.1 Multifamily Dwelling Unit Calculations—General

The *NEC* defines a dwelling unit as a single unit, providing complete and independent living facilities for one or more persons, including permanent provisions for living, sleeping, cooking, and sanitation [Article 100 Definitions]. **Figure 10-1**

A multifamily dwelling is a building that contains three or more dwelling units, **Figure 10–2**. A two-family dwelling is not considered a multifamily dwelling [Article 100 Definitions]. When determining the ungrounded conductors for multifamily dwelling units (**Figure 10–2**), apply the following steps:

> **AUTHOR'S COMMENT:** Hotels and motels without cooking areas are not considered dwelling units, and are covered in Unit 11 Commercial Load Calculations. **Figure 10-3**

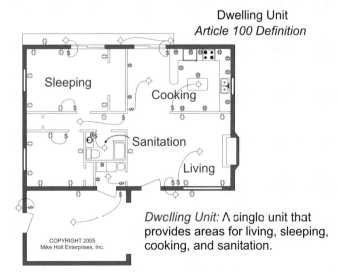

Dwelling Unit
Article 100 Definition

COPYRIGHT 2005
Mike Holt Enterprises, Inc.

Dwelling Unit: A single unit that provides areas for living, sleeping, cooking, and sanitation.

Figure 10–1

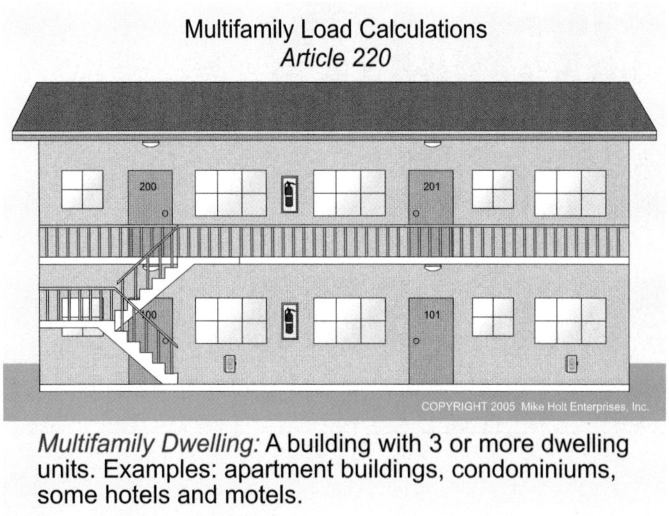

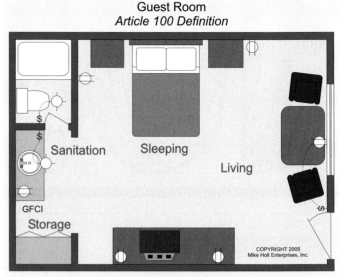

Multifamily Load Calculations
Article 220

Multifamily Dwelling: A building with 3 or more dwelling units. Examples: apartment buildings, condominiums, some hotels and motels.

Figure 10–2

Guest Room
Article 100 Definition

Sanitation   Sleeping
Living
GFCI
Storage

Guest Room: An accommodation combining living, sleeping, sanitary, and storage facilities.

Note: A guest room without provisions for cooking is not considered a dwelling unit. See Article 100 for the definition of "Dwelling Unit."

Figure 10–3

Step 1: General Lighting and Receptacles, Small-Appliance and Laundry Circuits [Table 220.42]

The *NEC* recognizes that the general lighting and general-use receptacles, and the small-appliance and laundry circuits will not all be on, or loaded, at the same time. It therefore permits the following demand factors to be applied to these loads [220.52]:

Step a: Total Connected Load—Determine the total connected general lighting and receptacle load (3 VA per sq ft) [Table 220.12], the two small-appliance circuits (1,500 VA each) [220.52(A)] and the laundry circuit load (1,500 VA) [220.52(B)] of all dwelling units. The laundry load (1,500 VA) can be omitted if laundry facilities, which are available to all building occupants, are provided on the premises [210.52(F) Ex 1].

Step b: Demand Factor—Apply the Table 220.42 demand factors to the total connected load (Step a). The first 3,000 VA is calculated at 100% demand, the next 117,000 VA (120,000 – 3,000) is calculated at 35% demand, and the remainder at 25% according to Table 220.42.

Step 2: Air-Conditioning versus Heat [220.51 and 220.60]

When the air-conditioning and heating loads are not on at the same time (simultaneously), it is permissible to omit the smaller of the two loads.

• Air-conditioning. The air-conditioning load must be calculated at 100%.

• Heat. Electric space-heating loads must be computed at 100% of the total connected load [220.51].

Step 3: Appliances [220.53]

A demand factor of 75% is permitted for four or more appliances fastened in place, such as a dishwasher, kitchen waste disposal, trash compactor, water heater, etc. This does not apply to space-heating equipment [220.51], clothes dryers [220.54], cooking appliances [220.55], or air-conditioning equipment.

Step 4: Clothes Dryers [220.54]

The feeder or service calculated load for household electric clothes dryers located in dwelling units must not be less than 5,000W (or 5,000 VA), or the nameplate rating (whichever is greater) and may be adjusted according to the demand factors listed in Table 220.54.

AUTHOR'S COMMENT: A dryer load is not required if the dwelling unit does not contain an electric dryer. Dryers in common laundry rooms must not have their loads calculated according to this method. This is covered in Unit 11.

Step 5: Cooking Equipment [220.55]

Household cooking appliances rated over 1 3/4 kVA can have their feeder and service loads calculated according to the demand factors of Table 220.55 and Notes.

Step 6: Feeder and Service Conductor Size

The conductors are sized according to Table 310.16. Conductors are presumed to be copper unless otherwise stated, and systems are presumed to be single-phase unless otherwise stated.

AUTHOR'S COMMENTS:

- Table 310.15(B)(6) can be used to size the 120/240V feeder conductors to the individual dwelling units of a multifamily dwelling, but Table 310.16 must be used to size service conductors that supply two or more dwelling units.

- 110.14(C)(1)(a) tells us that terminals are rated 60°C for equipment rated 100A or less unless marked 75°C. In real life, most terminals are now rated 75°C, so in this Unit, we will assume all terminals are rated 75°C unless 60°C is specified. Insulated conductors will be presumed to be 90°C rated. For exam purposes, read the problem carefully to be certain you know what terminal rating the exam question specifies. If unspecified, use the rules of 110.14(C).

PART A—STANDARD METHOD-FEEDER/ SERVICE LOAD CALCULATIONS

10.2 Multifamily Dwelling Unit Calculation Examples—Standard Method

Step 1: General Lighting, Small-Appliance, and Laundry Demand [Table 220.42]

▶ **General Lighting Load Example 1**

What is the general lighting and receptacle (including small-appliance circuits) calculated load for an apartment building that contains 20 units? Each apartment is 840 sq ft. *Note: Laundry facilities are provided on the premises for all tenants [210.52(F) Ex 1].* Figure 10-4

(a) 5,200 VA   (b) 40,590 VA
(c) 110,400 VA   (d) none of these

• Answer: (b) 40,590 VA

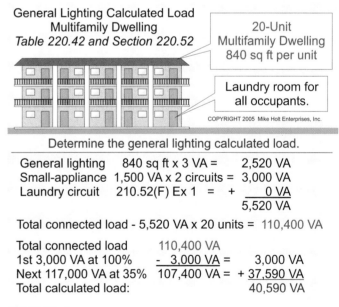

General Lighting Calculated Load
Multifamily Dwelling
Table 220.42 and Section 220.52

20-Unit Multifamily Dwelling 840 sq ft per unit

Laundry room for all occupants.

COPYRIGHT 2005 Mike Holt Enterprises, Inc.

Determine the general lighting calculated load.

General lighting	840 sq ft x 3 VA =	2,520 VA
Small-appliance	1,500 VA x 2 circuits =	3,000 VA
Laundry circuit	210.52(F) Ex 1 = +	0 VA
		5,520 VA

Total connected load - 5,520 VA x 20 units = 110,400 VA

Total connected load	110,400 VA	
1st 3,000 VA at 100%	- 3,000 VA =	3,000 VA
Next 117,000 VA at 35%	107,400 VA =	+ 37,590 VA
Total calculated load:		40,590 VA

Figure 10–4

General Lighting (840 sq ft x 3 VA)	2,520 VA		
Small-Appliance Circuits 2 x 1500 VA	3,000 VA		
Laundry Circuit	+ 0 VA		
Total Connected Load for one unit	5,520 VA		
Connected Load [Table 220.42] (5,520 VA x 20 units)	110,400 VA		
First 3,000 VA at 100%	– 3,000 VA	x 1.00 =	3,000 VA
Next 117,000 VA at 35%	107,400 VA	x 0.35 =	+ 37,590 VA
Total Calculated Load			40,590 VA

▶ **General Lighting Load Example 2**

What is the general lighting and receptacle calculated load for a 20-unit apartment building? Each unit is 990 sq ft.

(a) 74,700 VA   (b) 149,400 VA   (c) 51,300 VA   (d) 105,600 VA

• Answer: (c) 51,300 VA

General Lighting (990 sq ft x 3 VA)	2,970 VA		
Small-Appliance Circuits	3,000 VA		
Laundry Circuit	+ 1,500 VA		
Connected Load for one unit	7,470 VA		
Connected Load [Table 220.42] (7,470 VA x 20 units)	149,400 VA		
First 3,000 VA at 100%	– 3,000 VA	x 1.00 =	3,000 VA
	146,400 VA		
Next 117,000 VA at 35%	–117,000 VA	x 0.35 =	40,950 VA
Remainder VA at 25%	29,400 VA	x 0.25 =	+ 7,350 VA
Total Calculated Load			51,300 VA

Step 2: Air-Conditioning versus Heat [220.51]

▶ **Air-Conditioning versus Heat Example 1**

What is the calculated load for air-conditioning versus heat for a 40-unit multifamily building that has an A/C unit (3 hp, 230V) and two baseboard heaters (3 kVA) in each unit?

(a) 160 kVA (b) 240 kVA   (c) 60 kVA   (d) 50 kVA

• Answer: (b) 240 kVA
  Air-conditioning [Table 430.248] 230V x 17A = 3,910 VA per unit
  3,910 VA x 40 = 156,400 VA (156.4 kVA), (omit, smaller than heat) [220.60]
  Heat [220.51] 3 kVA x 2 units = 6 kVA x 40 units = 240 kVA

▶ **Air-Conditioning versus Heat Example 2**

What is the air-conditioning versus heat calculated load for a 25-unit multifamily building where each unit has a 3 hp, 230V A/C unit and 5 kVA electric heat?

(a) 160 kVA   (b) 125 kVA   (c) 6 kVA   (d) 5 kVA

• Answer: (b) 125 kVA
  Air-Conditioning [Table 430.248] 230V x 17A = 3,910 VA per unit
  3,910 VA x 25 units = 97,750 VA (97.75 kVA), (omit)
  Heat [220.51] 5 kVA x 25 units = 125 kVA

Step 3. Appliance Calculated Load [220.53]

► **Appliance Load Example 1**

What is the appliance calculated load for a 20-unit multifamily building that contains a 940 VA waste disposal, a 1,250 VA dishwasher, and a 4,500 VA water heater in each unit? **Figure 10-5**

(a) 100 kVA	(b) 134 kVA	(c) 7 kVA	(d) 5 kVA

• Answer: (a) 100 kVA

Waste Disposal	940 VA		
Dishwasher	1,250 VA		
Water Heater	+ 4,500 VA		
Connected Load per Unit	6,690 VA		
Total Connected Load	6.690 VA	x 20 units =	133,800 VA
Total Calculated Load	133,800 VA	x 0.75* =	100,350 VA

*Use the total number of appliances to determine if the 75% demand factor applies. In this case, there are 60 appliances on the service/feeder conductors [220.53].

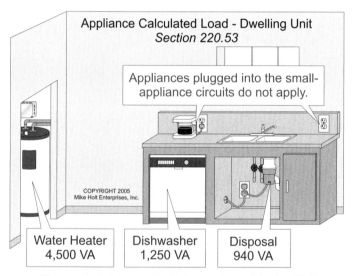

Appliance Calculated Load - Dwelling Unit
Section 220.53

Appliances plugged into the small-appliance circuits do not apply.

COPYRIGHT 2005
Mike Holt Enterprises, Inc.

Water Heater	Dishwasher	Disposal
4,500 VA	1,250 VA	940 VA

There are not enough appliances to apply the 75% demand factor to a single unit, but for the service calculation, there are 20 units with 3 appliances.

Waste disposer	940 VA
Dishwasher	1,250 VA
Water heater	4,500 VA
Connected load =	6,690 VA

6,690 VA x 20 units x 0.75 = 100,350 VA calculated load

Figure 10–5

▶ **Appliance Load Example 2**

What is the appliance calculated load for a 35-unit multifamily building that contains a 900 VA waste disposal, a 1,200 VA dishwasher, and a 5,000 VA water heater in each unit?

(a) 71 kVA (b) 142 kVA (c) 107 kVA (d) 186 kVA

• Answer: (d) 186 kVA

Waste Disposal	900 VA
Dishwasher	1,200 VA
Water Heater	+ 5,000 VA
Connected Load per Unit	7,100 VA

Total Connected Load	7,100 VA	x 35 units =	248,500 VA
Calculated Load	248,500 VA	x 0.75* =	186,375 VA

*Use the total number of appliances to determine if the 75% demand factor applies. In this case, there are 105 appliances on the service/feeder conductors [220.53].

Step 4: Household Dryer Calculated Load [220.54]

▶ **Dryer Load Example 1**

A 10-unit multifamily dwelling building contains a 4.5 kVA electric clothes dryer in each unit. What is the feeder/service dryer calculated load for the building?

(a) 5 kVA (b) 25 kVA (c) 60 kVA (d) none of these

• Answer: (b) 25 kVA

5 kVA is the minimum load for calculation [220.54]
Connected Load = 5 kVA x 10 units
Connected Load = 50 kVA

Calculated Load = Connected Load x Demand Factor [Table 220.54]
Calculated Load = 50 kVA x 0.50
Calculated Load = 25 kVA

▶ **Dryer Load Example 2**

A 20-unit multifamily dwelling building contains a 5.25 kVA electric clothes dryer in each unit. What is the feeder/service dryer calculated load for the building?

(a) 5 kVA (b) 27 kVA (c) 60 kVA (d) 39.9 kVA

• Answer: (d) 39.9 kVA

When the number of household electric dryers falls in the categories of 12 through 22, or 24 through 42, the formula used to determine the demand factor percent is specified in Table 220.54.

For 20 dryers, the demand factor percent is calculated by the following formula:

Dryer Demand Factor (Percent) = 47 – (number of dryers - 11)
Percent = 47 – (number of dryers – 11)
Percent = 47 – (20 dryers – 11)
Percent = 47 – 9
Percent = 38%

Calculated Load = Connected Load x Demand Factor Percent
Connected Load = 5.25 kVA x 20 units
Calculated Load = 5.25 kVA x 20 units x 0.38
Calculated Load = 39.9 kVA

Step 5: Household Cooking Equipment Calculated Load [220.55]

▶ **Table 220.55 Column C—not Over 12 kVA**

What is the feeder/service calculated load for five 9 kVA ranges?

(a) 9 kVA   (b) 45 kVA   (c) 20 kVA   (d) none of these

• Answer: (c) 20 kVA
   Over 8 3/4, under 12 kVA, look up in Column C kW Demand Load

▶ **Table 220.55, Note 1—Over 12 kVA with Equal Ratings**

What is the feeder/service calculated load for three 15.6 kVA ranges?

(a) 15 kVA   (b) 14 kVA   (c) 17 kVA   (d) 21 kVA

• Answer: (c) 17 kVA (closest answer)

Step a: Column C Demand Load for 3 units: 14 kVA.

Step b: The 15.6 kVA range exceeds 12 kVA by 3.6 kVA.
           Increase the Column C Demand Load by 5% for each kVA or major fraction of kVA in excess of 12 kVA.

Step c: 3.6 is 3 plus a major fraction, so increase the Column C value by 4 x 5% = 20%
           Increase the Column C load (14 kVA) by 20%: 14 kVA x 1.2 = 16.8 kVA.

▶ **Table 220.55, Note 2—Unequal Ratings Over 12 kVA**

What is the feeder/service calculated load for three ranges rated 9 kVA and three ranges rated 14 kVA?

(a) 36 kVA   (b) 42 kVA   (c) 78 kVA   (d) 22 kVA

• Answer: (d) 22 kVA

Step a: Determine the total connected load:

9 kVA (minimum 12 kVA)	3 ranges x 12 kVA =	36 kVA
14 kVA	3 ranges x 14 kVA =	42 kVA
Total Connected Load		78 kVA

Step b: Determine the average range rating:
           78 kVA/6 units = 13 kVA average rating.

Step c: Demand load Table 220.55 Column C:
           6 ranges = 21 kVA.

Step d: The average range (13 kVA) exceeds 12 kVA by 1 kVA. Increase the Column C Demand load (21 kVA) by 5%:
           Calculated Load = 21 kVA x 1.05 = 22.05 kVA.

▶ **Table 220.55, Note 3—Over 1 3/4 kVA and Less than 3 1/2 kVA—Column A**

What is the feeder/service calculated load for ten 3 kVA ovens?

(a) 10 kVA   (b) 30 kVA
(c) 15 kVA   (d) 20 kVA

- Answer: (c) 15 kVA (closest answer)
  Connected Load = 3 kVA x 10 units = 30 kVA
  Calculated Load = 30 kVA x 0.49
  Calculated Load = 14.70 kVA

▶ **Table 220.55, Note 3—3 1/4 to 8 3/4 kW—Column B**

What is the feeder/service calculated load for eight 6 kVA cooktops?

(a) 10 kVA   (b) 17 kVA
(c) 14.7 kVA   (d) 48 kVA

- Answer: (b) 17 kVA
  Connected Load = 6 kVA x 8 units = 48 kVA
  Calculated Load = 48 kVA x 0.36 kVA
  Calculated Load = 17.28 kVA

Step 6: Service Conductor Size [Table 310.16]

▶ **Service Conductor Size Example 1**

What size copper service conductors are required for a 120/240V, single-phase multifamily building that has a total calculated load of 93 kVA? **Figure 10-6**

(a) 300 kcmil   (b) 350 kcmil
(c) 500 kcmil   (d) 600 kcmil

- Answer: (d) 600 kcmil copper

  $I = VA/E$
  $I = 93,000\ VA/240V$
  $I = 388A$

  600 kcmil copper, rated 420A at 75°C [Table 310.16]

AUTHOR'S COMMENT: Table 310.15(B)(6) only applies to individual 120/240V dwelling units 400A or less for single-family, two-family, or multifamily buildings. In this building, Table 310.15(B)(6) can be used for the feeder to each apartment, but Table 310.16 must be used for sizing the service/feeder conductors that supply the entire building.

▶ **Service Conductor Size Example 2**

What size service conductors are required for a multifamily building that has a total calculated load of 270 kVA for a 120/208V, three-phase system? Service conductors are run in parallel in two raceways. **Figure 10-7**

(a) 2–300 kcmil per phase   (b) 2–350 kcmil per phase
(c) 2–500 kcmil per phase   (d) 2–600 kcmil per phase

- Answer: (c) 2–500 kcmil per phase

  $I = VA/(1.732 \times 208V)$

Conductor Sizing - Multifamily Dwelling
Table 310.16

120/240V Service Demand Load of 93 kVA

Requires 600 kcmil rated 420A at 75ºC

COPYRIGHT 2005 Mike Holt Enterprises, Inc.

Determine the service conductor size.

VA = 93 kVA x 1,000 = 93,000 VA

$I = \dfrac{VA}{E} = \dfrac{93,000\ VA}{240V} = 388A$

Step 2: Table 310.16, 75ºC column = 600 kcmil

Figure 10–6

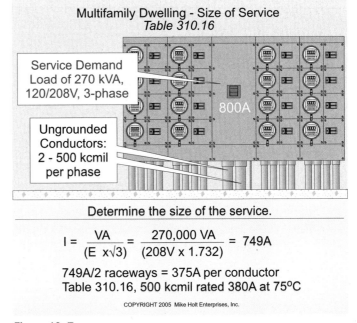

Multifamily Dwelling - Size of Service
Table 310.16

Service Demand Load of 270 kVA, 120/208V, 3-phase

Ungrounded Conductors: 2 - 500 kcmil per phase

800A

Determine the size of the service.

$I = \dfrac{VA}{(E \times \sqrt{3})} = \dfrac{270,000\ VA}{(208V \times 1.732)} = 749A$

749A/2 raceways = 375A per conductor
Table 310.16, 500 kcmil rated 380A at 75ºC

COPYRIGHT 2005 Mike Holt Enterprises, Inc.

Figure 10–7

I = 270,000 VA/(1.732 x 208V)
I = 749A

Amperes per Parallel Set = Amperes/Number of Parallel Sets
749A/2 conductors in parallel = 375A per conductor.

A 500 kcmil conductor has an ampacity of 380A [Table 310.16 at 75ºC]. Table 310.15(B)(6) does not apply to services or feeders for multifamily buildings.

Two sets of 500 kcmil conductors (380A x 2) can be protected by an 800A protection device. Their combined ampacity is 760A, but we are allowed to round up to the next standard size protection device [240.4(B) and 240.6(A)].

AUTHOR'S COMMENT: Note that throughout this book, we are using copper conductors unless otherwise specified.

10.3 Multifamily Dwelling Unit Calculations—Standard Method

▶ Standard Method Example

What is the calculated load for a 25-unit apartment building? The system voltage is 120/240V, single-phase. Each apartment is 1,000 sq ft, and contains the following:

Dishwasher	1.2 kVA
Waste Disposal	1.5 kVA
Water Heater	4.5 kVA
Dryer	4.5 kVA
Range	15.5 kVA
Air-conditioning (230V)	28 A
Electric Space Heating	7.5 kVA

Step 1: General Lighting, Small-Appliance, and Laundry Demand [Table 220.42]

General Lighting (1,000 sq ft x 3 VA) [220.12]	3,000 VA		
Small-Appliance Circuits [220.52(A)]	3,000 VA		
Laundry Circuit [220.52(B)]	+ 1,500 VA		
	7,500 VA		
Total Connected Load (7,500 VA x 25 units)	187,500 VA		
First 3,000 VA at 100%	− 3,000 VA	x 1.00 =	3,000 VA
	184,500 VA		
Next 117,000 VA at 35%	− 117,000 VA	x 0.35 =	40,950 VA
Remainder at 25%	67,500 VA	x 0.25 =	+ 16,875 VA
Total Calculated Load			60,825 VA

Step 2: Air-Conditioning versus Heat [220.51]

VA = V x A
Air-conditioning 230V x 28A = 6,440 VA
6,440 VA x 25 units = 161,000 VA, (omit) [220.60]
Heat [220.51] 7,500 VA x 25 units = 187,500 VA

Step 3: Appliance Calculated Load [220.53]

Dishwasher	1,200 VA		
Waste Disposal	1,500 VA		
Water Heater	+ 4,500 VA		
Connected Load	7,200 VA	x 25 units =	180,000 VA
Calculated Load	180,000 VA	x 0.75* =	135,000 VA

*Use the total number of appliances to determine if the 75% demand factor applies. In this case, there are 75 appliances on the service/feeder conductors [220.53]

Step 4: Dryer Calculated Load [220.54]

Dryers must be calculated at a minimum of 5,000 VA or the nameplate, whichever is larger [220.54].

Total Connected Load = 5 kVA x 25 units
Total Connected Load = 125,000 VA

Dryer Demand Factor (Percent) [Table 220.54]
Percent = 35 – 0.50 x (number of dryers – 23)
Percent = 35 – 0.50 x (25 dryers – 23)
Percent = 35 – (0.50 x 2)
Percent = 35 – 1
Percent = 34%

Calculated Load = Connected Load x Demand Factor Percent
Calculated Load = 125,000 VA x 0.34

Dryer Calculated Load = 42,500 VA

Step 5: Cooking Equipment Calculated Load [220.55]

Step a: Column C demand load for 25 units = 40 kVA. [Table 220.54]

Step b: 15.5 kVA – 12 kVA = 3.5 kVA.

Step c: Increase the Column C demand load (40 kVA) by 4 x 5% = 20%.

Step d: Range calculated load: 40 kVA x 1.2 = 48 kVA

Step 6: Service Conductor Size

Step a:	Total general lighting, small-appliance, and laundry calculated load	60,825 VA
Step b:	Total heat calculated load [220.51] (7,500 VA x 25 units)	187,500 VA
Step c:	Total appliance calculated load	135,000 VA
Step d:	Total dryer calculated load	42,500 VA
Step e:	Range calculated load	+ 48,000 VA
	Total Calculated Load	473,825 VA

Service Conductor Amperes = VA/E
Service Conductor Amperes = 473,825 VA/240V
Service Conductor Amperes = 1,974A

PART B—OPTIONAL METHOD-FEEDER/SERVICE LOAD CALCULATIONS

10.4 Multifamily Dwelling Unit Calculations [220.84]—Optional Method

Instead of sizing the ungrounded conductors according to the standard method from Article 220, Part III, the optional method in Part IV of Article 220 can be used for feeders and service conductors in multifamily dwelling units. Follow these steps for determining the calculated load:

The feeder/service calculated load for a building that has three or more dwelling units equipped with electric cooking equipment and either electric space heating or air-conditioning can be calculated in accordance with the demand factors of Table 220.84, based on the number of dwelling units. The feeder/service neutral calculated load must be determined in accordance with 220.61.

House loads [220.84(B)] are calculated in accordance with Article 220, Part III and then added to the Table 220.84 calculated load.

> **AUTHOR'S COMMENT:** House loads are those not directly associated with the individual dwelling units of a multifamily dwelling. Some examples of house loads might be landscape and parking lot lighting, common area lighting, common laundry facilities, common pool and recreation areas, etc.

Step 1: Total Connected Load [220.84(C)]

The following connected loads from all the dwelling units are added together, then the Table 220.84 demand factor is applied to get the calculated load:

- 3 VA per sq ft for general lighting and general-use receptacles.
- 1,500 VA for each small-appliance circuit (minimum of 2 circuits [220.52(A)]).
- 1,500 VA for each laundry circuit [220.52(B)].
- The nameplate rating of all appliances.
- The nameplate rating of all motors.
- The larger of the air-conditioning load or the space-heating load.

> **AUTHOR'S COMMENT:** A laundry circuit is not required for an individual dwelling unit if common laundry facilities are provided.

Step 2: Demand Load

The calculated load is determined by applying the demand factor from Table 220.84 to the total connected load (Step 1). The calculated load (kVA) can be converted to amperes by:

Single-Phase Formula: **Three-Phase Formula:**
   I = VA/E   I = VA/(1.732 x E)

Step 3: Feeder and Service Conductor Size

The ungrounded conductors are sized according to Table 310.16 based on the calculated load.

When do you use the standard method versus the optional method? For the purpose of exam preparation, always use the standard load calculation unless the question specifies the optional method. In the field, you will probably want to use the optional method because it results in a smaller service.

10.5 Multifamily—Optional Method Example 1 [220.84]

A 120/240V, single-phase system supplies a 12-unit multifamily building. Each 1,500 sq ft unit contains:

Waste Disposal	1.5 VA
Dishwasher	1.5 kVA
Water Heater	4 kVA
Washing Machine	1.2 kVA
Dryer	4.5 kVA
Range	14.4 kVA
A/C	3 hp
A/C Fan Motor	1/8 hp
Electric Space Heating	5 kVA

▶ **General Lighting Load Example**

Using the optional calculation method, what is the calculated load for the building's general lighting and general-use receptacles, and small-appliance and laundry circuits? *Note: The washing machine is calculated as part of the 1,500 VA laundry circuit.*

(a) 44 kVA   (b) 90 kVA   (c) 108 kVA   (d) 60 kVA

• Answer: (a) 44 kVA

General Lighting (1,500 sq ft x 3 VA)	4,500 VA
Small-Appliance Circuits (2 circuits x 1,500 VA)	3,000 VA
Laundry Circuit	+ 1,500 VA
Connected Load per Unit	9,000 VA

Total Connected Load	9,000 VA	x 12 units =	108,000 VA
Calculated Load	108,000 VA	x 0.41* =	44,280 VA

*Use the demand factor from Table 220.84

▶ **Air-Conditioning versus Heat Load Example**

Using the optional calculation method, what is the calculated load for the building's air-conditioning versus heat?

(a) 52 kVA   (b) 60 kVA   (c) 30 kVA   (d) 25 kVA

• Answer: (d) 25 kVA [220.84(C)(5)]

A/C (3 hp) 230V FLC = 17A [Table 430.248]
A/C VA = 230V x 17A [Table 430.248]   3,910 VA
Fan (1/8 hp) 230V x 1.45A* [Table 430.248]   + 334 VA
*One-half the value of a 1/4 hp motor [Table 430.248]   4,244 VA   x 12 units x 0.41 = 20,880 VA, (omit)

Heat [220.84(C)(5)]: 5,000W x 12 units = 60,000 VA x 0.41* = 24,600W.
* Use the demand factor from Table 220.84

▶ **Appliance Calculated Load Example**

Using the optional calculation method, what is the calculated load for the appliances that are fixed in place?

(a) 25 kVA   (b) 50 kVA   (c) 100 kVA   (d) 120 kVA

• Answer: (d) 120 kVA [220.84(C)(3)]

Dishwasher	1,500 VA
Water Heater	4,000 VA
Dryer (nameplate)	4,500 VA
Range (nameplate)	+ 14,400 VA
Calculated Load	24,400 VA

Calculated Load 24,400 VA   x 12 units x 0.41*   = 120,048 VA

*Use the demand factor from Table 220.84

Note: The washing machine is calculated as part of the laundry circuit in Step 1.

▶ **Total Calculated Loads**

General Lighting, Receptacle	44,280 VA
Heat Connected Load	24,600 VA
Appliances Connected Load	+120,048 VA
Total Calculated Load	188,928 VA

▶ **Service Conductor Size**

If the total calculated load equals 189 kVA, what is the service conductor size? The service is 120/240V, single-phase. Figure 10-8

(a) 600A   (b) 800A   (c) 1,000A   (d) 1,200A

• Answer: (b) 800A

I = VA/E
I = 189,000 VA/240V
I = 788A
800A service [240.6(A)]

Conductor size if paralleled in 2 raceways [240.4(B)]:
788A/2 raceways = 394A per conductor

Table 310.16, 600 kcmil rated 420A at 75°C

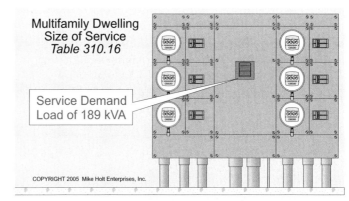

Multifamily Dwelling
Size of Service
Table 310.16

Service Demand
Load of 189 kVA

COPYRIGHT 2005 Mike Holt Enterprises, Inc.

Determine the size of the service.

VA = 189 kVA x 1,000 = 189,000 VA

$$I = \frac{VA}{E} = \frac{189,000 \text{ VA}}{240V} = 788A$$

788A/2 raceways = 394A per conductor
Table 310.16, 600 kcmil rated 420A at 75°C

Figure 10–8

10.6 Multifamily—Optional Method Example 2 [220.84]

Another method is to add all of the loads first, then apply the demand factor to the total connected load. A 120/240V, single-phase system supplies a 12-unit multifamily building. Each 1,500 sq ft unit contains:

Dishwasher	1.5 kVA
Water Heater	4 kVA
Washing Machine	1.2 kVA
Dryer	4.5 kVA
Range	14.4 kVA
A/C	3 hp
A/C Fan Motor	1/8 hp
Electric Space Heating	5 kVA

Using the optional method of calculation, what is the calculated load for the building's general lighting and general-use receptacles, and small-appliance and laundry circuits? *Note: The washing machine is calculated as part of the 1,500 VA laundry circuit.*

Step 1: Total Connected Load

Step a: Determine the General Lighting Load:

General Lighting (1,500 sq ft x 3 VA)	4,500 VA		
Small-Appliance Circuits (1,500 VA each)	3,000 VA		
Laundry Circuit	+1,500 VA		
Connected Load Per Unit	9,000 VA		
Total Connected Load	9,000 VA	x 12 units	= 108,000 VA

Step b: Determine the Appliance Calculated Load:

Using the optional method of calculation, what is the calculated load for the appliances that are fixed in place?

Dishwasher	1.5 kVA
Water Heater	4 kVA
Dryer	4.5 kVA
Range	14.4 kVA

Appliance Calculated Load	
Dishwasher	1,500 VA
Water Heater	4,000 VA
Dryer (nameplate)	4,500 VA
Range (nameplate)	+ 14,400 VA
	24,400 VA

Total Appliance Connected Load =	24,400 VA	x 12 units =	292,800 VA

Step c: Compare the Air-Conditioning versus Heat Load:

Using the optional method of calculation, what is the calculated load for the building's air-conditioning versus heat?

A/C	3 hp with 1/8 hp fan
Heat	5 kVA

A/C (3 hp) 230V x 17A [Table 430.248]	3,910 VA
Fan (1/8 hp) 230V x 1.45A*	+ 334 VA
	4,244 VA

*One-half the value of a 1/4 hp motor

A/C Connected Load		4,244 VA	x 12 units =	50,928 VA (omit)
Heat Connected Load =		5,000 VA	x 12 units =	60,000 VA

Step 2: Total Connected Loads

General Lighting, Receptacle	108,000VA
Heat Connected Load	60,000 VA
Appliances Connected Load	+292,800 VA
Total Connected Load	460,800 VA

Total Calculated Load	460,800 VA	x 0.41* =	188,928 VA

*[Table 220.84]

Step 3: Service Conductor Size

If the total calculated load equals 189 kVA, what is the service conductor size in amperes? The service is 120/240V, single-phase.

(a) 200A   (b) 400A   (c) 800A   (d) 1,200A

• Answer: (c) 800A
  [240.6(A)]

I = VA/E
I = 189,000 VA/240V
I = 788A

Conductor size if paralleled in 2 raceways [240.4(B)]:

788A/2 raceways = 394A per conductor [Table 310.16], 600 kcmil rated 420A at 75°C

Unit 10 Conclusion

As you have seen in Unit 10, the sizing of branch circuits, feeders, and service conductors for multifamily dwellings and single-family dwellings have much in common. The feeders to individual dwelling units are sized in the same manner whether that dwelling unit is a single-family dwelling or an individual unit of an apartment building. The *Code* allows the use of Table 310.15(B)(6) for sizing the feeders or service conductors to an individual dwelling unit; however, the conductors that feed the service to a multifamily dwelling must be sized using Table 310.16.

Some additional demand factors for multifamily dwellings are allowed, on the presumption that there will be diversity of usage between the various units. Dryers are allowed the demand factors of Table 220.54, which do not even begin to provide less than 100% demand until there are five units or more. Perhaps one of the most confusing single tables in the *NEC* is Table 220.55 for household ranges. This table is confusing for a number of reasons, one of which is because the first two columns are percentage multipliers, while the third column is a final kVA value. The notes to this table further complicate matters. Be sure you have studied this part of Unit 10 well and are able to complete the calculations using the range table as well as sizing the service for a multifamily dwelling unit.

(• Indicates that 75% or fewer of those who took this exam answered the question correctly.)

10.1 Multifamily Dwelling Unit Calculations—Standard Method

1. •Each unit of a 20-unit apartment building is 840 sq ft. What is the general lighting and general-use receptacle feeder/service calculated load for the building? *Note: Laundry facilities are provided on the premises for all tenants.*

    (a) 5,200 VA   (b) 40,590 VA   (c) 110,400 VA   (d) none of these

2. •Each unit of a 20-unit apartment building is 990 sq ft. What is the general lighting and general-use receptacle feeder/service calculated load for the building?

    (a) 74,700 VA   (b) 149,400 VA   (c) 51,300 VA   (d) 105,600 VA

3. A 40-unit multifamily building has an air-conditioner (3 hp, 230V) and two 3kW baseboard heaters in each unit. What is the feeder/service calculated load for the air conditioning and heat?

    (a) 160 kW   (b) 240 kW   (c) 60 kW   (d) 50 kW

4. Each unit of a 25-unit multifamily building has air-conditioning (3 hp, 230V) and electric heat (5 kW). What is the air conditioning and heat feeder/service calculated load?

    (a) 160 kW   (b) 125 kW   (c) 6 kW   (d) 5 kW

5. In a 16-unit multifamily building, each unit contains a waste disposal (940 VA), a dishwasher (1,250 VA), and a water heater (4,500 VA). What is the feeder/service calculated load for these appliances?

    (a) 100 kVA   (b) 134 kVA   (c) 80 kVA   (d) 5 kVA

6. Each unit in a 28-unit apartment building contains a waste disposal (900 VA), dishwasher (1,200 VA), and a water heater (5,000 VA). What is the feeder/service calculated load for the appliances?

    (a) 149 kVA   (b) 142 kVA   (c) 107 kVA   (d) 186 kVA

7. A multifamily dwelling (40 units) contains a 4.5 kW electric clothes dryer in each unit. What is the feeder/service calculated load for all of the dryers?

    (a) 53 kW   (b) 27 kW   (c) 60 kW   (d) none of these

8. What is the feeder/service calculated load for ten 5.25 kW dryers installed in dwelling units of a multifamily building?

    (a) 26 kW   (b) 37 kW   (c) 60 kW   (d) 40 kW

9. What is the feeder/service calculated load for twelve 3.25 kW ovens?

    (a) 10 kW   (b) 18 kW   (c) 15 kW   (d) 20 kW

10. What is the feeder/service calculated load for eight 7 kW counter-mounted cooktops?

    (a) 20 kW   (b) 17 kW   (c) 14.7 kW   (d) 48 kW

11. What is the feeder/service calculated load for five 12.4 kW ranges?

    (a) 9 kW   (b) 45 kW   (c) 20 kW   (d) none of these

12. •What is the feeder/service calculated load for three ranges rated 15.5 kW each?

    (a) 15 kW   (b) 14 kW   (c) 17 kW   (d) 21 kW

13. What is the feeder/service calculated load for three ranges rated 11 kW and three ranges rated 14 kW?

    (a) 36 kW   (b) 42 kW   (c) 78 kW   (d) 22 kW

14. •What size aluminum service conductors are required for a 120/240V, single-phase multifamily building that has a total calculated load of 90 kW?

    (a) 500 kcmil AL   (b) 600 kcmil AL   (c) 700 kcmil AL   (d) 800 kcmil AL

15. What size copper service conductors are required for a multifamily building that has a total calculated load of 260 kW for a 120/208V wye, three-phase system? The conductors are paralleled in two raceways.

    (a) 2 - 300 kcmil   (b) 2 - 350 kcmil   (c) 2 - 500 kcmil   (d) 2 - 600 kcmil

The following information applies to the next five questions. A multifamily building has 12 units. The system voltage is 120/240V, single-phase. Each is 1,500 sq ft and contains the following:

Dryer	4.5 kW
Washing Machine	1.2 kVA
Range	14.45 kW
Dishwasher	1.5 kVA
Water Heater	4 kW
Heat	5 kW
A/C	3 hp
A/C Fan Motor	1/8 hp (334 VA)

16. •What is the building's feeder/service calculated load for the general lighting and general-use receptacles, and the small-appliance and laundry circuits in VA?

    (a) 40 kVA   (b) 108 kVA   (c) 105 kVA   (d) 90 kVA

17. What is the building's feeder/service calculated load for the air conditioner (3 hp with a 1/8 hp compressor fan) versus electric heat (5 kW)?

    (a) 52 kW   (b) 60 kW   (c) 30 kW   (d) 105 kW

18. What is the building's feeder/service calculated load for the appliances in VA?

    (a) 40 kVA   (b) 55 kVA   (c) 43 kVA   (d) 50 kVA

19. What is the building's feeder/service calculated load for the 4.5 kW dryers?

    (a) 60.4 kW   (b) 27.6 kW   (c) 55.3 kW   (d) 45.7 kW

20. What is the building's feeder/service calculated load for the 14.45 kW range?

    (a) 27 kW   (b) 35 kW   (c) 168 kW   (d) 30 kW

21. If the total calculated load of a multifamily dwelling unit is 206 kVA, what is the minimum feeder/service conductor size? The system voltage is 120/240, single-phase.

    (a) 600A   (b) 800A   (c) 1,000A   (d) 1,200A

22. •If a service consists of three sets of parallel 400 kcmil conductors routed in three separate raceways, what size equipment bonding jumper is required for each service raceway?

    (a) 1 AWG   (b) 1/0 AWG   (c) 2/0 AWG   (d) 3/0 AWG

23. •If three sets of 400 kcmil copper service conductors are in parallel in three raceways, what is the minimum size grounding electrode conductor required?

    (a) 1/0 AWG   (b) 2/0 AWG   (c) 3/0 AWG   (d) 4/0 AWG

10.4 Multifamily Dwelling Unit Calculations [220.84]—Optional Method

24. •When determining the service (using the optional calculation method) for a multifamily dwelling, the total connected load must have the demand factors of Table 220.84 applied. When determining the total connected load, _____ must be used.

    (a) 125% of the air-conditioning load plus 100% of the space-heating load
    (b) the larger of the air-conditioning load or the space-heating load
    (c) the sum of the air-conditioning load and the space-heating load
    (d) 125% of the sum of the air-conditioning load and the space-heating load

25. A multifamily building has 60 units. Each unit is 1,500 sq ft. Using the optional dwelling unit calculations, what is the calculated load for the building's general lighting and general-use receptacles, and small-appliance and laundry circuits?

    (a) 145 kVA   (b) 190 kVA   (c) 108 kVA   (d) 130 kVA

26. A 60-unit multifamily dwelling has an air conditioner (3 hp with a 1/8 hp blower) and electric heat (5 kW) in each unit. Using the optional calculation method, what is the air-conditioning versus heat calculated load?

    (a) 50 kVA   (b) 61 kVA   (c) 30 kVA   (d) 72 kVA

27. Using the optional method for dwelling unit calculations, what is the fixed appliance portion of the 60-unit multifamily building's calculated load if each unit has a water heater (4 kW) and a dishwasher (1.5 kW)?

    (a) 80 kW   (b) 50 kW   (c) 30 kW   (d) 60 kW

28. Each unit of a 60-unit apartment building has a 4 kW dryer. Using the optional calculation method, the calculated load added to the service for the dryers is _____.

    (a) 75 kW   (b) 240 kW   (c) 72 kW   (d) 58 kW

29. Using the optional method for dwelling unit calculations, what is the dryer portion of a 60-unit multifamily building's calculated load if there is a 4.5 kW dryer in each unit?

    (a) 65 kW   (b) 25 kW   (c) 55 kW   (d) 75 kW

30. Using the optional method for dwelling unit calculations, what is the electric range portion of a 60-unit multifamily building's calculated load if each apartment has a 14 kW range?

    (a) 150 kW   (b) 50 kW   (c) 100 kW   (d) 200 kW

31. If the total calculated load for a multifamily dwelling is 270 kVA, what is the minimum feeder/service conductor size? The service is 120/208V, three-phase.

    (a) 600A   (b) 800A   (c) 1,000A   (d) 1,200A

32. Each unit of a 20-unit multifamily dwelling has 900 sq ft of living space and contains one of each of the following: air-conditioning (5 hp), heat (5 kW), water heater (5 kW), and range (14 kW). The service for this apartment building is approximately _____ if the optional method of calculation is used. (120/240V)

    (a) 200 kVA   (b) 250 kVA   (c) 280 kVA   (d) 320 kVA

33. •If two parallel service conductors per phase are installed in two raceways (500 kcmil in each raceway), what size equipment bonding jumper is required for each service raceway?

    (a) 2 AWG   (b) 1 AWG   (c) 1/0 AWG   (d) 2/0 AWG

34. •If two parallel service conductors per phase are installed in two raceways (500 kcmil in each raceway), what is the minimum size copper grounding electrode conductor required?

    (a) 1/0 AWG   (b) 2/0 AWG   (c) 3/0 AWG   (d) 4/0 AWG

Unit 10 Calculation Challenge Questions

(• Indicates that 75% or fewer of those who took this exam answered the question correctly.)

10.2 Multifamily Dwelling Unit Calculation Examples—Standard Method

General Lighting and Receptacle Calculations [Table 220.42]

1. Each dwelling unit of a 20-unit multifamily building has 900 square feet of living space. What is the general lighting and general-use receptacle load, before demand factors are applied, for the multifamily dwelling unit apartment building?

    (a) 45 kVA   (b) 60 kVA   (c) 37 kVA   (d) 54 kVA

2. A multifamily apartment building contains 20 units and each unit has 840 sq ft of living space. What is the general lighting service calculated load for the multifamily building if laundry facilities are provided on the premises for all tenants and no laundry circuit is installed in each unit?

    (a) 35 kVA   (b) 41 kVA   (c) 45 kVA   (d) 63 kVA

Appliance Demand Factors [220.53]

3. A multifamily apartment building contains 20 units. Each unit contains a waste disposal (900 VA), a dishwasher (1,200 VA), and a water heater (5,000 VA). What is the feeder calculated load for the appliances in this building?

    (a) 106,500 VA   (b) 117,100 VA   (c) 137,000 VA   (d) 60,000 VA

Dryer Calculation [220.54]

4. The nameplate rating for each household dryer in a 10-unit apartment building is 4 kW. This will add _____ to the service size.

    (a) 20 kW   (b) 25 kW   (c) 40 kW   (d) 50 kW

Ranges–Table 220.55, Note 1

5. •The calculated load for thirty 15.8 kW household ranges is _____.

    (a) 31 kW   (b) 47 kW   (c) 54 kW   (d) 33 kW

Ranges–Table 220.55, Note 2

6. What is the feeder calculated load for five 10 kW, five 14 kW, and five 16 kW household ranges?

    (a) 210 kW   (b) 30 kW   (c) 14 kW   (d) 33 kW

7. What kW needs to be added to service loads for ten 12 kW, eight 14 kW, and two 9 kW household ranges?

    (a) 33 kW   (b) 35 kW   (c) 36.75 kW   (d) 29.35 kW

Ranges–Table 220.55, Note 3

8. What is the minimum service calculated load for five 5 kW cooktops, two 4 kW ovens, and four 7 kW ranges?

    (a) 15.5 kW   (b) 8.8 kW   (c) 19.5 kW   (d) 18.2 kW

9.   •What is the maximum dwelling unit feeder/service calculated load for fifteen 8 kW cooking units?

(a) 38.4 kW   (b) 30 kW   (c) 120 kW   (d) none of these

Ranges – Table 220.55, Note 5

10.   A school has twenty 10 kW ranges installed in the home economics class. The minimum load this adds to the service is _____.

(a) 35 kW   (b) 44.8 kW   (c) 56 kW   (d) 160 kW

Neutral Calculation [220.61]

11.   The service neutral load for household electric clothes dryers must be calculated at _____ of the load as determined by 220.54.

(a) 50%   (b) 60%   (c) 70%   (d) 80%

12.   The feeder neutral demand for fifteen 9 kW cooking units is _____.

(a) 38.4 kW   (b) 30 kW   (c) 120 kW   (d) 21 kW

13.   What is the feeder neutral load for ten 5 kW household dryers?

(a) 17.5 kW   (b) 21.5 kW   (c) 27.5 kW   (d) 32.5 kW

14.   An 11-unit multifamily dwelling contains a 4 kW electric clothes dryer in each unit. What is the feeder/service neutral calculated load?

(a) 18.1 kW   (b) 22.3 kW   (c) 29.3 kW   (d) 32.9 kW

15.   •What is the dwelling unit service neutral load for ten 9 kW ranges?

(a) 12.4 kW   (b) 13.5 kW   (c) 15.5 kW   (d) 17.5 kW

(• Indicates that 75% or fewer of those who took this exam answered the question correctly.)

Article 517 Health Care Facilities (continued)

1. The receptacles or the cover plates for the receptacles supplied from the emergency system for essential electrical systems in nursing homes must have a distinctive color or marking so as to be readily identifiable.

    (a) True   (b) False

2. In a health care facility, receptacles and attachment plugs in a hazardous (classified) location within an anesthetizing area must be listed for use in Class I, Group _____ locations.

    (a) A   (b) B   (c) C   (d) D

3. Equivalent insulation and isolation to that required for the electrical distribution systems in patient care areas must be provided for communications, signaling systems, data system circuits, fire alarm systems, and systems less than _____, nominal in health care facilities.

    (a) 600V   (b) 120V   (c) 50V   (d) 24V

Article 518 Assembly Occupancies

This article covers all buildings or portions of buildings or structures specifically designed or intended for the assembly of 100 or more persons.

4. An assembly occupancy is a building, portion of a building, or structure designed or intended for the assembly of _____ or more persons.

    (a) 50   (b) 100   (c) 150   (d) 200

5. For temporary wiring in assembly occupancies, such as exhibition halls used for display booths, the wiring must be installed in accordance with Article 590, except _____.

    (a) the GFCI requirements of 590.6 do not apply
    (b) hard or extra-hard usage cords and cables are permitted to be laid on floors where protected from the general public
    (c) no cords are allowed
    (d) a and b

6. In assembly occupancies, nonmetallic raceways encased in not less than _____ of concrete are permitted.

    (a) 1 in.   (b) 2 in.   (c) 3 in.   (d) none of these

Article 520 Theaters, Audience Areas of Motion Picture and Television Studios, Performance Areas, and Similar Locations

This article covers all buildings or that part of a building or structure, indoor or outdoor, designed or used for presentation, dramatic, musical, motion picture projection, or similar purposes and to specific audience seating areas within motion picture or television studios

7. •Article 520 locations include the performance area, which encompasses the stage and audience seating area associated with a _____ stage structure, whether indoors or outdoors, which is used for the presentation of theatrical or musical productions or public presentations.

    (a) temporary   (b) permanent   (c) a or b   (d) a and b

8. The wiring methods in theaters, audience areas of motion picture and television studios, performance areas, and similar locations for control, signal, and communications circuits can be _____.

    (a) communications circuits as provided in Article 800
    (b) Class 2 remote-control and signaling circuits as provided in Article 725
    (c) type NM cable
    (d) a or b, but not c

9. On fixed stage equipment, portable strip lights and connector strips must be wired with conductors having insulation rated suitable for the temperature but not less than _____.

    (a) 75°C   (b) 90°C   (c) 125°C   (d) 200°C

10. Flexible conductors, including cable extensions, used to supply portable stage equipment must be _____ cords or cables.

    (a) listed   (b) extra-hard usage   (c) hard usage   (d) a and b

Article 525 Carnivals, Circuses, Fairs, and Similar Events

This article covers the installation of portable wiring and equipment for carnivals, circuses, exhibitions, fairs, traveling attractions, and similar functions, including wiring in or on all structures.

11. Electrical wiring in and around water attractions such as bumper boats for carnivals, circuses, and fairs must comply with the requirements of Article 680—Swimming Pools, Fountains, and Similar Installations.

    (a) True   (b) False

12. At carnivals, circuses, and similar events, electrical equipment and wiring methods in or on rides, concessions, or other units must be provided with mechanical protection where such equipment or wiring methods are subject to _____.

    (a) public access   (b) physical damage   (c) exposure to the weather   (d) operator access

13. At carnivals, circuses, and similar events, service equipment must be mounted on a solid backing and be installed so as to be protected from the weather, unless _____.

    (a) the location is a mild climate   (b) installed for less than 90 days
    (c) of weatherproof construction   (d) a or b

14. When installed indoors for carnivals, circuses, and fairs, flexible cords and flexible cables must be listed for wet locations and must be sunlight resistant.

    (a) True   (b) False

15. Wiring for an amusement ride, attraction, tent, or similar structure must not be supported by any other ride or structure unless specifically designed for the purpose.

    (a) True   (b) False

16. Wiring for temporary lighting located inside tents and concession areas at carnivals, circuses, and fairs must be securely installed, and where subject to physical damage, must be provided with mechanical protection.

    (a) True   (b) False

17. GFCI protection for personnel is required at carnivals, circuses, and fairs for all 15 and 20A, 125V, single-phase receptacle outlets that are readily accessible to the general public.

(a) True   (b) False

18. GFCI protection is not permitted at carnivals, circuses, and fairs for _____.

(a) sign lighting   (b) equipment that is not readily accessible to the general public
(c) egress lighting   (d) circuits servicing spot lights

Article 530 Motion Picture and Television Studios and Similar Locations

The requirements of this article apply to television studios and motion picture studios using either film or electronic cameras, and exchanges, factories, laboratories, stages, or a portion of the building in which film or tape more than 7/8 in. in width is exposed, developed, printed, cut, edited, rewound, repaired, or stored.

19. Each receptacle of dc plugging boxes must be rated at not _____ when used on a stage or set of a motion picture studio.

(a) more than 30A   (b) less than 20A   (c) less than 30A   (d) more than 20A

Article 540 Motion Picture Projection Rooms

The provisions of this article apply to motion picture projection rooms, motion picture projectors, and associated equipment of the professional and nonprofessional types using incandescent, carbon arc, xenon, or other light source equipment that develops hazardous gases, dust, or radiation.

20. A switch for the control of parking lights in a theater may be installed inside the projection booth.

(a) True   (b) False

Article 545 Manufactured Buildings

This article covers requirements for a manufactured building and building components as herein defined.

21. The *NEC* specifies wiring methods for prefabricated buildings (manufactured buildings).

(a) True   (b) False

22. Service-entrance conductors for a manufactured building must be installed _____.

(a) after erection at the building site
(b) before erection only where the point of attachment is known prior to manufacture
(c) before erection at the building site
(d) a or b

Article 547 Agricultural Buildings

The provisions of this article apply to agricultural buildings or those parts of buildings or adjacent areas where excessive dust or dust with water may accumulate, or where a corrosive atmosphere exists.

23. Agricultural buildings where a corrosive atmosphere exists include areas with conditions such as _____.

(a) poultry and animal excrement which may cause corrosive vapors
(b) corrosive particles which may combine with water
(c) an area that is damp and wet by reason of periodic washing
(d) all of these

24. The distribution point is also known as the _____.

   (a) center yard pole   (b) meter pole
   (c) common distribution point   (d) all of these

25. The purpose of the equipotential plane is to prevent a difference in voltage within the plane area.

   (a) True   (b) False

26. All cables installed in agricultural buildings must be secured within _____ of each cabinet, box, or fitting.

   (a) 8 in.   (b) 12 in.   (c) 10 in.   (d) 18 in.

27. In damp or wet locations of agricultural buildings, equipment enclosures and fittings must be located or equipped to prevent moisture from _____ within the enclosure, box, conduit body, or fitting.

   (a) entering   (b) accumulating   (c) a or b   (d) none of these

28. Where _____ may be present in an agricultural building, enclosures and fittings must have corrosion-resistance properties suitable for the conditions.

   (a) wet dust   (b) corrosive gases or vapors   (c) other corrosive conditions   (d) any of these

29. An equipotential plane is not required in dirt confinement areas containing metallic equipment that is accessible to animals and may become energized. GFCI protection must be provided for all 15 and 20A general-purpose receptacles located in the dirt confinement areas.

   (a) True   (b) False

30. Where livestock is housed, that portion of the equipment grounding conductor run underground to the building or structure from a distribution point must be insulated or covered _____.

   (a) aluminum   (b) copper   (c) copper-clad aluminum   (d) none of these

31. Outdoor livestock confinement areas, such as feedlots, must have equipotential planes installed around metallic equipment that is accessible to animals and may become energized. The equipotential plane must encompass the area around the equipment where the animal stands while accessing the equipment.

   (a) True   (b) False

Article 550 Mobile Homes, Manufactured Homes, and Mobile Home Parks

The provisions of this article cover the electrical conductors and equipment installed within or on mobile or manufactured homes, the conductors that connect mobile or manufactured homes to a supply of electricity, and the installation of electrical wiring, fixtures, and equipment.

32. In reference to mobile/manufactured homes, examples of portable appliances could be _____, but only if these appliances are cord connected and not hard wired.

   (a) refrigerators   (b) range equipment   (c) clothes washers   (d) all of these

33. For the purpose of the *Code*, unless otherwise indicated the term mobile home includes manufactured homes.

   (a) True   (b) False

34. The power supply to the mobile home must be _____.

(a) one listed 50A mobile home power-supply cord with attachment plug
(b) a permanently-installed feeder
(c) a or b
(d) none of these

35. Ground-fault circuit-interrupter (GFCI) protection in a mobile home is required for _____.

(a) receptacle outlets installed outdoors and in compartments accessible from outside
(b) receptacles within 6 ft of a wet bar sink and serving kitchen countertops
(c) all receptacles in bathrooms including receptacles in luminaires (light fixtures)
(d) all of these

36. The receptacle outlet for mobile and manufactured home heat tape that is used to protect cold water inlet piping must be _____ protected and it must be connected to an interior branch circuit other than a small-appliance branch circuit where all of the outlets of the circuit are on the load side of the _____.

(a) AFCI   (b) GFCI   (c) a or b   (d) none of these

37. All branch circuits that supply 15 and 20A, 125V outlets in bedrooms of mobile homes and manufactured homes must be protected by _____.

(a) GFCIs   (b) weatherproof-in-use covers
(c) AFCIs   (d) none of these

38. •What is the total park electrical wiring system load, after applying the demand factors permitted in Article 550, for a small mobile home park having six mobile homes?

(a) 4,640 VA   (b) 27,840 VA   (c) 96,000 VA   (d) none of these

39. Service equipment for a manufactured home can be installed in or on a manufactured home provided that all of seven conditions are met. Which of the following are included in the seven conditions?

(a) The manufacturer must include in its written installation instructions information indicating that the home must be secured in place by an anchoring system or installed on and secured to a permanent foundation.
(b) The manufacturer must include in its written installation instructions one method of grounding the service equipment at the installation site. The instructions must clearly state that other methods of grounding are found in Article 250.
(c) A red warning label must be mounted on or adjacent to the service equipment "WARNING DO NOT PROVIDE ELECTRICAL POWER UNTIL THE GROUNDING ELECTRODE SYSTEM IS INSTALLED AND CONNECTED."
(d) all of these

40. An outdoor disconnecting means for a mobile home must be installed so the bottom of the enclosure is not less than _____ above the finished grade or working platform.

(a) 1 ft   (b) 2 ft   (c) 3 ft   (d) 6 ft

41. Mobile home and manufactured home lot feeder circuit conductors must have adequate capacity for the loads supplied and must be rated at not less than _____ at 120/240V.

(a) 50A   (b) 60A   (c) 100A   (d) 200A

Article 551 Recreational Vehicles and Recreational Vchiolc Parks

The provisions of this article cover the electrical conductors and equipment other than low-voltage and automotive vehicle circuits or extensions thereof, installed within or on recreational vehicles, the conductors that connect recreational vehicles to a supply of electricity, and the installation of equipment and devices related to electrical installations within a recreational vehicle park.

42. A minimum of 20 percent of all recreational vehicle sites with electrical supply must each be equipped with a _____,125/250V receptacle.

(a) 15A   (b) 20A   (c) 30A   (d) 50A

43. •Electrical service and feeders of a recreational vehicle park must be calculated at a minimum of _____ per site equipped with only 20A supply facilities (not including tent sites).

(a) 1,200 VA   (b) 2,400 VA   (c) 3,600 VA   (d) 9,600 VA

Article 555 Marinas and Boatyards

This article covers the installation of wiring and equipment in the areas that comprise fixed or floating piers, wharves, docks, and other areas in marinas, boatyards, boat basins, boathouses, and similar occupancies that are used, or intended to be used, for the purpose of repair, berthing, launching, storing or fueling of small craft and the mooring of floating buildings. This article doesn't apply to docks or boathouses for single-family dwelling units.

44. Private, noncommercial docking facilities _____ for the use of the owner or residents of the associated single-family dwelling are not covered by Article 555.

(a) constructed   (b) occupied   (c) a or b   (d) a and d

45. A _____ is an enclosed assembly that can include receptacles, circuit breakers, fused switches, fuses, watt-hour meter(s), and monitoring means approved for marine use. All such enclosures must have a weep hole to discharge condensation.

(a) marine power receptacle   (b) marine outlet   (c) marine power outlet   (d) any of these

46. Service equipment for floating docks or marinas must be located _____ the floating structure.

(a) adjacent to   (b) on   (c) 100 ft from   (d) 20 ft from

47. The feeder for six 30A receptacles supplying shore power for boats must be calculated at _____ percent of the sum of the rating of the receptacles.

(a) 70   (b) 80   (c) 90   (d) 100

48. Where shore power accommodations provide two receptacles specifically for an individual boat slip, and these receptacles have different voltages, only the receptacle with the _____ is required to be calculated.

(a) smaller kW demand   (b) larger kW demand   (c) higher voltage   (d) none of these

49. The disconnecting means for a boat must be readily accessible, not more than _____ from the receptacle it controls and must be in the supply circuit ahead of the receptacle.

(a) 12 in.   (b) 24 in.   (c) 30 in.   (d) none of these

50. 15 and 20A, single-phase, 125V receptacles used for "other than shore power" in marinas used for storage, maintenance, or repair must be provided with _____.

(a) lockouts   (b) GFCI protection for personnel
(c) warning labels   (d) shore power adapters

51. Electrical wiring and equipment at marine craft repair facilities containing flammable or combustible liquids or gases must comply with the requirements contained in _____

(a) Article 511   (b) Article 555   (c) Article 513   (d) a and b

Article 590 Temporary Installations

This article applies to temporary power and lighting for construction, remodeling, maintenance, repair, demolitions, and decorative lighting. This article also applies when temporary installations are necessary.

52. There is no time limit for temporary electrical power and lighting except that it must be removed upon completion of _____, or similar activities.

    (a) construction or remodeling   (b) maintenance or repair
    (c) demolition of buildings   (d) all of these

53. Temporary electrical power and lighting is permitted during emergencies and for _____.

    (a) tests   (b) experiments   (c) developmental work   (d) all of these

54. Services for temporary installations are not required to comply with the requirements of Article 230.

    (a) True   (b) False

55. NM and NMC cables can be used for temporary wiring as branch circuits in structures of a height of _____.

    (a) 18 ft   (b) 3 stories   (c) 4 stories   (d) no limit

56. Single insulated open conductors can be used for a period not to exceed 90 days for holiday decorative lighting and similar purposes when the circuit voltage-to-ground does not exceed _____.

    (a) 50V   (b) 125V   (c) 150V   (d) 277V

57. Receptacles for construction sites must not be installed on the _____ as temporary lighting or connected to _____ that supply temporary lighting.

    (a) same branch circuit, the same feeders
    (b) same feeders, the same ungrounded conductor of multiwire branch circuits
    (c) same branch circuit, the same ungrounded conductor of multiwire circuits
    (d) all of these

58. At construction sites, boxes are not required for temporary wiring splices of _____.

    (a) multiconductor cords   (b) multiconductor cables   (c) a or b   (d) none of these

59. For temporary installations, cable assemblies, as well as flexible cords and flexible cables, must be supported at intervals that ensure protection from physical damage. Support must be in the form of _____ or similar type fittings installed so as not to cause damage.

    (a) staples   (b) cable ties   (c) straps   (d) any of these

60. All _____, 125V, single-phase receptacle outlets that are not a part of the permanent wiring of the building or structure and are in use by personnel for temporary power must have ground-fault circuit-interrupter protection for personnel.

    (a) 15A   (b) 20A   (c) 30A   (d) all of these

61. Receptacles rated other than 125V single-phase 15, 20, and 30A for temporary installations must be protected by _____.

    (a) a GFCI device   (b) the Assured Equipment Grounding Conductor Program
    (c) an AFCI device   (d) a or b

CHAPTER 6 SPECIAL EQUIPMENT

Article 600 Electric Signs and Outline Lighting

This article covers the installation of conductors and equipment for electric signs and outline lighting as defined in Article 100. Electric signs and outline lighting include all products and installations that utilize neon tubing, such as signs, decorative elements, skeleton tubing, or art forms.

62. Electric signs and outline lighting—fixed, mobile, or portable—are not required to be listed.

    (a) True   (b) False

63. Branch circuits that supply signs and outline lighting systems containing incandescent and fluorescent forms of illumination must be rated not to exceed _____.

    (a) 20A   (b) 30A   (c) 40A   (d) 50A

64. Metal poles used to support signs can contain the sign circuit conductors, provided the _____ are installed in accordance with the requirements contained in 410.15(B).

    (a) poles   (b) conductors   (c) safety chains   (d) a and b

65. The disconnecting means for each circuit leading to a sign located within a fountain must be located in accordance with _____.

    (a) 430.102   (b) 440.14   (c) 680.12   (d) any of these

66. Sign and outline lighting enclosures for live parts other than lamps and neon tubing must _____.

    (a) have ample structural strength and rigidity   (b) be constructed of metal or must be listed
    (c) be at least 0.016 in. thick if of sheet steel   (d) all of these

67. Neon tubing, other than _____ accessible to pedestrians, must be protected from physical damage.

    (a) Class I, Division 1 locations   (b) dry location portable signs
    (c) fixed equipment   (d) wet location portable signs

68. The spacing in signs and outline lighting between wood or other combustible materials and an incandescent or HID lamp or lampholder must not be less than _____.

    (a) 18 in.   (b) 2 ft   (c) 2 in.   (d) 6 in.

69. A portable or mobile electric sign in a wet or damp location must have a ground-fault circuit interrupter _____.

    (a) located on the sign
    (b) located in the power supply cord within 12 in. of the attachment plug
    (c) as an integral part of the attachment plug of the supply cord
    (d) b or c

70. Ballasts, transformers, and electronic power supplies for signs installed in suspended ceilings can be connected to the branch circuit by a _____.

    (a) fixed wiring method   (b) flexible wiring method   (c) flexible cord   (d) a or b

Article 604 Manufactured Wiring Systems

The provisions of Article 604 apply to field-installed manufactured wiring systems used for branch circuits, remote-control circuits, signaling circuits, and communications circuits in accessible areas. The components of a listed manufactured wiring system can be assembled together at the jobsite.

71. A manufactured wiring system is a system assembled by a manufacturer, which cannot be inspected at the building site without _____.

(a) a permit   (b) a manufacturer's representative present
(c) damage or destruction to the assembly   (d) an engineer's supervision

72. Manufactured wiring systems are permitted in _____ locations and in plenums and spaces used for environmental air, where installed in accordance with 300.22.

(a) accessible   (b) dry   (c) wet   (d) both a and b

73. Each section of a manufactured wiring system must be marked to identify _____.

(a) its location   (b) the type of cable, flexible cord, or conduit
(c) the size of the wires installed   (d) its suitability for wet or damp locations

Article 605 Office Furnishings (Wired Partitions)

This article covers electrical equipment, lighting accessories, and wiring systems used to connect, or contained in or on, relocatable partitions. Partitions can be fixed or freestanding and can have communications, signaling, and optical fiber cable wiring in addition to wiring for receptacles and lighting.

74. Wiring systems for the wiring of office furnishings must be identified as suitable for providing power for lighting accessories and appliances in wired partitions. These partitions are allowed to extend from the floor to above the ceiling.

(a) True   (b) False

75. Wired partitions for office furnishings that are fixed (secured to building surfaces) must be permanently connected to the building electrical system by a Chapter 3 wiring method.

(a) True   (b) False

Article 610 Cranes and Hoists

This article covers the installation of electrical equipment and wiring used in connection with cranes, monorail hoists, hoists, and all runways.

76. All exposed noncurrent-carrying metal parts of cranes, hoists, and accessories must _____ a continuous electrical conductor.

(a) be bonded with 6 AWG or larger conductors to   (b) be metallically joined together to
(c) have supplementary ground rods every 20 ft connected to   (d) not be grounded or made into

Article 620 Elevators, Escalators, and Moving Walks

This article covers the installation of electrical equipment and wiring used in connection with elevators, dumbwaiters, escalators, moving walks, wheelchair lifts, and stairway chair lifts.

77. •The minimum size parallel conductors permitted for elevator lighting are _____, provided the combined ampacity is equivalent to at least that of a 14 AWG wire.

(a) 14 AWG   (b) 20 AWG   (c) 16 AWG   (d) 1/0 AWG

78. A separate _____ is required for the elevator car lights, receptacle(s), auxiliary lighting power source, and ventilation on each elevator car.

(a) branch circuit   (b) disconnecting means   (c) connection   (d) none of these

79. An elevator machine room _____ must be located at the point of entry to such machine rooms/machinery spaces.

(a) directory
(b) lighting switch
(c) control circuit disconnecting means
(d) emergency exit map

80. A separate _____ must supply the elevator hoistway pit lighting and receptacle(s). The required lighting must not be connected to the load side of a ground-fault circuit interrupter.

(a) feeder
(b) sub-panel
(c) emergency system
(d) branch circuit

81. At least _____ 15 or 20A, 125V, single-phase, duplex receptacle(s) must be provided in the hoistway pit.

(a) one
(b) two
(c) three
(d) four

82. Where multiple driving machines are connected to a single elevator, escalator, moving walk, or pumping unit, there must be one disconnecting means to disconnect the _____.

(a) motor(s)
(b) control valve operating magnets
(c) a and b
(d) none of these

83. No provision must be made to open or close the disconnecting means for an elevator from any other part of the premises. If sprinklers are installed in hoistways, machine rooms, control rooms, machinery spaces, or control spaces, the disconnecting means is permitted to automatically _____ the power supply to the affected elevator(s) prior to the application of water.

(a) open
(b) close
(c) a or b
(d) none of these

84. Where there is more than one driving machine in an elevator machine room, the disconnecting means must be numbered to correspond to the identifying number of the _____.

(a) driving machine they control
(b) circuit feeding it
(c) panel it is fed from
(d) all of these

85. All 15 and 20A, 125V single-phase receptacles installed in machine rooms and machinery spaces for elevators, escalators, moving walks, and lifts must have ground-fault circuit-interrupter protection by a _____.

(a) GFCI receptacle
(b) GFCI circuit breaker
(c) a or b
(d) none of these

86. Each elevator must have a single means for disconnecting all ungrounded main power supply conductors for each unit _____.

(a) excluding the emergency power system
(b) including the emergency or standby power system
(c) excluding the emergency power system if it is automatic
(d) and the power supply may not be an emergency power system

Article 625 Electric Vehicle Charging Systems

Article 625 covers conductors and equipment external to electric vehicles that are used for electric vehicle charging. This only applies to automotive-type vehicles for highway use.

87. According to Article 625, automotive-type vehicles for highway use include _____.

(a) passenger automobiles
(b) trucks
(c) neighborhood electric vehicles
(d) all of these

88. For plug-connected electric vehicle supply equipment, the listed system of personnel protection can be _____.

    (a) an integral part of the attachment plug
    (b) in the power supply cable not more than 12 in. from the attachment plug
    (c) a or b
    (d) none of these

89. Electric vehicle supply equipment that is identified for and intended to be interconnected to a vehicle, and also serve _____, must be listed as suitable for that purpose.

    (a) as an optional standby system   (b) as an electric power production source
    (c) to provide bidirectional power feed   (d) all of these

Article 630 Electric Welders

Article 630 covers the wiring of arc welders, resistance welders, and other welding equipment connected to an electric supply system.

90. Feeder conductors that supply a group of welders must have an ampacity not less than the sum of the currents, as determined in accordance with 630.11(A) based on _____ percent of the two largest welders, 85 percent for the third largest welder, 70 percent for the fourth largest welder, and 60 percent for all remaining welders.

    (a) 90   (b) 100   (c) 125   (d) 250

91. A disconnecting means must be provided in the supply circuit for each arc welder that is not equipped with _____.

    (a) a governor   (b) a shunt-trip breaker
    (c) an integral disconnect   (d) ground-fault circuit-interrupter protection

92. Each resistance welder must have an overcurrent device rated or set at not more than _____ percent of the rated primary current of the welder.

    (a) 80   (b) 100   (c) 125   (d) 300

93. A _____ must be provided to disconnect each resistance welder and its control equipment from the supply circuit.

    (a) switch   (b) circuit breaker   (c) magnetic starter   (d) a or b

Article 640 Audio Signal Processing, Amplification, and Reproduction Equipment

This article covers equipment and wiring for audio signal generation, recording, processing, amplification and reproduction, distribution of sound, public address, speech input systems, temporary audio system installations, and electronic musical instruments such as electric organs, electric guitars, and electronic drums/percussion instruments.

94. Installed audio distribution cable that is not terminated at equipment and not identified for future use with a tag is considered abandoned.

    (a) True   (b) False

95. Amplifiers, loudspeakers, and other equipment covered by Article 640 must be so located or protected so as to guard against environmental or physical damage that might cause _____.

    (a) a fire   (b) shock   (c) personal hazard   (d) all of these

96. Audio system equipment supplied by branch-circuit power must not be located within _____ of the inside wall of a pool, spa, hot tub, fountain, or tidal high-water mark.

    (a) 2 ft   (b) 10 ft   (c) 5 ft   (d) 18 in.

97. Flexible cords and flexible cables are not allowed for the electrical connection of permanently installed equipment racks of audio systems to the premises wiring to facilitate access to equipment.

    (a) True   (b) False

98. The number of conductors permitted in a single conduit or tubing in a permanent audio system installation is not required to follow the percentage fill specified in Table 1, Chapter 9.

    (a) True   (b) False

Article 645 Information Technology Equipment

Article 645 covers equipment, power-supply wiring, equipment interconnecting wiring, grounding, and bonding of information technology equipment and systems, including terminal units in an information technology equipment room.

99. An information technology equipment room must have _____.

    (a) a disconnecting means complying with 645.10.   (b) a separate heating/ventilating/air-conditioning system
    (c) separation by fire-resistance rated walls, floors, and ceiling   (d) all of these

100. Branch-circuit conductors for data-processing equipment must have an ampacity not less than _____ of the total connected load.

    (a) 80 percent   (b) 100 percent   (c) 125 percent   (d) the sum

(• Indicates that 75% or fewer of those who took this exam answered the question correctly.)

1. In a location where flammable anesthetics are employed, the entire area that extends _____ is classified as Class I, Division 1.

   (a) upward to the structural ceiling   (b) upward to a level 8 ft above the floor
   (c) upward to a level 5 ft above the floor   (d) 10 ft in all directions

2. A mobile home not intended as a dwelling unit such as a unit used for offices, construction job dormitories, or other similar uses, is still required to meet all of the provisions of Article 550 including the capacity of the circuits and the service size.

   (a) True   (b) False

3. A professional-type projector uses _____film and has on each edge 212 perforations per meter, or a type using carbon arc, xenon, or other light source equipment that develops hazardous gases, dust, or radiation.

   (a) 35 mm   (b) 70 mm   (c) a or b   (d) none of these

4. A separate branch circuit must supply elevator machine room/machinery space lighting and receptacle(s). The required lighting must not be connected to the load side of _____.

   (a) a local subpanel   (b) an SWD-type circuit breaker
   (c) an HID-type circuit breaker   (d) a ground-fault circuit interrupter

5. All abandoned audio distribution cables must be removed.

   (a) True   (b) False

6. An electric vehicle that falls within the scope of Article 625 could be _____.

   (a) an automotive-type vehicle for highway use   (b) an automotive-type vehicle for off-road use
   (c) an electric golf cart   (d) any of these

7. At carnivals, circuses, and fairs GFCI protection is not required for receptacles that only facilitate the quick disconnecting and reconnecting of electrical equipment and are of the locking type.

   (a) True   (b) False

8. Audio system equipment (speakers) powered by a listed Class 2 power supply, or by the output of an amplifier listed for use with Class 2 wiring, must only be restricted in its placement by _____.

   (a) the manufacturer's recommendations   (b) 640.10(A), within 6 ft of water
   (c) the local authority having jurisdiction (d) the desires of the owner

9. Conductors that supply one or more resistance welders must be protected by an overcurrent device rated or set at not more than _____ percent of the conductor rating.

   (a) 80   (b) 100   (c) 125   (d) 300

10. Duty on escalator and moving walk driving machine motors must be rated as _____.

    (a) full time   (b) continuous   (c) various   (d) long term

11. Each arc welder must have overcurrent protection rated or set at not more than _____ percent of the rated primary current of the welder.

    (a) 100   (b) 125   (c) 150   (d) 200

12. Each commercial building, and each commercial occupancy with ground floor access for pedestrians, must have at least one outside sign outlet in an accessible location at each entrance. The outlet(s) must be supplied by a branch circuit rated at least _____ that supplies no other load.

    (a) 15A   (b) 20A   (c) a or b   (d) none of these

13. Each ride and concession at a carnival, circus, or similar event must be provided with a fused disconnect switch or circuit breaker within sight and within _____ of the operator's station. The disconnecting means must be readily accessible to the operator, including when the ride is in operation.

    (a) 25 ft   (b) 6 ft   (c) 18 in.   (d) 10 ft

14. Each sign and outline lighting system, or feeder/branch circuit supplying a sign or outline lighting system, must be controlled by an externally operable switch or circuit breaker that opens all _____ conductors.

    (a) ungrounded   (b) grounded   (c) grounding   (d) all of these

15. Electric vehicle supply equipment must have a listed system of protection against electric shock of personnel.

    (a) True   (b) False

16. Except as specifically modified by Article 590, all other requirements of the *Code* for permanent wiring apply to temporary wiring installations.

    (a) True   (b) False

17. Feeders to floating buildings are permitted to be installed in _____ where flexibility is required.

    (a) extra-hard usage portable power cable listed for both wet locations and sunlight resistance
    (b) liquidtight flexible metal conduit with approved fittings
    (c) liquidtight flexible nonmetallic conduit with approved fittings
    (d) all of these

18. For temporary wiring over 600V, nominal, suitable _____ must be provided to prevent access of other than authorized and qualified personnel.

    (a) fencing   (b) barriers   (c) signs   (d) a or b

19. General-purpose receptacles rated 125V, single-phase, _____ must be GFCI protected if they are located in an agricultural livestock building in an area that has an equipotential plane.

    (a) 15A   (b) 20A   (c) 30A   (d) a and b

20. In agricultural building locations where surfaces are periodically washed or sprayed with water, enclosures and fittings must be listed for use in wet locations and the enclosures must be weatherproof.

    (a) True   (b) False

21. In marinas and boatyards, transformers and enclosures must be specifically approved for the intended location. The bottom of enclosures for transformers must not be located below _____.

    (a) 2 ft above the dock   (b) 18 in. above the electrical datum plane
    (c) the electrical datum plane   (d) a dock

22. Loudspeakers of a permanent audio system which are installed in a fire-resistance rated partition, wall, or ceiling must be listed for the purpose or installed in an enclosure or recess that _____.

    (a) maintains the fire-resistance rating

    (b) is no more than 4 in. deep

    (c) is no more than 6 ft 6 in. high

    (d) all of these

23. Manufactured wiring systems must be constructed with _____.

    (a) listed Type AC or Type MC cable

    (b) 10 or 12 AWG copper-insulated conductors

    (c) conductors that are suitable for nominal 600V

    (d) all of these

24. Mobile home service equipment must be rated at not less than _____ at 120/240V, and provisions must be made for connecting a mobile home feeder assembly by a permanent wiring method.

    (a) 50A
    (b) 60A
    (c) 100A
    (d) 200A

25. Multiwire branch circuits for temporary wiring must be provided with a means to disconnect simultaneously all _____ conductors at the power outlet or panelboard where the branch circuit originated.

    (a) underground
    (b) overhead
    (c) ungrounded
    (d) grounded

26. Overhead wiring outside of tents and concession areas of carnivals and circuses which are accessible to pedestrians only, and where the voltage-to-ground does not exceed 150 must maintain a vertical clearance of _____ above finished grade, sidewalks, or from platforms, projections, or surfaces from which the wiring might be reached.

    (a) 3 ft
    (b) 6 ft
    (c) 8 ft
    (d) 10 ft

27. Receptacles that provide shore power for boats must be rated not less than _____ and must be of the single outlet type.

    (a) 15A
    (b) 20A
    (c) 30A
    (d) none of these

28. Signs and outline lighting system equipment installed in wet locations must be weatherproof and have drain holes unless they are listed watertight type.

    (a) True
    (b) False

29. Temporary wiring must be _____ immediately upon the completion of construction or purpose for which the wiring was installed.

    (a) disconnected
    (b) removed
    (c) de-energized
    (d) any of these

30. The bottom of sign and outline lighting enclosures must be at least _____ above areas accessible to vehicles unless protected from physical damage.

    (a) 12 ft
    (b) 14 ft
    (c) 16 ft
    (d) 18 ft

31. The conductors to the hoistway door interlocks from the hoistway riser of an elevator must be flame retardant and suitable for a temperature of not less than _____, and the conductors must be SF or the equivalent.

    (a) 200°C
    (b) 60°C
    (c) 90°C
    (d) 110°C

32. The demand used to calculate 45 receptacles in a boatyard feeder is _____ percent.

    (a) 90
    (b) 80
    (c) 70
    (d) 50

33. The disconnecting means for an elevator or escalator must be an enclosed externally operable fused motor-circuit switch or circuit breaker capable of _____.

    (a) interrupting 6 times the locked-rotor current

    (b) being locked in the open position

    (c) including overload protection

    (d) serving as a transfer switch

34. The distribution point is an electrical supply point from which _____ to agricultural buildings, associated farm dwelling(s), and associated buildings under single management are supplied.

(a) service drops or service laterals
(b) feeders or branch circuits
(c) a or b
(d) none of these

35. The electrical connection between mechanically contiguous wired partitions (for office furnishings) is permitted to be a flexible cord if the cord _____.

(a) is extra-hard usage with 12 AWG or larger conductors
(b) has an insulated equipment grounding conductor
(c) is no longer than 2 ft and terminates at an attachment plug and connector with strain relief
(d) all of these

36. The equipotential planes in an agricultural building must be bonded to the electrical grounding system. The bonding conductor must be copper, insulated, covered, or bare and not smaller than _____.

(a) 6 AWG
(b) 8 AWG
(c) 4 AWG
(d) 10 AWG

37. The lighting switch for hoistway pits must be readily accessible from the _____.

(a) pit access door
(b) elevator car
(c) floor of the pit
(d) machinery room

38. The maximum internal current that can flow through the line isolation monitor when any point of the isolated system is grounded must be _____ when used in a health care facility.

(a) 15A or less
(b) no more than 1A
(c) 1 mA
(d) 10 mA

39. The maximum spacing of receptacle outlets over countertops in the kitchen in a mobile home is _____.

(a) 6 ft
(b) 12 ft
(c) 3 ft
(d) none of these

40. The mobile home park secondary electrical distribution system to mobile home lots must be _____.

(a) 120/240V, single-phase, 3-wire
(b) 208/208V, three-phase, 4-wire
(c) either a or b
(d) none of these

41. The pilot light provided within a portable stage switchboard enclosure must have overcurrent protection rated or set at not more than _____.

(a) 10A
(b) 15A
(c) 20A
(d) 30A

42. The plans, specifications, and other building details for construction of manufactured buildings are included in the _____ details.

(a) manufactured building
(b) building component
(c) building structure
(d) building system

43. The provisions of Article 604 apply to field-installed manufactured wiring systems using off-site manufactured subassemblies for branch circuits, remote-control circuits, signaling circuits, and communications circuits in _____ areas.

(a) accessible
(b) only patient care
(c) hazardous (classified)
(d) concealed

44. The wiring methods permitted in theaters, audience areas of motion picture and television studios, performance areas, and similar locations are _____.

    (a) any metal raceway
    (b) nonmetallic raceways encased in 2 in. of concrete
    (c) Types MC or AC cable with an insulated equipment grounding conductor
    (d) any of these

45. The working space clearance for a distribution panelboard located in a recreational vehicle must be no less than _____.

    (a) 24 in. wide   (b) 30 in. deep   (c) 30 in. wide   (d) a and b

46. Type NM cable is an acceptable wiring method in agricultural buildings.

    (a) True   (b) False

47. Types NM and NMC cable are permitted to be used for temporary installations in any dwelling, building, or structure without height limitation or limitation by building construction type and without concealment when installed as _____.

    (a) branch circuits   (b) feeders   (c) a or b   (d) none of these

48. Vegetation cannot be used for support of overhead spans of _____.

    (a) branch circuits   (b) feeders
    (c) holiday lighting branch circuits with proper strain relief   (d) a or b

49. Where multiple services or separately derived systems or both supply rides, attractions, and other structures of carnival, circuses, fairs, and similar events, all sources of supply that serve rides, attractions, or other structures separated by less than _____ must be bonded to the same grounding electrode system.

    (a) 12 ft   (b) 8 ft   (c) 16 ft   (d) 6 ft

50. Which of the following wiring methods are permitted to be installed in an assembly occupancy?

    (a) Metal raceways.
    (b) Type MC cable.
    (c) Type AC cable containing an insulated equipment grounding conductor.
    (d) all of these

(• Indicates that 75% or fewer of those who took this exam answered the question correctly.)

1. Where a nonmetallic wireway is used as a pull box for insulated conductors 4 AWG or larger, the distance between raceway and cable entries enclosing the same conductor must not be less than that required in 314.28(A)(1) for straight pulls and 314.28(A)(2) for angle pulls.

    (a) True   (b) False

2. Where a portion of the dwelling unit basement is finished into one or more habitable rooms, each separate unfinished portion must have a receptacle outlet installed.

    (a) True   (b) False

3. Where a service raceway enters a building or structure from a(n) _____ it must be sealed in accordance with 300.5(G).

    (a) transformer vault   (b) underground distribution system
    (c) cable tray   (d) overhead rack

4. Where a transformer supplies an electric fire pump motor, it must be sized no less than _____ percent of the sum of the fire pump motor(s) and pressure maintenance pump motors, and 100 percent of any associated fire pump accessory equipment supplied by the transformer.

    (a) 100   (b) 125   (c) 250   (d) 300

5. Where a wireway is used as a pull box for insulated conductors 4 AWG or larger, the distance between raceway and cable entries enclosing the same conductor must not be less than that required in 314.28(A)(1) for straight pulls and 314.28(A)(2) for angle pulls.

    (a) True   (b) False

6. Where an ac system operating at less than 1,000V is grounded at any point, the _____ conductors must be run to each service disconnecting means and must be bonded to each disconnect enclosure.

    (a) ungrounded   (b) grounded   (c) grounding   (d) none of these

7. Where batteries are used for _____ in auxiliary engines of emergency systems, the authority having jurisdiction must require periodic maintenance.

    (a) starting   (b) control or ignition   (c) a and b   (d) none of these

8. Where batteries are used for _____ in auxiliary engines of legally required standby systems, the authority having jurisdiction must require periodic maintenance.

    (a) control   (b) starting or ignition   (c) a and b   (d) none of these

9. Where CNG (compressed natural gas) vehicles are repaired or stored, the area within _____ in. of the ceiling is classified as Class I, Division 2, except where ventilation of at least 1 cu ft per minute per sq ft (cfm/sq. ft) of ceiling area is taken from a point within 18 in. of the highest point in the ceiling of major repair garages.

    (a) 6   (b) 12   (c) 18   (d) 24

10.   Where communications wires and cables are installed in a raceway, the raceway must be of a type permitted in Chapter 3 and must be installed in accordance with Chapter 3 requirements, or a listed nonmetallic raceway may be used that complies with 800.182.

(a) True   (b) False

11.   Where conductors are run in parallel in multiple raceways or cables, the equipment grounding conductor, where used, must be run in parallel in each raceway or cable.

(a) True   (b) False

12.   Where fixed multioutlet assemblies used in other than dwelling units or the guest rooms of hotels or motels are employed, each _____ or fraction thereof of each separate and continuous length of multioutlet assembly must be considered as one outlet of not less than 180 VA capacity where appliances are unlikely to be used simultaneously.

(a) 5 ft   (b) 5 1/2 ft   (c) 6 ft   (d) 6 1/2 ft

13.   Where flexibility is necessary, securing LFMC is not required for lengths not exceeding _____ at terminals.

(a) 2 ft   (b) 3 ft   (c) 4 ft   (d) 6 ft

14.   Where flexible cords are used in ambient temperatures exceeding _____ the temperature correction factors from Table 310.16 that correspond to the temperature rating of the cord must be applied to the ampacity from Table 400.5(A) or 400.5(B).

(a) 60°C   (b) 30°C   (c) 75°C   (d) 90°C

15.   Where nails or screws are likely to penetrate nonmetallic-sheathed cable or electrical nonmetallic tubing installed through metal framing members, a steel sleeve, steel plate, or steel clip not less than _____ in thickness must be used to protect the cable or tubing. A thinner plate that provides equal or better protection may be used if listed and marked.

(a) 1/16 in.   (b) 1/8 in.   (c) 1/2 in.   (d) none of these

16.   Where nonmetal underground conduit with conductors (NUCC) enters a box, fitting, or other enclosure, a bushing or adapter must be provided to protect the conductor or cable from abrasion unless the design of the box, fitting, or enclosure is such as to afford equivalent protection.

(a) True   (b) False

17.   Where service entrance conductors are paralleled in two or more raceways or cables, the bonding jumper for each raceway or cable must be based on the size of the _____ in each raceway or cable.

(a) overcurrent protection for conductors   (b) grounded conductors
(c) service-entrance conductors   (d) sum of all conductors in the raceway

18.   Where the load is computed on volt-amperes per square meter or square foot basis, the wiring system up to and including the branch-circuit _____ must be provided to serve not less than the calculated load.

(a) wiring   (b) protection   (c) panelboard(s)   (d) all of these

19.   Where the premises wiring system contains feeders supplied from more than one voltage system, each ungrounded (hot) conductor, where accessible, must be identified by the system. Identification can be by _____ or other approved means. Such identification must be permanently posted at each feeder panelboard or similar feeder distribution equipment.

(a) color-coding   (b) marking tape   (c) tagging   (d) a, b, or c

20. Which of the following areas of an aircraft hangar are not classified as a Class I, Division 1 or 2 location?

(a) Any pit or depression below the level of the hangar floor.
(b) Areas adjacent to and not suitably cut off from the hangar.
(c) Areas within the vicinity of aircraft.
(d) Adjacent areas where adequately ventilated and where effectively cut off from the classified area of the hangar.

21. Which of the following conductor types are required to be used when FMC is installed in a wet location?

(a) THWN   (b) XHHW   (c) THW   (d) any of these

22. Which of the following is not a standard size for fuses or inverse-time circuit breakers?

(a) 45A   (b) 70A   (c) 75A   (d) 80A

23. A receptacle installed in a wet location, where the product intended to be plugged into it is not attended while in use, shall have an enclosure that is weatherproof with the attachment plug cap inserted or removed.

(a) True   (b) False

24. Which of the following switches must indicate whether they are in the open (off) or closed (on) position?

(a) General-use switches.   (b) Motor-circuit switches.   (c) Circuit breakers.   (d) all of these

25. Which of the following wiring methods are permitted in a Class I, Division 1 location?

(a) Threaded rigid metal conduit.   (b) Threaded IMC.
(c) MI cable.   (d) all of these.

26. Wiring methods and equipment installed behind panels designed to permit access (such as suspended-ceiling panels) must be so arranged and secured so as to allow the removal of panels and access to the electrical equipment.

(a) True   (b) False

27. Working space cannot be used for _____.

(a) storage   (b) raceways   (c) lighting   (d) accessibility

28. _____ is permitted to be installed in messenger-supported wiring.

(a) Multiconductor service-entrance cable   (b) Mineral-Insulated (Type MI) cable
(c) Multiconductor underground feeder cable   (d) all of these

29. •_____ identified for use on lighting track must be designed specifically for the track on which they are to be installed.

(a) Fittings   (b) Receptacles   (c) Devices   (d) all of these

30. •Aluminum and copper-clad aluminum of the same circular mil size and insulation have _____.

(a) the same physical characteristics   (b) the same termination
(c) the same ampacity   (d) different ampacities

31. •Warning signs for over 600V must read: "Warning—High Voltage—Keep Out."

(a) True   (b) False

32. •When devices or plug-in connections for tapping off feeders or branch circuits from busways include an externally operable fusible switch that is out of reach, _____ must be provided for operation of the disconnecting means from the floor.

    (a) ropes   (b) chains   (c) hook sticks   (d) any of these

33. •When the dc system consists of a _____, the grounding electrode conductor must not be smaller than the neutral conductor and not smaller than 8 AWG copper.

    (a) 2-wire balancer set   (b) 3-wire balancer set
    (c) balancer winding with overcurrent protection   (d) b or c

34. A _____ circuit is a circuit, other than field wiring, in which any arc or thermal effect produced under intended operating conditions of the equipment is not capable of igniting the flammable gas-air, vapor-air, or dust-air mixture under specified test conditions.

    (a) nonconductive   (b) branch   (c) nonincendive   (d) closed

35. A 10 AWG single strand (solid) copper wire has a cross-sectional area of _____

    (a) 0.008 sq in.   (b) 0.101 sq in.   (c) 0.012 sq in.   (d) 0.106 sq in.

36. A box must not be required where cables or conductors from cable trays are installed in bushed conduit and tubing used as support or protection against _____.

    (a) abuse   (b) unauthorized access (c) physical damage   (d) tampering

37. A capacitor operating at over 600V must be provided with means to reduce the residual voltage to 50V or less within _____ after it is disconnected from the source of supply.

    (a) 15 seconds   (b) 45 seconds   (c) 1 minute   (d) 5 minutes

38. A circuit breaker with a _____ voltage rating, such as 240V or 480V, is permitted to be used where the nominal voltage between any two conductors does not exceed the circuit breaker's voltage rating.

    (a) straight   (b) slash   (c) high   (d) low

39. A field-installed wiring system for branch circuits designed for installation under carpet squares is defined as _____.

    (a) underfloor wiring   (b) undercarpet wiring
    (c) flat conductor cable   (d) underfloor conductor cable

40. A fuse or an overcurrent trip unit of a circuit breaker must be connected in series with each ungrounded _____.

    (a) device   (b) conductor   (c) branch circuit   (d) all of these

41. A generator set for a required standby system must _____.

    (a) have means for automatically starting the prime movers
    (b) have two hours of fuel supply for full-demand operation available onsite if the prime mover is an internal combustion engine
    (c) not be solely dependent on public utility gas system
    (d) all of these

42. A large single panel, frame, or assembly of panels on which switches, overcurrent and other protective devices, buses, and instruments are mounted is a _____. They are generally accessible from the rear as well as from the front and are not intended to be installed in cabinets.

    (a) switchboard　　　　　(b) panel box　　　　　(c) switch box　　　　　(d) panelboard

43. A mobile home that is factory-equipped with gas or oil-fired central heating equipment and cooking appliances is permitted to be supplied with a listed mobile home power-supply cord rated _____.

    (a) 30A　　　　　(b) 35A　　　　　(c) 40A　　　　　(d) 50A

44. A motor for general use must be marked with a time rating of _____.

    (a) continuous　　　　　(b) 30 or 60 minutes　　　　　(c) 5 or 15 minutes　　　　　(d) any of these

45. A motor terminal housing with rigidly-mounted motor terminals must have a minimum of _____ between line terminals for a 230V motor.

    (a) 1/4 in.　　　　　(b) 3/8 in.　　　　　(c) 1/2 in.　　　　　(d) 5/8 in.

46. A vented alkaline-type battery operating at less than 250V must be installed with not more than _____ cells in the series circuit of any one tray.

    (a) 10　　　　　(b) 12　　　　　(c) 18　　　　　(d) 20

47. A(n) _____ system must supply major electrical equipment necessary for patient care and basic hospital operation.

    (a) emergency　　　　　(b) equipment　　　　　(c) life safety　　　　　(d) none of these

48. All accessible portions of abandoned network-powered broadband cable must be removed.

    (a) True　　　　　(b) False

49. All extensions from flat cable assemblies must be made by approved wiring methods within the _____ that is/are installed at either end of the flat cable assembly runs.

    (a) end-caps　　　　　(b) junction boxes　　　　　(c) surface metal raceway　　　　　(d) underfloor metal raceway

50. All fixed outdoor deicing and snow-melting equipment must be provided with a means for disconnection from all _____ conductors.

    (a) grounded neutral　　　　　(b) grounding　　　　　(c) ungrounded　　　　　(d) all of these

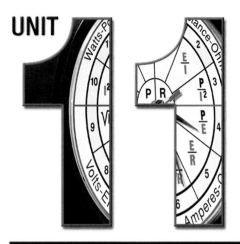

Commercial Calculations

Introduction

Commercial buildings are subjected to different patterns of use than are homes or multifamily dwellings. In a commercial building, there are certain loads (such as store lighting) that are in use for extended periods of time. In a home, it is expected that there will be a diversity of usage as discussed in Units 9 and 10, which allow us to apply demand factors to many of the loads used in dwelling units. There are some demand factors available for commercial buildings, but they are different from those allowed for dwelling calculations. It is important to study this unit carefully so you understand the proper application of demand factors in commercial calculations.

Be cautious when applying demand factors to commercial installations. For example, the demand factors for dryers in Table 220.54 are for dwelling units only and cannot be used for laundromats or similar locations. The range table of 220.55 is allowed only for dwelling unit use and cannot be applied to commercial kitchens. There are different rules, and in some cases different demand factors, for commercial occupancies.

Commercial occupancies include many different types of businesses and many different building uses. Some of the occupancies that are covered in this unit include; banks, stores, schools, restaurants, and office buildings. Some other locations with their own special requirements, such as marinas and mobile home parks, are also discussed.

Unit 11 includes some specific requirements for restaurant equipment, show-window lighting, sign lighting, multioutlet assemblies, electric welders, and heating and air-conditioning equipment. As you study this unit, pay careful attention to when demand factors can be applied, and also to when it is necessary to consider a load as continuous duty for conductor sizing.

PART A—GENERAL

11.1 General Requirements

Article 220 provides the requirements for branch circuits, feeders, and services. In addition to this article, other articles are applicable such as Branch Circuits—210, Feeders—215, Services—230, Overcurrent Protection—240, Wiring Methods—300, Conductors—310, Appliances—422, Electric Space-Heating Equipment—424, Motors—430 and Air-Conditioning—440.

11.2 Conductor Ampacity [Article 100]

The ampacity of a conductor is the rating, in amperes, that a conductor can carry continuously without exceeding its insulation temperature rating [*NEC* Definition—Article 100], Figure 11–1. The allowable ampacities listed in Table 310.16 are affected by ambient temperature, conductor insulation, and conductor bundling [310.10 and 310.15(B)]. Figure 11–2

> **AUTHOR'S COMMENT:** 110.14(C)(1)(a) tells us that terminals are rated 60°C for equipment rated 100A or less unless marked 75°C. In real life, most terminals are now rated 75°C, so in this Unit, we will assume all terminals are rated 75°C unless specified 60°C. For exam purposes, read the problem carefully to be certain you know what terminal rating the exam question specifies. If unspecified, use the rules of 110.14(C).

Conductors are presumed to be copper unless otherwise stated, and insulated conductors are presumed to be 90°C rated. Systems are presumed to be single-phase unless otherwise stated.

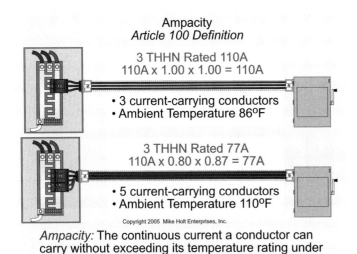

Ampacity
Article 100 Definition

3 THHN Rated 110A
110A x 1.00 x 1.00 = 110A

• 3 current-carrying conductors
• Ambient Temperature 86°F

3 THHN Rated 77A
110A x 0.80 x 0.87 = 77A

• 5 current-carrying conductors
• Ambient Temperature 110°F

Copyright 2005 Mike Holt Enterprises, Inc.

Ampacity: The continuous current a conductor can carry without exceeding its temperature rating under the conditions of use. See 310.10 and 310.15(B)(2)(a).

Figure 11–1

Continuous Loads

Conductors are sized at 125% of the continuous load before any adjustment factor and the overcurrent protection devices are sized at 125% of the continuous load [210.19(A), 215.2(A)(1), and 230.42].

Article 100 defines a continuous load as a load where the maximum current is expected to continue for 3 hours or more. Some *NEC* sections tell you when certain loads are continuous, such as 422.13 for some types of water heaters, or 424.3(B) for branch circuits for fixed electric space-heating equipment. Most commercial lighting and electric signs are considered continuous loads.

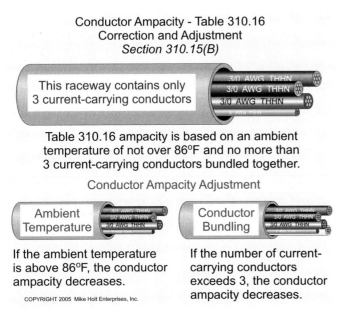

Conductor Ampacity - Table 310.16
Correction and Adjustment
Section 310.15(B)

This raceway contains only 3 current-carrying conductors

3/0 AWG THHN
3/0 AWG THHN
3/0 AWG THHN

Table 310.16 ampacity is based on an ambient temperature of not over 86°F and no more than 3 current-carrying conductors bundled together.

Conductor Ampacity Adjustment

Ambient Temperature

If the ambient temperature is above 86°F, the conductor ampacity decreases.

Conductor Bundling

If the number of current-carrying conductors exceeds 3, the conductor ampacity decreases.

COPYRIGHT 2005 Mike Holt Enterprises, Inc.

Figure 11–2

11.3 Conductor Overcurrent Protection [240.4]

The purpose of overcurrent protection devices is to protect conductors and equipment against excessive or dangerous temperatures [240.1 FPN]. There are many rules in the *NEC* for conductor protection, and there are many different installation applications where the general rule of protecting the conductor at its ampacity does not apply. Motor circuits, air-conditioning, tap conductors, etc. are examples. See 240.4 for specific rules on conductor overcurrent protection.

Next Size Up Okay [240.4(B)]. If the ampacity of a conductor does not correspond with the standard ampere rating of a fuse or circuit breaker as listed in 240.6(A), the next size up protection device is permitted. This only applies if the conductors do not supply multioutlet receptacles and if the next size up overcurrent protection device does not exceed 800A. Figure 11–3

Standard Size Overcurrent Devices [240.6(A)]. The following is a list of some of the standard ampere ratings for fuses and inverse-time circuit breakers: 15, 20, 25, 30, 35, 40, 45, 50, 60, 70, 80, 90, 100, 110, 125, 150, 175, 200, 225, 250, 300, 350, 400, 500, 600, 800, 1,000, 1,200, and 1,600A. Figure 11–4

11.4 Voltages [220.5(A)]

Unless other voltages are specified, branch-circuit, feeder, and service loads must be computed at a nominal system voltage of 120, 120/240, 120/208, 240, 277/480, or 480. Figure 11–5

11.5 Rounding an Ampere [220.5(B)]

Where calculations result in a fraction of 0.50A or less, such fractions can be dropped.

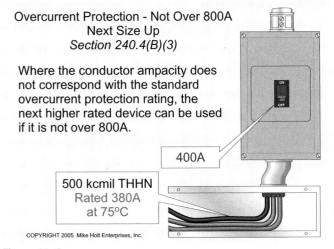

Overcurrent Protection - Not Over 800A
Next Size Up
Section 240.4(B)(3)

Where the conductor ampacity does not correspond with the standard overcurrent protection rating, the next higher rated device can be used if it is not over 800A.

400A

500 kcmil THHN
Rated 380A
at 75°C

COPYRIGHT 2005 Mike Holt Enterprises, Inc.

Figure 11–3

Standard Overcurrent Device Ratings
Section 240.6(A)

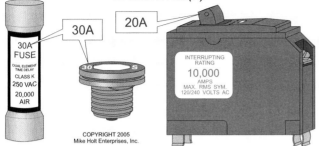

The standard ratings for fuses and inverse-time breakers include: 15, 20, 25, 30, 35, 40, 45, 50, 60, 70, 80, 90, 100, 110, 125, 150, 175, 200, 225, 250, 300, 350, 400, 450, 500, 600, 700, 800, 1000, 1200, 1600, 2000, 2500, 3000, 4000, 5000, and 6000A.

Figure 11–4

AUTHOR'S COMMENT: When do you round—after each calculation, or at the final calculation? The *NEC* isn't specific on this issue, but I guess it all depends on the answer you want to see!

▶ **Rounding Example**

According to 424.3(B), the branch-circuit conductors and overcurrent protection device for electric space-heating equipment must be sized no less than 125 percent of the total load. What size conductor is required to supply a 9 kVA (37.5A), 240V,

Nominal Voltages for Calculations
Section 220.5(A)

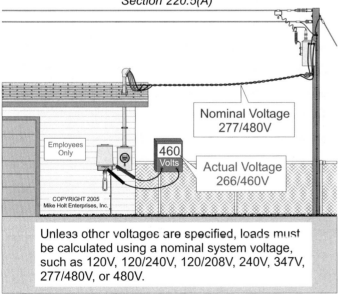

Unless other voltages are specified, loads must be calculated using a nominal system voltage, such as 120V, 120/240V, 120/208V, 240V, 347V, 277/480V, or 480V.

Figure 11–5

Rounding Amperes for Calculations
Section 220.5(B)

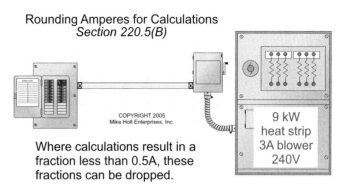

Where calculations result in a fraction less than 0.5A, these fractions can be dropped.

40.5A x 125% = 50.63A, Round up to 51A

Figure 11–6

single-phase fixed space heater with a 3A blower motor if the equipment terminals are rated 75°C? **Figure 11–6**

(a) 10 AWG   (b) 8 AWG
(c) 6 AWG   (d) 4 AWG

Answer: (c) 6 AWG

Step 1: Determine the total load
$$I = VA/E$$
$$I = 9{,}000 \text{ VA}/240\text{V}$$
$$I = 37.5\text{A}$$

Step 2: Conductor sized at 125% of the load.
Conductor Size = (37.5A + 3A) x 1.25
Conductor Size = 50.63A, round up to 51A

If we rounded down, then 8 AWG rated 50A at 75°C could be used, but since we have to round up, 6 AWG rated 65A at 75°C is required.

11.6 Air-Conditioning Branch Circuit

Branch-circuit conductors and overcurrent protection for air-conditioning equipment are marked on the equipment nameplate [110.3(B)]. The nameplate values are determined by the use of 440.32 for conductor sizing and 440.22(A) for short-circuit protection. 440.32 specifies that branch-circuit conductors must be sized no less than 125% of the air conditioner rating, and 440.22(A) specifies that the short-circuit protection device must be sized from 175% to 225% of the air-conditioning rating.

▶ **Air-Conditioning Branch Circuit [240.4(G)] Example**

An air conditioner has a motor-compressor rated-load amperage of 18A. The nameplate indicates a minimum circuit ampacity of 23A and a maximum fuse size of 40A. What size conductor and protection are required? **Figure 11–7**

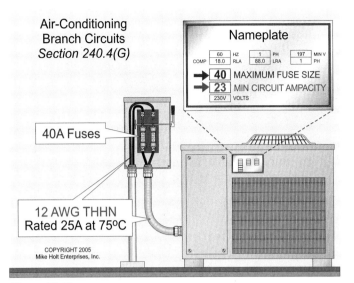

Air-Conditioning
Branch Circuits
Section 240.4(G)

Nameplate

| | 60 | HZ | 1 | PH | 197 | MIN V |
| COMP | 18.0 | RLA | 88.0 | LRA | 1 | PH |

40 MAXIMUM FUSE SIZE
23 MIN CIRCUIT AMPACITY
230V VOLTS

40A Fuses

12 AWG THHN
Rated 25A at 75°C

COPYRIGHT 2005
Mike Holt Enterprises, Inc.

Figure 11–7

(a) 12 AWG with a 40A breaker

(b) 12 AWG with a 40A fuse

(c) 14 AWG with a 30A breaker

(d) 10 AWG with a 40A breaker

• Answer: (b) 12 AWG with a 40A fuse

Conductor [440.32]. The conductor must be sized at no less than 125% of the motor-compressor rated-load current.
18A x 1.25 = 22.5A, 12 THHN rated at 25A at 75°C [Table 310-16]

Short-Circuit Protection [440.22(A)]. In this example, the short-circuit protection must be a fuse [110.3(B)] because the nameplate specified "fuse." However, the protection device must not be greater than 175% of the motor-compressor current.

Protection Size = 18A x 1.75
Protection Size = 31.5A
Next size down, 30A [240.6(A)]

Short-Circuit Protection [440.22(A)]

If difficulty is encountered in starting the A/C, the short-circuit ground-fault protection device may be increased, but it must be sized at not more than 225% of the motor rated-load current or the branch-circuit selection current, whichever is greater [440.22(A)].

Fuse size = 18A x 2.25
Fuse size = 40.5A
Next size down, 40A [240.6(A)]

AUTHOR'S COMMENT: I know many believe the conductor should be larger or the short-circuit protection smaller, but these are not the *NEC* requirements.

Air-Conditioning Feeder/Service Conductors

Feeder circuit conductors that supply air-conditioning equipment must be sized no less than 100% of the total load.

VA Rating—The VA rating of an air conditioner is determined by multiplying the voltage rating of the unit by its ampere rating. For the purpose of this textbook, we will determine the unit ampere rating by using motor FLC ratings as listed in Table 430.248 and Table 430.250.

▶ **Air-Conditioning Feeder/Service Conductor Example**

What is the calculated load required for the A/C equipment of a 12-unit office building where each unit contains a 5 hp, 230V air conditioner?

(a) 77 kVA   (b) 73 kVA
(c) 45 kVA   (d) none of these

• Answer: (a) 77 kVA
5 hp, 230V single phase A/C,
[Table 430.248] FLC = 28

VA = V x A
VA = 230V x 28A
VA = 6,440 VA

Connected Load = 6,440 VA x 12 units
Calculated Load = 77,280 VA
Calculated Load = 77.28 kVA

11.7 Dryers

The branch-circuit conductors and overcurrent protection device for commercial dryers are sized to the appliance nameplate rating. The feeder load for dryers is calculated at 100% of the appliance rating. Table 220.54 demand factors do not apply to commercial dryers.

Note: The NEC allows the use of kVA or kW interchangeably for ranges and clothes dryers.

▶ **Dryer Branch-Circuit Example**

What size branch-circuit conductor and overcurrent protection is required for a 7 kVA dryer rated 240V when the dryer is located in the common laundry room of a multifamily dwelling? Figure 11–8

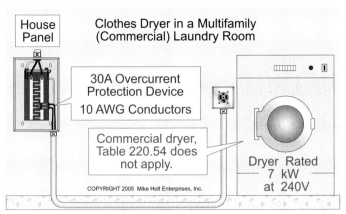

Clothes Dryer in a Multifamily (Commercial) Laundry Room

House Panel

30A Overcurrent Protection Device
10 AWG Conductors

Commercial dryer, Table 220.54 does not apply.

Dryer Rated 7 kW at 240V

COPYRIGHT 2005 Mike Holt Enterprises, Inc.

Determine branch-circuit protection and conductor size.

$$I = \frac{VA}{E} = \frac{7,000 \text{ VA}}{240V} = 29A$$

Table 310.16, use 10 AWG rated 35A at 75°C
240.6(A), 30A protection device

Figure 11–8

(a) 12 AWG with a 20A breaker
(b) 10 AWG with a 20A breaker
(c) 12 AWG with a 30A breaker
(d) 10 AWG with a 30A breaker

• Answer: (d) 10 AWG with a 30A breaker

I = VA/E
I = 7,000 VA/240V
I = 29A

The ampacity of the conductor and overcurrent device must not be less than 29A [240.4].

Table 310.16, a 10 AWG conductor at 75°C is rated 35A.

▶ **Dryer Feeder Example**

What is the feeder/service calculated load for ten 7 kVA dryers located in a laundry room?

(a) 70 kVA   (b) 52.5 kVA
(c) 35 kVA   (d) none of these

• Answer: (a) 70 kVA

The *NEC* does not permit a demand factor for commercial dryers, therefore the dryer load must be calculated at 100%: 7 kVA x 10 units = 70 kVA.

Note: If the dryers are on continuously, the conductor and protection device must be sized at 125% of the load [210.19(A), 210.20A(A), 215.2(A)(1), 215.3, and 230.42].

11.8 Electric Heat

Electric Heat Branch Circuit [424.3(B)]

The branch-circuit conductors and overcurrent protection device for electric heating must be sized not less than 125% of the total heating load including blower motors [210.19(A)(1) and 210.20(A)].

▶ **Electric Heat Example**

What size branch-circuit conductors and protection are required for a 15 kVA, 240V, three-phase heat strip with a 5.4A blower motor? Figure 11–9

(a) 10 AWG with 30A protection
(b) 6 AWG with 50A protection
(c) 8 AWG with 40A protection
(d) 6 AWG with 60A protection

• Answer: (d) 6 AWG with 60A protection [424.3(B)]

Conductors and protection must not be less than 125% of the total load.

I = VA/(E x 1.732)
I = 15,000 VA/(240V x 1.732)
I = 36.1A

I Total = 36.1A + 5.4A
I Total = 41.5A

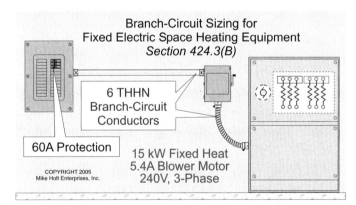

Branch-Circuit Sizing for Fixed Electric Space Heating Equipment
Section 424.3(B)

6 THHN Branch-Circuit Conductors

60A Protection

15 kW Fixed Heat
5.4A Blower Motor
240V, 3-Phase

COPYRIGHT 2005 Mike Holt Enterprises, Inc.

Determine the conductor size and protection.

Combined Load of Motors and Heaters

$$I \text{ (3-ph)} = \frac{VA}{(E \times \sqrt{3})} = \frac{15,000W}{(240V \times 1.732)} = 36.1A$$

Total Load = 36.1A + 5.4A = 41.5A
41.5A x 1.25 = 51.9A

Table 310.16 = 6 AWG wire rated 65A at 75°C

240.6(A) = 60A device

Figure 11–9

Multiply the total heating load by 125%

I Total = 41.5A x 1.25

I Total = 51.9A

Conductor sized to the 75ºC column ampacities of Table 310.16, 6 AWG rated 65A.

Overcurrent protection device sized no less than 52A, use a 60A protection device [240.4(B) and 240.6(A)].

Electric Heat Feeder/Service Demand Load [220.51]

The feeder/service load for electric space-heating equipment is calculated at 100% of the total heating load.

▶ **Electric Heat Feeder/Service Calculated Load Example**

What is the feeder/service calculated load for a building that has seven 10 kVA, 208V, three-phase heat strips with a 5.4A blower motor (1,945 VA) for each unit?

(a) 84 kVA	(b) 53 kVA
(c) 129 kVA	(d) 154 kVA

• Answer: (a) 84 kVA

Individual Heater Load = 10,000 VA + 1,945 VA
Individual Heater Load = 11,945 VA

Feeder/Service Calculated Load =
    11,945 VA x 7 heating units
Feeder/Service Calculated Load = 83,615 VA

11.9 Kitchen Equipment

Kitchen Equipment Branch Circuit

Branch-circuit conductors and overcurrent protection for commercial kitchen equipment are sized according to the appliance nameplate rating. Table 220.56 does not apply to branch circuits or dwelling units.

▶ **Kitchen Equipment Branch Circuit Example 1**

What is the branch-circuit calculated load (in amperes) for one 9 kVA oven rated 240V? Figure 11–10

(a) 38A	(b) 27A (c) 32A
(d) 33A	

• Answer: (a) 38A

I = VA/E
I = 9,000 VA/240V
I = 37.5A

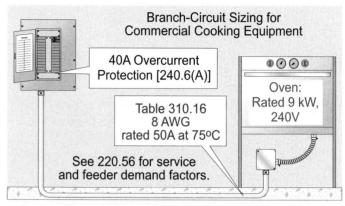

Branch-Circuit Sizing for Commercial Cooking Equipment

40A Overcurrent Protection [240.6(A)]

Oven: Rated 9 kW, 240V

Table 310.16 8 AWG rated 50A at 75ºC

See 220.56 for service and feeder demand factors.

Determine the branch-circuit load for the oven.

$$I = \frac{VA}{E} = \frac{9,000 \text{ VA}}{240V} = 37.5A$$

COPYRIGHT 2005 Mike Holt Enterprises, Inc.

Figure 11–10

▶ **Kitchen Equipment Branch Circuit Example 2**

What is the branch-circuit load for one 14.47 kVA, 208V, three-phase range?

(a) 60A	(b) 40A
(c) 50A	(d) 30A

• Answer: (b) 40A

I = VA/(E x 1.732)
I = 14,470 VA/(208V x 1.732)
I = 40.2A

Kitchen Equipment Feeder/Service Calculated Load [220.56]

The feeder/service calculated load for thermostatic control or intermittent use commercial kitchen equipment is determined by applying the demand factors from Table 220.56 to the total connected kitchen equipment load. The feeder or service calculated load cannot be less than the two largest appliance loads added together!

AUTHOR'S COMMENT: The demand factors of Table 220.56 do not apply to space-heating, ventilating, or air-conditioning equipment.

▶ **Kitchen Equipment Feeder/Service Example 1**

What is the calculated load for the following kitchen equipment loads? Figure 11–11

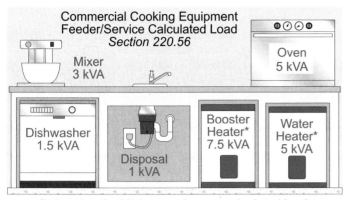

Commercial Cooking Equipment
Feeder/Service Calculated Load
Section 220.56

Mixer
3 kVA

Oven
5 kVA

Dishwasher
1.5 kVA

Disposal
1 kVA

Booster
Heater*
7.5 kVA

Water
Heater*
5 kVA

Determine the kitchen equipment calculated load.

Table 220.56, 6 units, 65% of connected load.

Water heater	5.00 kVA*	*The calculated load
Booster heater	7.50 kVA*	cannot be less than
Mixer	3.00 kVA	the sum of two
Oven	5.00 kVA	largest appliances.
Dishwasher	1.50 kVA	Water heater 5.00 kVA
Disposal	1.00 kVA	Booster heater 7.50 kVA
Total Connected	23.00 kVA	12.50 kVA
Table Demand	x 0.65	Feeder/Service
Demand	14.95 kVA	Calculated
		Load = 14.95 kVA

COPYRIGHT 2005 Mike Holt Enterprises, Inc.

Figure 11–11

Water Heater	5 kVA
Booster Heater	7.5 kVA
Mixer	3 kVA
Oven	5 kVA
Dishwasher	1.5 kVA
Waste Disposal	1 kVA

(a) 15 kVA   (b) 23 kVA
(c) 12.5 kVA   (d) none of these

• Answer: (a) 15 kVA

Water Heater	5.0 kVA
Booster Heater	7.5 kVA
Mixer	3.0 kVA
Oven	5.0 kVA
Dishwasher	1.5 kVA
Waste Disposal	+ 1.0 kVA
Total Connected	23.0 kVA

Calculated Load   23 kVA   x 0.65 =   14.95 kVA

Check the two largest appliances against the calculated load. In this case the two largest loads, the 5 kVA water heater plus the 7.5 kVA booster heater, total 12.5 kVA. This is smaller than the calculated load, so 14.95 kVA is the correct answer.

▶ **Kitchen Equipment Feeder/Service Example 2**

What is the calculated load for the following kitchen equipment loads?

Water Heater*	10 kVA
Booster Heater*	15 kVA
Mixer	4 kVA
Oven	6 kVA
Dishwasher	1.5 kVA
Waste Disposal	1 kVA

(a) 24.4 kVA   (b) 38.2 kVA
(c) 25.0 kVA   (d) 18.9

• Answer: (c) 25 kVA*

*The calculated load cannot be less than the sum of the two largest appliance loads 10 kVA + 15 kVA = 25 kVA.

Water Heater	10.0 kVA
Booster Heater	15.0 kVA
Mixer	4.0 kVA
Oven	6.0 kVA
Dishwasher	1.5 kVA
Waste Disposal	+ 1.0 kVA
Total Connected	37.5 kVA

Calculated Load =
    Connected Load x Demand Factor [Table 220.56]
Calculated Load = 37.5 kVA x 0.65
Calculated Load = 24.4 kVA

11.10 Laundry Equipment

Laundry equipment circuits are sized to the appliance nameplate rating. For exam purposes, it is generally accepted that a laundry circuit is not considered a continuous load and all commercial laundry circuits are assumed to be rated 1,500 VA, unless noted otherwise in the question.

▶ **Laundry Equipment Example**

What is the feeder/service calculated load for 10 washing machines located in a laundry room? Figure 11–12

(a) 1,500 VA   (b) 15,000 VA
(c) 1,125 VA   (d) none of these

• Answer: (b) 15,000 VA

Feeder/Service Calculated Load = 1,500 VA x 10 units
Feeder/Service Calculated Load = 15,000 VA

Commercial Laundry Circuits

Washers 75 Cents

Do Not Use Dye

10 Washing Machines Assume 1,500 VA Each

COPYRIGHT 2005 Mike Holt Enterprises, Inc.

Determine the feeder/service load for 10 washers.

1,500 VA x 10 units = 15,000 VA Calculated Load

Figure 11–12

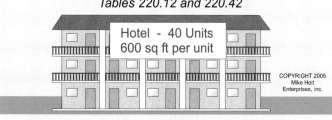

General Lighting Calculated Load - Hotel/Motel
Tables 220.12 and 220.42

Hotel - 40 Units
600 sq ft per unit

COPYRIGHT 2005 Mike Holt Enterprises, Inc.

Determine the general lighting calculated load.

Table 220.12, lighting load is 2 VA per sq ft.

600 sq ft x 40 x 2 VA per sq ft.   = 48,000 VA
Tbl 220.42, 1st 20,000 VA at 50%   – 20,000 VA = 10,000 VA
      Next 80,000 VA at 40%   28,000 VA = 11,200 VA
      Calculated Load   = 21,200 VA

Figure 11–13

11.11 Lighting—Demand Factors [Tables 220.12 and 220.42]

The *NEC* requires a minimum load per sq ft for general lighting depending on the type of occupancy [Table 220.12]. For the guest rooms of hotels and motels, hospitals, and storage warehouses, the general lighting demand factors of Table 220.42 can be applied to the general lighting load.

Hotel or Motel Guest Rooms—General Lighting [Tables 220.12 and 220.42]

The general lighting unit load of 2 VA per sq ft [Table 220.12] for the guest rooms of hotels and motels is permitted to be reduced according to the demand factors listed in Table 220.42.

General Lighting Demand Factors

First 20,000 VA at 50% demand factor
Next 80,000 VA at 40% demand factor
Remainder VA at 30% demand factor

▶ **Hotel General Lighting Calculated Load Example**

What is the general lighting calculated load for a 40-room hotel? Each unit contains 600 sq ft of living area. Figure 11–13

(a) 48 kVA   (b) 24 kVA
(c) 20 kVA   (d) 21 kVA

• Answer: (d) 21 kVA
  [Tables 220.12 and 220.42]

40 units x 600 sq ft x 2 VA   48,000 VA
First 20,000 VA at 50 %   – 20,000 VA x 0.50 =   10,000 VA
Next 80,000 VA at 40 %   28,000 VA x 0.40 = +11,200 VA
             21,200 VA

11.12 Lighting Without Demand Factors [215.2(A)(1), 230.42(A)(1), and Table 220.12]

The feeder/service general lighting load for commercial occupancies other than guest rooms of motels and hotels, hospitals, and storage warehouses is assumed to be continuous and must be calculated at 125% of the general lighting load as listed in Table 220.12.

▶ **Store Lighting Example**

What is the general lighting load for a 21,000 sq ft store? Figure 11–14

(a) 40 kVA   (b) 63 kVA
(c) 79 kVA   (d) 81 kVA

• Answer: (c) 79 kVA
  Store is 3 VA per sq ft [Table 220.12]

General Lighting Load = 21,000 sq ft x 3 VA
General Lighting Load = 63,000 VA
General Lighting Calculated Load = 63,000 VA x 1.25
General Lighting Calculated Load = 78,750 VA

▶ **Club Lighting Example**

What is the general lighting load for a 4,700 sq ft dance club?

(a) 4,700 VA   (b) 9,400 VA
(c) 11,750 VA   (d) 250 kVA

• Answer: (c) 11,750 VA

General Lighting Load at 125%
Table 220.12, Sections 215.2(A)(1) and 230.42(A)(1)

Determine the general lighting calculated load.

Table 220.12, store lighting is 3 VA per sq ft.
21,000 sq ft x 3 VA per sq ft = 63,000 VA lighting load
Store lighting is a continuous load at 125%
63,000 VA lighting load x 1.25 = 78,750 VA load

Figure 11–14

Club is 2 VA per sq ft [Table 220.12]

General Lighting Load = 4,700 sq ft x 2 VA
General Lighting Load = 9,400 VA
General Lighting Calculated Load = 9,400 VA x 1.25
General Lighting Calculated Load = 11,750 VA

▶ **School Lighting Example**

What is the general lighting load for a 125,000 sq ft school?

(a) 125 kVA   (b) 375 kVA
(c) 469 kVA   (d) 550 kVA

• Answer: (c) 469 kVA
School is 3 VA per sq ft [Table 220.12]

General Lighting Load = 125,000 sq ft x 3 VA
General Lighting Load = 375,000 VA
General Lighting Calculated Load = 375,000 VA x 1.25
General Lighting Calculated Load = 468,750 VA

11.13 Lighting-Miscellaneous

Show-Window Lighting [220.14(G) and 220.43(A)]

The feeder/service calculated load for each linear foot of show-window lighting must be calculated at 200 VA per ft. Show-window lighting is assumed to be a continuous load. See Example D3 in Annex D of the *NEC* for the requirements for show-window branch circuits.

Show-Window Lighting Load
Sections 220.14(G) and 220.43(A)

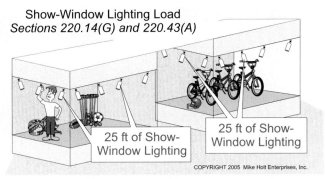

Determine the calculated load of show-window lighting.

50 linear ft of show-window lighting x 200 VA per ft =
10,000 VA lighting load

Continuous loads at 125%
10,000 VA show-window lighting load x 1.25 =
12,500 VA lighting load

Figure 11–15

▶ **Show-Window Load Example**

What is the feeder/service calculated load in kVA for 50 ft of show-window lighting? Figure 11–15

(a) 6 kVA   (b) 7.5 kVA
(c) 9 kVA   (d) 12.5 kVA

• Answer: (d) 12.5 kVA

Lighting Load = 50 ft x 200 VA per ft
Lighting Load = 10,000 VA
Lighting Calculated Load = 10,000 VA x 1.25
Lighting Calculated Load = 12,500 VA
Lighting Calculated Load in kVA = 12,500 VA/1,000
Lighting Calculated Load in kVA = 12.5 kVA

11.14 Multioutlet Receptacle Assembly [220.14(H)]

Each 5 ft or fraction of a foot, of multioutlet receptacle assembly must be considered to be 180 VA for feeder/service calculations where it is unlikely that appliances will be used simultaneously. When a multioutlet receptacle assembly is expected to have a number of appliances used simultaneously, each foot or fraction of a foot must be considered as 180 VA for feeder/service calculations. A multioutlet receptacle assembly is not generally considered to be a continuous load.

▶ **Multioutlet Receptacle Assembly Example**

What is the calculated load for 10 work stations, each of which has 10 ft of multioutlet receptacle assembly not used simultaneously and 3 ft of multioutlet receptacle assembly simultaneously used? Figure 11–16

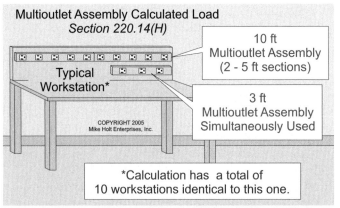

Multioutlet Assembly Calculated Load
Section 220.14(H)

10 ft
Multioutlet Assembly
(2 - 5 ft sections)

Typical
Workstation*

3 ft
Multioutlet Assembly
Simultaneously Used

COPYRIGHT 2005
Mike Holt Enterprises, Inc.

*Calculation has a total of
10 workstations identical to this one.

Determine the multioutlet assembly demand load.

Regular multioutlet assembly (180 VA per 5 ft)
10 ft multioutlet assembly x 10 stations = 100 ft
100 ft/5 ft = 20 sections x 180 VA = 3,600 VA

Simultaneously used multioutlet assembly (180 VA per ft)
3 ft multioutlet assembly x 10 stations = 30 ft
30 ft x 180 VA per ft = 5,400 VA

3,600 VA + 5,400 VA = 9,000 VA calculated load

Figure 11–16

(a) 5 kVA (b) 6 kVA
(c) 7 kVA (d) 9 kVA

• Answer: (d) 9 kVA

10 stations with 10 ft per station =
100 ft of multioutlet assembly not simultaneously used
10 stations with 3 ft per station =
30 ft of multioutlet assembly simultaneously used

100 ft/5 ft per section =
20 sections x 180 VA =   3,600 VA
30 ft/1 ft per section =
30 sections x 180 VA =   + 5,400 VA
Calculated Load   9,000 VA

11.15 Receptacle VA Load

The minimum load for each commercial or industrial general-use receptacle outlet is 180 VA per strap [220.14(I)]. Receptacles are generally not considered to be a continuous load. Figure 11–17

Number of Receptacles Permitted on a Circuit

The maximum number of receptacle outlets permitted on a commercial or industrial circuit depends on the circuit ampacity. The number of receptacles (straps) per circuit is calculated by dividing the VA rating of the circuit by 180 VA for each receptacle strap (also called a yoke).

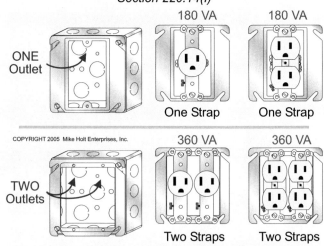

Commercial Receptacle Load
Section 220.14(I)

ONE Outlet

180 VA — One Strap
180 VA — One Strap

TWO Outlets

360 VA — Two Straps
360 VA — Two Straps

COPYRIGHT 2005 Mike Holt Enterprises, Inc.

Each 15 or 20A, 125V general-use receptacle outlet is considered as 180 VA per mounting strap.

Figure 11–17

▶ Receptacles per 20A Circuit [220.14(I)] Example

How many receptacle outlets are permitted on a 20A, 120V circuit? Figure 11–18

(a) 10 (b) 13
(c) 15 (d) 20

• Answer: (b) 13

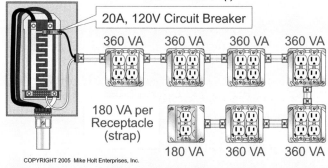

Number of Receptacles Per Circuit - Commercial
Section 220.14(I)

20A, 120V Circuit Breaker

360 VA 360 VA 360 VA 360 VA

180 VA per Receptacle (strap)

180 VA 360 VA 360 VA

COPYRIGHT 2005 Mike Holt Enterprises, Inc.

Determine how many receptacles on a 20A breaker.

Branch Circuit Load = Volts x Amperes
Branch Circuit Load = 120V x 20A
Branch Circuit Load = 2,400 VA
Each receptacle (strap) = 180 VA
2,400 VA load/180 VA per strap = 13 receptacles (straps)

Figure 11–18

The total circuit VA load for a 20A circuit is 120V x
20A = 2,400 VA

The number of receptacle outlets (straps) per circuit =
2,400 VA/180 VA

The number of receptacle outlets (straps) per circuit =
13 receptacles

Receptacle Feeder/Service Calculated Load [220.44]

In other than dwelling units, receptacle loads computed at not
less than 180 VA per outlet (strap) in accordance with 220.14(I),
and fixed multioutlet assemblies computed in accordance with
220.14(H), are permitted to be added to the lighting loads and
made subject to the demand factors given in Table 220.42, or
they are permitted to be made subject to the demand factors
given in Table 220.44. Receptacle loads are generally not considered to be a continuous load.

Table 220.44 Receptacle Demand Factors

First 10 kVA at 100% demand factor
Remainder kVA at 50% demand factor

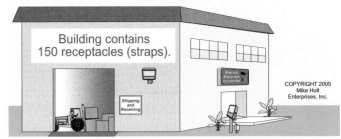

Receptacle Calculated Loads
Section 220.44

Building contains
150 receptacles (straps).

COPYRIGHT 2005
Mike Holt
Enterprises, Inc.

Determine the calculated load for 150 receptacles (straps).

220.14(I), each receptacle = 180 VA
Table 220.44: First 10 kVA at 100%, remainder at 50%

150 receptacles x 180 VA =	27,000 VA	
1st 10,000 VA at 100% =	-10,000 VA =	10,000 VA
Remainder at 50% =	17,000 VA =	+ 8,500 VA
Calculated Receptacle Load		= 18,500 VA

Figure 11–19

▶ **Receptacle Feeder/Service Calculated Load Using Table 220.44 Example**

What is the feeder/service calculated load for one hundred fifty, 20A, 125V general-use receptacles (straps) in a commercial building?
Figure 11–19

(a) 27 kVA   (b) 14 kVA   (c) 4 kVA   (d) 19 kVA

• Answer: (d) 19 kVA

Total receptacle load (150 receptacles x 180 VA)	27,000 VA		
First 10 kVA at 100%	– 10,000 VA	x 1.00 =	10,000 VA
Remainder at 50%	17,000 VA	x 0.50 =	+ 8,500 VA
Total Receptacle Calculated Load			18,500 VA

11.16 Banks and Offices—General Lighting and Receptacles [220.14(K)]

Receptacle Demand [Table 220.44]

The receptacle load is calculated at 180 VA for each receptacle strap [220.14(I)] if the number of receptacles is known, or 1 VA for each
sq ft of the building if the number of receptacles is unknown [220.14(K)(2)].

Banks and Office Buildings. The receptacle calculated load for banks and office buildings is the larger calculation of (1) or (2).

(1) Determine the receptacle calculated load at 180 VA per receptacle yoke [220.14(I)], then apply the demand factor from Table 220.44.

(2) Determine the receptacle calculated load at 1 VA per sq ft.

AUTHOR'S COMMENT: Not knowing the exact number of receptacles that will eventually be installed in an office building or bank is not
unusual. The main structure can be built, then individual office space that is rented out to each tenant will often have a custom installation, or a new tenant will remodel. 1 VA per sq ft allows a generic feeder/service demand for general receptacles.

▶ **Bank or Office General Lighting and Receptacle Example 1**

What is the feeder/service conductor calculated load for an 18,000 sq ft bank that has one hundred sixty 15A, 125V receptacles (straps)? Figure 11–20

(a) 15,400 VA   (b) 19,400 VA   (c) 28,800 VA   (d) 142 kVA

- Answer (b) 19,400 VA
  [220.14(K)(1) and 220.14(I)]
  160 receptacles (straps) x 180 VA = 28,800 VA

Total Receptacle Load =	28,800 VA		
First 10,000 at 100%	-10,000 VA	x 1.00 =	10,000 VA
Remainder at 50%	18,800 VA	x 0.50 =	+ 9,400 VA
Receptacle Calculated Load			19,400 VA

220.14(K)(2), 18,000 x 1 VA per sq ft = 18,000 VA (smaller answer, omit)

▶ **Bank or Office General Lighting and Receptacle Example 2**

What is the feeder/service conductor calculated load for an 18,000 sq ft bank that has one hundred forty receptacles (straps)? Figure 11–21

(a) 15,000 VA   (b) 18,000 VA   (c) 23,000 VA   (d) 31,000 VA

- Answer: (b) 18,000 VA
  [220.14(K)(1)]
  140 receptacles x 180 VA

Total Receptacle Load =	25,200 VA		
First 10,000 VA at 100%	− 10,000 VA	x 1.00 =	10,000 VA
Remainder at 50%	15,200 VA	x 0.50 =	+ 7,600 VA
Receptacle Calculated Load			17,600 VA (omit)

220.14(K)(2), 18,000 sq ft x 1 VA per sq ft = 18,000 VA

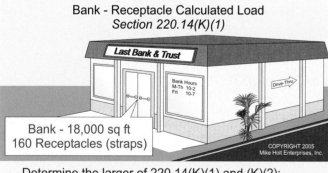

Bank - Receptacle Calculated Load
Section 220.14(K)(1)

Last Bank & Trust

Bank - 18,000 sq ft
160 Receptacles (straps)

Determine the larger of 220.14(K)(1) and (K)(2):
220.14(K)(1),
160 receptacles x 180 VA = 28,800 VA
First 10,000 VA at 100% - 10,000 VA = 10,000 VA
Remainder at 50%   18,800 VA = + 9,400 VA
Receptacle Demand Load   19,400 VA

220.14(K)(2), 18,000 sq ft x 1 VA per ft = 18,000 VA

Figure 11–20

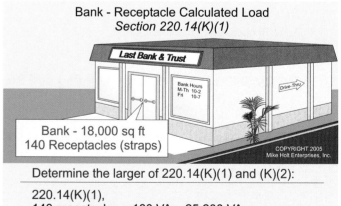

Bank - Receptacle Calculated Load
Section 220.14(K)(1)

Last Bank & Trust

Bank - 18,000 sq ft
140 Receptacles (straps)

Determine the larger of 220.14(K)(1) and (K)(2):
220.14(K)(1),
140 receptacles x 180 VA = 25,200 VA
First 10,000 VA at 100% - 10,000 VA = 10,000 VA
Remainder at 50%   15,200 VA = 7,600 VA
Receptacle Demand Load   17,600 VA

220.14(K)(2), 18,000 sq ft x 1 VA per ft = 18,000 VA

Figure 11–21

11.17 Signs [220.14(F) and 600.5]

The *NEC* requires each commercial occupancy that is accessible to pedestrians to be provided with at least one 20A branch circuit for a sign [600.5(A)]. The load for the required exterior signs or outline lighting must be a minimum of 1,200 VA [220.14(F)]. A sign outlet is considered to be a continuous load and the feeder/service conductor must be sized at 125% of the continuous load [215.2(A)(1) and 230.42].

▶ **Sign Calculated Load Example**

What is the feeder/service conductor calculated load for one electric sign? Figure 11–22

(a) 1,200 VA　　　　　　　　(b) 1,500 VA
(c) 1,920 VA　　　　　　　　(d) 2,400 VA

• Answer: (b) 1,500 VA

Feeder/Service Calculated Load = 1,200 VA x 1.25
Feeder/Service Calculated Load = 1,500 VA

PART B—STANDARD METHOD— FEEDER/SERVICE LOAD CALCULATIONS

11.18 Feeder/Service Load Calculation

For exam preparation purposes, you are not usually expected to calculate the total feeder/service calculated load for a commercial building. However, you are expected to know how to determine

the calculated load for the individual loads (Steps 1a through 1j below). For your own personal knowledge, you can use the following steps to determine the total calculated load for a commercial building for the purpose of sizing the service.

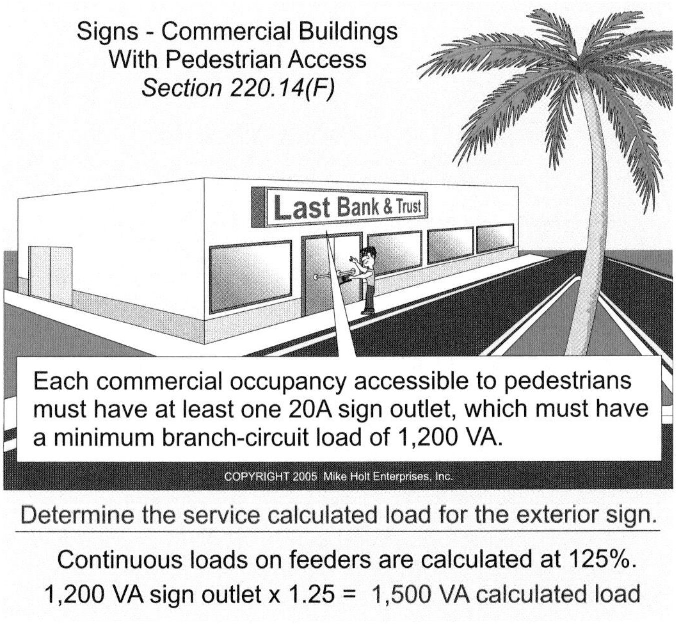

Step 1: Determine the Calculated Load for Each Type of Load

Step a:　Determine the general lighting load: Table 220.12 and Table 220.42.

Step b:　Determine the receptacle calculated load [220.44].

Step c:　Determine the appliance calculated load at 100% [220.14(A)].

Step d:　Determine the calculated load for show windows at 125% [220.43].

Step e:　Determine the calculated load for multioutlet assembly [220.14(H)].

Step f:　Determine the larger of:
Air-conditioning at 100% [220.50].
Heat at 100% [220.51].

Step g:　Determine the calculated load for educational cooking equipment [Table 220.55 Note 5].

Step h:　Determine the kitchen equipment calculated load [Table 220.56].

Step i:　All other noncontinuous loads at 100% [215.2(A)(1) and 230.42(A)].

Step j:　All other continuous loads at 125% [215.2(A)(1) and 230.42(A)].

Step 2: Determine the Total Calculated Load

Add up the individual calculated loads from Steps 1a through 1j.

Step 3: Determine the Feeder/Service Size

Divide the total calculated load (Article 220, Part III) by the system voltage.

Single-phase: I = VA/E
Three-phase: I = VA/(E x 1.732)

11.19 Neutral Calculations [220.61]

The neutral load is the maximum unbalanced calculated load between the grounded neutral conductor and any one ungrounded (hot) conductor as determined by the calculations in Article 220, Part III. This means that line-to-line loads are not considered when sizing the grounded neutral conductor [220.61(A)].

Signs - Commercial Buildings With Pedestrian Access
Section 220.14(F)

Last Bank & Trust

Each commercial occupancy accessible to pedestrians must have at least one 20A sign outlet, which must have a minimum branch-circuit load of 1,200 VA.

COPYRIGHT 2005 Mike Holt Enterprises, Inc.

Determine the service calculated load for the exterior sign.

Continuous loads on feeders are calculated at 125%.
1,200 VA sign outlet x 1.25 = 1,500 VA calculated load

Figure 11–22

Reduction Over 200A [220.61(B)(2)]

The feeder/service calculated load for 3-wire single-phase or 4-wire three-phase systems supplying linear loads can be reduced for that portion of the unbalanced load over 200A by taking it times a multiplier of 70 percent.

▶ **Reduction Over 200A Example**

What is the adjusted neutral load for a 120/240V, 3-wire feeder where the calculated neutral load is 400A?

(a) 400A	(b) 340A
(c) 300A	(d) 500A

• Answer: (b) 340A

Total Neutral Load	400A		
First 200A at 100%	− 200A	x 1.00 =	200A
Remainder at 70%	200A	x 0.70 = +	140A
Neutral Calculated Load			340A

Reduction not Permitted [220.61(C)]

The neutral calculated load cannot be reduced for 3-wire, single-phase circuits consisting of two line wires and the neutral conductor of a 4-wire, three-phase wye-connected system [220.61(C)(1)]. This is because the neutral conductor of a 3-wire circuit connected to a 4-wire, three-phase wye-connected system carries approximately the same current as the phase conductors. See 310.15(B)(4)(b). This can be proven with the following formula:

◆ **I Neutral Formula**

$$I_{Neutral} = \sqrt{[(I_{Line1}^2 + I_{Line2}^2) - (I_{Line1} \times I_{Line2})]}$$

I_{Line1} = Neutral Current of Line 1

I_{Line2} = Neutral Current of Line 2

▶ **Three-Wire Wye Neutral Current [220.61(C)(1)] Example**

What is the neutral calculated load for a balanced 300A, 3-wire, 120/208V feeder supplied from a 4-wire, three-phase wye-connected system? Figure 11–23

(a) 100A	(b) 200A
(c) 300A	(d) none of these

• Answer: (c) 300A

$$I_{Neutral} = \sqrt{[(I_{Line1}^2 + I_{Line2}^2) - (I_{Line1} \times I_{Line2})]}$$

$$I_{Neutral} = \sqrt{[(300A^2 + 300A^2) - (300A \times 300A)]}$$

$$I_{Neutral} = \sqrt{(180,000A - 90,000A)}$$

$$I_{Neutral} = \sqrt{90,000A}$$

$$I_{Neutral} = 300A$$

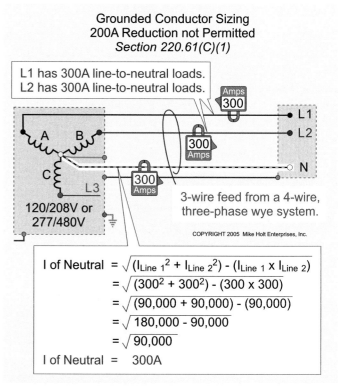

Grounded Conductor Sizing
200A Reduction not Permitted
Section 220.61(C)(1)

L1 has 300A line-to-neutral loads.
L2 has 300A line-to-neutral loads.

3-wire feed from a 4-wire, three-phase wye system.

120/208V or 277/480V

COPYRIGHT 2005 Mike Holt Enterprises, Inc.

$$I \text{ of Neutral} = \sqrt{(I_{Line\ 1}^2 + I_{Line\ 2}^2) - (I_{Line\ 1} \times I_{Line\ 2})}$$
$$= \sqrt{(300^2 + 300^2) - (300 \times 300)}$$
$$= \sqrt{(90,000 + 90,000) - (90,000)}$$
$$= \sqrt{180,000 - 90,000}$$
$$= \sqrt{90,000}$$

$$I \text{ of Neutral} = 300A$$

Figure 11–23

Nonlinear Loads [220.61(C)(2)]

The neutral calculated load cannot be reduced for nonlinear loads supplied from a 4-wire, three-phase, wye-connected system because they produce triplen harmonic currents that add on the neutral conductor, which can require the neutral conductor to be larger than the ungrounded conductors. See 220.61(C)(2), 220.61(C)(2) FPN No. 2, and 310.15(B)(4)(c). Figure 11–24

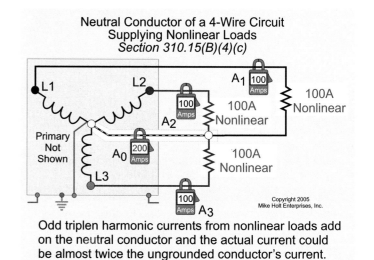

Neutral Conductor of a 4-Wire Circuit
Supplying Nonlinear Loads
Section 310.15(B)(4)(c)

100A Nonlinear

100A Nonlinear

100A Nonlinear

Primary Not Shown

Copyright 2005
Mike Holt Enterprises, Inc.

Odd triplen harmonic currents from nonlinear loads add on the neutral conductor and the actual current could be almost twice the ungrounded conductor's current.

Figure 11–24

PART C—EXAMPLES

11.20 Bank (120/240V, single-phase)

What is the feeder/service calculated load for a bank with the loads shown in **Figure 11–25**?

(1) Air-conditioning [Table 430.248]
    10 hp, single-phase FLC = 50A
    VA = (230V x 50A)   11,500 VA

(2) Heat [220.51 and 220.60] 10,000 VA (omit)

(3) Lighting [Table 220.12]
    General Lighting 30,000 sq ft x 3.5 VA = 105,000 VA*
    General Lighting Calculated Load = 105,000 VA x 1.25 =   131,250 VA*

    Actual Lighting Connected Load = 200 units x 120V x 1.65A
    Actual Lighting Connected Load = 39,600 VA

    Actual Lighting Calculated Load = 39,600 VA x 1.25 = 49,500 VA, (omit)

(4) Sprinkler Pump Motor 5 hp, single-phase FLC = 28A [Table 430.248]
    VA = V x A
    VA = 230V x 28A =   6,440 VA

    Note: Some exams use 240V (the system nominal voltage) instead of 230V
    which is the actual motor voltage of this problem, so be aware of this possibility.

(5) For Banks and Office Buildings, the receptacle load is calculated by using
    the larger of the computed load from 220.14 or 1 VA per sq ft [220.14(K)].

    Receptacles [220.44] (400 receptacles (straps) x 180 VA)   72,000 VA
    First 10 kVA at 100%   −10,000 VA   x 1.00 =   10,000 VA*
    Remainder at 50%   62,000 VA   x 0.50 =   31,000 VA*

    Or use 1 VA per sq ft if larger [220.14(K)] 30,000 sq ft x 1 VA = 30,000 VA (omit)

(6) Individual Circuits (30 circuits x 120V x 20A)   72,000 VA*

(7) Sign [220.14(F)] (1,200 VA x 1.25)   1,500 VA*

*Indicates neutral load.

Summary	Conductor	Neutral
(1) Air Conditioner	11,500 VA	0 VA
(3) Lighting	131,250 VA	131,250 VA
(4) Sprinkler Pump	6,440 VA	0 VA
(5) Receptacles	41,000 VA	41,000 VA
(6) Individual Circuits	72,000 VA	72,000 VA
(7) Sign	1,500 VA	1,500 VA
Largest Motor 25%	+ 1,610 VA	+ 1,610 VA
	265,300 VA	245,750 VA

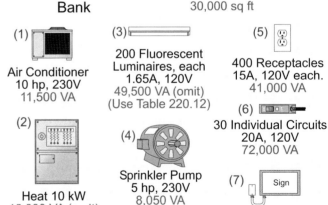

Bank   30,000 sq ft

(1) Air Conditioner 10 hp, 230V 11,500 VA

(3) 200 Fluorescent Luminaires, each 1.65A, 120V 49,500 VA (omit) (Use Table 220.12)

(5) 400 Receptacles 15A, 120V each. 41,000 VA

(2) Heat 10 kW 10,000 VA (omit)

(4) Sprinkler Pump 5 hp, 230V 8,050 VA

(6) 30 Individual Circuits 20A, 120V 72,000 VA

(7) Sign 1- 20A, 120V 1,500 VA

VA totals for items 1 through 7 above are calculated loads.

COPYRIGHT 2005 Mike Holt Enterprises, Inc.

Figure 11–25

Feeder/Service Calculated Load:

I = VA/E
I = 265,300 VA/240V
I = 1,105A

Grounded Neutral Amperes:

The grounded neutral conductor is permitted to be reduced according to the requirements of 220.61(B)(2) for that portion of the unbalanced load that exceeds 200A. Since this system is a 120/240V, single-phase system, we are permitted to reduce the neutral by multiplying that portion that exceeds 200A by 70%.

I = VA/E
I = 245,750 VA/240V
I = 1,024A

First 200A at 100%	200A	x 1.00	200A
Remainder at 70%	824A	x 0.70	+ 577A
			777A

Bank Summary Questions

The service overcurrent protection device must be sized no less than 1,105A. The service conductors must have an ampacity no less than the overcurrent protection device rating [240.4(C)]. The grounded neutral conductor must not be less than 777A.

▶ **Overcurrent Protection Example**

What size service overcurrent protection device is required?

(a) 800A   (b) 1,000A
(c) 1,200A   (d) 1,600A

• Answer: (c) 1,200A [240.6(A)].

▶ **Service Ungrounded Conductor Size Example**

What size service THHN conductors are required in each raceway if the service is paralleled in four raceways?

(a) 250 kcmil   (b) 300 kcmil
(c) 350 kcmil   (d) 400 kcmil

• Answer: (c) 350 kcmil

When the overcurrent device is over 800A, the ampacity of the conductors must be equal to, or greater than, the rating of the overcurrent device. In this example, the overcurrent device is 1,200A, so the ampacity of the conductors must be 1,200A or more [240.4(C)].

1,200A/4 raceways = 300A per raceway, sized based on 75°C terminal rating [110.14(C)(2)]

350 kcmil rated 310A x 4 = 1,240A [Table 310.16]

Note: 300 kcmil THHN has an ampacity of 320A at 90°C, but we must size the conductors at 75°C, not 90°C!

▶ **Service Grounded Neutral Conductor Size Example**

What size grounded neutral service conductor is required in each of the four raceways?

(a) 1/0 AWG   (b) 2/0 AWG
(c) 3/0 AWG   (d) 4/0 AWG

• Answer: (c) 3/0 AWG

The grounded neutral service conductor must be sized no less than the largest requirement of the following:

(1) 12 1/2% of the area of the ungrounded conductor:

Total Area of Ungrounded Conductors = 350,000 cmil x 4
Total Area of Ungrounded Conductors = 1,400,000 cmil
Minimum Area of Neutral Conductors = 1,400,000 cmil x 0.125 = 175,000 cmil [250.24(C)(1)]
175,000 cmil/4 raceways = 43,750 cmil, 3 AWG per raceway [Chapter 9, Table 8].

(2) When paralleling conductors, no grounded neutral conductor can be smaller than 1/0 AWG [310.4].

(3) The service neutral conductor must have an ampacity of at least 777A, as calculated previously [220.61(B)(2)].

777A/4 raceways = 194A, Table 310.16, 3/0 AWG is required at 75°C [110.14(C)]

▶ **Grounding Electrode Conductor Size [250.66(B)] Example**

What size grounding electrode conductor is required to a concrete-encased electrode?

(a) 4 AWG   (b) 1/0 AWG
(c) 2/0 AWG   (d) 3/0 AWG

• Answer: (a) 4 AWG

11.21 Marina [555.12]

The *NEC* permits a demand factor to apply to the receptacle outlets for boat slips at a marina. The demand factors of Table 555.12 are based on the number of receptacles on the feeder. The receptacles must also be balanced between the lines to determine the number of receptacles on any given line.

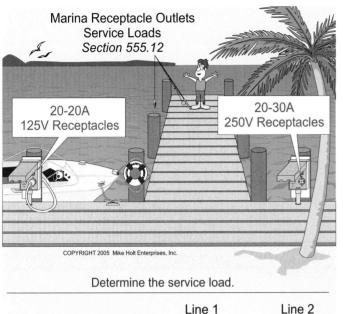

Marina Receptacle Outlets
Service Loads
Section 555.12

20-20A
125V Receptacles

20-30A
250V Receptacles

COPYRIGHT 2005 Mike Holt Enterprises, Inc.

Determine the service load.

	Line 1	Line 2
20- 30A 250V receptacles	20 x 30A	20 x 30A
20- 20A 125V receptacles	10 x 20A	10 x 20A
	30- 800A	30- 800A

555.12, demand load for 30 receptacle is 70%.
800A x 0.7 demand factor = 560A load per line

Figure 11–26

▶ **Marina Receptacle Outlet Demand [555.12] Example**

The calculated load is based on the number of receptacles. Balance the receptacles to determine the maximum number of receptacles on any line.

What size 120/240V, single-phase, service is required for a marina that has twenty 30A, 250V receptacles and twenty 20A, 125V receptacles? Figure 11–26

    (a) 200A   (b) 420A

    (c) 560A   (d) 720A

    • Answer: (c) 560A

	Line 1	Line 2
Twenty 30A, 250V	20 x 30A	20 x 30A
Ten 20A, 125V	+ 10 x 20A	+ 10 x 20A
Thirty receptacles	30- 800A	30- 800A

    Table 555.12, 30 receptacles = 0.70 demand factor

    Calculated Load Per Line =

        Connected Load per Line x Demand Factor

    Calculated Load per Line = 800A x 0.70

    Calculated Load per Line = 560A per line

11.22 Mobile/Manufactured Home Park [550.31]

The service calculated load for a mobile/manufactured home park is sized according to the demand factors of Table 550.31 to the larger of 16,000 VA for each mobile/manufactured home lot, or the calculated load for each mobile/manufactured home site according to 550.18.

▶ **Mobile/Manufactured Home Park Example**

A mobile home park's electrical wiring systems must be calculated at 120/240V based on the larger of the following [550.31]:

(1) 16,000 VA for each mobile home lot.

(2) The load calculated in accordance with 550.18 for the largest typical mobile home that each lot will accept.

It is permissible to calculate the feeder or service load in accordance with the demand factor percents in Table 550.31. It is also permitted to size service and feeder conductors to an individual mobile home in accordance with 310.15(B)(6)

What is the feeder/service calculated load for a mobile/manufactured home park that has facilities for 35 sites? The system is 120/240V, single-phase. Figure 11–27

    (a) 400A   (b) 560A   (c) 800A   (d) 1,000A

    • Answer: (b) 560A

    Since no calculated load in accordance with 550.18 is given, just use 16,000 VA per site [550.31(1)].

    Table 550.31, 35 sites = 0.24 demand factor.
    16,000 VA x 35 sites x 0.24 = 134,400 VA

    $I = VA/E$
    $I = 134,000 \text{ VA}/240\text{V}$
    $I = 560\text{A}$

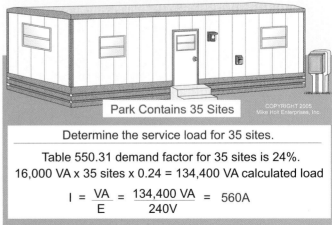

Mobile/Manufactured Home Park Site Calculated Load
Section 550.31

Park Contains 35 Sites

COPYRIGHT 2005
Mike Holt Enterprises, Inc.

Determine the service load for 35 sites.

Table 550.31 demand factor for 35 sites is 24%.
16,000 VA x 35 sites x 0.24 = 134,400 VA calculated load

$$I = \frac{VA}{E} = \frac{134,400 \text{ VA}}{240\text{V}} = 560\text{A}$$

Figure 11–27

11.23 Office Building (277/480V, Three-phase)

For the purpose of the example shown in Figure 11-28, this 28,000 sq ft office building has a 277/480V three-phase service. Some of the loads are supplied by an owner-supplied transformer with a 480V primary and a 120/208V secondary. Because primary VA is the same as secondary VA, all the loads can be calculated together regardless of voltage or whether the load is on the 277/480V service or the 120/208V transformer. Figure 11–28

(1) Air-Conditioning (Table 430.250)

460V x 7.6A x 1.732 = 6,055 VA
Connected Load = 6,055 VA x 15 units   90,825 VA

(2) Lighting (calculated VA from *NEC* tables) [215.2(A)(1) and Table 220.12]

28,000 sq ft x 3.5 VA x 1.25 = 122,500 VA (omit)
Lighting, Electric Discharge (Actual) [215.2(A)(1) and 230.42]
VA = 500 lights x 277V x 0.75A = 103,875 VA
Calculated VA = 103,875 VA x 1.25
Calculated Load =   129,844 VA*

(3) Lighting, Track (Actual) [220.43(B)] 150 VA per 2 ft

200 ft/2 ft = 100 sections
Connected VA = 100 sections x 150 VA
Connected VA = 15,000 VA
Calculated VA = 15,000 VA x 1.25
Calculated VA =   18,750 VA*

(4) Receptacles [220.44] (Actual) 200 receptacles (straps) x 180 VA =   36,000 VA

Multioutlet Assembly [220.14(H)]

147 ft/5 ft = thirty 5 ft sections, not simultaneously used
VA = 30 sections x 180 VA   5,400 VA
20 ft Simultaneously used
20 ft x 180 VA   3,600 VA
                                                                         45,000 VA
First 10 kVA at 100%   – 10,000 VA x 1.00   10,000 VA
Remainder at 50% [Table 220.44]   35,000 VA x 0.50   + 17,500 VA
                                                                         27,500 VA (omit)

Compare this to General Lighting Load calculated at 1 VA/sq ft
and use the larger of the two [220.14(K)(2)].
28,000 sq ft x 1 VA per sq ft =   28,000 VA*

(5) 30 Individual Computer Circuits

VA = V x A
VA = 120V x 20A
Calculated Load = 2,400 x 30 circuits   72,000 VA*

(6) Sign [220.14(F)] 1,200 VA x 1.25   1,500 VA*

*Indicates neutral load.

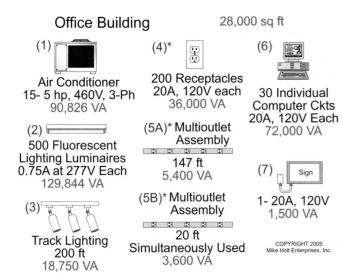

Office Building   28,000 sq ft

(1) Air Conditioner
15- 5 hp, 460V, 3-Ph
90,826 VA

(2) 500 Fluorescent
Lighting Luminaires
0.75A at 277V Each
129,844 VA

(3) Track Lighting
200 ft
18,750 VA

(4)* 200 Receptacles
20A, 120V each
36,000 VA

(5A)* Multioutlet
Assembly
147 ft
5,400 VA

(5B)* Multioutlet
Assembly
20 ft
Simultaneously Used
3,600 VA

(6) 30 Individual
Computer Ckts
20A, 120V Each
72,000 VA

(7) 1- 20A, 120V Sign
1,500 VA

COPYRIGHT 2005
Mike Holt Enterprises, Inc.

*In a bank or office building, the larger of 220.14(K)(1) and 220.14(K)(2) determines the calculated receptacle load of general-use receptacles and multioutlet assemblies.

VA totals for items 1 through 7 above are calculated loads.

Figure 11–28

Summary	Conductor	Neutral
(1) Air-Conditioning	90,825 VA	0 VA
(2) Lighting (actual)	129,844 VA	129,844 VA
(3) Lighting (track)	18,750 VA	18,750 VA
(4) Receptacles (VA per sq ft)	28,000 VA	28,000 VA
(5) Computer circuits	72,000 VA	72,000 VA
(6) Sign	+ 1,500 VA	+ 1,500 VA
Calculated Load	340,919 VA	250,094 VA

Feeder/Service Calculated Load:

$I = VA/(E \times 1.732)$

$I = 340,919 \text{ VA}/(480V \times 1.732)$

$I = 410A$

Grounded Neutral Conductor:

$I = VA/(E \times 1.732)$

$I = 250,094/(480V \times 1.732)$

$I = 301A$

Office Building Summary Questions

The service overcurrent protection device and conductor must be sized no less than 410A and the grounded neutral conductor must not be less than 301A.

▶ **Overcurrent Protection Example**

What size service overcurrent protection device is required?

(a) 300A (b) 350A
(c) 450A (d) 500A

• Answer: (c) 450A [240.6(A)]

Since the total calculated load for the overcurrent device is 410A, the minimum service permitted is 450A.

▶ **Service Conductor Size Example**

What size service conductors are required if the total calculated load is 410A?

(a) 300 kcmil (b) 400 kcmil
(c) 500 kcmil (d) 600 kcmil

• Answer: (d) 600 kcmil rated 420A at 75°C [240.4(B) and Table 310.16]

The service conductors must have an ampacity of at least 410A protected by a 450A overcurrent protection device [240.4(B)] and the conductors must be selected based on 75°C insulation rating [110.14(C)(2)].

▶ **Service Grounded Neutral Conductor Size Example**

What size service grounded neutral conductor is required for this service if the maximum unbalanced load is 301A?

(a) 4/0 AWG (b) 250 kcmil
(c) 300 kcmil (d) 350 kcmil

• Answer: (d) 350 kcmil

The grounded neutral conductor must be sized no less than the larger of the following:

(1) The required grounding electrode conductor [250.24(C) and Table 250.66], 1/0 AWG.

(2) An ampacity of at least 300A, Table 310.16, 350 kcmil is rated 310A at 75°C [110.14(C)].

Note: Because there are 125A of electric-discharge lighting [103,875 VA/(480 x 1.732)], the grounded neutral conductor is not permitted to be reduced for that portion of the load in excess of 200A [220.61(C)(2)].

11.24 Recreational Vehicle Park [551.73]

Recreational vehicle parks are calculated according to the demand factors of Table 551.73. The total calculated load is based on:

- 2,400 VA for each site with 20A, 120V supply facilities,
- 3,600 VA for each site with 20A and 30A, 120V supply facilities, and
- 9,600 VA for each site with 50A, 120/240V supply facilities.

▶ **Recreational Vehicle Park Example**

What is the calculated load for a recreational vehicle park that has ten 20A supply facilities, fifteen 20 and 30A supply facilities, and twenty 50A supply facilities? The system is 120/240V, single-phase. Figure-11-29

(a) 420A (b) 460A
(c) 520A (d) 600A

• Answer: (b) 460A

The service for the recreational vehicle park is sized according to the demand factors of Table 551.73

Ten 20A sites (2,400 VA x 10 sites)	24,000 VA
Fifteen 20A and 30A sites (3,600 VA x 15 sites)	54,000 VA
Twenty 50A sites (9,600 VA x 20 sites)	+ 192,000 VA
Connected Load	270,000 VA

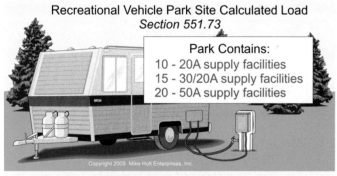

Recreational Vehicle Park Site Calculated Load
Section 551.73

Park Contains:
10 - 20A supply facilities
15 - 30/20A supply facilities
20 - 50A supply facilities

Determine the service demand load for 45 sites.

Determine VA of all sites, apply Tbl 551.73 demand factor

20A site	= 2,400 VA per site x 10 sites =	24,000 VA
30/20A site	= 3,600 VA per site x 15 sites =	54,000 VA
50A site	= 9,600 VA per site x 20 sites =	192,000 VA
Total connected site VA	45 sites =	270,000 VA

Table 551.73 demand for 45 sites = 41%
270,000 VA x 0.41 = 110,700 VA calculated load

$$I = \frac{VA}{E} = \frac{110,700\ VA}{240V} = 461A$$

Figure 11–29

Calculated Load = 270,000 VA x 0.41 [Table 551.73]
Calculated Load = 110,700 VA

I = VA/E
I = 110,700 VA/240V
I = 461A

11.25 Restaurant—Standard Load Calculation (120/208V, Three-phase) Figure 11–30

(1) Air-Conditioning 20 hp, 208V three-phase FLC = 59.4A [Table 430.250]

VA = E x I x 1.732
VA = 208V x 59.4A x 1.732
VA = 21,399 VA

(2) Kitchen Equipment [220.56]

Ovens, 10 kVA x 2 units =	20.0 kVA
Mixers, 3 kVA x 2 units =	6.0 kVA
Water Heater, 7.5 kVA x 1 unit =	+ 7.5 kVA
Total Connected	33.5 kVA

Apply 70% demand factor for 5 pieces of Kitchen Equipment [Table 220.56]

Calculated Load = Connected Load x Demand Factor
Calculated Load = 33,500 VA x 0.70
Calculated Load = 23,450 VA

(3) Lighting [215.2(A)(1), 230.42, and Table 220.12]

8,400 sq ft x 2 VA = 16,800 VA
Calculated Load = 16,800 VA x 1.25
Calculated Load = 21,000 (omit)

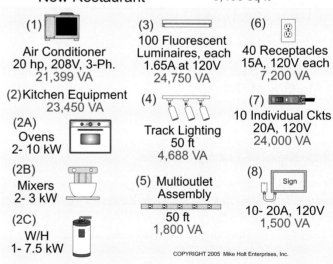

New Restaurant   8,400 sq ft

(1) Air Conditioner
20 hp, 208V, 3-Ph.
21,399 VA

(2) Kitchen Equipment
23,450 VA

(2A) Ovens
2- 10 kW

(2B) Mixers
2- 3 kW

(2C) W/H
1- 7.5 kW

(3) 100 Fluorescent Luminaires, each 1.65A at 120V
24,750 VA

(4) Track Lighting
50 ft
4,688 VA

(5) Multioutlet Assembly
50 ft
1,800 VA

(6) 40 Receptacles
15A, 120V each
7,200 VA

(7) 10 Individual Ckts
20A, 120V
24,000 VA

(8) Sign
10- 20A, 120V
1,500 VA

COPYRIGHT 2005 Mike Holt Enterprises, Inc.

Figure 11–30

Lighting, Electric Discharge (Actual) [215.2(A)(1) and 230.42]

Connected Load = 100 luminaires x 120V x 1.65A
Calculated Load = 19,800 VA x 1.25 = 24,750 VA

(4) Track Lighting, 150 VA for every 2 ft
[220.43(B), 215.2(A)(1), and 230.42]

50/2 = 25 sections
VA = 25 sections x 150 VA
VA = 3,750 VA

Calculated Load = 3,750 VA x 1.25
Calculated Load = 4,688 VA

(5) Multioutlet Assembly, not simultaneous used [220.14(H)]

50/5 = ten 5 ft sections
VA = 10 sections x 180 VA
VA = 1,800 VA

(6) Receptacles (Actual) [220.44], 40 receptacles (straps) x 180 VA =7,200 VA

The demand factor for under 10 kVA is 100%, and the sum of the receptacle and multioutlet assembly in this example is less than 10 kVA, so no reduction is allowed [Table 220.44].

(7) Individual circuits, 10 circuits x 20A x 120V = 24,000 VA

(8) Sign [220.14(F), 215.2(A)(1), and 230.42], 1,200 VA x 1.25 = 1,500 VA

Summary	Conductor
(1) Air-Conditioning	21,399 VA
(2) Kitchen Equipment	23,450 VA
(3) Lighting (actual)	24,750 VA
(4) Lighting (track)	4,688 VA
(5) Multioutlet Assembly	1,800 VA
(6) Receptacles (actual)	7,200 VA
(7) Individual Circuits	24,000 VA
(8) Sign	+ 1,500 VA
	108,787 VA

Feeder/Service Calculated Load:

$I = VA/(E \times 1.732)$
$I = 108,787 \text{ VA}/(208 \times 1.732)$
$I = 302A$

Restaurant Standard Load Calculation Summary Questions

The service conductors and overcurrent protection device must be sized no less than 302A.

▶ **Overcurrent Protection Example**

What size service overcurrent protection device is required?

(a) 300A   (b) 350A
(c) 450A   (d) 500A

• Answer: (b) 350A
[240.6(A)]

Since the total calculated load for the overcurrent device is 302A, the minimum service permitted is 350A [240.6(A)].

▶ **Service Conductor Size Example**

What size service conductors are required?

(a) 4/0 AWG   (b) 250 kcmil
(c) 300 kcmil   (d) 400 kcmil

• Answer: (d) 400 kcmil

The service conductors must have an ampacity of at least 302A and be protected by a 350A protection device [240.4(B)]. The next size up is permitted and the conductors must be selected according to Table 310.16, 350 kcmil is based on 75°C insulation rating [110.14(C)(2)] and is rated 335A.

PART D—OPTIONAL METHOD— FEEDER/SERVICE LOAD CALCULATIONS

11.26 New Restaurant—Optional Method [220.88]

An optional method of calculating the service load is permitted for a new restaurant that has electric space heating or electric air-conditioning, or both. The following steps can be used to determine the service size:

Step 1: Determine the total connected load. Add the nameplate rating of all loads at 100% and include both the air-conditioning and heat load [Table 220.88 Note].

Step 2: Apply the demand factors from Table 220.88 to the total connected load calculated in Step 1.

▶ **All-Electric Restaurant Example**

What is the calculated load for an all-electric restaurant (120/208V, three-phase) that has a total connected load of 300 kVA?

(a) 420A	(b) 472A
(c) 520A	(d) 600A

• Answer: (b) 472A

Total Connected Load   300 kVA
First 200 kVA at 80% – 200 kVA x 0.80 = 160 kVA
201-325 kVA at 10%   100 kVA x 0.10 = +10 kVA
Total Calculated Load   170 kVA

$I = VA/(E \times 1.732)$
$I = 170{,}000\ VA/(208V \times 1.732)$
$I = 472A$

▶ **Not All-Electric Restaurant Example**

What is the calculated load for a not all-electric restaurant (120/208V, three-phase) that has a total connected load of 300 kVA?

(a) 420A	(b) 460A
(c) 520A	(d) 695A

• Answer: (d) 695A

Total Connected Load   300 kVA
First 200 kVA at 100% – 200 kVA x 1.00 = 200 kVA
201-325 kVA at 50%   100 kVA x 0.50 = + 50 kVA
Total Calculated Load   250 kVA

$I = VA/(E \times 1.732)$
$I = 250{,}000\ VA/(208V \times 1.732)$
$I = 694A$

▶ **New Restaurant—Optional Method [220.88] Example**

Using the optional method, what is the service size for a new restaurant with the loads listed in Figure 11–31?

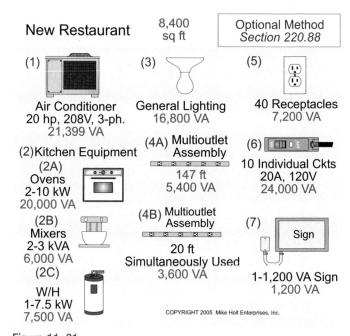

Figure 11–31

Step 1: Determine the total connected load.

(1) Air-Conditioning calculated [Table 430.250]

20 hp, 208V, three-phase FLC = 59.4A

VA = E x I x 1.732
VA = 208V x 59.4A x 1.732
VA =   21,399 VA

(2) Kitchen equipment

Ovens 10 kVA x 2 units	20,000 VA
Mixers 3 kVA x 2 units	6,000 VA
Water Heaters 7.5 kVA x 1 unit	+7,500 VA
	33,500 VA

Kitchen Equipment Load   33,500 VA

(3) Lighting [Table 220.12]
8,400 sq ft x 2 VA   16,800 VA

(4) Multioutlet assembly [220.14(H)]
147 ft/5 ft = thirty 5 ft sections not simultaneously used

180 VA x 30	5,400 VA
Simultaneously used, 180 VA x 20	+3,600 VA
	9,000 VA

Multioutlet Total   9,000 VA

(5) Receptacles [220.14(I)]
180 VA x 40 receptacles   7,200 VA

(6) Individual circuits
120V x 20A x 10 circuits   24,000 VA

(7) Sign [220.14(F) and 600.5]   1,200 VA

Summary	Conductor
(1) Air-Conditioning	21,399 VA
(2) Kitchen Equipment	33,500 VA
(3) Lighting	16,800 VA
(4) Multioutlet Assembly	9,000 VA
(5) Receptacles	7,200 VA
(6) Individual Circuits	24,000 VA
(7) Sign	+ 1,200 VA
Total Connected Load	113,099 VA

Step 2: Apply the demand factors from Table 220.88 to the total connected load.

All-Electric

If the restaurant is all-electric, a demand factor of 80% is permitted to apply to the first 200 kVA.

Calculated Load = Connected Load x Demand Factor [Table 220.80]
Calculated Load = 113,099 VA x 0.80
Calculated Load = 90,479 VA

$I = VA/(E \times 1.732)$
$I = 90,479 \text{ VA}/(208 \times 1.732)$
$I = 251A$

Not All-Electric

If the restaurant is not all-electric, then a demand factor of 100% applies to the first 200 kVA.

113,099 VA at 100% = 113,099 VA

$I = VA/(E \times 1.732)$
$I = 113,099 \text{ VA}/(208 \times 1.732)$
$I = 314A$

11.27 School—Optional Method [220.86]

An optional method of calculating the service load for a school is permitted. The following steps can be used to determine the service size:

Step 1: Add the nameplate rating of all loads at 100% including the larger of the A/C versus electric space-heating load.

Step 2: Determine the average VA per sq ft by dividing the total connected load (Step 1) by the sq ft of the building.

Step 3: Determine the calculated VA per sq ft by applying the Table 220.86 demand factors to the average VA per sq ft.

Step 4: Determine the feeder/service VA by multiplying the calculated VA per sq ft (Step 3) by the sq ft of the school building.

▶ **School—Optional Method Example**

What is the service size for the following loads? The system voltage is 120/208V, three-phase. **Figure 11–32**

(a) 300A (b) 400A
(c) 500A (d) 600A

• Answer: (c) 500A

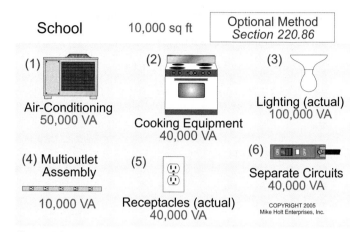

School   10,000 sq ft   Optional Method Section 220.86

(1) Air-Conditioning 50,000 VA
(2) Cooking Equipment 40,000 VA
(3) Lighting (actual) 100,000 VA
(4) Multioutlet Assembly 10,000 VA
(5) Receptacles (actual) 40,000 VA
(6) Separate Circuits 40,000 VA

COPYRIGHT 2005 Mike Holt Enterprises, Inc.

Figure 11–32

Step 1: Add the nameplate rating of all loads at 100% including the larger of the A/C versus electric space-heating load.

(1) Air-conditioning	50,000 VA
(2) Cooking equipment	40,000 VA
(3) Lighting	100,000 VA
(4) Multioutlet assembly	10,000 VA
(5) Receptacles	40,000 VA
(6) Separate circuits	40,000 VA
	280,000 VA

Step 2: Determine the average VA per sq ft (total connected load/sq ft area):

Average VA per sq ft = total connected load/sq ft
Average VA per sq ft = 280,000 VA/10,000 sq ft
Average VA per sq ft = 28 VA per sq ft

Step 3: Apply the demand factors from Table 220.86 to the VA per sq ft

Average VA per sq ft	28 VA	
First 3 VA at 100%	– 3 VA x 1.00 =	3.00 VA
	25 VA	
Next 17 VA at 75%	– 17 VA x 0.75 =	12.75 VA
Remainder at 25%	8 VA x 0.25 =	2.00 VA
Demand VA per sq ft =		17.75 VA

Step 4: Net VA per sq ft

Net VA per sq ft = Demand VA per sq ft x sq ft
Net VA per sq ft = 17.75 VA x 10,000 sq ft
Net VA per sq ft= 177,500 VA

Three Phase Service Size:
$I = VA/(E \times 1.732)$
$I = 177,500 \text{ VA}/(208 \times 1.732)$
$I = 493A$

PART E—ELECTRIC WELDERS

11.28 Arc Welders

Ampacity of Supply Conductors—Individual Welders

The supply conductors for arc welders must have an ampacity not less than the welder nameplate rating. If the nameplate rating isn't available, the supply conductors must have an ampacity not less than the rated primary current as adjusted by the multiplier in Table 630.11(A), based on the duty cycle of the welder.

Table 630.11(A) Duty Cycle Multiplication Factors for Arc Welders

Duty Cycle	Nonmotor Generator	Motor Generator
100	1.00	1.00
90	0.95	0.96
80	0.89	0.91
70	0.84	0.86
60	0.78	0.81
50	0.71	0.75
40	0.63	0.69
30	0.55	0.62
20 or less	0.45	0.55

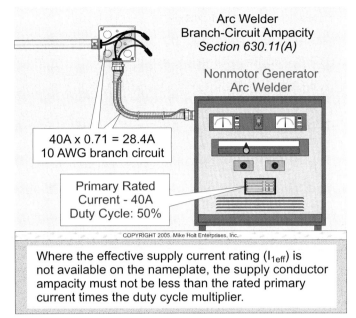

Arc Welder
Branch-Circuit Ampacity
Section 630.11(A)

Nonmotor Generator
Arc Welder

40A x 0.71 = 28.4A
10 AWG branch circuit

Primary Rated
Current - 40A
Duty Cycle: 50%

COPYRIGHT 2005. Mike Holt Enterprises, Inc.

Where the effective supply current rating (I_{1eff}) is not available on the nameplate, the supply conductor ampacity must not be less than the rated primary current times the duty cycle multiplier.

Figure 11–33

▶ **Individual Welders Example**

A nonmotor-generator arc welder has a primary current rating of 40A with a duty cycle of 50 percent. The branch-circuit conductor for the welder must not be sized less than: Figure 11–33

(a) 15A   (b) 20A
(c) 25A   (d) 30A

• Answer: (d) 30A
40A x 0.71 = 28.4A, 10 AWG [Table 310.16].

Ampacity of Supply Conductors—Group of Welders

Feeder conductors that supply a group of welders must have a minimum ampacity not less than the sum of the currents as determined in 630.11(A), based on 100 percent of the two largest welders, 85 percent for the third largest welder, 70 percent for the fourth largest welder, and 60 percent for all remaining welders.

> **AUTHOR'S COMMENT:** This calculation method provides an ample margin of safety under high-production conditions.

▶ **Group of Welders Example**

What is the feeder conductor for five 50A nonmotor-generator welders with a duty cycle of 50 percent?

(a) 1 AWG   (b) 2 AWG
(c) 3 AWG   (d) 4 AWG

• Answer: (a) 1 AWG

Welder 1: 50A x 0.71 = 35.5A x 100% =	35.50A
Welder 2: 50A x 0.71 = 35.5A x 100% =	35.50A
Welder 3: 50A x 0.71 = 35.5A x 85% =	30.18A
Welder 4: 50A x 0.71 = 35.5A x 70% =	24.85A
Welder 5: 50A x 0.71 = 35.5A x 60% =	21.30A
Total Calculated Load	147.33A

Conductor size from Table 310.16 is 1/0 AWG, rated 150A

Overcurrent Protection

Where the calculated overcurrent protection value does not correspond to the standard protection device ratings in 240.6(A), the next higher standard rating is permitted.

Welders. Each welder must have overcurrent protection rated at not more than 200 percent of the maximum rated supply current at the maximum rated output nameplate, or not more than 200 percent of the rated primary current of the welder.

Conductors. The conductors must be protected by an overcurrent device rated at not more than 200 percent of the conductor rating.

▶ **Overcurrent Protection Example**

What is the maximum overcurrent protection device rating for 10 THHN used for an arc welder branch circuit?

(a) 30A   (b) 40A
(c) 50A   (d) 70A

• Answer: (d) 70A
  10 AWG at 75°C is rated 35A [Table 310.16]
  35A x 2 = 70A maximum overcurrent protection device size

Disconnecting Means

A disconnecting means is required for each arc welder that isn't equipped with an integral disconnect.

11.29 Resistance Welders

Ampacity of Supply Conductors—Individual Welders

The ampacity of the supply conductors for varied duty-cycle welders must not be less than 70 percent of the rated primary current for seam and automatically fed welders, and 50 percent of the rated primary current for manually operated welders.

The ampacity of the supply conductors for welders with a specific duty cycle and nonvarying current levels must have an ampacity not less than the rated primary current as adjusted by the multipliers in Table 630.31(A)(2), based on the duty cycle of the welder.

Table 630.31(A)(2) Duty Cycle Multiplication Factors for Resistance Welders

Duty Cycle	Multiplier
50	0.71
40	0.63
30	0.55
25	0.50
20	0.45
15	0.39
10	0.32
7.5	0.27
5 or less	0.22

▶ **Individual Welders Example**

What size branch-circuit conductor is required for a 50A resistance welder having a duty cycle of 50 percent?

(a) 6 THHN   (b) 8 THHN
(c) 4 THHN   (d) 2 THHN

• Answer: (b) 8 THHN
  50A x 0.71 = 25.5A
  8 AWG at 75°C is rated 50A [Table 310.16]

Ampacity of Supply Conductors—Group of Welders

Feeder conductors that supply a group of resistance welders must have an ampacity not less than the sum of the value determined using 630.31(A)(2) for the largest welder in the group, plus 60 percent of the values determined for all remaining welders.

▶ **Group of Welders Example**

What is the feeder conductor for five 50A resistance welders with a duty cycle of 50 percent?

(a) 2 THHN   (b) 3 THHN
(c) 1 THHN   (d) 4 THHN

• Answer: (c) 1 THHN
  Conductor size from Table 310.16 is 1 AWG, rated 130A

Welder 1: 50A x 0.71 = 35.5A x 100% =	35.50A
Welder 2: 50A x 0.71 = 35.5A x 60% =	21.30A
Welder 3: 50A x 0.71 = 35.5A x 60% =	21.30A
Welder 4: 50A x 0.71 = 35.5A x 60% =	21.30A
Welder 5: 50A x 0.71 = 35.5A x 60% =	21.30A
Total Calculated Load	120.70A

1 AWG at 75°C is rated 130A [Table 310.16]

Overcurrent Protection

Where the calculated overcurrent protection value does not correspond with the standard protection device ratings in 240.6(A), the next higher standard rating is permitted.

Welders. Each welder must have overcurrent protection set at not more than 300 percent of the rated primary current.

Conductors. Branch-circuit conductors must be protected by an overcurrent device rated at not more than 300 percent of the conductor rating.

Disconnecting Means

A switch or circuit breaker is required to disconnect each resistance welder and its control equipment from the supply circuit.

11.30 Light Industrial Calculation

Calculate the service size for a light industrial manufacturing building with the following loads:

- Lighting, 11,600 VA, comprised of electric-discharge luminaries operating at 277V
- Twenty-two 20A, 125V receptacle outlets on general-purpose branch circuits, supplied by a separately derived system
- Air compressor, 460V, three-phase, 7 1/2 hp
- Grinder, 460V, three-phase, 1 1/2 hp
- Five 50A nonmotor-generator arc welders with a duty cycle of 50 percent (nameplate: 50A, 480V)
- Three industrial process dryers, 480V, three-phase, 15 kVA each (assume continuous duty during shifts)

Step 1: Determine the noncontinuous loads and motor loads. The noncontinuous and motor loads can be combined [430.24].

(1) Noncontinuous Loads

    (a) Receptacle load [220.44] 22 receptacles at 180 VA   3,960 VA

    (b) Welder Load [630.11(A) and Table 630.11(A)]
        A multiplication factor of 0.71 is allowed for 50% duty cycle
        Each welder: 480V x 50A x .71 = 17,040 VA

        Welder demand factors for 5 welders: [630.11(B)]

First welder	100%
Second welder	100%
Third welder	85%
Fourth welder	70%
Fifth welder	60%

        17,040 VA x 100% =   17,040 VA
        17,040 VA x 100% =   17,040 VA
        17,040 VA x 85% =   14,484 VA
        17,040 VA x 70% =   11,928 VA
        17,040 VA x 60% =   <u>10,224 VA</u>
                               70,716 VA

        Welder total calculated load =   70,716 VA

        Total noncontinuous loads (receptacles and welders) =   74,676 VA

(2) Motor Loads [430.24 and Table 430.250]

    (a) Air compressor: 7 1/2 hp FLC = 11A [Table 430.250]
        460V x 11A x 1.732 =   8,764 VA

    (b) Grinder: 1 1/2 hp FLC = 3A [Table 430.250]
        3A x 460V x 1.732 =   2,390 VA

    (c) Largest motor, additional 25%: 8,764 x 25% =   2,191 VA

    Total motor loads =   13,345 VA

    Total noncontinuous loads and the motor loads [430.24] =   88,021 VA

Step 2: Determine the continuous loads:

(1) General lighting =   11,600 VA

(2) 3 Industrial process dryers 15 kVA each =   <u>45,000 VA</u>
                                                               56,600 VA

   Total continuous loads =   56,600 VA

Step 3: Determine the overcurrent protection [215.3]:

The overcurrent protective device must be sized at 125% of the continuous load, plus the noncontinuous load:

(1) Noncontinuous load =   88,021 VA

(2) Continuous load (56,600 VA x 1.25) =   <u>70,750 VA</u>
                                                              158,771 VA

   Total VA   158,771 VA

Step 4: Convert to amperes to size the overcurrent protection:

I = VA/(E x 1.732)
I = 158,771 VA/(480V x 1.732)
I = 190.98A

Overcurrent Protection Device = 200A [240.6]
Conductors at 75°C = 3/0 AWG [110.14(C)(1)(b) and Table 310.16]

Unit 11 Conclusion

This unit showed that the calculations used to size feeders and service conductors for commercial installations do not include the same demand factors allowed for dwelling units. The nature of nondwelling occupancies does not lead to the same kinds of diversity of usage found in homes and apartment buildings. Accordingly, Unit 11 provided a variety of examples to help acquaint you with the *Code* requirements for commercial service sizing.

Article 220 is not the only *Code* article where service calculation requirements are contained. We referred to Article 550 for mobile home parks, Article 551 for recreational vehicle parks, Article 555 for marinas, Article 630 for electric welders, Article 440 for hermetic air-conditioning equipment, and Article 430 for information on motors. When performing commercial service calculations, be careful to look at all of the components of the installation to determine if some other article of the *Code* includes information pertinent to your installation.

Certain demand factors may be applied to commercial services. When dealing with individual branch circuits and feeders for continuous loads remember to use a 125 percent multiplier. This carries over to the continuous duty portions of loads when determining the actual feeder and service conductors for commercial occupancies. There are optional calculations that are allowed for some commercial installations, so be certain to read problems carefully so you will employ the correct method.

Unit 11 Calculation Practice Questions

(• Indicates that 75% or fewer of those who took this exam answered the question correctly.)

PART A—GENERAL

11.2 Conductor Ampacity [Article 100]

1. The _____ of a conductor is the rating in amperes it can carry continuously without exceeding its insulation temperature rating. The allowable ampacities, as listed in Table 310.16, are affected by ambient temperature, current flow, conductor insulation, and conductor bundling [310.10].

   (a) load rating   (b) ampacity   (c) calculated load   (d) continuous factor

11.3 Conductor Overcurrent Protection [240.4]

2. The purpose of _____ is to protect circuit conductors against excessive or dangerous temperatures. If the ampacity of a conductor does not correspond with the standard ampere rating of a fuse or circuit breaker, the next size up protection device is permitted. This applies only if the conductors do not supply multioutlet receptacles and if the next size up overcurrent protection device does not exceed 800A.

   (a) short-circuit protection   (b) ground-fault protection   (c) overload protection   (d) overcurrent protection

3. The following is a partial list of standard ampere ratings for overcurrent protection devices (fuses and inverse-time circuit breakers): 15, 25, 35, 45, 80, 90, 110, 175, 250, and 350.

   (a) True   (b) False

11.4 Voltages [220.5(A)]

4. Unless other voltages are specified, branch-circuit, feeder, and service loads are calculated at a nominal system voltage of _____.

   (a) 600Y/347V   (b) 240/120V   (c) 120/208V   (d) any of these

11.5 Rounding an Ampere [220.5(B)]

5. Where a calculation results in a fraction of an ampere that is _____ or less, that fraction is permitted to be dropped.

   (a) 0.05   (b) 0.50   (c) 0.49   (d) 0.51

11.6 Air-Conditioning Branch Circuit

6. What is the feeder or service calculated load required for the air conditioning of a 6-unit office building? Each unit contains one air-conditioner rated 3 hp, 230V, single-phase.

   (a) 13.2 kVA   (b) 23.4 kVA   (c) 45.5 kVA   (d) 52.1 kVA

11.7 Dryers

7. What size branch-circuit conductor and overcurrent protection is required for a 5 kW dryer rated 240V located in the laundry room of a multifamily dwelling?

    (a) 12 AWG with a 20A overcurrent protection device
    (b) 10 AWG with a 20A overcurrent protection device
    (c) 12 AWG with a 30A overcurrent protection device
    (d) 10 AWG with a 30A overcurrent protection device

8. What is the feeder and service calculated load for eight 6.75 kW dryers in a commercial laundromat?

    (a) 70 kW   (b) 54 kW   (c) 35 kW   (d) 27 kW

11.8 Electric Heat

9. •What size conductor and protection is required for a 480V, 15 kW, single-phase heat strip that has a 1.6A blower motor?

    (a) 10 AWG with 30A protection   (b) 6 AWG with 45A protection
    (c) 10 AWG with 40A protection   (d) 4 AWG with 70A protection

10. What is the feeder and service calculated load in VA for a building that has four 230V, 20 kW, single-phase heat strips, each of which has a 5.4A blower motor?

    (a) 100 kW   (b) 50 kW   (c) 125 kW   (d) 85 kW

11.9 Kitchen Equipment

11. What is the branch-circuit calculated load in amperes for one 11.4 kW oven rated 240V?

    (a) 60A   (b) 27A   (c) 48A   (d) 33A

12. •What is the feeder and service calculated load for the following commercial kitchen equipment?

Water Heater	9 kW
Booster Heater	12 kW
Mixer	3 kW
Oven	2 kW
Dishwasher	1.5 kW
Waste Disposal	1 kW

    (a) 19 kW   (b) 21 kW   (c) 29 kW   (d) 12 kW

13. What is the feeder and service calculated load for the following commercial kitchen equipment?

Water Heater	14 kW
Booster Heater	11 kW
Mixer	7 kW
Oven	9 kW
Dishwasher	1.5 kW
Waste Disposal	3 kW

    (a) 25 kW   (b) 30 kW   (c) 20 kW   (d) 45 kW

11.10 Laundry Equipment

14. What is the feeder and service calculated load for seven commercial washing machines at 1,500 VA each?

    (a) 10,500 VA   (b) 15,000 VA   (c) 1,125 VA   (d) none of these

11.11 Lighting—Demand Factors [Tables 220.12 and 220.42]

15. What is the general lighting and general-use receptacle feeder or service calculated load for a 24-room motel, where each unit is 685 sq ft?

    (a) 10 kVA   (b) 15 kVA   (c) 20 kVA   (d) 25 kVA

16. What is the general lighting and general-use receptacle feeder or service calculated load for a 250,000 sq ft storage warehouse that has 200 receptacles?

    (a) 25 kVA   (b) 56 kVA   (c) 95 kVA   (d) 105 kVA

11.12 Lighting Without Demand Factors [Table 220.12, 215.2(A)(1), and 230.42(A)(1)]

17. What is the feeder and service general lighting calculated load for a 3,200 sq ft dance club?

    (a) 3,200 VA   (b) 6,400 VA   (c) 8,000 VA   (d) 12,000 VA

18. What is the feeder and service general lighting load for a 90,000 sq ft school?

    (a) 238 kVA   (b) 338 kVA   (c) 90 kVA   (d) 270 kVA

11.13 Lighting—Miscellaneous

19. How many 2 x 4 fluorescent luminaires, each rated 277V, 0.80A, can be connected to a 20A circuit? The four lamps are rated 40W each and the luminaire is to be on for more than three hours.

    (a) 5   (b) 7   (c) 9   (d) 20

20. How many 360W, 120V incandescent luminaires that operate continuously can be connected to a 20A, 120V circuit?

    (a) 5   (b) 7   (c) 9   (d) 12

21. •What is the VA demand feeder and service load for 130 ft of show-window lighting?

    (a) 26 kVA   (b) 33 kVA   (c) 9 kVA   (d) 11 kVA

11.14 Multioutlet Receptacle Assembly [220.14(H)]

22. What is the feeder calculated load for 50 ft of multioutlet assembly and 10 ft of multioutlet assembly simultaneously used?

    (a) 3,600 VA   (b) 12,000 VA   (c) 7,200 VA   (d) 5,500 VA

11.15 Receptacles VA Load [220.44]

23. How many receptacle outlets are permitted on a 20A, 120V circuit in a commercial occupancy?

    (a) 10   (b) 13   (c) 15   (d) 20

24. What is the service calculated load for 110 receptacles (15 or 20A, 125V) in a commercial building?

    (a) 5 kVA   (b) 10 kVA   (c) 15 kVA   (d) 20 kVA

25. What is the service calculated load for the general lighting and receptacles for a 30,000 sq ft bank?

    (a) 111 kVA   (b) 151 kVA   (c) 123 kVA   (d) 175 kVA

26. •What is the general lighting and receptacle calculated load for a 10,000 sq ft office building with 75 receptacles?

    (a) 25 kVA   (b) 35 kVA   (c) 45 kVA   (d) 56 kVA

11.17 Signs [220.14(F) and 600.5]

27. What is the feeder calculated load for sizing the overcurrent protection device for one electric sign?

    (a) 1,400 VA   (b) 1,500 VA   (c) 1,920 VA   (d) 2,400 VA

PART B—STANDARD LOAD CALCULATIONS
11.19 Neutral Calculations [220.61]

28. What is the neutral current for a balanced 150A, 3-wire, 120/208V feeder?

    (a) 0A   (b) 150A   (c) 250A   (d) 300A

PART C—EXAMPLES
11.21 Marina [555.12]

29. A marina has the following: 24 slips with 20A, 250V receptacles, and 30 slips with 30A, 250V receptacles. What size service is required for the marina?

    (a) 400A   (b) 550A   (c) 900A   (d) 1,000A

30. What size conductor is required for the service if the total calculated load for each phase is 570A and the service is paralleled in two raceways?

    (a) 4/0 AWG   (b) 250 kcmil   (c) 300 kcmil   (d) 350 kcmil

11.22 Mobile/Manufactured Home Park [550.31]

31. What is the feeder and service calculated load for a mobile home park that has the facilities for 42 sites? The system is 120/240V, single-phase.

    (a) 644A   (b) 512A   (c) 732A   (d) 452A

11.24 Recreational Vehicle Park [551.73]

32. A recreational vehicle park has 17 dedicated tent sites with only 20A, 240V receptacles, 35 sites with 20 and 30A, 240V receptacles, and 10 sites with 50A, 240V receptacles. The feeder and service calculated load is approximately _____.

    (a) 355A   (b) 450A   (c) 789A   (d) 1,114A

PART D—OPTIONAL LOAD CALCULATIONS

11.26 New Restaurant—Optional Method [220.88]

33. A new restaurant has a total connected load of 400 kVA and is all electric. What is the calculated load for the service?

    (a) 210 kVA   (b) 325 kVA   (c) 300 kVA   (d) 275 kVA

34. A new restaurant has a total connected load of 400 kVA and is not all electric. What is the calculated load for the service?

    (a) 296 kVA   (b) 325 kVA   (c) 300 kVA   (d) 275 kVA

11.27 School—Optional Method [220.86]

35. A 28,000 sq ft school has a total connected load of 590,000 VA. What is the calculated load using the optional method?

    (a) 350 kVA   (b) 400 kVA   (c) 450 kVA   (d) 500 kVA

(• Indicates that 75% or fewer of those who took this exam answered the question correctly.)

PART A—GENERAL

11.9 Kitchen Equipment

1. What is the kitchen equipment calculated load for one 14 kW range, one 1.5 kW water heater, one 3/4 kW mixer, one 2 kW dishwasher, one 3 kW booster heater, and one 3 kW coffee machine?

    (a) 17 kW   (b) 14 kW   (c) 15 kW   (d) 24 kW

11.11 Lighting—Demand Factors [Tables 220.12 and 220.42]

2. •Each unit of a 100-unit hotel is 12 x 15 ft. In addition, there is a 60 x 20 ft office and there are hallways of 120 sq ft. What is the general lighting calculated load?

    (a) 29 kVA   (b) 37 kVA   (c) 23 kVA   (d) 25 kVA

11.15 Receptacles VA Load

3. If in the hall and other areas of a motel there are 100 receptacle outlets (not in the motel rooms), the calculated load added to the service for these receptacles is _____.

    (a) 0 VA   (b) 10,000 VA   (c) 14,000 VA   (d) 20,000 VA

4. What is the receptacle calculated load for a 20,000 sq ft office building?

    (a) 10,000 VA   (b) 40,000 VA   (c) 30,000 VA   (d) 15,000 VA

PART B—STANDARD LOAD CALCULATIONS

11.16 Banks and Offices—General Lighting and Receptacles [220.14(k)]

5. What is the general lighting and general-use receptacle load for a 30,000 sq ft bank?

    (a) 162 kVA   (b) 123 kVA   (c) 173 kVA   (d) 151 kVA

11.19 Neutral Calculations [220.61]

6. •A 120/208V, three-phase service has a total connected load of 1,450A:
    (1) 600A of these are phase-to-phase loads
    (2) 300A are balanced 120V fluorescent lighting
    (3) 550A are other 120V loads
    The neutral calculated load for this service is _____.

    (a) 1,150A   (b) 650A   (c) 745A   (d) 420A

PART C—EXAMPLES

11.21 Marina [555.12]

7.   A marina shore power facility has twenty 20A, 240V receptacles, seventeen 30A, 240V receptacles, and seven 50A, 240V receptacles. After applying demand factors, the service calculated load for the shore power boxes is _____.

   (a) 1,260A   (b) 630A   (c) 1,160A   (d) 625A

11.22 Mobile/Manufactured Home Park [550.31]

8.   A 75-site mobile home park is designed for mobile homes that have a 14,000 VA load per site. The service calculated load for the park is _____.

   (a) 1,200 kVA   (b) 264 kVA   (c) 222 kVA   (d) 201 kVA

11.24 Recreational Vehicle Park [551.73]

9.   A recreational vehicle park has 42 sites: 3 sites equipped with 50A, 120/240V supply facilities; 30 sites equipped with 20 and 30A, 120/240V supply facilities; and 9 sites equipped with 20A 120/240V supply facilities. The minimum feeder calculated load for these sites would be _____.

   (a) 158 kVA   (b) 101 kVA   (c) 139 kVA   (d) 65 kVA

PART D—OPTIONAL LOAD CALCULATIONS

11.26 New Restaurant—Optional Method [220.88]

10.   •A new restaurant has a total connected lighting load of 30 kVA. The kitchen equipment includes two gas stoves, one gas grill, three gas ovens, one 75-gallon gas water heater, one 5 kW dishwasher, two 2 kW coffee makers, five 2 kW kitchen appliances on their own circuit, and ten 1.5 kVA small-appliance circuits. Using the optional method, the service calculated load is closest to _____.

   (a) 64 kVA   (b) 50 kVA   (c) 45 kVA   (d) 38 kVA

11.27 School—Optional Method [220.86]

11.   •Using the optional method, what is the calculated load (VA per sq ft) for a 10,000 sq ft school that has a total connected load of 320 kVA?

   (a) 15.75 VA per sq ft   (b) 18.75 VA per sq ft   (c) 29.00 VA per sq ft   (d) 12.75 VA per sq ft

12.   Using the optional method, what is the total kVA calculated load for a 20,000 sq ft school that has a total connected load of 160 kVA?

   (a) 135 kVA   (b) 106 kVA   (c) 120 kVA   (d) 112 kVA

(• Indicates that 75% or fewer of those who took this exam answered the question correctly.)

Article 645 Information Technology Equipment (continued)

1. Cables listed for the purpose can be used to interconnect separate data-processing units in information technology equipment rooms. Where run on the surface of the floor, the cables must be protected by _____.

    (a) a GFCI circuit breaker   (b) approved means   (c) duct tape   (d) metal raceways only

2. Under a raised floor, liquidtight flexible metal conduit is permitted to enclose branch-circuit conductors for information technology communications equipment.

    (a) True   (b) False

3. Ventilation in the underfloor area of an information equipment room can be used in that room only, and the ventilation system must be arranged so that upon the detection of fire or products of combustion in the underfloor area, the circulation of air will cease.

    (a) True   (b) False

4. _____ cables such as CL2, CM, or CATV are permitted within the raised floor area of an information technology equipment room.

    (a) Control   (b) Signal   (c) Communications   (d) all of these

5. Abandoned cables under an information technology room raised floor must be removed, unless the cables are contained within a metal raceway.

    (a) True   (b) False

6. Signal and communications cables that extend beyond the information technology equipment room are required to comply only with Article 645.

    (a) True   (b) False

7. Where a pushbutton is used as a means to disconnect power in the information technology equipment room, pushing the button "in" must disconnect the power.

    (a) True   (b) False

8. Each unit of an information technology system supplied by a branch circuit must have a manufacturer's nameplate that includes the _____.

    (a) rating in volts   (b) operating frequency   (c) maximum load in amperes   (d) all of these

Article 647 Sensitive Electronic Equipment

A technical power system (called "balanced power" by some) is a separately derived, 120V line-to-line, single-phase, 3-wire system with 60V-to-ground used for sensitive electronic equipment.

9. The purpose of a 60/120V power system is to reduce objectionable noise in sensitive electronic equipment locations. Its use is restricted to _____ occupancies that are under close supervision by qualified personnel.

    (a) commercial   (b) industrial   (c) a and b   (d) none of these

10. Junction boxes used in sensitive electronic equipment systems must be clearly marked to indicate _____.

   (a) the installer's name   (b) the system voltage   (c) the distribution panel   (d) b and c

11. Voltage drop on sensitive electronic equipment systems must not exceed _____ percent for branch circuits.

   (a) 1.5   (b) 3   (c) 2.5   (d) 5

12. Permanently wired utilization equipment and receptacles in sensitive electronic equipment systems must be grounded with a separate equipment grounding conductor run with the circuit conductors to an equipment grounding bus prominently marked _____.

   (a) "Technical Equipment Ground"   (b) "Equipment Ground Bar"
   (c) "Green"   (d) "Isolation Bonding"

Article 660 X-Ray Equipment

This article covers all X-ray equipment operating at any frequency or voltage for industrial or other nonmedical or nondental use.

13. X-ray equipment mounted on a permanent base equipped with wheels and/or casters for moving while completely assembled is defined as _____.

   (a) portable   (b) mobile   (c) movable   (d) room

14. The ampacity requirements for a disconnecting means for X-ray equipment must be based on the greater of _____ percent of the input required for the momentary rating or 100 percent of the input required for the long-time rating.

   (a) 125   (b) 100   (c) 50   (d) none of these

15. Size 18 or 16 AWG fixture wires are permitted for the control and operating circuits of X-ray and auxiliary equipment when protected by an overcurrent protection device not larger than _____.

   (a) 15A   (b) 20A   (c) 25A   (d) 30A

Article 670 Industrial Machinery

This article covers the definition of, the nameplate data for, and the size and overcurrent protection of supply conductors to industrial machinery.

16. Where overcurrent protection is provided as part of an industrial machine, the machine must be marked to read, _____.

   (a) "Overcurrent Protection Provided At Machine Supply Terminals"
   (b) "This Unit Contains Overcurrent Protection"
   (c) "Fuses Or Circuit Breaker Enclosed"
   (d) "Overcurrent Protected"

Article 675 Electrically Driven or Controlled Irrigation Machines

The provisions of this article apply to electrically driven or controlled irrigation machines, and to the branch circuits and controllers for such equipment.

17. An electrically driven or controlled machine with one or more motors that are not hand-portable, and used primarily to transport and distribute water for agricultural purposes, is called a(n) _____.

   (a) irrigation machine   (b) electric water distribution system
   (c) center pivot irrigation machine   (d) automatic water distribution system

Article 680 Swimming Pools, Spas, Hot Tubs, Fountains, and Similar Installations

The scope of Article 680 is limited to the installation of electric wiring and equipment that supplies swimming, wading, therapeutic and decorative pools, fountains, hot tubs, spas, and hydromassage bathtubs, whether permanently installed or storable.

18. •A spa or hot tub is a hydromassage pool or tub for recreational or therapeutic use designed for the immersion of users. They are not generally designed or intended to have the contents drained or discharged after each use.

    (a) True   (b) False

19. A wet-niche luminaire (lighting fixture) is intended to be installed in a _____.

    (a) transformer   (b) forming shell   (c) hydromassage bathtub   (d) all of these

20. Fixed or stationary pool, outdoor spa, and hot tub equipment is permitted to be cord-and-plug connected to facilitate the removal or disconnection for maintenance or repair. The flexible cord must _____.

    (a) not exceed 3 ft except for storable pools
    (b) have a copper equipment grounding conductor not smaller than 12 AWG
    (c) terminate in a grounding-type attachment plug
    (d) all of these

21. Overhead utility service conductors that operate at not over 750 volts-to-ground must maintain a _____ clearance in any direction to the water level, edge of water surface, base of diving platform, or permanently anchored raft.

    (a) 14 ft   (b) 16 ft   (c) 20 ft   (d) 22 1/2 ft

22. Overhead network-powered broadband communications systems conductors must be located no less than _____ from the water's edge of swimming and wading pools, or the base of diving structures.

    (a) 10 ft   (b) 12 ft   (c) 18 ft   (d) none of these

23. Underground rigid nonmetallic wiring located less than 5 ft from the inside wall of a pool or spa must be buried not less than _____

    (a) 6 in.   (b) 10 in.   (c) 12 in.   (d) 18 in.

24. Underground outdoor pool or spa equipment rooms or pits must have adequate drainage to prevent water accumulation during normal operation or filter maintenance.

    (a) True   (b) False

25. The "maintenance" disconnect for pool equipment applies to all utilization equipment, including lighting.

    (a) True   (b) False

26. Pool-associated motors must be grounded using a minimum size 12 AWG insulated copper conductor and this grounding conductor must be installed in any wiring method employed, which could include _____.

    (a) rigid nonmetallic conduit   (b) electrical metallic tubing where installed on or within buildings
    (c) flexible metal conduit   (d) a or b

27. Receptacles that provide power for water-pump motors or for other loads directly related to the circulation and sanitation system must be located at least _____ from the inside walls of the pool.

    (a) 3 ft   (b) 5 ft   (c) 10 ft   (d) 12 ft

28. One 15 or 20A, single-phase, 125V receptacle can be installed not less than _____, measured horizontally, from the inside wall of the pool at a dwelling unit if the dimensions of the lot do not allow the required receptacle outlet to be 10 ft from the water.

    (a) 3 ft   (b) 5 ft   (c) 6 ft   (d) none of these

29. All outdoor 15 and 20A, single-phase, 125V through 250V receptacles for pool, spa, and hot tub pump motors must be _____.

    (a) AFCI protected   (b) GFCI protected   (c) approved   (d) listed

30. Luminaires or ceiling fans mounted less than 12 ft above the water level cannot be installed above or within _____ of an outdoor pool, fountain, or spa.

    (a) 3 ft   (b) 5 ft   (c) 10 ft   (d) 8 ft

31. A pool transformer used for the supply of underwater luminaires, together with the transformer enclosure, is required to _____.

    (a) be of the isolated-winding type with an ungrounded secondary
    (b) have a grounded metal barrier between the primary and secondary windings
    (c) be listed for the purpose
    (d) all of these

32. Forming shells for wet-niche luminaires must be installed with the top level of the fixture lens not less than _____ below the normal water level of the pool or spa.

    (a) 6 in.   (b) 12 in.   (c) 18 in.   (d) 24 in.

33. All wet-niche luminaires installed in swimming pools must be removable from the water for relamping or normal maintenance and must be installed in such a manner that personnel can reach the luminaire for relamping, maintenance, or inspection _____.

    (a) while the pool is drained   (b) while the person is on the deck or a dry location
    (c) during construction   (d) all of these

34. Electrical metallic tubing is permitted for branch-circuit wiring for underwater luminaires where installed on buildings. Where installed within buildings, electrical nonmetallic tubing, Type MC cable, or electrical metallic tubing is permitted.

    (a) True   (b) False

35. A pool light junction box that is connected to a conduit that extends directly to a forming shell or mounting bracket of a no-niche luminaire (fixture) must be _____ for this use.

    (a) listed   (b) labeled   (c) marked   (d) a and b

36. Junction boxes for pool lighting must not be located less than _____ from the inside wall of a pool unless separated by a fence or wall.

    (a) 3 ft   (b) 4 ft   (c) 6 ft   (d) 8 ft

37. The enclosure for a transformer or ground-fault circuit interrupter connected to a conduit that extends directly to a pool light forming shell must be _____ for this purpose.

    (a) labeled   (b) listed   (c) identified   (d) a and b

38. The feeder to a swimming pool panelboard at a separate building or structure is permitted to be supplied with any Chapter 3 wiring method provided the feeder has a separate insulated copper equipment grounding conductor.

    (a) True   (b) False

39. •When installing equipotential bonding of pool and spa equipment, a solid 8 AWG copper conductor must be run back to the service equipment. This conductor must be unbroken.

(a) True   (b) False

40. •When bonding together pool reinforcing steel and welded wire fabric (wire-mesh) with tie-wire, the tie-wires must be _____.

(a) stainless steel   (b) accessible   (c) made tight   (d) none of these

41. •Which of the following must be bonded?

(a) Metal parts of electrical equipment associated with the pool water circulating system.   (b) Pool structural steel.
(c) Metal fittings within or attached to the pool.   (d) all of these

42. The components that are required to be connected to the equipotential bonding grid of a swimming pool must be connected using a minimum size of 8 AWG solid _____ conductor.

(a) insulated   (b) bare   (c) covered   (d) any of these

43. The electric motors, controllers, and wiring for an electrically operated pool cover must be _____.

(a) located at least 5 ft from the inside wall of the pool   (b) separated from the pool by a permanent barrier
(c) both a and b   (d) either a or b

44. Radiant heating cables embedded in or below the pool deck _____.

(a) must not be installed within 5 ft horizontally from the inside walls of the pool
(b) must be mounted at least 12 ft vertically above the pool deck
(c) are not permitted
(d) none of these

45. 15 and 20A, single-phase, 125V receptacles located within _____ of the inside walls of a storable pool must be protected by a ground-fault circuit interrupter.

(a) 8 ft   (b) 10 ft   (c) 15 ft   (d) 20 ft

46. In spas or hot tubs, a clearly labeled emergency shutoff or control switch for the purpose of stopping the motors(s) that provide power to the recirculation system and jet system must be installed. The emergency shutoff control switch must be _____ to the users and located not less than 5 ft away, and within sight of, the spa or hot tub. This requirement does not apply to single-family dwelling units.

(a) accessible   (b) readily accessible   (c) available   (d) none of these

47. Listed packaged spa or hot tub equipment assemblies or self-contained spas or hot tubs installed outdoors are permitted to use flexible connections utilizing _____.

(a) liquidtight flexible metal conduit or liquidtight flexible nonmetallic conduit in lengths of not more than 6 ft.
(b) cord-and-plug connections with cords not longer than 15 ft, where GFCI protected
(c) a or b
(d) none of these

48. The interior wiring for the motor, heater, and control loads that are part of an outdoor installation of a self-contained spa or hot tub, at a one-family dwelling or structure associated with a one-family dwelling, can use any Chapter 3 wiring method that contains an insulated 12 AWG or larger copper equipment grounding conductor.

(a) True   (b) False

49. At least one 15 or 20A, 125V receptacle must be located a minimum of _____ (and a maximum of 10 ft) from the inside wall of a spa or hot tub installed indoors.

(a) 2 ft   (b) 5 ft   (c) 18 in.   (d) no minimum

50. Receptacles that provide power for an indoor spa or hot tub must be _____.

(a) 240V minimum   (b) GFCI protected   (c) a or b   (d) a and b

51. Luminaires and ceiling fans located over or within 5 ft, measured horizontally, from the inside walls of an indoor spa or hot tub must have a mounting height of not less than _____ above the maximum water level when GFCI protection is provided.

(a) 4.7 ft   (b) 5 ft   (c) 7 ft 6 in.   (d) 12 ft

52. Surface-mounted luminaires _____ located over or within 5 ft, measured horizontally, from the inside walls of an indoor spa or hot tub are permitted to be installed at less than 7 ft 6 in. above the maximum water level when GFCI protection is provided.

(a) with a glass or plastic globe
(b) with a nonmetallic body or a metallic body isolated from contact
(c) suitable for use in a damp location
(d) all of these

53. Metal fittings within or attached to an indoor spa or hot tub structure must be _____.

(a) bonded   (b) insulated   (c) removed   (d) concealed

54. Metal conduit and metal piping within _____ of the inside walls of an indoor spa or hot tub, and not separated from the indoor spa or hot tub by a permanent barrier, must be bonded.

(a) 4 ft   (b) 5 ft   (c) 7 ft   (d) 12 ft

55. Small conductive surfaces of an indoor spa or hot tub, such as air and water jets not likely to become energized, are not required to be bonded. Other nonelectric equipment, such as towel bars or mirror frames, which are not connected to metallic piping, are not required to be bonded.

(a) True   (b) False

56. All metal parts associated with an indoor spa or hot tub must be bonded by _____.

(a) the interconnection of threaded metal piping and fittings
(b) metal-to-metal mounting on a common frame or base
(c) a copper bonding jumper (insulated, covered, or bare) not smaller than 8 AWG solid
(d) any of these

57. The branch circuit supplying submersible fountain equipment must be _____, unless the equipment is listed for operation at not more than 15V and is supplied by a pool transformer complying with 680.23(A)(2).

(a) 240V   (b) protected by a ground-fault circuit interrupter
(c) both a and b   (d) none of these

58. The maximum length of exposed cord in a fountain must be _____.

(a) 3 ft   (b) 4 ft   (c) 6 ft   (d) 10 ft

59. All metal piping systems associated with a fountain must be bonded to the equipment grounding conductor of the _____.

(a) branch circuit supplying the fountain   (b) bonding grid
(c) equipotential plane   (d) locally driven ground rod

60. All cord-and-plug connected equipment in fountains _____ must have ground-fault circuit-interrupter protection.

    (a) except pumps
    (b) including power-supply cords
    (c) less than 6 ft high
    (d) except power supply cords

61. Each circuit supplying a sign within or adjacent to a fountain must _____.

    (a) have ground-fault circuit-interrupter protection
    (b) be equipped with a lock out
    (c) operate at less than 50V
    (d) be an intrinsically safe circuit

62. All 15 and 20A, single-phase, 125V through 250V receptacles located within _____ of a fountain edge must have GFCI protection.

    (a) 8 ft
    (b) 10 ft
    (c) 15 ft
    (d) 20 ft

63. GFCI protection is required for all 125V, single-phase receptacles not exceeding 30A and located within 5 ft measured _____ from the inside walls of a hydromassage bathtub.

    (a) vertically
    (b) horizontally
    (c) across
    (d) none of these

64. All metal piping systems, metal parts of electrical equipment, and pump motors associated with a hydromassage tub must be bonded together with a(n) _____ solid copper bonding jumper not smaller than 8 AWG.

    (a) insulated
    (b) covered
    (c) bare
    (d) any of these

Article 690 Solar Photovoltaic Systems

The provisions of this article apply to solar photovoltaic electrical energy systems that may be interactive with other electrical power production sources or stand-alone, with or without electrical energy storage such as batteries. These systems may have ac or dc output for utilization.

65. Any structure with a photovoltaic power system that is not connected to a utility service source and is a stand-alone system must have a permanent plaque or directory on the exterior of the structure that identifies the location of system disconnecting means and states that the structure contains a stand-alone electrical power system.

    (a) True
    (b) False

Article 692 Fuel Cell Systems

This article identifies the requirements for the installation of fuel cell power systems, which may be stand-alone or interactive with other electrical power production sources and may be with or without electrical energy storage such as batteries. These systems may have ac or dc output for utilization.

66. A fuel cell is an electrochemical system that consumes fuel to produce an electric current. The main chemical reaction used in a fuel cell to produce electrical power is not combustion.

    (a) True
    (b) False

67. The fuel cell system must be evaluated and _____ for its intended application prior to installation.

    (a) approved
    (b) identified
    (c) listed
    (d) marked

Article 695 Fire Pumps

Article 695 covers the electric power sources and interconnecting circuits for electric motor-driven fire pumps. It also covers switching and control equipment dedicated to fire pump drivers. Article 695 doesn't apply to sprinkler system pumps in one- and two-family dwellings or to pressure maintenance (jockey) pumps.

68. For fire pump motors, the _____ must be selected to carry indefinitely the sum of the locked-rotor current of the fire pump motor(s), pressure maintenance pump motor(s), and the full-load current of any associated fire pump accessory equipment connected to this power supply.

(a) overcurrent protective device(s)   (b) pump motor conductors
(c) a and b   (d) none of these

69. The primary overcurrent protective device for a transformer supplying a fire pump must carry the sum of the locked-rotor current of the fire pump motor(s) and pressure maintenance pump motor(s), and the full-load current of any associated fire pump accessory equipment when connected to this power supply _____.

(a) for 15 minutes   (b) for 45 minutes   (c) for 3 hours   (d) indefinitely

70. The _____ for a transformer that supplies fire pumps must carry indefinitely the sum of the locked-rotor current of the fire pump motor(s) and the pressure maintenance pump motor(s), and the full-load current of the associated fire pump accessory equipment when connected to this power supply.

(a) primary overcurrent protective device(s)   (b) pump motor conductors
(c) both a and b   (d) none of these

71. Feeder conductors supplying fire pump motors and accessory equipment must be sized no less than _____ percent of the sum of the motor full-load currents as listed in Article 430, plus 100 percent of the ampere rating of the fire pump accessory equipment.

(a) 100   (b) 125   (c) 250   (d) 600

72. Ground-fault protection of equipment _____ for fire pumps.

(a) is not permitted   (b) is permitted
(c) is allowed   (d) must be approved by the AHJ

73. When a fire pump motor is operating at 115 percent of its full-load current rating, the supply voltage at the motor terminals must not drop more than _____ percent below the voltage rating of the motor.

(a) 5   (b) 10   (c) 15   (d) any of these

Chapter 7 Special Conditions

Article 700 Emergency Power Systems

The requirements of Article 700 apply only to the wiring methods for "emergency systems" that are essential for safety to human life and required by federal, state, municipal, or other regulatory codes. When normal power is lost, emergency systems must be capable of supplying emergency power in 10 seconds or less.

74. Emergency systems are generally installed where artificial illumination is required for safe exiting and for panic control in buildings occupied by large numbers of persons, such as _____ and similar institutions.

(a) hotels   (b) theaters and sports arenas
(c) health care facilities   (d) all of these

75. Except as modified by Article 700, all requirements contained in the *NEC* Chapters 1 through 4 apply to installations of emergency systems.

    (a) True   (b) False

76. Emergency systems that are tested upon installation and found to be acceptable to the authority having jurisdiction (AHJ) are not required to undergo any future tests unless the equipment is modified.

    (a) True   (b) False

77. A written record must be kept of required tests and maintenance on emergency systems.

    (a) True   (b) False

78. An emergency system must have adequate capacity to safely carry _____ that are expected to operate simultaneously on the emergency system.

    (a) all of the loads   (b) 80 percent of the total loads
    (c) up to 200A of the loads   (d) 300 percent of the total loads

79. A portable or temporary alternate source _____ whenever the emergency generator is out of service for major maintenance or repair.

    (a) is not required   (b) is recommended   (c) must be available   (d) must be avoided

80. An emergency transfer switch can supply _____.

    (a) emergency loads   (b) computer equipment   (c) UPS equipment   (d) all of these

81. A sign _____ be placed at the service-entrance equipment indicating the type and location of on-site emergency power sources.

    (a) must   (b) should   (c) is not required to   (d) is not allowed to

82. Emergency circuit wiring must be designed and located to minimize the hazards that might cause failure because of _____.

    (a) flooding   (b) fire   (c) icing   (d) all of these

83. A storage battery supplying emergency lighting and power must maintain not less than 87 1/2 percent of full voltage at total load for a period of at least _____ hour(s).

    (a) 1   (b) 1 1/2   (c) 2   (d) 2 1/2

84. Where a generator for emergency circuits is installed outdoors and equipped with a readily accessible disconnecting means located within sight of the building or structure supplied, an additional disconnecting means is not required where ungrounded conductors pass through the building or structure.

    (a) True   (b) False

85. In emergency systems, no appliances and no lamps other than those required for emergency use, may be supplied by _____.

    (a) emergency lighting circuits   (b) multiwire branch circuits
    (c) HID rated circuit breakers   (d) a and b

86. The switches installed in emergency lighting circuits must be arranged so that only _____ will have control of emergency lighting.

    (a) the authority having jurisdiction   (b) authorized persons
    (c) automated means   (d) qualified persons

87. All manual switches for controlling emergency circuits must be in locations convenient to authorized persons responsible for their _____.

(a) maintenance   (b) actuation   (c) inspection   (d) evaluation

88. The alternate source for emergency systems must be required to have ground-fault protection of equipment.

(a) True   (b) False

Article 701 Legally Required Standby Power Systems

Legally required standby systems provide electric power to aid in firefighting, rescue operations, control of health hazards, and similar operations, and are required by federal, state or municipal governments, or other regulatory codes. When normal power is lost, legally required systems must be capable of automatically supplying standby power in 60 seconds or less, instead of the 10 seconds or less required of emergency systems.

89. A legally required standby system is intended to automatically supply power to _____.

(a) those systems classed as emergency systems   (b) selected loads
(c) a and b   (d) none of these

90. Legally required standby systems that are tested upon installation and found to be acceptable to the authority having jurisdiction (AHJ) are not required to undergo any future tests unless the equipment is modified.

(a) True   (b) False

91. A written record must be kept of required tests and maintenance on legally required standby systems.

(a) True   (b) False

92. A legally required standby system must have adequate capacity to safely carry _____ that are expected to operate simultaneously on the standby system.

(a) all of the loads   (b) 80 percent of the total loads
(c) up to 200A of the loads   (d) 300 percent of the total loads

93. The alternate power source (generator, UPS, etc.) is permitted to supply legally required standby and optional standby system loads where automatic selective load pickup and load shedding is provided as needed to ensure adequate power to the legally required standby systems.

(a) True   (b) False

94. Means to bypass and isolate the transfer switch equipment are not permitted on legally required standby systems.

(a) True   (b) False

95. Audible and visual signal devices must be provided on legally required standby systems, where practicable, to indicate _____.

(a) derangement of the standby source   (b) that the standby source is carrying load
(c) that the battery charger is not functioning   (d) all of these

96. Legally required standby system wiring is permitted to occupy the same raceways, cables, boxes, and cabinets with other general-purpose wiring.

(a) True   (b) False

97. Where a generator for legally required circuits is installed outdoors and equipped with a readily accessible disconnecting means located within sight of the building or structure supplied, an additional disconnecting means is not required where ungrounded conductors pass through the building or structure.

    (a) True   (b) False

98. Individual unit equipment (battery packs) for legally required standby illumination must consist of _____.

    (a) a rechargeable battery with a battery charging means
    (b) provisions for one or more lamps on the equipment, remote, or both
    (c) a relaying device arranged to energize the lamps automatically upon failure
    (d) all of these

99. The branch circuit feeding the unit equipment for legally required standby illumination must be the same branch circuit that serves the normal lighting in the area, but the unit must be connected ahead of any local switches.

    (a) True   (b) False

100. The alternate source for legally required standby systems is not required to have ground-fault protection of equipment.

    (a) True   (b) False

(• Indicates that 75% or fewer of those who took this exam answered the question correctly.)

1. Power cables, communications cables, connecting cables, interconnecting cables, and receptacles associated with the information technology equipment are permitted under a raised floor, provided the area under the floor is not accessible after installation.

   (a) True   (b) False

2. A disconnecting means for X-ray equipment must have adequate capacity for at least _____ percent of the input required for the momentary rating of the equipment or _____ percent of the input required for the long-time rating of the equipment, whichever is greater

   (a) 50, 100   (b) 100, 100   (c) 50, 125   (d) 125, 125

3. A ground-fault circuit interrupter (GFCI) must be installed in the branch circuit supplying swimming pool luminaires that operate at more than _____ to eliminate shock hazard during relamping.

   (a) 6V   (b) 14V   (c) 15V   (d) 18V

4. A portable electric sign cannot be placed in or within _____ from the inside walls of a fountain.

   (a) 3 ft   (b) 5 ft   (c) 10 ft   (d) none of these

5. A sign must be placed at the service equipment indicating the _____ of on-site legally required standby power sources.

   (a) type   (b) location   (c) manufacturer   (d) a and b

6. A spa or hot tub installed outdoors is permitted to be bonded by metal-to-metal mounting on a common frame. The metal bands or hoops used to secure wooden staves _____.

   (a) are not required to be bonded   (b) must be bonded
   (c) must be covered with insulating material   (d) are not allowed

7. All exposed noncurrent-carrying metal parts of an information technology system must be _____.

   (a) grounded in accordance with Article 250   (b) double insulated
   (c) fed from GFCI-protected circuits   (d) a or b

8. An assembly of electrically interconnected electrolytic cells supplied by a source of dc power is called a(n) _____.

   (a) battery pack   (b) cell line   (c) electrolytic cell bank   (d) battery storage bank

9. An underground rigid nonmetallic raceway must be not less than _____ from the inside wall of the pool or spa, unless space limitations prevent otherwise.

   (a) 8 ft   (b) 10 ft   (c) 5 ft   (d) 25 ft

10. Article 700 applies to the installation, operation, and maintenance of emergency systems consisting of circuits and equipment intended to supply, distribute, and control electricity for _____ in required facilities when the normal electrical supply or system is interrupted.

    (a) illumination   (b) power   (c) HVAC systems only (d) a and b

11. Branch-circuit wiring for underwater luminaires must be installed in _____.

    (a) rigid metal conduit or intermediate metal conduit
    (b) liquidtight flexible nonmetallic conduit or rigid nonmetallic conduit
    (c) any raceway wiring method
    (d) a or b

12. Cables for communications systems such as _____ must be located no less than 10 ft from the water's edge of swimming and wading pools, diving structures, observation stands, towers, or platforms.

    (a) telephone   (b) radio   (c) CATV   (d) all of these

13. Conductors supplying a single fire pump motor must be sized in accordance with the requirements of 430.22 and 695.7.

    (a) True   (b) False

14. Electrical devices and controls not associated with an spa or hot tub must be located a minimum of _____ from the inside walls of the indoor spa or hot tub, or be bonded to the indoor spa or hot tub system.

    (a) 4.7 ft   (b) 5 ft   (c) 7 ft 6 in.   (d) 12 ft

15. Emergency lighting systems must be designed and installed so that the failure of any individual lighting element, such as the burning out of a light bulb, will not leave in total darkness any space that requires emergency illumination.

    (a) True   (b) False

16. Emergency transfer equipment, including automatic transfer switches, must be _____.

    (a) automatic   (b) identified for emergency use
    (c) approved by the authority having jurisdiction   (d) any of these

17. Equipment for a fountain that is supplied by a flexible cord must have all exposed noncurrent-carrying metal parts grounded by an insulated copper equipment grounding conductor that is an integral part of the cord.

    (a) True   (b) False

18. Ground-fault circuit interrupters (GFCI) protecting a 120V wet-niche light on a pool or spa must only be of the circuit-breaker type.

    (a) True   (b) False

19. Hydromassage bathtub equipment must be _____ without damaging the building structure or building finish.

    (a) readily accessible   (b) accessible   (c) within sight   (d) none of these

20. In dwelling units, a 125V receptacle is required to be installed a minimum of 10 ft and a maximum of 20 ft from the inside wall of the pool.

    (a) True   (b) False

21. In outdoor pool areas, ceiling-suspended (paddle) fans installed above the pool or the area extending _____ horizontally from the inside walls of the pool must be installed at a height not less than 12 ft above the maximum water level of the pool.

    (a) 3 ft   (b) 5 ft   (c) 10 ft   (d) 12 ft

22. In swimming pools, the junction box connected to a conduit that extends to the forming shell of the luminaire (fixture) must be listed as a pool light junction box. In addition, when the luminaire operates at over 15V, the junction box must be located not less than _____ above the ground level or pool deck, or not less than _____ above the maximum water level.

    (a) 8 in., 4 in.   (b) 4 in., 8 in.   (c) 6 in., 12 in.   (d) 12 in., 6 in.

23. Interconnecting cables under raised floors that support information technology equipment must be listed as Type _____ cable having adequate fire-resistant characteristics suitable for use under raised floors of an information technology equipment room.

    (a) RF   (b) UF   (c) LS   (d) DP

24. Junction boxes connected to a conduit that extends directly to a forming shell must be provided with a number of grounding terminals that must be no fewer than _____ the number of conduit entries.

    (a) one more than   (b) two more than   (c) the same as   (d) none of these

25. Luminaires installed in fountains must be _____.

    (a) installed with the top of the luminaire lens below the normal water level
    (b) listed for above-water use
    (c) a and b
    (d) a or b

26. Metal parts of electric equipment associated with an indoor spa or hot tub water circulating system must be bonded.

    (a) True   (b) False

27. Panelboards for sensitive electronic equipment systems are allowed to be standard single-phase panelboards with the requirements that _____.

    (a) 2-pole common-trip circuit breakers are used
    (b) circuit breakers are identified for operation at the system voltage
    (c) the system is clearly marked on the face of the panel or inside cover
    (d) all of these

28. Power to fire pump motors must be supplied by a reliable source. This source must have the capacity to carry the locked-rotor current of the fire pump motor(s), the pressure maintenance pump motors, and the full-load current of any associated fire pump equipment. This source can be _____.

    (a) a separate service or a tap located ahead of but not within the utility service-disconnecting means
    (b) an on-site power supply, such as a generator
    (c) a or b
    (d) a and b

29. Receptacles must not be less than _____ from the inside walls of a storable pool.

    (a) 8 ft   (b) 10 ft   (c) 15 ft   (d) 20 ft

30. Receptacles rated 125V, and 30A or less, within 10 ft of the inside walls of an indoor spa or hot tub, must be _____.

    (a) removed   (b) on individual circuits only
    (c) GFCI protected   (d) at least 12 in. above the maximum water level

31. Recessed luminaires _____ located over or within 5 ft, measured horizontally, from the inside walls of an indoor spa or hot tub are permitted to be installed at less than 7 ft 6 in. above the maximum water level when GFCI protection is provided.

    (a) with a glass or plastic lens   (b) with nonmetallic or electrically isolated metal trim
    (c) suitable for use in a damp location   (d) all of these

32. Secondary overcurrent protection is permitted for transformers supplying fire pumps.

    (a) True   (b) False

33. Stainless steel, brass, copper, or copper alloy clamps labeled as being suitable for the purpose are acceptable for connection of the bonding conductor to the equipotential bonding grid of a swimming pool.

    (a) True   (b) False

34. Structures with a utility service and a photovoltaic system must have a permanent plaque or directory that identifies the location of the service-disconnecting means and the photovoltaic system disconnecting means, if they are not at the same location.

    (a) True   (b) False

35. Testing all emergency lighting and power systems during maximum anticipated load conditions must be avoided so as not to tax the emergency system unnecessarily.

    (a) True   (b) False

36. Testing all legally required standby system lighting and power systems during maximum anticipated load conditions must be avoided so as not to tax the standby system unnecessarily.

    (a) True   (b) False

37. The branch-circuit overcurrent protection devices for legally required standby systems must be accessible only to _____.

    (a) the authority having jurisdiction   (b) authorized persons
    (c) the general public   (d) qualified persons

38. The branch-circuit overcurrent protection devices in emergency circuits must be accessible to _____ only.

    (a) the authority having jurisdiction   (b) authorized person
    (c) the general public   (d) qualified persons

39. The electric motor and controller for an electrically operated pool cover must be _____.

    (a) GFCI protected   (b) located at least 10 ft from the inside wall of the pool.
    (c) both a and b   (d) either a or b

40. The maintenance disconnecting means required for swimming pool equipment must be _____.

    (a) readily accessible   (b) within sight of its equipment
    (c) accessible   (d) a and b

41. The pool structure, including the reinforcing metal of the pool shell and deck, must be bonded together.

    (a) True   (b) False

42. The scope of Article 680 includes _____.

    (a) wading and decorative pools   (b) fountains
    (c) hydromassage bathtubs   (d) all of these

43. To ensure that the emergency system meets or exceeds the original installation specification, the _____ must conduct or witness an acceptance test of the complete emergency system upon installation and periodically afterward.

    (a) electrical engineer   (b) authority having jurisdiction
    (c) qualified person   (d) manufacturer's representative

44. To ensure that the legally required standby system meets or exceeds the original installation specification, the _____ must conduct or witness an acceptance test of the complete emergency system upon installation.

    (a) electrical engineer   (b) authority having jurisdiction
    (c) qualified person   (d) manufacturer's representative

45. Transfer equipment for legally required systems, including automatic transfer switches, must be _____. Transfer equipment must be designed and installed to prevent the inadvertent interconnection of normal and alternate sources of supply in any operation of the transfer equipment.

    (a) automatic   (b) identified for standby use
    (c) approved by the authority having jurisdiction   (d) all of these

46. Under raised floors of information technology equipment rooms, power cables, communications cables, connecting and interconnecting cables, and associated boxes, connectors, plugs, and receptacles listed as part of or for information technology equipment _____.

    (a) are not allowed   (b) must be secured in place
    (c) are not required to be secured in place (d) must be installed only in rigid metal conduit

47. Voltage drop on sensitive electronic equipment systems must not exceed _____ percent for feeder and branch-circuit conductors combined.

    (a) 1.5   (b) 3   (c) 2.5   (d) 5

48. Where acceptable to the authority having jurisdiction (AHJ), connections ahead of and not within the same cabinet, enclosure, or vertical switchboard section as the service-disconnecting means are permitted for _____ standby service.

    (a) emergency   (b) legally required   (c) optional   (d) all of these

49. Where an internal combustion engine is used as the prime mover for an emergency system, an on-site fuel supply must be provided for not less than _____ hours of full-demand operation of the system.

    (a) 2   (b) 3   (c) 4   (d) 5

50. Wiring from emergency source or emergency source distribution overcurrent protection to emergency loads must be kept entirely independent of all other wiring and equipment except in _____.

    (a) transfer equipment enclosures
    (b) exit or emergency luminaires supplied from two sources
    (c) a common junction box attached to exit or emergency luminaires supplied from two sources
    (d) all of these

(• Indicates that 75% or fewer of those who took this exam answered the question correctly.)

1. All lights and receptacles installed in theater dressing rooms adjacent to the mirrors and above the dressing table counter(s), must be controlled by wall switches in the dressing rooms.

    (a) True   (b) False

2. All theater fixed stage switchboards that are not completely enclosed, dead-front and dead-rear or recessed into a wall, must be provided with a metal hood extending the full length of the board to protect all equipment on the board from falling objects.

    (a) True   (b) False

3. An apparatus enclosed in a case that is capable of withstanding an explosion of a specified gas or vapor that may occur within it, and of preventing the ignition of a specified gas or vapor surrounding the enclosure by sparks, flashes, or explosion of the gas or vapor within, and that operates at such an external temperature that a surrounding flammable atmosphere will not be ignited is defined as a(n) _____.

    (a) overcurrent protection device   (b) thermal apparatus
    (c) explosionproof apparatus   (d) bomb casing

4. An atmosphere classified as Group E contains combustible metal dusts.

    (a) True   (b) False

5. An autotransformer, used as part of a ballast for supplying lighting units and which raises the voltage to more than 300V, must be supplied by a(n) _____ system.

    (a) high-leg   (b) grounded   (c) listed   (d) identified

6. An electrically operated pipe organ must have both the generator and motor frame grounded or _____.

    (a) the generator and motor must be effectively insulated from ground
    (b) the generator and motor must be effectively insulated from ground and from each other
    (c) the generator must be effectively insulated from ground and from the motor driving it
    (d) both must have double insulation

7. An irrigation machine may have hand-portable motors.

    (a) True   (b) False

8. An open span length of 200 ft for antenna conductors of hard-drawn copper located at an amateur transmitting and receiving station requires a minimum conductor size of _____.

    (a) 14 AWG   (b) 12 AWG   (c) 10 AWG   (d) 8 AWG

9. Audible and visual signal devices for an emergency system must be provided, when practicable, for the purpose(s) of indicating _____.

    (a) that the battery is carrying load   (b) derangement of the emergency source
    (c) that the battery charger is not functioning   (d) all of these

10. Bare conductors must be securely and rigidly supported so that the minimum clearance between bare current-carrying metal parts of different potential mounted on the same surface will not be less than 2 in., nor less than _____, for parts that are in free air.

    (a) 1/4 in.   (b) 1/2 in.   (c) 1 in.   (d) 2 in.

11. Cablebus is ordinarily assembled at the _____.

    (a) point of installation   (b) manufacturer's location   (c) distributor's location   (d) none of these

12. Class 2 and 3 control conductors must be installed in raceways including _____ when used in hoistways.

    (a) rigid metal conduit   (b) electrical metallic tubing   (c) intermediate metal conduit   (d) all of these

13. Conductors located above a heated ceiling are considered as operating in an ambient temperature of _____.

    (a) 86°C   (b) 30°C   (c) 50°C   (d) 20°C

14. Conductors supplying outlets for arc and xenon projectors of the professional type must not be smaller than _____ and must be of sufficient size for the projector employed.

    (a) 12 AWG   (b) 10 AWG   (c) 8 AWG   (d) 6 AWG

15. Conductors with thermoplastic and fibrous outer braid, such as TBS insulation, are used for wiring _____.

    (a) switchboards only   (b) in a dry location   (c) in a wet location   (d) luminaires

16. Conduit bodies containing conductors larger than 6 AWG must have a cross-sectional area at least twice that of the largest conduit to which they are connected.

    (a) True   (b) False

17. Dry-type transformers installed indoors rated over _____ must be installed in a vault.

    (a) 1,000V   (b) 112 1/2 kVA   (c) 50,000V   (d) 35,000V

18. Each continuous-duty motor of _____ or less that is not permanently installed, not automatically started, and is within sight of the controller, is permitted to be protected against overload by the branch-circuit short-circuit and ground-fault protective device.

    (a) 1 hp   (b) 2 hp   (c) 3 hp   (d) 4 hp

19. Each electric appliance must be provided with a(n) _____ giving the identifying name and the rating in volts and amperes, or in volts and watts.

    (a) pamphlet   (b) nameplate   (c) auxiliary statement   (d) owner's manual

20. Electric equipment must not be installed in rooms or pits that do not have drainage that adequately prevents water accumulation only during abnormal operation.

    (a) True   (b) False

21. Electric heaters of the cord-and-plug connected immersion type must be constructed and installed so that current-carrying parts are effectively _____ from electrical contact with the substance in which they are immersed.

    (a) isolated   (b) protected   (c) insulated   (d) all of these

22. Electric pipe organ circuits must be arranged so that all 26 AWG and 28 AWG conductors are protected from overcurrent by an overcurrent protection device rated at not more than _____.

    (a) 20A   (b) 15A   (c) 6A   (d) none of these

23. Except by special permission, no conductor larger than _____ AWG can be installed in a cellular metal floor raceway.

    (a) 1/0   (b) 4/0   (c) 1   (d) no restriction

24. Feeders supplying 15 and 20A receptacle branch circuits are permitted to be protected by a ground-fault circuit interrupter in lieu of the provisions for such interrupters as specified in 210.8 and Article 590.

    (a) True   (b) False

25. Fixed electric space-heating equipment must be installed to provide the _____ spacing between the equipment and adjacent combustible material, unless it has been found to be acceptable where installed in direct contact with combustible material.

    (a) required   (b) minimum   (c) maximum   (d) safest

26. Flat conductor cable cannot be installed in _____.

    (a) dwelling units   (b) schools   (c) hospitals   (d) any of these

27. FMT must be used _____.

    (a) in dry and damp locations   (b) for direct burial   (c) in lengths over 6 ft   (d) for a maximum of
                                                                                                 1,000V

28. For applications where underground circuits must be buried deeper than shown in a specific underground ampacity table or figure, the following ampacity derating factor is permitted to be used: _____ percent per increased foot of depth for all values of Rho.

    (a) 3   (b) 6   (c) 9   (d) 12

29. For cellular concrete floor raceways, junction boxes must be _____ the floor grade and sealed against the free entrance of water or concrete.

    (a) leveled to   (b) above   (c) below   (d) perpendicular to

30. For each farm building or load supplied by _____ or more branch circuits, the load for feeders, service-entrance conductors, and service equipment must be computed in accordance with demand factors not less than indicated in Table 220.102.

    (a) one   (b) two   (c) three   (d) four

31. For services exceeding 600V, nominal, the isolating switch must be accessible to _____.

    (a) all occupants   (b) qualified personnel only   (c) a height of 8 ft   (d) any of these

32. For straight pulls, the length of a pull box must not be less than _____ times the outside diameter, over sheath, of the largest shielded or lead-covered conductor or cable entering the box on systems over 600V.

    (a) 18   (b) 16   (c) 36   (d) 48

33. General-use _____ switches must be used only to control permanently-installed incandescent luminaires unless otherwise listed for control of other loads.

    (a) dimmer   (b) fan speed control   (c) timer   (d) all of these

34. General-use branch circuits using flat conductor cable must not exceed _____.

    (a) 15A   (b) 20A   (c) 30A   (d) 40A

35. Ground-fault protection of equipment must be provided for electric heat tracing and heating panels installed on pipelines or vessels except in certain industrial installations where there is alarm indication of ground faults.

    (a) True   (b) False

36. If a set of 120/240V service conductors terminates at a through-the-roof raceway or approved support, with less than 6 ft of these conductors passing over the roof overhang, the minimum clearance above the roof for these service conductors is _____.

    (a) 12 in.   (b) 18 in.   (c) 2 ft   (d) 5 ft

37. In a cablebus, the size and number of conductors must be that for which the cablebus is designed, and in no case smaller than _____ AWG.

    (a) 1/0   (b) 2/0   (c) 3/0   (d) 4/0

38. In anesthetizing locations, low-voltage equipment that is frequently in contact with the bodies of persons or has exposed current-carrying elements must _____.

    (a) operate on an electrical potential of 10V or less   (b) be moisture resistant
    (c) be intrinsically safe or double-insulated   (d) all of these

39. In Article 200, connected so as to be capable of carrying current (as distinguished from connection through electromagnetic induction) defines the term _____.

    (a) effectively grounded (b) electrically connected (c) grounded system (d) none of these

40. In cellular concrete floor raceways, a cell is defined as a single, enclosed _____ space in a floor made of precast cellular concrete slabs, the direction of the cell being parallel to the direction of the floor member.

    (a) circular   (b) oval   (c) tubular   (d) hexagonal

41. In health care facilities, patient bed receptacles located in general care areas must be supplied by at least two branch circuits, generally one from the normal system and one from the emergency system. The branch circuits for these receptacles are allowed to originate from two separate transfer switches on the emergency system.

    (a) True   (b) False

42. In locations where electrical equipment is likely to be exposed to _____, enclosures or guards must be so arranged and of such strength as to prevent such damage.

    (a) air circulation   (b) physical damage   (c) magnetic fields   (d) weather

43. In network-powered broadband communications systems, all separate electrodes can be bonded together using a minimum size jumper of _____ copper.

    (a) 10 AWG   (b) 8 AWG   (c) 6 AWG   (d) 4 AWG

44. Incandescent luminaires must be marked with the maximum lamp wattage. Luminaires requiring ballasts or transformers must be plainly marked with their electrical _____ and the manufacturer's name, trademark, or other suitable means of identification.

    (a) characteristics   (b) rating   (c) frequency   (d) none of these

45. Individual open conductors and cables other than service-entrance cables must not be installed within _____ of grade level or where exposed to physical damage.

    (a) 8 ft   (b) 10 ft   (c) 12 ft   (d) 15 ft

46. Knife switches rated for more than 1,200A at 250V or less _____.

    (a) are used only as isolating switches   (b) may be opened under load
    (c) should be placed so that gravity tends to close them   (d) should be connected in parallel

47. Lampholders installed in wet or damp locations must be of the _____ type.

    (a) waterproof   (b) weatherproof   (c) moistureproof   (d) moisture-resistant

48. Lampholders installed over highly combustible material must be of the _____ type.

    (a) industrial   (b) switched   (c) unswitched   (d) residential

49. Loop wiring in an underfloor raceway _____ to be a splice or tap.

    (a) is considered   (b) must not be considered   (c) is not permitted   (d) none of these

50. Luminaires with more than one lampholder must be wired so that the _____ of each lampholder is connected to the same circuit conductor or terminal.

    (a) stem   (b) arm   (c) supplemental protection   (d) screw-shell

UNIT 12

Delta/Delta and Delta/Wye Transformers

Introduction

In 1885 George Westinghouse, the head of Westinghouse Electric Company, bought the patent rights to a system of dynamos, transformers, and motors from inventor Nikola Tesla. The development of alternating-current electricity by both Tesla and Westinghouse faced opposition from the public, including Thomas Edison who argued that ac was dangerous and a hazard to health. Edison was a strong proponent of direct-current distribution systems, and in order to emphasize to the public the dangers of alternating current, he launched a smear campaign that included advocating the adoption of ac for use by the State of New York in electrocution to impose the death penalty for capital crimes. This campaign was successful, and New York did select ac to power the first electric chair in 1889. The process of electrocution by this device was referred to as being "Westinghoused."

Westinghouse went on to prove the viability of alternating-current systems in 1893 by providing the lighting system for the entire Columbian exposition in Chicago. Then in 1896, Westinghouse successfully placed generating stations at Niagara Falls to provide power to Buffalo, New York over 20 miles away. In order to efficiently distribute power over long distances, Westinghouse developed the transformer from Tesla's patents.

Transformers are an essential component in the distribution of ac power. Basic transformer concepts were introduced in Unit 4. This unit will delve into a deeper study including three-phase transformers of delta-delta and delta-wye configurations. Common transformer connections, and some of the essentials concerning the voltage, current, and power relationships in transformers are also explained.

DEFINITIONS

Delta-Connected Transformer. Delta-connected transformers have three transformer windings connected end to end with each other. The line conductors are connected to each point where two windings meet. This system is called a Delta System because when it's drawn out it looks like a triangle (Greek symbol Delta for the letter D). **Figure 12–1**

> **AUTHOR'S COMMENT:** **Figure 12–2** shows other styles used for representing delta/delta transformers and some typical relationships between the primary and secondary windings. For the purpose of this unit, we will be using the Greek letter Delta shown in **Figure 12–1**.

kVA Rating. Transformers are rated in kilovolt-amperes (kVA) and are sized to the VA rating of the loads they supply.

Relationship of Delta-Delta Transformers

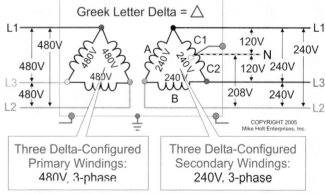

Delta-cofigured transformers have three transformer windings connected end-to-end with each other.

Figure 12–1

Mike Holt Enterprises, Inc. • www.NECcode.com • 1.888.NEC.CODE

511

Relationship of Delta-Delta Transformers

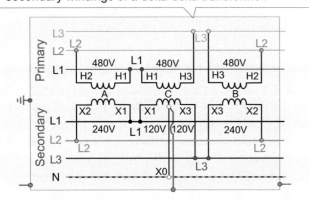

This graphic shows other styles sometimes used for representing the relationships between the primary and secondary windings of a delta-delta transformer.

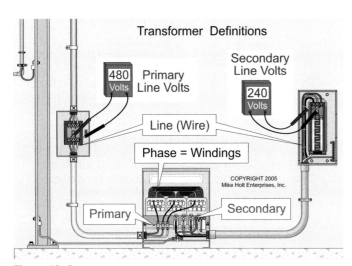

Figure 12–2

Line. The circuit conductors. Figure 12–3

Line Current. The current on the ungrounded conductors: Figure 12–4

* **Line Current (single-phase) or**
  I = VA/E

* **Line Current (three-phase)**
  I = VA/(E x 1.732)

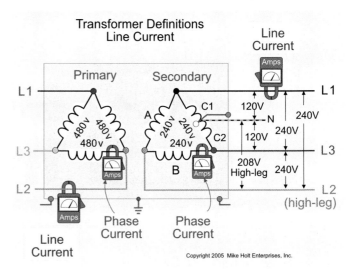

Figure 12–4

In a delta-configured system, the line current is greater than the phase current by a factor of 1.732 (the square root of three).

Line = 100A, Phase = 57.74A

In a wye-configured system, the line current is equal to the phase current.

Line = 100A, Phase = 100A

Line Voltage. The voltage between any two ungrounded conductors. Figure 12–5

In a delta-configured system, the line voltage equals the phase voltage.

Example: Line = 240V, Phase = 240V

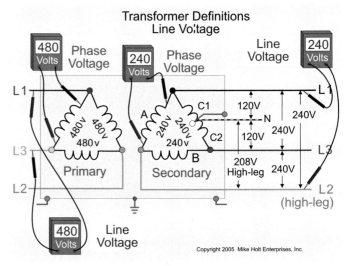

Figure 12–3

Figure 12–5

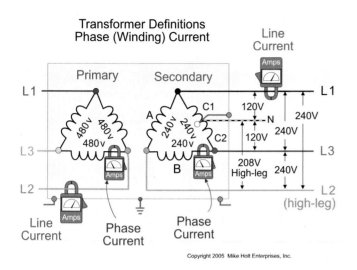

Figure 12–6

In a wye-configured system, the line voltage is greater than the phase voltage by a factor of 1.732.

Example: Line = 208V, Phase = 120V

Phase (Winding). The coil-shaped conductors that serve as the primary or secondary of a transformer. A transformer phase is often called the transformer winding.

Phase Current. The current flowing through the transformer winding. **Figure 12–6**

In a delta-configured system, the phase current is less than the line current by a factor of 1.732.

Line = 100A, Phase = 57.74A

In a wye-configured system, the phase current is equal to the line current.

Line = 100A, Phase = 100A

Phase Load. The VA load on the transformer winding.

Phase Load Delta (Winding). The phase load is the load on the transformer winding. **Figure 12–7**

The phase load of a three-phase, 240V load = Line Load/3

Line = 18 kVA, Phase = 6 kVA

The phase load of a single-phase, 240V load = the line load.

Line = 10 kVA, Phase = 10 kVA

The phase load of a single-phase, 120V load = the line load.

Line = 3 kVA, Phase = 3 kVA

Phase Load Wye (Winding). The phase load is the load on the transformer winding. **Figure 12–8**

The phase load of a three-phase, 208V load = Line Load/3.

Line = 18 kVA, Phase = 6 kVA

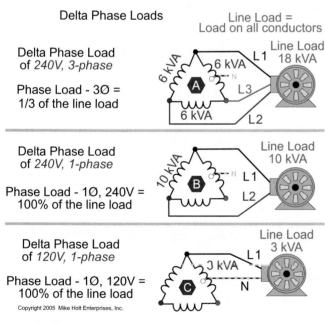

Figure 12–7

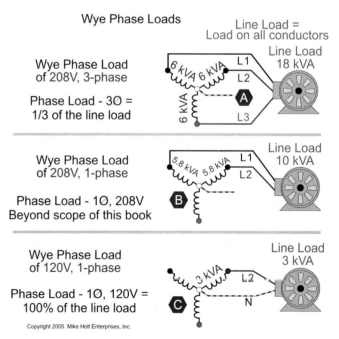

Figure 12–8

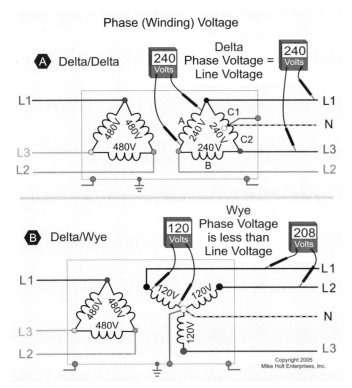

Figure 12–9

The approximate phase load of a single-phase 208V load = Phase Current x Phase Voltage. Because of the out-of-phase relationships of the internal windings, this value will be larger than the result of dividing the Line Load by 2.

Line = 10 kVA, Phase = 5.8 kVA

AUTHOR'S COMMENT: Many think that the phase load should be 5 kVA instead of 5.8 kVA. The reason for this is beyond the scope of this unit. Understanding this is not necessary for taking exams, and would not affect normal transformer sizing.

The approximate phase load of a single-phase, 120V load = the line load.

Line = 3 kVA, Phase = 3 kVA

Phase Voltage (Winding Voltage). The phase voltage is the internal transformer voltage generated across any one winding of a transformer. The secondary winding voltage versus the secondary line voltage:

In a delta-configured system, the phase voltage is equal to the line voltage. **Figure 12–9A**

Line = 240V, Phase = 240V

In a wye-configured system, the phase voltage is less than the line voltage by a factor of 1.732. **Figure 12–9B**

Line = 208V, Phase = 120V

AUTHOR'S COMMENT: Remember that in a delta-configured secondary, line voltage equals phase voltage. In a wye-configured secondary, phase voltage is different than line voltage. Earlier in this unit we explained that in a delta-configured secondary, line current is different than phase current. In a wye-connected secondary, line current is the same as phase current.

Turns Ratio. The relationship between the number of primary winding turns and the number of secondary winding turns.

Turns Ratio Voltage. The comparison between the primary phase voltage and the secondary phase voltage.

The ratio is the relationship between the number of primary winding turns, as compared to the number of secondary winding turns. The ratio is a comparison between the primary phase voltage and the secondary phase voltage. For typical delta/delta systems under 600 volts, the ratio is 2:1. For typical wye-connected systems under 600 volts, the ratio is 4:1. **Figure 12–10**

An example of a delta/delta-configured system with a ratio of 2:1:

Primary = 480V, Secondary = 240V

An example of a delta/wye-configured system with a ratio is 4:1:

Primary = 480V, Secondary = 120V

Unbalanced Load (Neutral Current). The unbalanced load is the load on the secondary grounded neutral conductors.

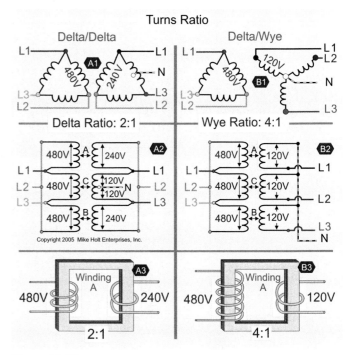

Figure 12–10

Unbalanced Neutral Load—Delta Secondary. The neutral current (unbalanced load) is calculated by subtracting the Line 3 current from the Line 1 current.

◆ **I Neutral Formula (Delta Secondary)**

$$I_{Neutral} = I_{Line\ 1} - I_{Line\ 3}$$

AUTHOR'S COMMENT: In a delta-connected 120/240V system, line 2 is called the "high-leg", or "wild leg." Line 2 (high-leg) voltage-to-ground is approximately 208V; therefore, no neutral loads are connected to this line.

Unbalanced Neutral Load—Wye Secondary. The neutral current (unbalanced load) is calculated by using the following formula:

◆ **I Neutral Formula (Wye Secondary)**

$$I_{Neutral} = \sqrt{[(I_{Line1}^2 + I_{Line2}^2 + I_{Line3}^2) - [(I_{Line1} \times I_{Line2}) + (I_{Line2} \times I_{Line3}) + (I_{Line1} \times I_{Line3})]]}$$

Winding (Phase). The coil-shaped conductors that serve as the primary or secondary of a transformer. A winding is also called the phase.

Wye-Configured Transformers. Wye-configured transformers have one lead from each of three windings connected to a common point. The other leads from each of the windings are connected to the line conductors. A wye-configured secondary is often represented with a Y shape arrangement of the windings. Figure 12–11

AUTHOR'S COMMENT: Figure 12–12 shows other styles used for representing delta/wye transformers and some typical relationships between the primary and secondary windings.

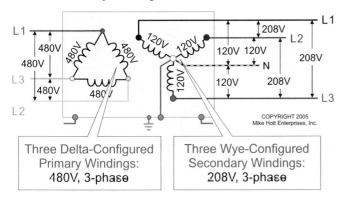

Wye-Configured Transformer

Three Delta-Configured Primary Windings: 480V, 3-phase

Three Wye-Configured Secondary Windings: 208V, 3-phase

Wye-configured transformers have one lead from each of three windings connected to a common point.

Figure 12–11

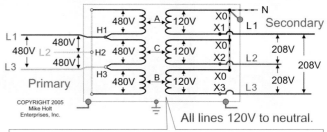

Relationship of Delta-Wye Transformers

All lines 120V to neutral.

This graphic shows other styles sometimes used for representing the relationships between the primary and secondary windings of a delta-wye transformer.

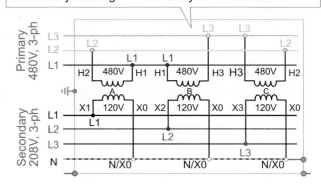

Figure 12–12

12.1 Current Flow

When a load is connected to the secondary of a transformer, current will flow through the secondary and primary windings. Figure 12–13

AUTHOR'S COMMENTS:

• The primary and secondary line currents are inversely proportional to the voltage ratio of the transformer. This means that the winding with the most number of turns will have a higher voltage and lower current as compared to the winding with the least number of turns, which will have a lower voltage and higher current. Figure 12–14

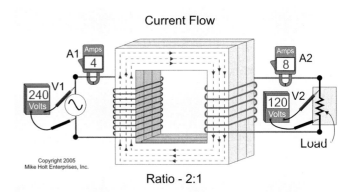

Current Flow

Ratio - 2:1

Figure 12–13

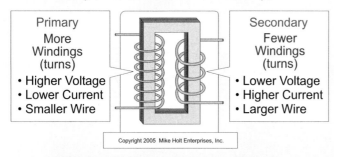

Step-Down Transformer Relationships

Primary
More Windings (turns)
• Higher Voltage
• Lower Current
• Smaller Wire

Secondary
Fewer Windings (turns)
• Lower Voltage
• Higher Current
• Larger Wire

Copyright 2005 Mike Holt Enterprises, Inc.

Note: This graphic is comparing one winding of the primary to one winding of the secondary

Figure 12–14

- In a typical step-down transformer, the primary has more windings, higher voltage, lower current, and smaller wire. The secondary has fewer windings, lower voltage, higher current, and larger wire. See **Figure 12–14**.

Tables 12-1 and 12-2 show the current relationship between kVA and voltage for common size transformers:

Table 12–1
Single-Phase Transformers I = VA/E

kVA Rating	Current at 208V	Current at 240V	Current at 480V
7.5	36A	31A	16A
10.0	48A	42A	21A
15.0	72A	63A	31A
25.0	120A	104A	52A
37.5	180A	156A	78A

Table 12–2
Three-Phase Transformers I = VA/(E x $\sqrt{3}$)

kVA Rating	Current at 208V	Current at 240V	Current at 480V
15.0	42A	36A	18A
22.5	63A	54A	27A
30.0	83A	72A	36A
37.5	104A	90A	45A
45.0	125A	108A	54A
50.0	139A	120A	60A
75.0	208A	180A	90A
112.5	313A	271A	135A

PART A—DELTA/DELTA TRANSFORMERS

12.2 Delta Transformer Voltage

In a delta-configured, three-phase transformer, the line voltage equals the phase voltage ($E_{Line} = E_{Phase}$). **Figure 12–15**

Primary Delta Voltage. See **Figure 12–15**.

Line Voltage	Phase Voltage
L_1 to L_2 = 480V	Phase A winding = 480V
L_2 to L_3 = 480V	Phase B winding = 480V
L_3 to L_1 = 480V	Phase C winding = 480V

Secondary Delta Voltage. See **Figure 12–15**.

Line Voltage	Phase Voltage	Neutral Voltage
L_1 to L_2 = 240V	Phase A winding = 240V	Neutral to L_1 = 120V
L_2 to L_3 = 240V	Phase B winding = 240V	Neutral to L_2 = 208V
L_3 to L_1 = 240V	Phase C winding = 240V	Neutral to L_3 = 120V

12.3 Delta High-Leg

The terms "high-leg," "wild leg," or "bastard leg" are used to identify the conductor of a delta-connected system that has a voltage rating of 208V-to-ground. The high-leg voltage is the vector sum of the voltage of transformers A and C1, or transformers B and C2, which equal 120V x 1.732 = 208V for a 120/240V secondary. **Figure 12–16**

> **AUTHOR'S COMMENT:** The actual voltage of the high-leg is often less than the nominal system voltage because of voltage drop.

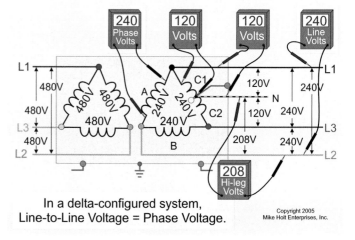

Delta/Delta Line and Phase Voltage Relationships

In a delta-configured system,
Line-to-Line Voltage = Phase Voltage.

Copyright 2005 Mike Holt Enterprises, Inc.

Figure 12–15

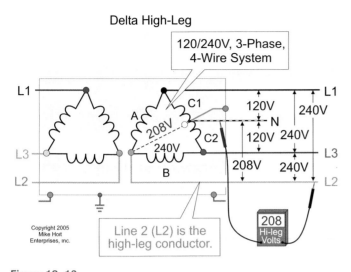

Delta High-Leg

120/240V, 3-Phase, 4-Wire System

Line 2 (L2) is the high-leg conductor.

Figure 12–16

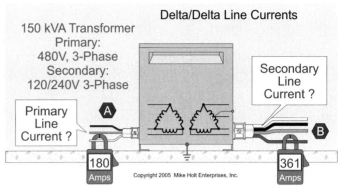

Delta/Delta Line Currents

150 kVA Transformer
Primary:
480V, 3-Phase
Secondary:
120/240V 3-Phase

Primary Line Current ?

Secondary Line Current ?

180 Amps   361 Amps

Determine the primary and secondary line current.

Formula: $I\ Line = \dfrac{Line\ Power}{(Line\ Volts \times \sqrt{3})} = \dfrac{VA}{(E \times \sqrt{3})}$

Primary Line Current: $I\ Line = \dfrac{150{,}000\ VA}{(480V \times 1.732)} = 180\ A$ **(A)**

Secondary Line Current: $I\ Line = \dfrac{150{,}000\ VA}{(240V \times 1.732)} = 361\ A$ **(B)**

Figure 12–17

▶ **High-Leg Voltage Example**

What is the actual voltage of the high-leg if the delta-configured secondary is 115/230V, three-phase?

(a) 115V   (b) 230V
(c) 199V   (d) 240V

• Answer: (c) 199V
High-Leg Voltage = (Line Voltage/2) x 1.732
High-Leg Voltage = 115V x 1.732
High-Leg Voltage = 199.18V

12.4 Delta Line Currents

In a delta-configured transformer, the line current does not equal the phase current. The line current of a three-phase transformer can be calculated by the formula:

◆ **Delta Line Current Formula**
Single-phase: I = VA/E
Three-phase: I = VA/(E x 1.732)

▶ **Primary Line Current Example**

What is the primary line current for a 480V to 120/240V, 150 kVA, three-phase transformer? Figure 12–17A

(a) 416A   (b) 360A
(c) 180A   (d) 144A

• Answer: (c) 180A
I_{Line} = VA/(E x 1.732)
I_{Line} = 150,000 VA/(480V x 1.732)
I_{Line} = 180A

▶ **Secondary Line Current Example**

What is the secondary line current for a 480V to 240V, 150 kVA, three-phase transformer? Figure 12–17B

(a) 416A   (b) 361A
(c) 180A   (d) 144A

• Answer: (b) 361A
I_{Line} = VA/(E x 1.732)
I_{Line} = 150,000 VA/(240V x 1.732)
I_{Line} = 361A

12.5 Delta Phase Currents

The phase current of a transformer winding is calculated by dividing the phase VA by the phase volts:

◆ **Delta Phase Current Formula**
$I_{Phase} = VA_{Phase}/E_{Phase}$

The phase load of a three-phase, 240V load = line load/3.
The phase load of a single-phase, 240V load = line load.
The phase load of a single-phase, 120V load = line load.

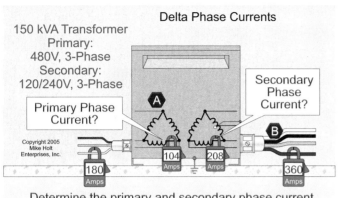

Delta Phase Currents

150 kVA Transformer
Primary:
480V, 3-Phase
Secondary:
120/240V, 3-Phase

Primary Phase Current?

Secondary Phase Current?

Copyright 2005
Mike Holt
Enterprises, Inc.

180 Amps   104 Amps   208 Amps   360 Amps

Determine the primary and secondary phase current.

Formula: $I\ Phase = \dfrac{Phase\ Power}{Phase\ Volts^*} = \dfrac{VA}{E}$

Primary Phase Current: $I\ Phase = \dfrac{50,000\ VA}{480V^*} = 104\ A$ **A**

Secondary Phase Current: $I\ Phase = \dfrac{50,000\ VA}{240V^*} = 208\ A$ **B**

*Note: The voltage of each phase individually is 1-phase.

Figure 12–18

▶ **Primary Phase Current Example**

What is the primary phase current for a 480V to 120/240V, 150 kVA, three-phase transformer? Figure 12–18A

(a) 416A   (b) 360A   (c) 180A   (d) 104A

• Answer: (d) 104A

$I_{Phase} = VA_{Phase}/E_{Phase}$

$VA_{Phase} = 150,000\ VA/3\ Phases$
$VA_{Phase} = 50,000\ VA$

$I_{Phase} = 50,000\ VA/480V$
$I_{Phase} = 104A$

▶ **Secondary Phase Current Example**

What is the secondary phase current for a 480V to 120/240V, 150 kVA, three-phase transformer? Figure 12–18B

(a) 416A   (b) 360A   (c) 208A   (d) 104A

• Answer: (c) 208A

Phase Power = 150,000 VA/3 Phases
Phase Power = 50,000 VA

$I_{Phase} = 50,000\ VA/240V$
$I_{Phase} = 208A$

12.6 Delta Phase versus Line Current

Since each line conductor from a delta transformer is actually connected to two transformer windings (phases), the effects of loading on the line (conductors) can be different than on the phase (winding).

Phase VA (Three-Phase)

Because each line from a delta-configured transformer is connected to two transformer phases, the line current from a three-phase load will be greater than the phase current by a factor of 1.732.

$I_{Line} = VA_{Line}/(E_{Line} \times 1.732)$

$I_{Phase} = I_{Line}/1.732$

$I_{Phase} = VA_{Phase}/E_{Phase}$

A 240V, 36 kVA, three-phase load has the following effect on a delta system: Figure 12–19

Line: Total line power = 36 kVA

$I_{Line} = VA_{Line}/(E_{Line} \times 1.732)$

$I_{Line} = 36,000VA/(240V \times 1.732)$

$I_{Line} = 87A$

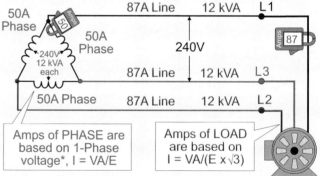

Delta Phase Versus Line - "3-Phase Loads"

50A Phase   87A Line   12 kVA   L1

50A Phase   240V

240V 12 kVA each   87A Line   12 kVA   L3

50A Phase   87A Line   12 kVA   L2

Amps of PHASE are based on 1-Phase voltage*, I = VA/E

Amps of LOAD are based on I = VA/(E x √3)

Copyright 2005 Mike Holt Enterprises, Inc.

Line is 36 kVA
240V 3-Phase

Determine the phase and line current.

Phase Current	Formula:	$I\ Phase = \dfrac{Phase\ Power}{^*Phase\ Volts} = \dfrac{VA}{E}$
Phase Power = 12 kVA per winding		$I\ Phase = \dfrac{12,000\ VA}{^*240V} = 50A$
Line Current	Formula:	$I\ Line = \dfrac{Line\ Power}{Line\ Volts} = \dfrac{VA}{(E \times \sqrt{3})}$
Line Power = 36 kVA		$I\ Line = \dfrac{36,000\ VA}{(240V \times 1.732)} = 87A$

Figure 12–19

Phase: Total phase power = 12 kVA (winding)

$I_{Phase} = VA_{Phase}/E_{Phase}$

$I_{Phase} = 12,000\ VA/240V$

$I_{Phase\ =}\ 50A$

or

$I_{Phase} = I_{Line}/1.732$

$I_{Phase} = 87A/1.732$

$I_{Phase} = 50A$

Phase VA (Single-Phase) 240V

The single-phase line current is equal to the phase current.

$I_{Line} = VA_{Line}/E_{Line}$

$I_{Phase} = VA_{Phase}/E_{Phase}$

A 240V, 10 kVA, single-phase load has the following effect on a delta/delta system: Figure 12–20

Line: Total line power = 10 kVA

$I_{Line} = VA_{Line}/E_{Line}$

$I_{Line} = 10,000\ VA/240V$

$I_{Line} = 42A$

Phase: Phase power = 10 kVA (winding)

$I_{Phase} = VA_{Phase}/E_{Phase}$

$I_{Phase} = 10,000\ VA/240V$

$I_{Phase} = 42A$

Phase VA (Single-Phase) 120V

A 120V, 3 kVA, single-phase load has the following effect on the system: Figure 12–21

Line: Line power = 3 kVA

$I_{Line} = VA_{Line}/E_{Line}$

$I_{Line} = 3,000\ VA/120V$

$I_{Phase} = 25A$

Phase: Phase power = 3 kVA (C1 or C2 winding)

$I_{Phase} = VA_{Phase}/E_{Phase}$

$I_{Phase} = 3,000\ VA/120V$

$I_{Phase} = 25A$

12.7 Delta Current Triangle

The three-phase line and phase currents of a delta system are not equal; the difference is the square root of three (1.732).

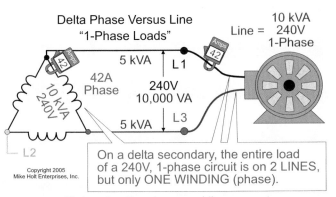

Determine the phase and line current.

Phase Current	Line Current
Phase Power = 10 kVA (winding)	Line Power = 10 kVA
Formula: I Phase = $\dfrac{\text{Phase Power}}{\text{Phase Volts}} = \dfrac{VA}{E}$	
I Phase = $\dfrac{10,000\ VA}{240V}$ = 42A	I Line = $\dfrac{10,000\ VA}{240V}$ = 42A

Figure 12–20

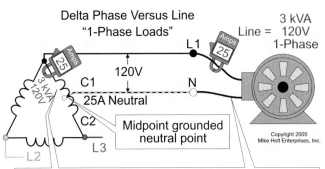

Determine the phase and line current.

Phase Current	Line Current
Phase Power = 3 kVA (C1 or C2 winding)	Line Power = 3 kVA
Formula. I Phase = $\dfrac{\text{Phase Power}}{\text{Phase Volts}} \_ \dfrac{VA}{E}$	
I Phase = $\dfrac{3,000\ VA}{120V}$ = 25A	I Line = $\dfrac{3,000\ VA}{120V}$ = 25A

Figure 12–21

◆ **Delta Current Formula**

$I_{Line} = I_{Phase} \times 1.732$ or $I_{Phase} = I_{Line}/1.732$

The delta triangle can be used to calculate delta three-phase line and phase currents. Place your finger over the desired item and the remaining items show the formula to use. **Figure 12–22**

12.8 Delta Transformer Balancing

To properly size a delta-configured transformer, the transformer must have the loads balanced among the windings.

Step 1: Determine the VA rating of all loads.

Step 2: Balance the loads on the transformer windings as follows:

Three-Phase Loads: one-third of the load on Phase A, one-third of the load on Phase B, and one-third of the load on Phase C.

240V, Single-Phase Loads: 100% of the load on Phase A or B. It is permissible to place some 240V, single-phase load on Phase C when necessary for balance.

120V loads: 100% of the load on C1 or C2.

▶ **Delta Transformer Balancing Example**

Balance and size a 480V to 120/240V, three-phase transformer for the following loads: one 240V, 36 kVA, three-phase heat strip; two 240V, 10 kVA, single-phase loads; and three 120V, 3 kVA loads. **Figure 12–23**

	Phase A (L1 and L2)	Phase B (L2 and L3)	C1 (L1)	C2 (L3)	Line Total
One 240V, 36 kVA, three-phase	12,000 VA	12,000 VA	6,000 VA	6,000 VA	36,000 VA
Two 240V, 10 kVA, single-phase	10,000 VA	10,000 VA			20,000 VA
Three 120V, 3 kVA, single-phase	+_____	+_____	+ **6,000 VA**	+ **3,000 VA**	+ 9,000 VA
	22,000 VA	22,000 VA	12,000 VA	9,000 VA	65,000 VA

Bold indicates neutral (120V) load.

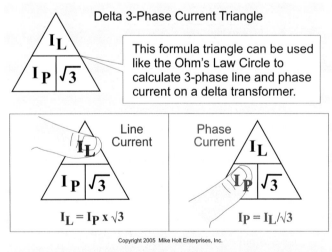

Delta 3-Phase Current Triangle

This formula triangle can be used like the Ohm's Law Circle to calculate 3-phase line and phase current on a delta transformer.

$I_L = I_P \times \sqrt{3}$

$I_P = I_L/\sqrt{3}$

Copyright 2005 Mike Holt Enterprises, Inc.

Note: The DELTA triangle is used to calculate current of a delta system. The WYE triangle is used to calculate voltage of a wye system.

Figure 12–22

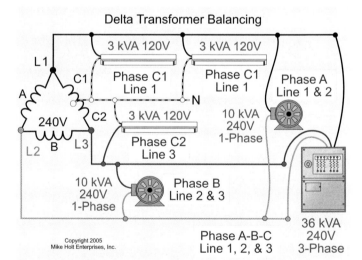

Delta Transformer Balancing

Copyright 2005
Mike Holt Enterprises, Inc.

Note: This diagram is showing transformer balancing. For the sake of simplicity, overcurrent protection for these circuits is not shown.

Figure 12–23

12.9 Delta Transformer Sizing

Once you balance the transformer, size it according to the load of each phase. The "C" transformer must be sized using two times the highest of "C1" or "C2." The "C" transformer is actually a single unit. If one side has a larger load, that side determines the transformer size.

▶ **Delta Transformer Sizing Example**

What size 480 to 120/240V transformer is required for the following loads: one 240V, 36 kVA, three-phase heat strip; two 240V, 10 kVA, single-phase loads; and three 120V, 3 kVA loads?

(a) three single-phase, 25 kVA transformers   (b) one three-phase, 75 kVA transformer

(c) a or b   (d) none of these

- Answer: (c) a or b
  Phase winding A = 22 kVA
  Phase winding B = 22 kVA
  Phase winding C = (12 kVA of C1 x 2)
  Phase winding C = 24 kVA

12.10 Delta Panel Balancing

When balancing a panelboard in VA, be sure that three-phase loads are split one-third on each line, 240V, single-phase loads are split one-half on each line, and 120V loads are placed on line 1 or line 3.

▶ **Delta Panel Example**

Balance a 120/240V, three-phase panelboard for the following loads: one 240V, 36 kVA, three-phase heat strip; two 240V, 10 kVA, single-phase loads; and three 120V, 3 kVA loads.

	Line 1	Line 2	Line 3	Line Total
240V, 36 kVA, three-phase	12,000 VA	12,000 VA	12,000 VA	36,000 VA
240V, 10 kVA, single-phase	5,000 VA	5,000 VA		10,000 VA
240V, 10 kVA, single-phase		5,000 VA	5,000 VA	10,000 VA
Three 120V, 3 kVA	+ **6,000 VA**	+_____	+ **3,000 VA**	+ 9,000 VA
	23,000 VA	22,000 VA	20,000 VA	65,000 VA

Bold indicates neutral (120V) load.

12.11 Delta Panelboard and Conductor Sizing

To size the panelboard and its conductors, you must balance the loads in amperes.

▶ **Delta Conductors Sizing Example**

Balance a 120/240V, three-phase panelboard for the following loads: one 36 kVA, 240V, three-phase heat strip; two 10 kVA, 240V, single-phase loads; and three 3 kVA, 120V loads.

	Line 1	Line 2	Line 3	Line Amperes
240V, 36 kVA, three-phase	87A	87A	87A	36,000 VA/(240V x 1.732)
240V, 10 kVA, single-phase	42A	42A		10,000 VA/240V
240V, 10 kVA, single-phase		42A	42A	10,000 VA/240V
Three 120V, 3 kVA	**+ 50A**	+_____	**+ 25A**	3,000 VA/120V
	179A	171A	154A	

Bold indicates neutral (120V) load.

Panel loads must be balanced in amperes rather than VA to avoid errors. The following example demonstrates the error that will occur if panel loads are balanced in VA.

The line current of a three-phase load is calculated by the formula:

$I_{Line} = VA_{Line}/(E_{Line} \times 1.732)$

$I_{Line} = 36,000 \text{ VA}/(240V \times 1.732)$

$I_{Line} = 87A$ per line

Note: If the per line power of 12,000 VA is divided by one line voltage of 120V, the result is an incorrect line current of 12,000 VA/120V = 100A.

12.12 Delta Neutral Current

The neutral current is calculated by subtracting Line 3 neutral current from Line 1 neutral current. Line-to-line loads don't count.

◆ **Delta Neutral Current Formula**

$I_{Neutral} = I_{Line\ 1} - I_{Line\ 3}$

No neutral loads are connected to Line 2 (high-leg) because the voltage from this line-to-ground is 208V.

▶ **Delta Neutral Current Example**

What is the neutral current for the following loads: one 240V, 36 kVA, three-phase heat strip; two 240V, 10 kVA, single-phase loads; and three 3 kVA, 120V loads? In our current example, Line 1 neutral current = 50A and Line 3 neutral current = 25A.

(a) 0A   (b) 25A   (c) 50A   (d) 100A

• Answer: (b) 25A
   Neutral current = 50A - 25A
   Neutral current = 25A

	Line 1	Line 2	Line 3	Ampere Calculation
240V, 36 kVA, three-phase	87A	87A	87A	36,000 VA/(240V x 1.732)
240V, 10 kVA, 240V, single-phase	42A	42A		10,000 VA/240V
240V, 10 kVA, 240V, single-phase		42A	42A	10,000 VA/240V
Three 120V, 3 kVA	**50A**		**25A**	3,000 VA/120V

Bold indicates neutral (120V) load.

12.13 Delta Maximum Unbalanced Load

The maximum unbalanced load is the actual current on the grounded neutral conductor.

▶ Maximum Unbalanced Load Example

What is the maximum unbalanced load for the following loads: one 240V, 36 kVA, three-phase heat strip; two 240V, 10 kVA, single-phase loads; and three 3 kVA, 120V loads?

(a) 0A	(b) 25A	(c) 50A	(d) none of these

• Answer: (c) 50A

The maximum unbalanced current equals the line with the largest neutral current.

	Line 1	Line 2	Line 3	Ampere Calculation
240V, 36 kVA, three-phase	87A	87A	87A	6,000 VA/(240V x 1.732)
240V, 10 kVA, single-phase	42A	42A		10,000 VA/240V
240V, 10 kVA, single-phase		42A	42A	10,000 VA/240V
Three 120V, 3 kVA, single-phase	**50A**		**25A**	3,000 VA/120V

Bold indicates neutral (120V) load.

12.14 Delta/Delta Example

240V, 18 kVA three-phase space heating   10 hp, 240V, three-phase A/C   Two—240V, 14 kVA, single-phase ranges
240V, 10 kVA, single-phase water heater   Two – 3 hp, 240V, single-phase motors   120V, 4.5 kVA dishwasher
Eight – Lighting circuits 120V, 1.5 kVA

Note: The NEC allows the use of kVA or kW interchangeably for ranges and clothes dryers [220.54 and 220.55].

Motor VA

Single-phase VA = Table Volts x Table Amperes [Table 430.248]
3 hp 230V FLC = 17A [Table 430.248]
3 hp VA = 230V x 17A = 3,910 VA
Three-phase VA = Table Volts x Table Amperes x 1.732 [Table 430.250]
10 hp 230V FLC = 28A [Table 430.250]
10 hp A/C VA = 230V x 28A x 1.732 = 11,154 VA, (omit) [220.60]

Note: Some exam testing agencies use 240V instead of the table volts.

	Phase A (L1 and L2)	Phase B (L2 and L3)	C1 (L1)	C2 (L3)	Line Total
Space Heating 18 kVA (omit A/C)	6,000 VA	6,000 VA	3,000 VA	3,000 VA	18,000 VA
Ranges 240V, 14 kVA, single-phase	14,000 VA	14,000 VA			28,000 VA
Water Heater 240V, 10 kVA, single-phase	10,000 VA				10,000 VA
3 hp, 240V, single-phase motor		3,910 VA			3,910 VA
3 hp, 240V, single-phase motor		3,910 VA			3,910 VA
Dishwasher 120V, 4.5 kVA			**4,500 VA**		4,500 VA
Lighting (8 – 1.5 kVA), 120V	+	+	+ **4,500 VA**	+ **7,500 VA**	+ 12,000 VA
	30,000 VA	27,820 VA	12,000 VA	10,500 VA	80,320 VA

Note: Phase totals (30,000 VA, 27,820 VA, 22,500 VA) should add up to the Line total (80,320 VA). This is done as a check to make sure all items have been accounted for and added correctly.

Bold indicates neutral (120V) load.

▶ **Transformer Size Example**

What size transformers are required?

> (a) three 30 kVA, single-phase transformers
> (b) one 90 kVA, three-phase transformer
> (c) a or b
> (d) none of these
>
> • Answer: (c) a or b
>   Phase A = 30 kVA
>   Phase B = 28 kVA
>   Phase C = 24 kVA (12 kVA x 2)

▶ **High-Leg Voltage Example**

What is the high-leg voltage to the grounded conductor ?

> (a) 120V   (b) 208V
> (c) 230V   (d) 240V
>
> • Answer: (b) 208V

The voltage relationships between transformer windings of "A" and "C1" or transformer windings of "B" and "C2" are such that the voltages are not a simple addition of the phase winding voltages. There is an out-of-phase relationship between the phases which requires a vectorial addition that is beyond the scope of this textbook. The resulting voltage from the high-leg to the grounded conductor can be found by multiplying the line-to-grounded conductor voltage by 1.732. High-leg voltage = 120V x 1.732 = 208V.

▶ **Neutral kVA Example**

What is the maximum kVA on the grounded conductor?

> (a) 3 kVA   (b) 6 kVA   (c) 7.5 kVA   (d) 9 kVA
>
> • Answer: (d) 9 kVA

Note: If the Phase C2 loads are not on, then phase C1 neutral loads would impose a 9 kVA load to the neutral. (4.5 kVA + 4.5 kVA). This does not include the 6 kVA on transformer "C" from the heater load since there are no neutrals involved.

▶ **Maximum Unbalanced Current Example**

What is the maximum unbalanced load on the grounded conductor?

> (a) 25A   (b) 50A   (c) 75A   (d) 100A
>
> • Answer: (c) 75A
>
> I = VA/E
> I = 9,000 VA/120V
> I = 75A

Note: The grounded conductor must be sized to carry the maximum unbalanced current, which in this case is 75A.

▶ **Neutral Current Example**

What is the current on the grounded neutral conductor?

> (a) 0A   (b) 13A
> (c) 25A   (d) 50A
>
> • Answer: (b) 13A
>
> L1 = 9,000 VA/120V
> L1 = 75A
>
> L2 = 7,500 VA/120V
> L2 = 62.5A
>
> Neutral Current = 75A − 62.5A
> Neutral Current = 12.5A

▶ **Phase Load (Single-Phase) Example**

What is the phase load of each 3 hp, 240V, single-phase motor?

> (a) 1,855 VA   (b) 3,910 VA
> (c) 978 VA   (d) none of these
>
> • Answer: (b) 3,910 VA
>   FLC = 17A [Table 430.248]
>
>   VA = 230V x 17A
>   VA = 3,910 VA

On a delta system, a 240V, single-phase load is 100% on one transformer.

▶ **Phase Load (Three-Phase) Example**

What is the phase load for the 10 hp, three-phase motor?

> (a) 11,154 VA   (b) 3,718 VA
> (c) 5,577 VA   (d) 6,440 VA
>
> • Answer: (b) 3,718 VA
>
>   VA = Volts x Amperes x 1.732
>   10 hp FLC = 28A [Table 430.250]
>   VA = 230V x 28A x 1.732
>   VA = 11,154 VA
>
>   Phase Load = 11,154 VA/3 phases
>   Phase Load = 3,718 VA per phase

▶ **High-Leg Conductor Size Example**

If only the three-phase, 18 kVA load is on the high-leg, what is the current on the high-leg conductor?

> (a) 25A   (b) 43A
> (c) 73A   (d) 97A
>
> • Answer: (b) 43A

To calculate current on any conductor:

> $I = VA/(E \times 1.732)$
> $I = 18{,}000 \text{ VA}/(240V \times 1.732)$
> $I = 43.3A$

▶ **Voltage Ratio Example**

What is the phase voltage ratio of the transformer?

    (a) 4:1   (b) 1:4   (c) 1:2   (d) 2:1

    • Answer: (d) 2:1

      480 primary phase volts to 240 secondary phase volts

      Turns Ratio = 480V/240V
      Turns Ratio = 2:1

▶ **Panel Loading—VA Example**

Balance the loads on the panelboard in VA.

	Line 1	Line 2	Line 3	Line Total
Space Heating 18 kVA, 240V, three-phase	6,000 VA	6,000 VA	6,000 VA	18,000 VA
Ranges 14 kVA, 240V, single-phase	7,000 VA	7,000 VA		14,000 VA
Ranges 14 kVA 240V, single-phase		7,000 VA	7,000 VA	14,000 VA
Water Heater 240V, single-phase	5,000 VA	5,000 VA		10,000 VA
3 hp, 240V, single-phase Motor		1,955 VA	1,955 VA	3,910 VA
3 hp, 240V, single-phase Motor		1,955 VA	1,955 VA	3,910 VA
Dishwasher 120V, single-phase	**4,500 VA**			4,500 VA
Lighting (8 circuits) 120V, single-phase	**+ 4,500 VA**	_____	**+ 7,500 VA**	+12,000 VA
	27,000 VA	28,910 VA	24,410 VA	80,320 VA

Bold indicates neutral (120V) loads.

▶ **Panel Sizing—Amperes Example**

Balance the loads from the previous example on the panelboard in amperes.

	Line 1	Line 2	Line 3	Ampere Calculation
Space Heating 18 kVA, 240V, three-phase	43A	43A	43A	18,000 VA/(240V x 1.732)
Ranges 14 kVA, 240V, single-phase	58A	58A		14,000 VA/240V
Ranges 14 kVA, 240V, single-phase		58A	58A	14,000 VA/240V
Water Heater 10 kVA, 240V, single-phase	42A	42A		10,000 VA/240V
3 hp, 240V, single-phase Motor		17A	17A	FLC
3 hp, 240V, single-phase Motor		17A	17A	FLC
Dishwasher 120V, single-phase	**38A**			4,500 VA/120V
Lighting (8 circuits) 120V, single-phase	**+ 38A**	+ _____	**+ 63A**	7,500 VA/120V
	219A	235A	198A	

Bold indicates neutral (120V) loads.

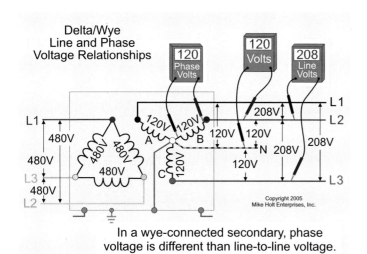

Figure 12–24

In a wye-connected secondary, phase voltage is different than line-to-line voltage.

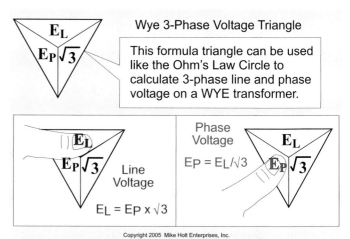

Note: The WYE triangle is used to calculate the voltage of a wye system. The DELTA triangle is used to calculate the current of a delta system.

Figure 12–25

PART B—DELTA/WYE TRANSFORMERS

12.15 Wye Transformer Voltage

In a wye-configured transformer, the line voltage is greater than the phase voltage by a factor of 1.732. Figure 12–24

Delta Primary Voltage

Line Voltage	Phase Voltage
L_1 to L_2 = 480V	Phase Winding A = 480V
L_2 to L_3 = 480V	Phase Winding B = 480V
L_3 to L_1 = 480V	Phase Winding C = 480V

Wye Secondary Voltage

Line Voltage	Phase Voltage	Neutral Voltage
L_1 to L_2 = 208V	Phase Winding A = 120V	Neutral to L_1 = 120V
L_2 to L_3 = 208V	Phase Winding B = 120V	Neutral to L_2 = 120V
L_3 to L_1 = 208V	Phase Winding C = 120V	Neutral to L_3 = 120V

12.16 Wye Voltage Triangle

The line voltage and phase voltage of a wye-connected system are not the same. They differ by a factor of 1.732.

◆ **Wye Line Voltage Formula**
   Line Voltage $E_{Line} = E_{Phase}$ x 1.732

◆ **Wye Phase Voltage Formula**
   Phase Voltage $E_{Phase} = E_{Line}$ /1.732

The wye voltage triangle can be used to calculate wye, three-phase, line and phase voltage, Figure 12–25. Place your finger over the desired item, and the remaining items show the formula to use. These formulas can be used when either one of the phase or line voltages is known.

12.17 Wye Transformers Current

In a wye-configured transformer, the three-phase and single-phase, 120V line current equals the phase current ($I_{Phase} = I_{Line}$). Figure 12–26

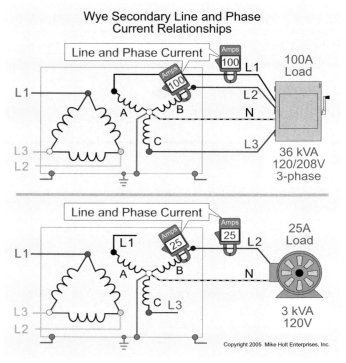

Figure 12–26

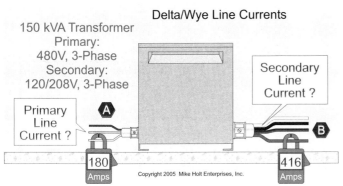

Delta/Wye Line Currents

150 kVA Transformer
Primary:
480V, 3-Phase
Secondary:
120/208V, 3-Phase

Primary Line Current ?

A

Secondary Line Current ?

B

180 Amps

416 Amps

Copyright 2005 Mike Holt Enterprises, Inc.

Determine the primary and secondary line current.

Formula: $I \text{ Line} = \dfrac{\text{Line Power}}{(\text{Line Volts} \times \sqrt{3})} = \dfrac{VA}{(E \times \sqrt{3})}$

Primary Line Current: $I \text{ Line} = \dfrac{150{,}000 \text{ VA}}{(480V \times 1.732)} = 180 \text{ A}$ **A**

Secondary Line Current: $I \text{ Line} = \dfrac{150{,}000 \text{ VA}}{(208V \times 1.732)} = 416 \text{ A}$ **B**

Figure 12–27

12.18 Wye Line Current

The line current of both delta and wye three-phase transformers can be calculated by the following formula:

◆ **Wye Line Current Formula**

$I_{Line} = VA_{Line}/(E_{Line} \times 1.732)$

▶ **Primary Line Current Question**

What is the primary line current for a 150 kVA, 480V to 120/208V, three-phase transformer? Figure 12–27A

   (a) 416A   (b) 360A
   (c) 180A   (d) 144A

   • Answer: (c) 180A

$I_{Line} = VA_{Line}/(E_{Line} \times 1.732)$
$I_{Line} = 150{,}000 \text{ VA}/(480V \times 1.732)$
$I_{Line} = 180A$

▶ **Secondary Line Current Question**

What is the secondary line current for a 150 kVA, 480V to 120/208V, three-phase transformer? Figure 12–27B

   (a) 416A   (b) 360A
   (c) 180A   (d) 144A

   • Answer: (a) 416A

$I_{Line} = VA_{Line}/(E_{Line} \times 1.732)$
$I_{Line} = 150{,}000 \text{ VA}/(208V \times 1.732)$
$I_{Line} = 416A$

12.19 Wye Phase Current

The phase current of a wye-configured transformer winding is the same as the line current. The phase current of a delta-configured transformer winding is less than the line current by a factor of 1.732.

▶ **Primary Phase Current Question**

What is the primary phase current for a 150 kVA, 480 to 120/208V, three-phase transformer? Figure 12–28A

   (a) 416A   (b) 360A
   (c) 180A   (d) 104A

   • Answer: (d) 104A

$I_{Line} = VA_{Line}/(E_{Line} \times 1.732)$
$I_{Line} = 150{,}000 \text{ VA}/(480V \times 1.732)$
$I_{Line} = 180A$

$I_{Phase} = VA_{Phase}/E_{Phase}$
$I_{Phase} = 50{,}000 \text{ VA}/480V$
$I_{Phase} = 104A$

or

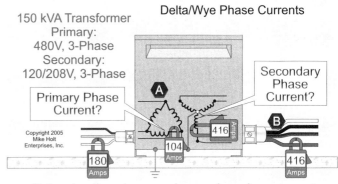

Delta/Wye Phase Currents

150 kVA Transformer
Primary:
480V, 3-Phase
Secondary:
120/208V, 3-Phase

Primary Phase Current?

A

Secondary Phase Current?

B

Copyright 2005 Mike Holt Enterprises, Inc.

104 Amps

416 Amps

180 Amps

416 Amps

Determine the primary and secondary phase current.

Formula: $I \text{ Phase} = \dfrac{\text{Phase Power}}{\text{Phase Volts}^*} = \dfrac{VA}{E}$

Primary Phase Current $I \text{ Phase} = \dfrac{50{,}000 \text{ VA}}{480V^*} = 104 \text{ A}$ **A**

Secondary Phase Current $I \text{ Phase} = \dfrac{50{,}000 \text{ VA}}{120V^*} = 416 \text{ A}$ **B**

*Note: The voltage of each phase individually is 1-phase.

Figure 12–28

$I_{Phase} = I_{Line}/1.732$
$I_{Phase} = 180A/1.732$
$I_{Phase} = 104A$

▶ **Secondary Phase Current Question**

What is the secondary phase current for a 150 kVA, 480 to 120/208V, three-phase transformer? Figure 12–28B

    (a) 416A   (b) 360A
    (c) 208A   (d) 104A

    • Answer: (a) 416A

$I_{Phase} = VA_{Line}/(E_{Line} \times 1.732)$
$I_{Phase} = 150,000 \text{ VA}/(208 \times 1.732)$
$I_{Phase} = 416A$

or

$I_{Phase} = VA_{Phase}/E_{Phase}$
$I_{Phase} = 50,000 \text{ VA}/120V$
$I_{Phase} = 416A$

12.20 Wye Phase versus Line Current

Since each line conductor from a wye transformer is connected to a different transformer winding (phase), the effects of three-phase loading on the line are the same as the phase. Figure 12–29

▶ **Phase versus Line, 208V, Three-Phase Example**

A 36 kVA, 208V, three-phase load has the following effect on the system:

Phase: Phase power = 12 kVA (any winding)
$I_{Phase} = VA_{Phase}/E_{Phase}$
$I_{Phase} = 12,000 \text{ VA}/120V$
$I_{Phase} = 100A$

Line: Line power = 36 kVA
$I_{Line} = VA_{Line}/(E_{Line} \times 1.732)$
$I_{Line} = 36,000 \text{ VA}/(208V \times 1.732)$
$I_{Line} = 100A$

▶ **Phase versus Line, 208V, Single-Phase Example**

A 10 kVA, 208V, single-phase load has the following effect on the system. Figure 12–30

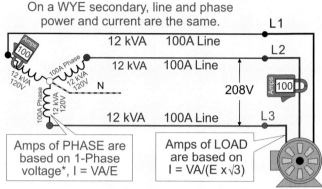

Wye Phase Versus Line - "3-Phase Loads"

On a WYE secondary, line and phase power and current are the same.

Amps of PHASE are based on 1-Phase voltage*, I = VA/E

Amps of LOAD are based on I = VA/(E x √3)

Line is 36 kVA 208V, 3-Phase

Copyright 2005 Mike Holt Enterprises, Inc.

Determine the phase and line current.

Phase Current	Formula:	I Phase = $\dfrac{\text{Phase Power}}{\text{*Phase Volts}} = \dfrac{VA}{E}$
Phase Power = 12 kVA per winding		I Phase = $\dfrac{12,000 \text{ VA}}{\text{*120V}} = 100A$
Line Current	Formula:	I Line = $\dfrac{\text{Line Power}}{\text{Line Volts}} = \dfrac{VA}{(E \times \sqrt{3})}$
Line Power = 36 kVA		I Line = $\dfrac{36,000 \text{ VA}}{(208V \times 1.732)} = 100A$

Figure 12–29

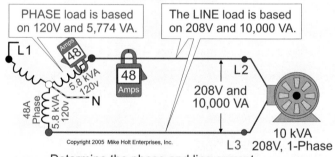

Wye Secondary Phase Versus Line "1-Phase Loads"

PHASE load is based on 120V and 5,774 VA.

The LINE load is based on 208V and 10,000 VA.

208V and 10,000 VA

10 kVA 208V, 1-Phase

Copyright 2005 Mike Holt Enterprises, Inc.

Determine the phase and line current.

Phase Current	Line Current
Phase Power = 5 kVA (winding)	Line Power = 10 kVA
Formula: I Phase = $\dfrac{\text{Phase Power}}{\text{Phase Volts}} = \dfrac{VA}{E}$	
I Phase = $\dfrac{5,774 \text{ VA}}{120V} = 48A$	I Line = $\dfrac{10,000 \text{ VA}}{208V} = 48A$

Figure 12–30

Line: Line power = 10 kVA

$I_{Line} = VA_{Line}/E_{Line}$

$I_{Line} = 10,000\ VA/208V$

$I_{Line} = 48A$

Phase: Phase Power = 5.8 kVA (winding)

$I_{Phase} = VA_{Phase}/E_{Phase}$

$I_{Phase} = 5,774\ VA/120V$

$I_{Phase} = 48.1A$

AUTHOR'S COMMENT: A 10 kVA load does not balance out to 5 kVA per phase on a 208V single-phase system. This is because the two windings providing 208V are out of phase with each other. Vectorial math is beyond the scope of this unit. The approximate load on each phase winding can be found by multiplying the phase voltage times the phase current.

$VA_{Phase} = E_{Phase}\ x\ I_{Phase}$

$VA_{Phase} = 120V\ x\ 48.1A$

$VA_{Phase} = 5,774\ VA$

▶ **Phase Load (Single-Phase) 120V Example**

A 3 kVA, 120V, single-phase load has the following effect on the system. Figure 12–31

Phase: Phase Power = 3 kVA (any winding)

$I_{Phase} = VA_{Phase}/E_{Phase}$

$I_{Phase} = 3,000\ VA/120V$

$I_{Phase} = 25A$

Line: Line Power = 3 kVA

$I_{Line} = VA_{Line}/E_{Line}$

$I_{Line} = 3,000\ VA/120V$

$I_{Line} = 25A$

12.21 Wye Transformer Balancing

To properly size a delta/wye transformer, the secondary transformer phases (windings) or the line conductors must be balanced. Balancing the panel (line conductors) is identical to balancing the transformer for wye-configured transformers! The following steps should be helpful to balance the transformer:

Step 1: Determine the VA rating of all loads.

Step 2: Split three-phase loads: one-third on Phase A; one-third on Phase B; and one-third on Phase C.

Step 3: Split single-phase, 208V loads (largest to smallest): one-half on each phase (A to B, B to C, or A to C).

Step 4: Place 120V loads (largest to smallest): 100% on any phase.

▶ **Transformer Balancing Example**

Balance and size a 480V to 120/208V, three-phase transformer for the following loads: a 36 kVA, 208V, three-phase heat strip; two 10 kVA, 208V, single-phase loads; and three 3 kVA, 120V loads. Figure 12–32

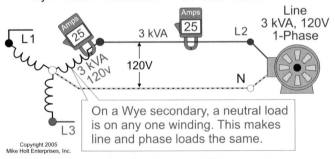

Wye Phase Versus Line - "1-Phase Loads"

On a Wye secondary, a neutral load is on any one winding. This makes line and phase loads the same.

Determine the phase and line current.

Phase Current Phase Power = 3 kVA	Line Current Line Power = 3 kVA
Formula: $I\ Phase = \dfrac{Phase\ Power}{Phase\ Volts} = \dfrac{VA}{E}$	
$I\ Phase = \dfrac{3,000\ VA}{120V} = 25A$	$I\ Line = \dfrac{3,000\ VA}{120V} = 25A$

Figure 12–31

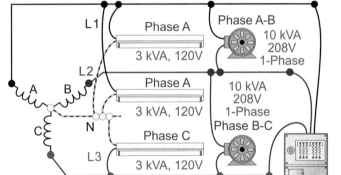

Wye Transformer Loading and Balancing

Note: This diagram is showing transformer balancing. For the sake of simplicity, overcurrent protection for these circuits is not shown.

36 kVA
208V
3-Phase

Figure 12–32

	Phase A (L1)	Phase B (L2)	Phase C (L3)	Line Total
36 kVA, 208V, three-phase	12 kVA	12 kVA	12 kVA	36 kVA
10 kVA, 208V, single-phase	5 kVA	5 kVA		10 kVA
10 kVA, 208V, single-phase		5 kVA	5 kVA	10 kVA
Three 3 kVA, 120V	**+ 6 kVA**	+_____	**+ 3 kVA**	+ 9 kVA
	23 kVA	22 kVA	20 kVA	65 kVA

Bold indicates neutral (120V) loads.

12.22 Wye Transformer Sizing

Once you balance the transformer, you can size the transformer according to the load on each phase.

▶ Transformer Sizing Example

What size 480 to 120/208V, three-phase transformer is required for the following loads: a 208V, 36 kVA, three-phase heat strip; two 208V, 10 kVA, single-phase loads; and three 120V, 3 kVA loads?

(a) three single-phase, 25 kVA transformers   (b) one three-phase, 75 kVA transformer

(c) a or b   (d) none of these

- Answer: (c) a or b
  Phase A = 23 kVA
  Phase B = 22 kVA
  Phase C = 20 kVA

	Phase A (L1)	Phase B (L2)	Phase C (L3)	Line Total
36 kVA, 208V, three-phase	12 kVA	12 kVA	12 kVA	36 kVA
10 kVA, 208V, single-phase	5 kVA	5 kVA		10 kVA
10 kVA, 208V, single-phase		5 kVA	5 kVA	10 kVA
Three 3 kVA, 120V	**+ 6 kVA**	+_____	**+ 3 kVA**	+ 9 kVA
	23 kVA	22 kVA	20 kVA	65 kVA

Bold indicates neutral (120V) loads.

12.23 Wye Panel Balancing

When balancing a panelboard in VA, be sure that three-phase loads are split one-third on each line, 208V, single-phase loads are split one-half on each line, and 120V loads are placed on any line.

▶ Panel Balancing Example

Balance and size a 120/208V, three-phase panelboard in kVA for the following loads: a 36 kVA, 208V, three-phase heat strip; two 10 kVA, 208V, single-phase loads; and three 3 kVA, 120V loads.

	Line 1	Line 2	Line 3	Line Total
36 kVA, 208V, three-phase	12 kVA	12 kVA	12 kVA	36,000 VA
10 kVA, 208V, single-phase	5 kVA	5 kVA		10,000 VA
10 kVA, 208V, single-phase		5 kVA	5 kVA	10,000 VA
Two 3 kVA, 120V	**6 kVA**			6,000 VA
One 3 kVA, 120V	+ _____	+ _____	**+ 3 kVA**	+ 3,000 VA
	23 kVA	22 kVA	20 kVA	65,000 VA

Bold indicates neutral (120V) loads.

12.24 Wye Panelboard and Conductor Sizing

When selecting and sizing the panelboard and conductors, the line loads must be balanced in amperes.

▶ Panelboard Conductor Sizing Example

Balance and size a 120/208V, three-phase panelboard in amperes for the following loads: a 36 kVA, 208V, three-phase heat strip; two 10 kVA, 208V, single-phase loads; and three 3 kVA, 120V loads.

	Line 1	Line 2	Line 3	Ampere Calculation
36 kVA, 208V, three-phase	100A	100A	100A	36,000/(208V x 1.732)
10 kVA, 208V, single-phase	48A	48A		10,000 VA/208V
10 kVA, 208V, single-phase		48A	48A	10,000 VA/208V
Two 3 kVA, 120V	**50A**			6,000 VA/120V
One 3 kVA, 120V	+ _____	+ _____	**+ 25A**	3,000 VA/120V
	198A	196A	173A	

Bold indicates neutral (120V) loads.

12.25 Wye Neutral Current

To determine the neutral current of a wye-connected system, use the following formula:

◆ I Neutral Formula

$I_{Neutral} = \sqrt{[(I_{Line1}^2 + I_{Line2}^2 + I_{Line3}^2) - [(I_{Line1} \times I_{Line2}) + (I_{Line2} \times I_{Line3}) + (I_{Line1} \times I_{Line3})]]}$

▶ Neutral Current Example

Based on the previous example, balance and size the neutral current for the following loads: a 208V, 36 kVA, three-phase heat strip; two 208V, 10 kVA, single-phase loads; and three 3 kVA, 120V loads. The neutral loads are: $L_1 = 50A$, $L_2 = 0A$, $L_3 = 25A$.

(a) 0A   (b) 25A   (c) 43A   (d) 50A

• Answer: (c) 43A

$I_{Neutral} = \sqrt{[(I_{Line1}^2 + I_{Line2}^2 + I_{Line3}^2) - [(I_{Line1} \times I_{Line2}) + (I_{Line2} \times I_{Line3}) + (I_{Line1} \times I_{Line3})]]}$

$I_{Neutral} = \sqrt{[(50A^2 + 0A^2 + 25A^2) - [(50A \times 0A) + (0A \times 25A) + (50A \times 25A)]}$

$I_{Neutral} = \sqrt{[(2,500A + 625A) - 1,250A]}$

$I_{Neutral} = \sqrt{1,875A}$

$I_{Neutral} = 43.3A$

12.26 Wye Maximum Unbalanced Load

The maximum unbalanced load is the actual current on the grounded neutral conductor.

▶ **Maximum Unbalanced Load Example**

Balance and size the maximum unbalanced load for the following loads: a 208V, 36 kVA, three-phase heat strip; two 208V, 10 kVA, single-phase loads; and three 120V, 3 kVA loads. The line to neutral loads are: $L_1 = 50A$, $L_2 = 0A$, $L_3 = 25A$.

    (a) 0A   (b) 25A   (c) 50A   (d) 100A

    • Answer: (c) 50A

The maximum unbalanced current equals the largest line neutral current.

	Line 1	Line 2	Line 3	Ampere Calculation
336 kVA, 208V, three-phase	100A	100A	100A	36,000/(208V x 1.732)
10 kVA, 208V, single-phase	48A	48A		10,000 VA/208V
10 kVA, 208V, single-phase		48A	48A	10,000 VA/208V
Two 3 kVA, 120V	**50A**			6,000 VA/120V
One 3 kVA, 120V	+_____	+_____	+ **25A**	3,000 VA/120V
	198A	196A	173A	

Bold indicates neutral (120V) loads.

12.27 Delta/Wye Example

Space Heating (18 kVA) 208V, three-phase
A/C motor (10 hp) 208V, three-phase
Two Ranges (14 kVA) 208V, single-phase
Water Heater (10 kVA) 208V, single-phase
Two 3 hp motors, 208V, single-phase
Dishwasher (4.5 kVA) 120V
Eight Lighting circuits (1.5 kVA), 120V

Motor VA

Single-phase VA = Table Volts x Table Ampere
3 hp, 208V FLC = 18.7A [Table 430.248]
Motor VA = 208V x 18.7A
Motor VA = 3,890 VA

To find the phase VA of a wye transformer, take the phase current times the phase voltage. This does not equal the motor VA due to the out-of-phase relationship of the wye windings.
VA per phase = 120V x 18.7A
VA per phase = 2,244 VA

Three-phase VA = Table Volts x Table Amperes x 1.732
10 hp, three-phase, A/C motor 208V FLC = 30.8A [Table 430.250]
A/C, VA = 208V x 30.8A x 1.732
A/C VA = 11,096 VA (omit, smaller than 18 kVA space heat [220.60])

	Phase A (L1)	Phase B (L2)	Phase C (L3)	Line Total
Space-Heating (18 kVA) 208V, three-phase (A/C omitted)	6,000 VA	6,000 VA	6,000 VA	18,000 VA
Ranges 14 kVA, 208V, single-phase	7,000 VA	7,000 VA		14,000 VA
Ranges 14 kVA, 208V, single-phase		7,000 VA	7,000 VA	14,000 VA
Water Heater 10 kVA 208V, single-phase	5,000 VA		5,000 VA	10,000 VA
3 hp, 208V, single-phase Motor	2,244 VA	2,244 VA		3,890 VA
3 hp, 208V, single-phase Motor		2,244 VA	2,244 VA	3,890 VA
Dishwasher 4.5 kVA, 120V			**4,500 VA**	4,500 VA
Lighting (8 – 1.5 kVA circuits)	**+ 6,000 VA**	**+ 3,000 VA**	**+ 3,000 VA**	+12,000 VA
	26,244 VA	27,488 VA	27,744 VA	80,280 VA

Bold indicates neutral (120V) loads.

AUTHOR'S COMMENT: The phase total will not add up to the same as the line total on a wye-configured system when there are 208V single-phase loads included. The phase kVA load will be greater than the line kVA load because the internal windings providing 208V are out-of-phase with each other. Vectorial math is beyond the scope of this unit.

▶ Transformer Sizing Example

What size transformers are required?

(a) three 30 kVA, single-phase transformers
(b) one 90 kVA, three-phase transformer
(c) a or b
(d) none of these

• Answer: (c) a or b
 Phase A = 27 kVA
 Phase B = 28 kVA
 Phase C = 28 kVA

▶ Maximum kVA on Neutral Example

What is the maximum kVA on the neutral?

(a) 3 kVA   (b) 6 kVA   (c) 7.5 kVA   (d) 9 kVA

• Answer: (c) 7.5 kVA
 120V loads only; don't count phase-to-phase (208V) loads. Line 3 (7,500 VA) is the largest in this example.

▶ Maximum Neutral Current Example

What is the maximum current on the neutral?

(a) 50A   (b) 63A   (c) 75A   (d) 100A

• Answer: (b) 63A

 Single-phase I = VA/E
 I = 7,500 VA/120V
 I = 63A

The neutral must be sized to carry the maximum unbalanced neutral current, which in this case is 63A.

▶ **Neutral Current Example**

What is the current on the neutral?

(a) 25A   (b) 33A   (c) 50A   (d) 63A

• Answer: (b) 33A

$I_{Neutral} = \sqrt{[(I_{Line1}^2 + I_{Line2}^2 + I_{Line3}^2) - [(I_{Line1} \times I_{Line2}) + (I_{Line2} \times I_{Line3}) + (I_{Line1} \times I_{Line3})]]}$

$L_1 = 6,000 \text{ VA}/120\text{V}$
$L_1 = 50\text{A}$
$L_2 = 3,000 \text{ VA}/120\text{V}$
$L_2 = 25\text{A}$
$L_3 = 7,500 \text{ VA}/120\text{V}$
$L_3 = 63\text{A}$

$I_{Neutral} = \sqrt{[(50A^2 + 25A^2 + 63A^2) - [(50A \times 25A) + (25A \times 63A) + (50A \times 63A)]]}$
$I_{Neutral} = \sqrt{[(2,500A + 625A + 3.969A) - (1,250A + 1,575A + 3,150A)]}$
$I_{Neutral} = \sqrt{(7,049A - 5,975A)}$
$I_{Neutral} = \sqrt{1,119A}$
$I_{Neutral} = 33A$

▶ **Phase Load 208V, Single-Phase Example**

What is the per phase load of each 3 hp, 208V, single-phase motor?

(a) 2,244 VA   (b) 3,910 VA   (c) 978 VA   (d) none of these

• Answer: (a) 2,244 VA

Single-Phase Motor VA = Table Volts x Table Amperes
3 hp, 208 FLC = 18.7A [Table 430.248]
Motor VA = 208V x 18.7A = 3,890 VA

AUTHORS' COMMENT: This 3,890 VA line load does not balance out to 1,945 VA per phase on a 208V single-phase load. The actual phase load is closer to 2,244 VA. This is because the two windings providing 208V are out-of-phase with each other. Vectorial math is beyond the scope of this unit. The approximate load on each phase winding can be found by multiplying the phase voltage times the phase current

$VA_{Phase} = E_{Phase} \times I_{Phase}$
$VA_{Phase} = 120\text{V} \times 18.7\text{A}$
$VA_{Phase} = 2,244 \text{ VA}$

▶ **Phase Load 208V, Three-Phase Example**

What is the per phase load for the 18 kVA , 208V, three-phase space heating?

(a) 11,154 VA   (b) 3,699 VA   (c) 6,000 VA   (d) none of these

• Answer: (c) 6,000 VA

Three-Phase Motor VA = Table Volts x Table Amperes x 1.732
10 hp 208V FLC = 30.8A [Table 430.250]
VA = 208V x 30.8A x 1.732
VA = 11,096 VA
Three-phase load is on three phases = 11,095 VA/3 phases = 3,699 VA per phase

▶ Voltage Ratio Example

What is the phase voltage ratio of the transformer?

    (a) 4:1   (b) 1:4   (c) 1:2   (d) 2:1

    • Answer: (a) 4:1

    Turns Ratio = Primary-Phase Volts to Secondary-Phase Volts
    Turns Ratio = 480V/120V
    Turns Ratio = 4:1

Balance Panel—VA

Balance the loads on the panelboard in VA.

	Line 1	Line 2	Line 3	Line Total
Space Heating 18 kVA, three-phase (A/C omitted)	6,000 VA	6,000 VA	6,000 VA	18,000 VA
Ranges 14 kVA, 208V, single-phase	7,000 VA	7,000 VA		14,000 VA
Ranges 14 kVA, 208V, single-phase		7,000 VA	7,000 VA	14,000 VA
Water Heater 10 kVA, 208V, single-phase	5,000 VA		5,000 VA	10,000 VA
3 hp, 208V, single-phase	2,244 VA	2,244 VA		3,890 VA
3 hp, 208V, single-phase		2,244 VA	2,244 VA	3,890 VA
Dishwasher 4.5 kVA, 120V			4,500 VA	4,500 VA
Lighting (8 – 1.5 kVA circuits)	+ 6,000 VA	+ 3,000 VA	+ 3,000 VA	+ 12,000 VA
	26,244 VA	27,488 VA	27,744 VA	80,280 VA

Panelboard Balancing and Sizing

Balance the previous example loads on the panelboard in amperes.

	Line 1	Line 2	Line 3	Ampere Calculations
Space Heating 18 kVA, three-phase	50.0A	50.0A	50.0A	18,000 VA/(208V x 1.732)
Range 14 kVA, 208V, single-phase	67.0A	67.0A		14,000 VA/208V
Range 14 kVA, 208V, single-phase		67.0A	67.0A	14,000 VA/208V
Water Heater 10 kVA, 208V, single-phase	48.0A		48.0A	10,000 VA/208V
3 hp, 208V, single-phase Motor	18.7A	18.7A		Motor FLC
3 hp, 208V, single-phase Motor		18.7A	18.7A	Motor FLC
Dishwasher, 4.5 kVA, 120V			38.0A	4,500 VA/120V
Lighting (8 – 1.5 kVA circuits)	+ 50.0A	+ 25.0A	+ 25.0A	1,500 VA/120V
	233.7A	246.4A	246.7A	

12.28 Delta versus Wye

Delta

Delta phase voltage is the same as the line voltage.

$$E_{Phase} = E_{Line} \text{ or } E_{Line} = E_{Phase}$$

Delta phase current is different than the line current. The line current is greater than the phase current by a factor of the square root of three (1.732).

$$I_{Line} = I_{Phase} \times 1.732 \text{ or } I_{Phase} = I_{Line}/1.732$$

Wye

Wye phase voltage is different than line voltage. Line voltage is greater than phase voltage by a factor of the square root of three (1.732).

$$E_{Line} = E_{Phase} \times 1.732 \text{ or } E_{Phase} = E_{Line}/1.732$$

Phase current is the same as line current.

$$I_{Phase} = I_{Line} \text{ or } I_{Line} = I_{Phase}$$

Unit 12 Conclusion

Transformers are indispensable for the distribution of alternating-current electricity that is so essential for the daily conveniences we take for granted. This unit included some basic transformer principles and some very important information on connections for delta and wye-configured transformer banks. A basic understanding of transformer connections and transformer principles is important to the work of an electrician.

The voltage and current relationships between the individual transformer winding and the line are distinctly different between delta-configured and wye-configured systems. We explained the fact that in delta transformers, the winding voltage is equal to the line voltage, for example 240V. The line-to-ground voltage is taken from a winding center tap, and so it is simply one-half the line-to-line voltage, or 120V in a 240V transformer. In a wye-connected system, the line voltage is found by multiplying the winding voltage by the square root of three, which can be expressed as 1.732. The voltage-to-ground is the same as the winding voltage. Therefore, you can tell by looking at a system voltage if the system is delta configured (120/240V) or wye configured (120/208V) because in a delta system the line-to-ground voltage is one-half the line-to line-voltage, while in a wye system the line voltage is 1.732 times the line-to-ground voltage.

This unit included some more advanced information that discussed the internal current and voltage of three-phase transformers. An electrical exam may include some of this type of information, but not usually in great detail. Hopefully, you have not come away from this unit feeling that you have been "Westinghoused."

Unit 12 Calculation Practice Questions

(• Indicates that 75% or fewer of those who took this exam answered the question correctly.)

Definitions

1. Delta-configured means that the windings of three single-phase transformers are connected in _____ with each other. A delta-connected transformer is represented by the Greek letter delta.

    (a) series   (b) parallel   (c) series-parallel   (d) a and b

2. What 4-wire system is called the high-leg system because the voltage from one conductor to ground is between 190 and 208 volts-to-ground?

    (a) Delta   (b) Wye

3. The term _____ is used to identify the ungrounded (hot) conductors in an electrical system.

    (a) load   (b) line   (c) system   (d) grounded

4. The _____ voltage is the voltage measured between any two ungrounded (hot) conductors.

    (a) load   (b) line   (c) grounded   (d) any of these

5. •The term "phase current" is used to identify the current flowing through the transformer winding. For _____-connected systems, the phase current will be less than the line current and for _____-connected systems, the phase current will be the same as the line current.

    (a) wye, wye   (b) delta, delta   (c) wye, delta   (d) delta, wye

6. The term "phase load" is used to identify the load on the transformer winding. For delta-configured systems, the phase load will be equal to _____.

    (a) three-phase, 240V load = line load/3   (b) single-phase, 240V load = line load
    (c) single-phase, 120V load = line load   (d) all of these

7. The term "phase voltage" is used to identify the internal voltage of a single transformer winding. For _____-connected systems, the phase voltage will be equal to the line voltage and for _____-connected systems, the phase voltage is less than the line voltage.

    (a) wye, wye   (b) delta, delta   (c) wye, delta   (d) delta, wye

8. The turns ratio is the relationship between the number of primary windings compared to the number of secondary windings. This is the same as the turns ratio between the primary phase voltage and the secondary phase voltage. For a delta/delta system, the phase voltage ratio is ____ and for a delta/wye system, the phase voltage ratio will be _____.

    (a) 1:2, 1:4   (b) 2:1, 4:1   (c) 4:1, 2:1   (d) none of these

9. What is the turns ratio for a 480V to 120/208V, three-phase delta/wye-configured transformer?

    (a) 4:1   (b) 1:4   (c) 1:2   (d) 2:1

10. •The term "unbalanced load" is intended to identify the load on the secondary grounded conductor. For _____-configured systems, the unbalanced load is determined by the formula:

$$I_{Neutral} = \sqrt{[(I_{Line1}^2 + I_{Line2}^2 + I_{Line3}^2) - [(I_{Line1} \times I_{Line2}) + (I_{Line2} \times I_{Line3}) + (I_{Line1} \times I_{Line3})]]}$$

(a) delta   (b) wye   (c) a or b   (d) none of these

11. The unbalanced load in amperes for a _____-configured system can be calculated by the formula:

$$I_{Neutral} = I_{Line1} - I_{Line3}$$

(a) delta   (b) wye   (c) a or b   (d) none of these

12. _____-connected means a connection of three single-phase transformer windings to a common point (neutral), with the other end of each winding connected to the line conductors.

(a) Delta   (b) Wye   (c) a or b   (d) none of these

12.1 Current Flow

13. When a load is connected to the secondary winding of a transformer, current will flow through the secondary winding. The current flowing in the secondary creates an electromagnetic field that opposes the primary electromagnetic field.

(a) True   (b) False

14. In a delta-configured transformer, the ratio of the primary-to-secondary line current will be directly proportional (the same ratio) to the voltage turns ratio.

(a) True   (b) False

PART A—DELTA/DELTA TRANSFORMERS

12.2 Delta Transformer Voltage

15. In a delta-configured transformer, the line voltage is equal to the phase voltage.

(a) True   (b) False

12.3 Delta High-Leg

16. If the secondary voltage of a delta/delta transformer is 220/110V, the high-leg voltage-to-ground (or neutral) is approximately _____.

(a) 191V   (b) 196V   (c) 202V   (d) 208V

12.4 Delta Line Currents

17. In a delta-configured transformer, the line current equals the phase current.

(a) True   (b) False

18. What is the primary line current for a fully loaded 45 kVA, 480V to 120/240V, three-phase transformer?

(a) 124A   (b) 108A   (c) 54A   (d) 43A

19. What is the secondary line current for a fully loaded 45 kVA, 480V to 240V, three-phase transformer?

(a) 124A   (b) 108A   (c) 54A   (d) 43A

12.5 Delta Phase Currents

20.   The phase current of a transformer winding is calculated by dividing the phase load by the phase volts:

   $I_{Phase} = VA_{Phase}/E_{Phase}$.

   (a) True   (b) False

21.   What is the primary phase current for a fully loaded 15 kVA, 480V to 120/240V, single-phase transformer?

   (a) 124A   (b) 62A   (c) 45A   (d) 31A

22.   What is the secondary phase current for a fully loaded 15 kVA, 480V to 120/240V, single-phase transformer?

   (a) 124A   (b) 63A   (c) 45A   (d) 31A

12.6 Delta Phase versus Line Current

23.   A 15 kVA, 240V, three-phase load has the following effect on a delta system:

   (a) I_{Line} = 15,000 VA/(240V x 1.732) = 36A   (b) I_{Phase} = 5,000 VA/240V = 21A
   (c) $I_{Line} = I_{Phase}$ x 1.732 = 21A x 1.732 = 36A   (d) all of these

24.   •A 5 kVA, 240V, single-phase load has the following effect on a delta/delta system:

   (a) Line Power = 5 kVA   (b) Phase Power = 5 kVA
   (c) I_{Phase} = 5,000 VA/240V = 21A   (d) all of these

25.   •A 2 kVA, 120V, single-phase load has the following effect on a delta system:

   (a) Line Power = 2 kVA   (b) I_{Line} = 2,000 VA/120V = 17A
   (c) Phase Power = 2 kVA (C1 or C2 winding)   (d) all of these

12.7 Delta Current Triangle

26.   The line and phase current of a delta system are not equal. The difference between line and phase current can be described by which of the following equations?

   (a) $I_{Line} = I_{Phase}$ x 1.732   (b) $I_{Phase} = I_{Line}/1.732$ (c) a and b   (d) none of these

12.8 and 12.9 Delta Transformer Balancing and Sizing

27.   To properly size a delta/delta transformer, the transformer must be balanced in kVA. Which of the following steps should be used to balance the transformer?

   (a) three-phase loads, split 1/3 on Phase A, 1/3 on Phase B, and 1/3 on Phase C.
   (b) single-phase, 240V loads, place 100% on Phase A or Phase B.
   (c) 120V loads, place 100% on Phase C1 or C2.
   (d) all of these

28.   •Balance and size a 480V to 120/240V, three-phase delta transformer for the following loads: one 18 kVA, three-phase heat strip; two 5 kVA, single-phase, 240V loads; and three 2 kVA 120V loads. What size transformer is required?

   (a) three single-phase, 12.5 kVA transformers   (b) one three-phase, 37.5 kVA transformer
   (c) a or b   (d) none of these

12.10 Delta Panel Balancing

29. When balancing a panelboard for a delta system, be sure to split the three-phase VA load so that one-third is on each line; split the 240V, single-phase VA load so that 50 percent is on each line; and place 120V, single-phase VA loads so that they are balanced as equally as possible on each line.

(a) True   (b) False

30. •Balance a 120/240V delta three-phase panelboard in kVA for the following loads: one 18 kVA, three-phase heat strip; two 5 kVA, single-phase, 240V loads; and three 2 kVA 120V loads.

(a) The largest line load will not exceed 13 kVA.   (b) The smallest line load is at least 10 kVA.
(c) The total load is equal to 34 kVA.   (d) all of these.

12.11 Delta Panelboard and Conductor Sizing

31. When selecting and sizing panelboards and conductors, the line loads must be balanced in amperes. Balance a 120/240V, three-phase panelboard in amperes for the following loads: one 18 kVA, three-phase heat strip; two 5 kVA, single-phase, 240V loads; and three 2 kVA 120V loads.

(a) The largest line is 98A.   (b) The smallest line is 81A.
(c) Each line is equal to 82A.   (d) a and b

12.12 Delta Neutral Current

32. What is the neutral current for: one 18 kVA, three-phase heat strip; two 5 kVA, single-phase, 240V loads; and three 2 kVA 120V loads?

(a) 17A   (b) 34A   (c) 0A   (d) a and b

12.13 Delta Maximum Unbalanced Load

33. •What is the maximum unbalanced load in amperes for: one 18 kVA, three-phase heat strip; two 5 kVA, single-phase, 240V loads; and three 2 kVA 120V loads?

(a) 25A   (b) 34A   (c) 0A   (d) none of these

34. What is the phase load for an 18 kVA, three-phase heat strip?

(a) 18 kVA   (b) 9 kVA   (c) 6 kVA   (d) 3 kVA

35. •On a delta system, what is the transformer winding phase load for a 5 kVA, single-phase, 240V load?

(a) 5 kVA   (b) 2.5 kVA   (c) 1.25 kVA   (d) none of these

36. What is the current on the high-leg if the only load on the high-leg is a 12 kW, 240V, three-phase load?

(a) 29A   (b) 43A   (c) 73A   (d) 97A

37. What is the turns ratio of a 480V to 120/240V transformer?

(a) 4:1   (b) 1:4   (c) 1:2   (d) 2:1

PART B—DELTA/WYE TRANSFORMERS
12.15 Wye Transformer Voltage

38. In a wye-configured transformer, the line voltage is the same as the phase voltage.

(a) True   (b) False

12.17 Wye Transformers Current

39. In a wye-configured transformer, the line current is the same as the phase current.

   (a) True   (b) False

12.18 Wye Line Current

40. The line current for both delta and wye-configured three-phase transformers can be calculated by the formula:
   $I_{Line} = VA_{Line}/(E_{Line} \times 1.732)$.

   (a) True   (b) False

41. What is the primary line current for a fully loaded 22 kVA, 480V to 120/208V, three-phase transformer?

   (a) 61A   (b) 54A   (c) 26A   (d) 22A

42. What is the secondary line current for a fully loaded 22 kVA, 480V to 120/208V, three-phase transformer?

   (a) 61A   (b) 54A   (c) 27A   (d) 22A

12.19 Wye Phase Current

43. The phase current of a wye-configured transformer will be the same as the line current. The phase current of a delta-configured transformer is less than the line current by a factor of 1.732 (square root of 3).

   (a) True   (b) False

44. •What is the primary phase current for a 22 kVA, 480V to 120/208V, three-phase delta/wye transformer?

   (a) 15A   (b) 22A   (c) 36A   (d) 61A

45. •What is the secondary phase current for a 22 kVA, 480V to 120/208V, three-phase delta/wye transformer?

   (a) 15A   (b) 22A   (c) 36A   (d) 61A

12.20 Wye Phase versus Line Current

46. Since each line conductor from a wye transformer is connected to a different transformer winding (phase), the effects of loading on the line are the same as the phase. A 12 kVA, 208V, three-phase load has the following effect on the system:

   (a) $I_{Line} = VA_{Line}/(E_{Line} \times 1.732) = 12,000VA/(208V \times 1.732) = 33A$

   (b) Phase Power = 4 kVA

   (c) $I_{Phase} = VA_{Phase}/E_{Phase} = 4,000 \, VA/120V = 33A$

   (d) all of these

47. A 2 kVA, 120V, single-phase load has the following effect on the system:

   (a) Line Power = 2 kVA

   (b) $I_{Line} = VA/E = 2,000 \, VA/120V = 17A$

   (c) $I_{Phase} = VA_{Phase}/E_{Phase} = 2,000 \, VA/120V = 17A$

   (d) all of these

48. •What is the phase load (load per transformer winding) for a 7.5 hp, 208V, three-phase motor?

(a) 2,906 VA   (b) 8,718 VA   (c) 4,359 VA   (d) none of these

12.21 and 12.22 Wye Transformer Balancing and Sizing

49. To properly size a delta/wye transformer, the secondary transformer phases (windings) or the line conductors must be balanced. Balancing the panel (line conductors) is identical to balancing the transformer for wye-configured transformers. Which of the following steps should be used to balance the transformer?

(a) Three-phase loads, split one-third on each phase.   (b) Single-phase, 208V loads, split one-half on each phase.
(c) 120V loads, place 100% on any phase.   (d) all of these

12.24 Wye Panelboard and Conductor Sizing

50. •When selecting and sizing panelboards and conductors, the line loads must be balanced in amperes. Balance a 120/208V, three-phase panelboard in amperes for the following loads: one 18 kVA, 208V, three-phase heat strip; two 5 kVA, single-phase, 208V loads; and three 2 kVA, 120V loads.

(a) The largest line current is 108A.   (b) The smallest line is 91A.
(c) a and b   (d) none of these

12.25 Wye Neutral Current

51. The neutral current for a 3-wire circuit from a 4-wire wye-configured system can be determined by the following formula:

$$I_{Neutral} = \sqrt{[(I_{Line\ 1}^2 + I_{Line\ 2}^2 + I_{Line\ 3}^2) - [(I_{Line\ 1} \times I_{Line\ 2}) + (I_{Line\ 2} \times I_{Line\ 3}) + (I_{Line\ 1} \times I_{Line\ 3})]]}$$

(a) True   (b) False

52. •What is the maximum neutral current for: one 18 kVA, three-phase heat strip; two 5 kVA, single-phase, 208V loads; and three 2 kVA, 120V loads?

(a) 17A   (b) 29A   (c) 34A   (d) a and b

12.26 Wye Maximum Unbalanced Load

53. •What is the maximum unbalanced load in amperes for: one 18 kVA, three-phase heat strip; two 5 kVA, single-phase, 208V loads; and three 2 kVA, 120V loads?

(a) 17A   (b) 34A   (c) 0A   (d) a and b

12.28 Delta versus Wye

54. Which of the following statements are true for wye systems?

(a) Phase current is the same as line current: $I_{Phase} = I_{Line}$.   (b) Phase voltage is the same as the line voltage.
(c) $E_{Line} = E_{Phase} \times 1.732$ (d) a and c

55. Which of the following statements are true for delta systems?

(a) Phase voltage is the same as line voltage: $E_{Phase} = E_{Line}$.
(b) Phase current is the same as the line current.
(c) Line current is greater than phase current: $I_{Line} = I_{Phase} \times 1.732$.
(d) a and c

(• Indicates that 75% or fewer of those who took this exam answered the question correctly.)

PART A—DELTA/DELTA TRANSFORMERS

12.8 and 12.9 Delta Transformer Balancing and Sizing

The following loads are to be connected to a delta/delta three-phase transformer with a 480V primary and a 120/240V secondary rating. Balance the loads as closely as possible, then answer questions 56 through 62 based on this information.

Heat 18 kW, 230V, three-phase heat
A/C 25 hp, 230V, three-phase synchronous motor
Two 1 hp, 230V, single-phase motors
Two 2 hp, 115V, single-phase motors
Three 1,900W, 115V lighting loads

1. •If three single-phase transformers are connected in series, what size transformers are required for the loads?

   (a) 10/10/10 kVA   (b) 15/15/15 kVA   (c) 10/10/20 kVA   (d) 15/15/10 kVA

2. •The line VA load of the 25 hp, three-phase synchronous motor will be _____ VA.

   (a) 9,700   (b) 21,100   (c) 32,000   (d) 48,000

3. •After balancing the 120V loads, the maximum unbalanced neutral current in amperes is _____.

   (a) 27A   (b) 1.5A   (c) 48A   (d) 148A

4. •The transformer phase load of one 1 hp, 115V motor will be _____.

   (a) 1,380 VA   (b) 2,760 VA   (c) 1,840 VA   (d) 1,150 VA

5. •The line load of one of the 1 hp, 230V motors will be _____.

   (a) 1,380 VA   (b) 2,760 VA   (c) 1,840 VA   (d) 1,150 VA

6. •The transformer phase VA load of the 25 hp, 230V, three-phase synchronous motor is closest to _____.

   (a) 3,520 VA   (b) 7,038 VA   (c) 21,100 VA   (d) 32,100 VA

7. •If the only load on the high-leg is the three-phase, 25 hp motor, the high-leg conductor will have to be sized for a minimum of _____.

   (a) 13A   (b) 66A   (c) 18A   (d) 22A

Answer the next two questions based on this information: A three-phase, 37.5 kVA delta/delta transformer has a primary of 480V and a secondary of 120/240V.

8. •The primary line current is closest to _____.

   (a) 45A   (b) 90A   (c) 50A   (d) 65A

9. •The maximum size overcurrent device for primary only protection of the 37.5 kVA delta/delta transformer is _____.

    (a) 40A   (b) 45A   (c) 50A   (d) 60A

Answer the next question based on this information:

    Seven heaters 1,500W, 120V
    Five 3 kW, 240V, single-phase heaters
    Equipment circuits 30 kW, 120V
    Lighting circuits 40 kW, 120V

10. •If a three-phase, 37.5 kVA, center-tapped, delta/delta transformer that has a primary voltage of 480V and secondary voltage of 120/240V has only the 120V loads listed connected to its secondary, what is the total kW load on this transformer?

    (a) 30 to 40 kW   (b) 50 to 60 kW   (c) 80 to 90 kW   (d) over 100 kW

11. •The total load on a center-tapped 120/240V transformer (delta/delta) is 100 kW which consists of 80 kW of 120V balanced loads and 20 kW of 240V loads. What is the maximum unbalanced current on the grounded conductor?

    (a) 167A   (b) 0A   (c) 192A   (d) 333A

12. •The phase current flowing though the secondary winding for a delta/delta, three-phase transformer is _____ if the load is 30,000 VA, 240V, three-phase.

    (a) 125A   (b) 72A   (c) 42A   (d) none of these

13. •What is the secondary line current for a 45 kVA delta/delta transformer that has a line voltage turns ratio of 2:1, if the primary operates at 460V?

    (a) 113A   (b) 55A   (c) 36A   (d) cannot be determined

14. •A 4,160V to 240V, three-phase transformer is connected delta/delta. The secondary phase current is 300A and the secondary line voltage is 240V. How much current will be flowing in the conductors supplying the transformer (line current)?

    (a) 17A   (b) 20A   (c) 50A   (d) 30A

15. •The three-phase transformer connection giving the highest secondary line voltage is _____. Assume the primary line voltage is 480V.

    (a) wye primary, delta secondary   (b) delta primary, delta secondary
    (c) wye primary, wye secondary   (d) delta primary, wye secondary

PART B—DELTA/WYE TRANSFORMERS

12.21 and 12.22 Wye Transformer Balancing and Sizing

16. •What is the primary line current for a delta/wye 480V to 120/208V, three-phase transformer that has a secondary line current of 200A?

    (a) 31A   (b) 72A   (c) 87A   (d) 53A

17. •The secondary line current for a wye-connected transformer will be approximately _____ if the secondary phase voltage is 277V and the load is 10 kVA, three-phase.

    (a) 7A   (b) 12A   (c) 32A   (d) none of these

Answer the next question based on this information:

> One motor, 15 hp, 208V, three-phase
> Two dryers, 1.5 kW, 208V, single-phase
> Four lighting circuits, 3 kW, 120V
> One cooktop, 8 kW, 208V, single-phase
> Five heaters, 2.5 kW, 208V, single-phase each

18. •Each 2.5 kW heat strip has a line load of _____.

(a) 1,250W   (b) 12,500W   (c) 2,500W   (d) no load

19. •The VA load per line for a 15 hp, 208V, three-phase motor can be determined by which of these formulas?

(a) 1.732 x E x I   (b) (E x I)/1.732   (c) E x I   (d) none of these

20. •If a three-phase motor has a total load of 12,000 VA and is connected to a delta/wye transformer, the load on one phase of the secondary will be _____.

(a) 12,000 VA   (b) 4,000 VA   (c) 3,000 VA   (d) 1,500 VA

21. •A three-phase, 480Y to 120/208V transformer provides power to nine 2,000 VA, 120V lights and nine 2,000W, 208V heaters. The maximum neutral current is _____.

(a) 50A   (b) 75A   (c) 87A   (d) 95A

22. •The load of a 10 hp, three-phase, 120/208V motor on each phase is closest to _____.

(a) 3,700 VA   (b) 5,500 VA   (c) 4,300 VA   (d) 11,100 VA

Answer the next question based on this information:

> The system is a three-phase, 120/208V system and the loads are as follows:
> Nine 2 kVA, three-phase, 120V lighting loads
> Five 3 kVA, 120V, single-phase loads

23. •The neutral conductor must be sized to carry _____.

(a) 10A   (b) 25A   (c) 90A   (d) 100A

(• Indicates that 75% or fewer of those who took this exam answered the question correctly.)

Article 702 Optional Standby Power Systems

Optional standby systems are intended to protect public or private facilities or property where life safety doesn't depend on the performance of the system. These systems are typically installed to provide an alternate source of electric power for such facilities as industrial and commercial buildings, farms, and residences, and to serve loads that, when stopped during any power outage, could cause discomfort, serious interruption of a process, or damage to a product or process. Optional standby systems are intended to supply on-site generated power to loads selected by the customer either automatically or manually.

1.   Article 702 applies to _____ generators used for backup power to telecommunications facilities, water and wastewater pump stations, as well as homes and offices.

(a) permanently installed   (b) portable   (c) a and b   (d) none of these

2.   Optional standby systems must have adequate capacity and rating for the supply of _____.

(a) all emergency lighting and power loads
(b) all equipment intended to be operated at one time
(c) 100 percent of the appliance loads and 50 percent of the lighting loads
(d) 100 percent of the lighting loads and 75 percent of the appliance loads

3.   For optional standby systems, the temporary connection of a portable generator without transfer equipment is permitted, where written safety procedures are in place and conditions of maintenance and supervision ensure that only qualified persons will service the installation, and where the normal supply is physically isolated by _____.

(a) a lockable disconnecting means   (b) the disconnection of the normal supply conductors
(c) an extended power outage   (d) a or b

4.   A sign must be placed at the service-entrance equipment indicating the _____ of on-site optional standby power sources.

(a) type   (b) location   (c) manufacturer   (d) a and b

5.   If the transfer switch for a portable generator switches the _____ conductor, then it is being used as a separately derived system and the portable generator must be grounded in accordance with 250.30.

(a) phase   (b) equipment grounding   (c) grounded   (d) all of these

6.   Where a generator for an optional standby system is installed outdoors and equipped with a readily accessible disconnecting means located _____, an additional disconnecting means is not required where ungrounded conductors serve or pass through the building or structure.

(a) inside the building or structure   (b) within sight of the building or structure
(c) inside the generator enclosure   (d) a or c

Article 720 Circuits and Equipment Operating at Less Than 50V

Article 720 applies to electrical installations that operate below 50V, either direct current or alternating current. Other installations that operate below 50V and are covered in Articles 411, 551, 650, 669, 725, and 760 aren't required to comply with Article 720.

7.   Circuits and equipment operating at less than 50V must use receptacles that are rated at not less than _____.

(a) 10A   (b) 15A   (c) 20A   (d) 30A

Article 725 Class 1, Class 2, and Class 3 Remote-Control, Signaling, and Power-Limited Circuits

Article 725 contains the requirements for remote-control, signaling, and power-limited circuits that aren't an integral part of a device or appliance.

- Remote-Control Circuit—A circuit that controls other circuits through a relay or solid-state device. For example, a circuit that controls the coil of a motor starter or lighting contactor.
- Signaling Circuit—A circuit that supplies energy to an appliance or device that gives a visual and/or audible signal. For example, a circuit for doorbells, buzzers, code-calling systems, signal lights, annunciators, burglar alarms, and other indication or alarm devices.

8.   Due to its power limitations, a Class 2 circuit is safe from a fire initiation standpoint and provides acceptable protection from electric shock

(a) True   (b) False

9.   All accessible portions of abandoned Class 2, Class 3, and PLTC cables must be removed.

(a) True   (b) False

10.   Class 1, 2, and 3 cables installed _____ on the surface of ceilings and sidewalls must be supported by the building structure in such a manner that the cable will not be damaged by normal building use.

(a) exposed   (b) concealed   (c) hidden   (d) a and b

11.   Remote-control circuits to safety-control equipment must be classified as _____ if the failure of the equipment to operate introduces a direct fire or life hazard.

(a) Class 1   (b) Class 2   (c) Class 3   (d) Class I, Division 1

12.   Where damage to remote-control circuits of safety control equipment would introduce a hazard, all conductors of such remote-control circuits shall be installed in rigid metal conduit, intermediate metal conduit, rigid nonmetallic conduit, electrical metallic tubing, Type MI cable, Type MC cable, or be otherwise suitably protected from physical damage.

(a) True   (b) False

13.   A Class 1 signaling circuit must not exceed _____.

(a) 130V   (b) 150V   (c) 220V   (d) 600V

14.   Class 1 circuit conductors supplied by the secondary of a single-phase transformer having only a 2-wire (single-voltage) secondary are permitted to be protected by overcurrent protection provided on the primary side of the transformer, provided _____.

(a) primary protection is in accordance with 450.3
(b) primary protection does not exceed the value determined by multiplying the secondary conductor ampacity by the secondary to primary transformer voltage ratio
(c) branch-circuit conductors are 90-degree rated
(d) a and b.

15. Power-supply and Class 1 circuit conductors are permitted to occupy the same cable, enclosure, or raceway _____.

(a) only where the equipment powered is functionally associated
(b) only where the circuits involved are not a mixture of ac and dc
(c) under no circumstances
(d) none of these

16. When required, the maximum overcurrent protection in amperes for a noninherently-limited Class 2 remote-control circuit is _____.

(a) 1.0A (b) 2.0A (c) 5.0A (d) 7.5A

17. Equipment supplying Class 2 or Class 3 circuits must be durably marked where plainly visible to indicate _____.

(a) each circuit that is a Class 2 or Class 3 circuit (b) the circuit VA rating
(c) the size of the conductors serving each circuit (d) all of these

18. Conductors of Class 2 and Class 3 circuits must not be placed in any enclosure, raceway, cable, or similar fittings with conductors of Class 1 or electric light or power conductors, except when they are _____.

(a) insulated for the maximum voltage (b) totally comprised of aluminum conductors
(c) separated by a barrier (d) all of these

19. Class 2 and Class 3 circuits are permitted within the same cable, raceway, or enclosure provided that the insulation of the Class 2 circuit conductors meet the requirements for Class 3 circuits.

(a) True (b) False

20. Raceways must not be used as a means of support for Class 2 or Class 3 circuit conductors.

(a) True (b) False

21. The accessible portion of abandoned Class 2 and Class 3 cables installed in duct, plenums, or other spaces used for environmental air must be _____.

(a) removed (b) identified as abandoned (c) a or b (d) none of these

22. Class 2 or Class 3 cables installed in hazardous (classified) locations must be Type _____, as permitted by 501.4(B), 502.4(B), and 504.20.

(a) CL2R (b) PLTC (c) CL2P (d) CL3P

23. Class 2 and Class 3 riser cables listed as suitable for use in a vertical run in a shaft, or from floor to floor are _____.

(a) CL2P and CL3P (b) CL2R and CL3R (c) CL2 and CL3 (d) PLCT

Article 727 Instrumentation Tray Cable (Type ITC)

Instrumentation tray cable (ITC) is used in industrial establishments where the conditions of maintenance and supervision assure that only qualified persons will service the installation.

24. Instrumentation tray cable is used for instrumentation and control circuits operating at _____.

(a) 300V or less and 0.5A or less (b) 150V or less and 5A or less
(c) 480V or less and 10A or less (d) over 600V

25. Type ITC cable can be installed with power, lighting, and Class 1 circuits.

    (a) True   (b) False

26. Overcurrent protection for Type ITC cable must not exceed _____ for 20 AWG and larger conductors.

    (a) 3A   (b) 5A   (c) 10A   (d) 15A

Article 760 Fire Alarm Systems

Article 760 covers the installation of wiring and equipment for fire alarm systems. Fire alarm systems include fire detection and alarm notification, voice communications, guard's tour, sprinkler waterflow, and sprinkler supervisory systems.

27. Article 760 covers the requirements for the installation of wiring and equipment of _____.

    (a) communications systems   (b) antennas   (c) fire alarm systems   (d) fiber optics

28. Class 2, Class 3, and PLTC cables that are not terminated at equipment and not identified for future use with a tag will be considered as abandoned.

    (a) True   (b) False

29. Fire alarm circuits installed in ducts, plenums, and other air-handling spaces must be installed in accordance with the requirements contained in 300.22.

    (a) True   (b) False

30. Fire alarm circuits installed in _____ locations must comply with 110.11, 300.6, and 310.9.

    (a) corrosive   (b) damp   (c) wet   (d) any of these

31. Exposed fire alarm circuit cables must be supported by the building structure using straps, staples, hangers, or similar fittings designed and installed so as not to damage the cable.

    (a) True   (b) False

32. Fire alarm circuits must be identified at all terminal and junction locations. The identification must be in a manner that will prevent unintentional interference with the fire alarm signaling circuit during _____.

    (a) installation   (b) testing and servicing   (c) renovations   (d) all of these

33. The power source for a nonpower-limited fire alarm (NPLFA) circuit cannot be supplied through a(n) _____.

    (a) ground-fault circuit interrupter   (b) arc-fault circuit interrupter
    (c) inverse-time circuit breaker   (d) a or b

34. Overcurrent protection devices for nonpower-limited fire alarm (NPLFA) circuits must be located at the point where the conductor to be protected _____.

    (a) terminates at the load   (b) is spliced to any other conductor
    (c) receives its supply   (d) none of these

35. Nonpower-limited fire alarm (NPLFA) circuit conductors are permitted to be in the same cable, enclosure, or raceway with power-supply circuits only where connected to the same equipment.

    (a) True   (b) False

36.   Conductors for nonpower-limited fire alarm circuits must be _____.

       (a) solid copper   (b) stranded copper   (c) copper or aluminum   (d) a or b

37.   Where installed exposed, fire alarm cables must be _____.

       (a) adequately supported   (b) installed in such a way as to be protected against physical damage
       (c) none of these   (d) a and b

38.   Exposed power-limited fire alarm circuit cables may be installed in _____ when passing through a floor or wall to a height of 7
       ft above the floor, unless adequate protection is afforded by the building construction or an equivalent solid guard is provided.

       (a) rigid metal conduit   (b) rigid nonmetallic conduit   (c) electrical metallic tubing   (d) any of these

39.   The listing requirements for power-limited fire alarm (PLFA) circuit sources are found in Tables 12(A) and 12(B) of _____.

       (a) Article 760   (b) Chapter 9   (c) Article 300   (d) Annex C

40.   Power-limited fire alarm circuits are permitted to be reclassified and installed as _____ if the power-limited fire alarm circuit
       markings required by 760.42 are eliminated, and the entire circuit is installed in a Chapter 3 wiring method in accordance with
       Part II of Article 760.

       (a) intrinsically safe circuits   (b) ground-fault protected circuits
       (c) nonpower-limited circuits   (d) Class I, Division 2

41.   Conductors of lighting or power may occupy the same enclosure or raceway with conductors of power-limited fire alarm circuits.

       (a) True   (b) False

42.   Audio system circuits described in 640.9(C) and using Class 2 or Class 3 wiring methods are not permitted to be installed in the
       same cable or raceway with _____.

       (a) other audio system circuits   (b) power-limited fire alarm conductors or cables
       (c) a or b   (d) none of these

43.   Power-limited fire alarm circuit cables installed within buildings in an air-handling space used for environmental air must use
       _____ conductors when not installed in a raceway.

       (a) FPL   (b) CL3P   (c) OFNP   (d) FPLP

44.   Coaxial cables used in power-limited fire alarm systems must have an overall insulation rating of not less than _____.

       (a) 100V   (b) 300V   (c) 600V   (d) 1,000V

Article 770 Optical Fiber Cables and Raceways

Article 770 covers the installation of optical fiber cables, which contain optical fibers used to transmit light for control, signaling, and
communication. This article also contains the installation requirements for raceways that contain and support the optical fiber cables.
Requirements are also contained in this article for composite cables (often called "hybrid" in the field) that combine optical fibers with
current-carrying metallic conductors.

45.   All accessible portions of abandoned optical fiber cable must be removed.

       (a) True   (b) False

46. Conductive optical fiber cables contain noncurrent-carrying conductive members such as metallic _____.

    (a) strength members   (b) vapor barriers   (c) armor or sheath   (d) any of these

47. When optical fiber cable is installed in a raceway, the raceway must be of a type permitted in Chapter 3 and the raceway must be installed in accordance with Chapter 3 requirements.

    (a) True   (b) False

48. Access to equipment must not be prohibited by an accumulation of optical fiber cables that prevent the removal of access panels. This includes suspended-ceiling panels.

    (a) True   (b) False

49. Exposed optical fiber cables must be supported by the building structure using straps, staples, hangers, or similar fittings designed and installed so as not to damage the cable.

    (a) True   (b) False

50. _____ is a conductive, general-purpose type of optical fiber cable that may be installed as wiring within buildings.

    (a) FPLP   (b) CL2P   (c) OFPN   (d) OFC

51. Optical fibers are permitted within the same composite cable as electric light, power, and Class 1 circuits operating at 600V, or less where the functions of the optical fibers and the electrical conductors are associated.

    (a) True   (b) False

52. Optical fibers are permitted in the same cable, and conductive and nonconductive optical fiber cables are permitted in the same cable tray, enclosure, or raceway with conductors of Class 2 and Class 3 circuits in compliance with Article 725.

    (a) True   (b) False

53. Types OFNG, OFN, OFCG, and OFC optical fiber cables may be used as risers when _____.

    (a) encased in a metal raceway
    (b) located in a fireproof shaft having a fire-stop at each floor
    (c) none of these
    (d) a or b

54. Optical fiber riser cables listed as suitable for use in a vertical run in a shaft or from floor to floor are Types _____.

    (a) OFNP and OFCP   (b) OFNR and OFCR   (c) OFNG and OFCG   (d) OFN and OFC

55. Optical fiber cables listed as suitable for general-purpose use, with the exception of risers, plenums, and other space used for environmental air are Types _____.

    (a) OFNP and OFCP   (b) OFNR and OFCR   (c) OFNG and OFCG   (d) OFN and OFC

Chapter 8 Communications Systems

Article 800 Communications Circuits

This article covers the installation requirements for telephone wiring and for other related telecommunications purposes such as computer Local Area Networks (LANs), and outside wiring for fire and burglar alarm systems connected to central stations.

56. Communications circuits and equipment installed in a location that is _____ in accordance with Article 500 must comply with the applicable requirements contained in Chapter 5.

    (a) designed   (b) classified   (c) located   (d) approved

57. Equipment intended to be electrically connected to a telecommunications network must be listed for the purpose.

    (a) True   (b) False

58. Communications cables installed _____ on the surface of ceilings and sidewalls must be supported by the building structure in such a manner that the cable will not be damaged by normal building use.

    (a) exposed   (b) concealed   (c) hidden   (d) a and b

59. Where overhead communications wires and cables enter buildings, they must _____.

    (a) where practicable, be located below the electric light or power conductors
    (b) not be attached to a cross-arm that carries electric light or power conductors
    (c) have a vertical clearance of not less than 8 ft from all points of roofs above which they pass
    (d) all of these

60. The metallic sheath of communications cable entering buildings must be _____.

    (a) grounded at the point of emergence through an exterior wall
    (b) grounded at the point of emergence through a concrete floor slab
    (c) interrupted as close to the point of entrance as practicable by an insulating joint
    (d) any of these

61. Limiting the length of the primary protector grounding conductors for communications circuits on one- and two-family dwellings reduces differences in potential between the building's _____ and communications systems during lightning events.

    (a) power   (b) fire alarm   (c) lighting   (d) lightning protection

62. In communications circuits, all separate electrodes are permitted to be bonded together using a minimum jumper size of _____ copper.

    (a) 10 AWG   (b) 8 AWG   (c) 6 AWG   (d) 4 AWG

63. Communications wires and cables are not required to be listed and marked where the length of the cable within the building, measured from its point of entrance, does not exceed_____ and the cable enters the building from the outside and is terminated in an enclosure or on a listed primary protector.

    (a) 25 ft   (b) 30 ft   (c) 50 ft   (d) 100 ft

64. Communications cable risers penetrating more than one floor, or cables installed in vertical runs in a shaft, must be Type CMR. Listed communications cables are also allowed when _____.

(a) encased in metal raceways

(b) located in a fireproof shaft with firestops at each floor

(c) a or b

(d) none of these

65. Communications plenum cable must be _____ as being suitable for use in ducts, plenums, and other spaces used for environmental air.

(a) marked (b) identified (c) approved (d) listed

Article 810 Radio and Television Equipment

This article covers antenna systems for radio and television receiving equipment, amateur radio transmitting and receiving equipment, and certain features of transmitter safety. It also includes antennas such as multi-element, vertical rod and dish, and the wiring and cabling that connect them to the equipment.

66. Coaxial cables that connect antennas to equipment must be installed in accordance with Article 820.

(a) True (b) False

67. Soft-drawn or medium-drawn copper lead-in conductors for receiving antenna systems are permitted where the maximum span between points of support is less than _____.

(a) 35 ft (b) 30 ft (c) 20 ft (d) 10 ft

68. Outdoor antennas and lead-in conductors for radio and television equipment must not cross over open conductors of electric light or power circuits, and must be kept well away from all such circuits to avoid the possibility of accidental contact. Where proximity to open electric light or power service conductors of less than 250V between conductors cannot be avoided, the installation must provide a clearance of at least _____.

(a) 2 ft (b) 6 ft (c) 8 ft (d) 5 ft

69. The receiving station outdoor wire-strung antenna conductor with a span of 75 ft must be at least _____ if a copper-clad steel conductor is used.

(a) 10 AWG (b) 12 AWG (c) 14 AWG (d) 17 AWG

70. Underground antenna conductors for radio and television receiving equipment must be separated at least _____ from any light, power, or Class 1 circuit conductors.

(a) 6 ft (b) 5 ft (c) 12 in. (d) 18 in.

71. Indoor antenna lead-in conductors for radio and television receiving equipment are permitted to be in the same enclosure with conductors of other wiring systems where separated by an effective, permanently installed barrier.

(a) True (b) False

72. Antenna discharge units must be located outside the building. They may never be located indoors.

(a) True (b) False

73. The grounding conductor for an antenna mast or antenna discharge unit must be run to the grounding electrode in as straight a line as practicable.

(a) True (b) False

74. If a separate grounding electrode is installed for the radio and television equipment, it must be bonded to the building's electrical power grounding electrode system with a conductor not smaller than _____ AWG.

(a) 10   (b) 8   (c) 6   (d) 1/0

75. Unshielded lead-in antenna conductors for amateur transmitting stations attached to buildings must be firmly mounted at least _____ clear of the surface of the building on nonabsorbent insulating supports.

(a) 1 in.   (b) 2 in.   (c) 3 in.   (d) 4 in.

Article 820 Community Antenna Television (CATV) and Radio Distribution Systems

This article covers the installation of coaxial cables to distribute limited-energy high-frequency signals for television, cable TV, and closed-circuit television (CCTV), which is often used for security purposes. This article also covers premises wiring of satellite TV systems where the dish antenna is outside and covered by Article 810.

76. CATV cable not terminated at equipment and not identified for future use with a tag is considered abandoned.

(a) True   (b) False

77. The coaxial cable for community antenna television (CATV) and radio systems is permitted to deliver low-energy power to equipment that is directly associated with the radio frequency distribution system if voltage is not over _____ volts and if the current supply is from a transformer or other energy-limiting device.

(a) 600   (b) 120   (c) 60   (d) 1,000

78. CATV cables installed _____ on the surface of ceilings and sidewalls must be supported by the building structure in such a manner that the cable will not be damaged by normal building use.

(a) exposed   (b) concealed   (c) hidden   (d) a and b

79. Where practicable, coaxial cables for a CATV system must be separated by at least _____ from lightning conductors.

(a) 3 in.   (b) 6 in.   (c) 6 ft   (d) 2 ft

80. The conductor used to ground the outer cover of a coaxial cable must be _____.

(a) insulated   (b) 14 AWG minimum   (c) bare   (d) a and b

81. Limiting the length of the primary protector grounding conductors for community antenna television and radio systems on one- and two-family dwellings reduces differences in potential between the building's _____ and communications systems during lightning events.

(a) power   (b) fire alarm   (c) lighting   (d) lightning protection

82. The grounding conductor for a CATV system must be connected to the nearest accessible location included on the list in 820.100(B)(1) when the building _____.

(a) has a grounding means   (b) is without a grounding means
(c) has an emergency transfer switch   (d) is wired using a metallic cable or raceway system

83. A bonding jumper not smaller than _____ copper or equivalent must be connected between the antenna system's grounding electrode and the power grounding electrode system at the building or structure served where separate electrodes are used for the CATV system.

(a) 12 AWG   (b) 8 AWG   (c) 6 AWG   (d) 4 AWG

84. Coaxial cable is permitted to be placed in a raceway, compartment, outlet box, or junction box with the conductors of light or power circuits, or Class 1 circuits when _____.

    (a) installed in rigid metal conduit   (b) separated by a permanent barrier
    (c) insulated   (d) none of these

85. CATV cables installed in ducts, plenums, and other spaces used for environmental air, and not inside of a raceway, must be Type CATVP.

    (a) True   (b) False

Article 830 Network-Powered Broadband Communications Systems

This article contains the installation requirements for network-powered broadband communications systems where powered from the communications utility network for voice, audio, video, data, and interactive services through a network interface unit (NIU). An example of a network-powered broadband communications system is hybrid fiber-coaxial (HFC) cable used for video/audio conferencing or interactive multimedia entertainment systems.

86. Network-powered broadband cable not terminated at equipment and not identified for future use with a tag is considered abandoned.

    (a) True   (b) False

87. Network-powered broadband cables installed _____ on the surface of ceilings and sidewalls must be supported by the structural components of the building in such a manner that the cable will not be damaged by normal building use.

    (a) exposed   (b) concealed   (c) hidden   (d) a and b

88. Where network-powered broadband communications system aerial cables are installed outside and entering buildings, they must _____.

    (a) be located below the electric light or power conductors, where practicable
    (b) not be attached to a cross-arm that carries electric light or power conductors
    (c) have a vertical clearance of not less than 8 ft from all points of roofs above which they pass
    (d) all of these

89. In one- and two-family and multifamily dwellings, the grounding conductor for network-powered broadband communications systems must be as short as permissible, not to exceed _____ in length.

    (a) 5 ft   (b) 6 ft   (c) 10 ft   (d) 20 ft

90. In one- and two-family dwellings where it is not practicable to achieve an overall maximum primary protector grounding conductor length of 20 ft or less for network-powered broadband communications systems, a separate _____ communications ground rod must be driven and be bonded to the power grounding electrode system with a 6 AWG conductor.

    (a) 5 ft   (b) 8 ft   (c) 10 ft   (d) 20 ft

91. Network-powered broadband communications system cables must be separated at least 2 in. from conductors of _____ circuits.

    (a) power   (b) electric light   (c) Class 1   (d) any of these

Chapter 9 Tables

Conductor and Raceway Specifications

92. The percentage of conduit fill for two conductors is _____ percent.

(a) 40   (b) 31   (c) 53   (d) 30

93. When calculating raceway conductor fill, equipment grounding conductors must _____.

(a) not be counted   (b) have the actual dimensions used
(c) not be counted if in a nipple   (d) not be counted if for a wye three-phase balanced load

94. When conduit nipples 24 in. or shorter are installed, the ampacity adjustment factor for more than three current-carrying conductors _____ to this condition.

(a) does not apply   (b) must be applied

95. The inside diameter of 1 in. IMC is _____

(a) 1.000 in.   (b) 1.105 in.   (c) 0.826 in.   (d) 0.314 in.

96. The circular mil area of a 12 AWG conductor is _____.

(a) 10,380   (b) 26,240   (c) 6,530   (d) 6,350

97. A 10 AWG 7-strand copper wire has a cross-sectional area of _____

(a) 0.007 sq in.   (b) 0.011 sq in.   (c) 0.012 sq in.   (d) 0.106 sq in.

98. A 250 kcmil bare cable has a conductor diameter of _____

(a) 0.557 in.   (b) 0.755 in.   (c) 0.575 in.   (d) 0.690 in.

99. The ac ohms-to-neutral impedance per 1,000 ft of 2/0 AWG copper conductor in a steel raceway is _____.

(a) 0.06 ohms   (b) 0.10 ohms   (c) 0.22 ohms   (d) 0.11 ohms

100. Annex C contains tables that list the number of conductors or fixture wires permitted in a raceway when the conductors are all of the same size and type.

(a) True   (b) False

(• Indicates that 75% or fewer of those who took this exam answered the question correctly.)

1. Optional standby systems are typically installed to provide an alternate source of power for _____.

   (a) data-processing and communication systems
   (b) emergency systems for health care facilities
   (c) emergency systems for hospitals
   (d) none of these

2. •Cables and conductors of Class 2 and Class 3 circuits _____ be placed in any cable, cable tray, compartment, enclosure, manhole, outlet box, device box, raceway, or similar fitting with conductors of electric light, power, Class 1, nonpower-limited fire alarm circuits, and medium power network-powered broadband communications circuits.

   (a) may   (b) must not   (c) a and b   (d) none of these

3. A rigid metal conduit nipple (1 1/2 in.) with three conductors can be filled to an area of _____

   (a) 0.882 sq in.   (b) 1.072 sq in.   (c) 1.243 sq in.   (d) 1.343 sq in.

4. Access doors to the transmitter enclosure of a radio or TV station must have interlocks to disconnect the power to the transmitter when any access door is opened, if the voltage between conductors is over _____.

   (a) 150V   (b) 250V   (c) 350V   (d) 480V

5. Access to electrical equipment must not be denied by an accumulation of cables that prevents removal of panels, including suspended-ceiling panels.

   (a) True   (b) False

6. Access to equipment must not be denied by an accumulation of (CATV) wires and cables that prevent the removal of panels. This does not apply to suspended-ceiling panels.

   (a) True   (b) False

7. Access to equipment must not be prohibited by an accumulation of _____ that prevents the removal of access panels. This includes suspended-ceiling panels.

   (a) wires   (b) cables   (c) ductwork   (d) a and b

8. An outdoor wire-strung antenna conductor of a receiving station with a 75 ft span using a hard-drawn copper conductor must not be less than _____.

   (a) 10 AWG   (b) 12 AWG   (c) 14 AWG   (d) 17 AWG

9. Audible and visual signal devices must be provided on optional standby systems, where practicable, to indicate _____.

   (a) derangement of the optional standby source
   (b) that the optional standby source is carrying load
   (c) that the battery charger is not functioning
   (d) a and b

10. Audio system circuits described in 640.9(C), and using Class 2 or Class 3 wiring methods, are not permitted to be installed in the same cable or raceway with _____.

    (a) other audio system circuits
    (b) Class 2 conductors or cables
    (c) Class 3 conductors or cables
    (d) b or c

11.   Cables and conductors of two or more power-limited fire alarm circuits can be installed in the same cable, enclosure, or raceway.

(a) True   (b) False

12.   Class 1 control circuits using 18 AWG conductors must use insulation types including _____.

(a) RFH-2, RFHH-2, or RFHH-3   (b) TF, TFF, TFN, or TFFN
(c) RHH, RHW, THWN, or THHN   (d) a and b

13.   Class 1, 2, and 3 cables installed _____ to framing members must be protected against physical damage from penetration by screws or nails by 1 1/4 in. separation from the framing member or by a suitable metal plate in accordance with 300.4(D).

(a) exposed   (b) concealed   (c) parallel   (d) all of these

14.   Class 2 and Class 3 cables listed as suitable for general-purpose use with the exception of risers, ducts, plenums, and other spaces used for environmental air, are _____.

(a) CL2P and CL3P   (b) CL2R and CL3R   (c) CL2 and CL3   (d) PLCT

15.   Class 2 or Class 3 cables, installed in vertical runs penetrating more than one floor or installed in a shaft, must be type _____.

(a) CL2R   (b) CL3R   (c) CL2P   (d) a or b

16.   Class 2, Class 3, and PLTC cable that is not terminated at equipment and not identified for future use with a tag is considered abandoned.

(a) True   (b) False

17.   Coaxial cables for community antenna television systems installed in vertical runs and penetrating more than one floor or cables installed in vertical runs in a shaft, must be Type _____.

(a) CATV   (b) CATVX   (c) CATVR   (d) any of these

18.   Communications _____ cable must be listed as being suitable for use in a vertical run in a shaft, or from floor to floor, and must also be listed as having fire-resistant characteristics capable of preventing the carrying of fire from floor to floor.

(a) plenum   (b) riser   (c) general-purpose   (d) none of these

19.   Communications cables not terminated at both ends with a connector or other equipment and not identified for future use with a tag are considered abandoned.

(a) True   (b) False

20.   Communications wires and cables must be separated by at least 2 in. from conductors of _____ circuits.

(a) power   (b) lighting   (c) Class 1   (d) any of these

21.   Community antenna television (CATV) and radio system coaxial cables are not required to be listed and marked where the length of the cable within the building, measured from its point of entrance, does not exceed _____, the cable enters the building from the outside, and the cable is terminated at a grounding block.

(a) 25 ft   (b) 30 ft   (c) 50 ft   (d) 100 ft

22.   Conductive optical fiber cables are permitted to occupy the same cable tray or raceway with conductors for electric light, power, and Class 1 circuits.

(a) True   (b) False

23. Each conductor of a lead-in from an outdoor antenna must be provided with a listed antenna discharge unit.

    (a) True   (b) False

24. Exposed network-powered broadband cables must be secured to structural components by straps, staples, hangers, or similar fittings designed and installed so as not to damage the cable.

    (a) True   (b) False

25. Fire alarm cables installed _____ to framing members must be protected against physical damage from penetration by screws or nails by 1 1/4 in. separation from the framing member or by a suitable metal plate in accordance with 300.4(D).

    (a) exposed   (b) concealed   (c) parallel   (d) all of these

26. Fire alarm circuits installed in any _____ must be installed in accordance with Articles 500 through 516 and Article 517, Part IV.

    (a) outdoor location   (b) hazardous (classified) location
    (c) place of assembly   (d) patient care area

27. Fire alarm equipment supplying PLFA circuits must be durably marked where plainly visible to indicate each circuit that is _____.

    (a) supplied by a nonpower-limited fire alarm circuit   (b) a power-limited fire alarm circuit
    (c) a fire alarm circuit   (d) none of these

28. Fire alarm systems include _____.

    (a) fire detection and alarm notification   (b) guard's tour
    (c) sprinkler water flow   (d) all of these

29. For nonpower-limited fire alarm circuits, an 18 AWG conductor is considered protected if the overcurrent device protecting the system is not over _____.

    (a) 15A   (b) 10A   (c) 20A   (d) 7A

30. If the transfer switch for a portable generator does not switch the _____ conductor, then it is not a separately derived system and the equipment grounding conductor must be bonded to the system grounding electrode.

    (a) phase   (b) equipment grounding   (c) grounded   (d) all of these

31. In one- and two-family dwellings where it is not practicable to achieve an overall maximum primary protector grounding conductor length of 20 ft for communications systems, a separate _____ or longer communications ground rod must be driven and it must be bonded to the power grounding electrode system with a 6 AWG conductor.

    (a) 5 ft   (b) 8 ft   (c) 10 ft   (d) 20 ft

32. In one- and two-family dwellings where it is not practicable to achieve an overall maximum grounding conductor length of _____ for CATV, a separate ground must be used as specified in 250.52(A)(5), (6), or (7). It must be bonded to the power grounding electrode system with a copper conductor no smaller than 6 AWG.

    (a) 5 ft   (b) 8 ft   (c) 10 ft   (d) 20 ft

33. Listed plenum optical fiber raceways, listed riser optical fiber raceways, or listed general-purpose optical fiber raceways installed in accordance with 770.154 can be installed as _____ in any type of listed raceway permitted in Chapter 3.

    (a) innerduct   (b) ductfill   (c) busway   (d) a or b

34. Nonconductive optical fiber cable contains no metallic members and no other _____ materials.

(a) electrically conductive   (b) inductive   (c) synthetic   (d) insulating

35. Nonpower-limited fire alarm circuit conductors of sizes _____ must be of the types included in 760.27(B) or other types of insulation listed for nonpower-limited fire alarm circuit use. Conductors larger than 16 AWG must comply with Article 310.

(a) 16 and 18 AWG   (b) 14 and 12 AWG   (c) 14 AWG and larger   (d) all of these

36. Optical fiber plenum cables listed as suitable for use in ducts, plenums, and other space used for environmental air are Types _____.

(a) OFNP and OFCP   (b) OFNR and OFCR   (c) OFNG and OFCG   (d) OFN and OFC

37. Outdoor antennas and lead-in conductors must be securely supported and the lead-in conductors must be securely attached to the antenna, but they must not be attached to the electric service mast.

(a) True   (b) False

38. Overcurrent protection devices for Class 1 circuit protection must be located at the point where the conductor to be protected _____.

(a) terminates to the load   (b) is spliced to any other conductor
(c) receives its supply   (d) none of these

39. Power-limited fire alarm cables installed as wiring within buildings must be _____ as being resistant to the spread of fire.

(a) marked FR   (b) listed   (c) identified   (d) color-coded

40. Splices and terminations of nonpower-limited fire alarm circuits must be made in _____ fittings, boxes, enclosures, fire alarm devices, or utilization equipment.

(a) identified   (b) listed   (c) approved   (d) none of these

41. The ac ohms-to-neutral impedance per 1,000 ft of 4/0 AWG aluminum in a steel raceway is the same as the ohms-to-neutral impedance of 1,000 ft of _____ copper installed in a steel raceway.

(a) 1 AWG   (b) 1/0 AWG   (c) 2/0 AWG   (d) 250 kcmil

42. The area in sq in. for a 1/0 AWG bare aluminum conductor is _____

(a) 0.087 sq in.   (b) 0.109 sq in.   (c) 0.137 sq in.   (d) 0.173 sq in.

43. The conductors contained within Type ITC cable must be rated 300V, and not smaller than _____ AWG nor larger than _____ AWG.

(a) 18,10   (b) 16, 8   (c) 22, 12   (d) 14, 1/0

44. The cross-section area (sq in.) of a 12 THHN is _____.

(a) 0.0133   (b) 0.0233   (c) 0.0321   (d) 0.0147

45. The grounding conductor for an antenna mast or antenna discharge unit must not be smaller than 10 AWG copper.

(a) True   (b) False

46. The grounding conductor for an antenna must be _____.

(a) True   (b) False

47. The outer conductive shield of a coaxial cable must be grounded at the building premises as close to the point of cable entrance or attachment as practicable.

(a) True   (b) False

48. When conduit nipples 24 in. or shorter are installed, the ampacity adjustment factor for more than three current-carrying conductors _____ to this condition.

(a) does not apply   (b) must be applied

49. When practical, a separation of at least _____ must be maintained between communications wires and cables on buildings and lightning conductors.

(a) 6 ft   (b) 8 ft   (c) 10 ft   (d) 12 ft

50. Where exposed to contact with electric light or power conductors, the noncurrent-carrying metallic members of optical fiber cables entering buildings must be _____.

(a) grounded as close as possible to emergence through an exterior wall
(b) grounded as close as possible to emergence through a concrete floor slab
(c) interrupted as close to the point of entrance as practicable by an insulating joint
(d) any of these

(• Indicates that 75% or fewer of those who took this exam answered the question correctly.)

1. Means must be provided to disconnect simultaneously all _____ supply conductors to the phase converter.

    (a) ungrounded   (b) grounded   (c) grounding   (d) all of these

2. No _____ splices or taps may be made within or on a luminaire (fixture).

    (a) unapproved   (b) untested   (c) uninspected   (d) unnecessary

3. Nonmetallic cable trays must be made of _____ material.

    (a) fire-resistant   (b) waterproof   (c) corrosive   (d) flame-retardant

4. On circuits over 600V, nominal, where energized live parts are exposed, the minimum clear workspace must not be less than _____ high.

    (a) 3 ft   (b) 5 ft   (c) 6 ft   (d) 6 1/2 ft

5. Open conductors entering or leaving locations subject to dampness, wetness, or corrosive vapors must have _____ formed on them and must then pass upward and inward from the outside of the buildings, or from the damp, wet, or corrosive location, through noncombustible, nonabsorbent, insulating tubes.

    (a) weather heads   (b) drip loops   (c) identification   (d) blisters

6. Open conductors must be separated by at least _____ from metal raceways, piping, or other conducting material, and from any exposed lighting, power, or signaling conductor, or must be separated by a continuous and firmly fixed nonconductor in addition to the insulation of the conductor.

    (a) 2 in.   (b) 2 1/2 in.   (c) 3 in.   (d) 3 1/2 in.

7. Overload relays and other devices for motor overload protection that are not capable of _____ must be protected by fuses or circuit breakers, or a motor short-circuit protector.

    (a) opening short circuits   (b) clearing overloads   (c) opening ground faults   (d) a or c

8. Receptacles, receptacle housings, and self-contained devices used with flat conductor cable systems must be _____.

    (a) rated a minimum of 20A   (b) rated a minimum of 15A   (c) identified for this use   (d) none of these

9. Resistance heating elements of embedded deicing and snow-melting _____ must not be installed where they bridge expansion joints unless provision is made for expansion and contraction.

    (a) cables   (b) units   (c) panels   (d) all of these

10. Resistance-type heating elements in electric space-heating equipment must be protected at not more than _____.

    (a) 95 percent of the nameplate value   (b) 60A
    (c) 48A   (d) 150 percent of the rated current

11. Service-entrance conductors entering, or on the exterior of, buildings or other structures must be insulated.

    (a) True   (b) False

12. Service-lateral conductors must have _____.

    (a) adequate mechanical strength   (b) sufficient ampacity for the loads computed
    (c) a and b   (d) none of these

13. Sheet steel boxes not over 100 cu in. in size must be made from steel at least _____ thick.

    (a) 0.0625 in.   (b) 0.0757 in.   (c) 0.075 in.   (d) 0.025 in.

14. Single, locking, and grounding-type receptacles for water-pump motors or other loads directly related to the circulation and sanitation system of a permanently installed pool or fountain can be located _____ from the inside walls of the pool or fountain, if the receptacle is GFCI protected.

    (a) 3 to 6 ft   (b) 5 to 10 ft   (c) 10 to 15 ft   (d) 10 to 20 ft

15. Switchboards that have any exposed live parts must be installed in permanently _____ locations, and then only where under competent supervision and accessible only to qualified persons.

    (a) dry   (b) mounted   (c) supported   (d) all of these

16. The _____ of conductors used in prewired ENT manufactured assemblies must be identified by means of a printed tag or label attached to each end of the manufactured assembly.

    (a) type   (b) size   (c) quantity   (d) all of these

17. The ac ohms-to-neutral impedance per 1,000 ft of 4/0 AWG aluminum conductor in a steel raceway is _____.

    (a) 0.06 ohms   (b) 0.10 ohms   (c) 0.22 ohms   (d) 0.11 ohms

18. The ampacity of supply branch-circuit conductors and the overcurrent protection devices for X-ray equipment must not be less than _____.

    (a) 50 percent of the momentary rating   (b) 100 percent of the long-time rating
    (c) the larger of a or b   (d) the smaller of a or b

19. The authority having jurisdiction may judge a location utilized for _____ as non-hazardous, providing there is positive ventilation and the conditions of the *Code* are met.

    (a) drying or curing   (b) dipping and coating   (c) spraying operations   (d) none of these

20. The building disconnecting means for a one-circuit installation that supplies only limited loads of a single branch circuit must have a rating of not less than _____.

    (a) 15A   (b) 20A   (c) 25A   (d) 30A

21. The continuous current-carrying capacity of 1 1/2 sq in. copper busbar mounted in an unventilated enclosure is _____.

    (a) 500A   (b) 750A   (c) 650A   (d) 1,500A

22. The essential electrical systems in a health care facility must have sources of power from _____.

(a) a normal source generally supplying the entire electrical system
(b) one or more alternate sources for use when the normal source is interrupted
(c) a or b
(d) a and b

23. The flexible cord conductor identification of the grounded circuit conductor required in the *Code* must consist of one of six methods. One method is a tracer in a braid of any color contrasting with that of the braid and _____ in the braid of the other conductor or conductors.

(a) a solid color   (b) no tracer   (c) two tracers   (d) none of these

24. The ground-fault protection system for service equipment must be _____ when first installed on site.

(a) a Class A device   (b) identified   (c) turned on   (d) performance tested

25. The maximum load permitted on a heating element in a pool heater must not exceed _____.

(a) 20A   (b) 35A   (c) 48A   (d) 60A

26. The minimum depth of clear working space in front of electrical equipment for 5,000V, nominal-to-ground is _____ when there are exposed live parts on both sides of the workspace.

(a) 4 ft   (b) 5 ft   (c) 6 ft   (d) 9 ft

27. The minimum size conductor for operating control and signaling circuits in an elevator is _____.

(a) 20 AWG   (b) 16 AWG   (c) 14 AWG   (d) 12 AWG

28. The minimum size conductor permitted for Type MC cable is _____ AWG.

(a) 18 copper   (b) 14 copper   (c) 12 copper   (d) none of these

29. The minimum spacing of busbars of opposite polarity held in free air inside a panelboard is _____ when operating at not over 125V, nominal.

(a) 1/2 in.   (b) 1 in.   (c) 2 in.   (d) 4 in.

30. The *NEC* requires series-rated installations to be field-marked to indicate the maximum level of fault current for which the system has been installed.

(a) True   (b) False

31. The percentage of conduit fill for five conductors is _____ percent.

(a) 35   (b) 60   (c) 40   (d) 55

32. The photovoltaic disconnecting means must _____.

(a) be installed at a readily accessible location either outside of a building or structure or inside nearest the point of entrance of the system conductors
(b) be suitable for the prevailing conditions
(c) consist of not more than six switches or six circuit breakers
(d) all of these

33. The residual voltage of a capacitor, rated not over 600V, must be reduced to 50V or less within _____ after the capacitor is disconnected from the source of supply.

    (a) 15 seconds   (b) 45 seconds   (c) 1 minute   (d) 2 minutes

34. The size of the branch-circuit overcurrent protective devices and conductors for an electrode-type boiler, rated less than 50 kW and not greater than 600V, must be calculated on the basis of _____.

    (a) 125 percent of the total load excluding motors   (b) 125 percent of the total load including motors
    (c) 150 percent of the nameplate value   (d) 100 percent of the nameplate value

35. Type FC cable is an assembly of parallel conductors formed integrally with an insulating material web specifically designed for field installation in surface metal raceways.

    (a) True   (b) False

36. Type IGS cable is a factory assembly of one or more conductors, each individually insulated and enclosed in a loose-fit, nonmetallic flexible conduit as an integrated gas spacer cable rated _____ volts.

    (a) 0 through 6,000   (b) 600 through 6,000   (c) 0 through 600   (d) 3,000 through 6,000

37. Type MI cable must be securely supported at intervals not exceeding _____.

    (a) 3 ft   (b) 3 1/2 ft   (c) 5 ft   (d) 6 ft

38. When determining the number of conductors that are considered as current-carrying, a grounding conductor is _____.

    (a) counted as one current-carrying conductor
    (b) considered to be a current-carrying conductor but not counted
    (c) considered to be a noncurrent-carrying conductor and is not counted
    (d) counted as one conductor for each ground wire in the raceway

39. When individual open conductors enter a building or other structure through tubes, _____ must be formed on the conductors before they enter the tubes.

    (a) drop loops   (b) knots   (c) drip loops   (d) none of these

40. When the calculated number of conductors, all of the same size, that may be installed in a conduit or in tubing includes a decimal, the next higher whole number must be used when this decimal is _____ or larger.

    (a) 0.40   (b) 0.60   (c) 0.70   (d) 0.80

41. When used as open wiring on insulators, conductors that are _____ AWG or larger, supported on solid knobs, must be securely tied to the knobs by tie wires having an insulation equivalent to that of the conductor.

    (a) 14   (b) 12   (c) 10   (d) 8

42. Where knob-and-tube conductors pass through wood cross members in plastered partitions, conductors must be protected by noncombustible, nonabsorbent, insulating tubes extending not less than _____ beyond the wood member.

    (a) 2 in.   (b) 3 in.   (c) 4 in.   (d) 6 in.

43. Where practicable, a separation of at least _____ must be maintained between any network-powered broadband communications cable on buildings and lightning conductors.

    (a) 6 ft   (b) 8 ft   (c) 10 ft   (d) 12 ft

44. Where the outer sheath of Type MI cable is made of copper, it must provide an adequate path for equipment grounding purposes.

    (a) True   (b) False

45. Which of the following statements about Type MI cable is correct?

    (a) It may be used in any hazardous location.
    (b) A single run of cable must not contain more than the equivalent of four quarter bends.
    (c) It must be securely supported at intervals not exceeding 10 ft.
    (d) none of these

46. It is permissible to extend busways vertically through dry floors if totally enclosed (unventilated) where passing through, and for a minimum distance of _____ above the floor to provide adequate protection from physical damage.

    (a) 6 ft   (b) 6 1/2 ft   (c) 8 ft   (d) 10 ft

47. For installations consisting of not more than two 2-wire branch circuits, the building disconnecting means must have a rating of not less than _____.

    (a) 15A   (b) 20A   (c) 25A   (d) 30A

48. HDPE is permitted to be installed _____.

    (a) where subject to chemicals for which the conduit is listed
    (b) in cinder fill
    (c) in direct burial installations in earth or concrete
    (d) all of these

49. Power distribution blocks installed in metal wireways must be listed.

    (a) True   (b) False

50. The requirements in "Annexes" must be complied with.

    (a) True   (b) False

Index

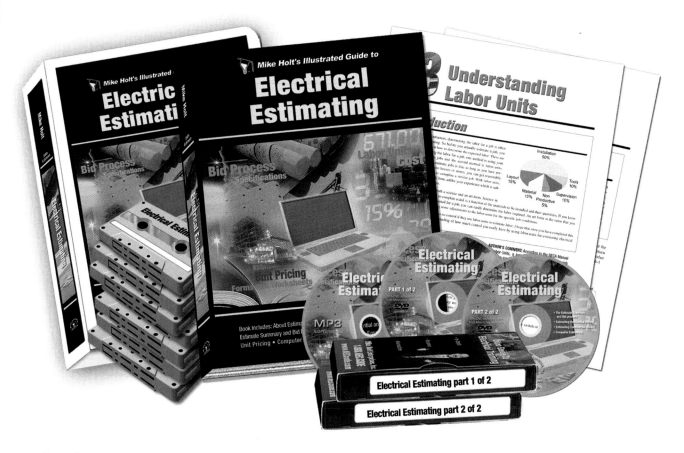

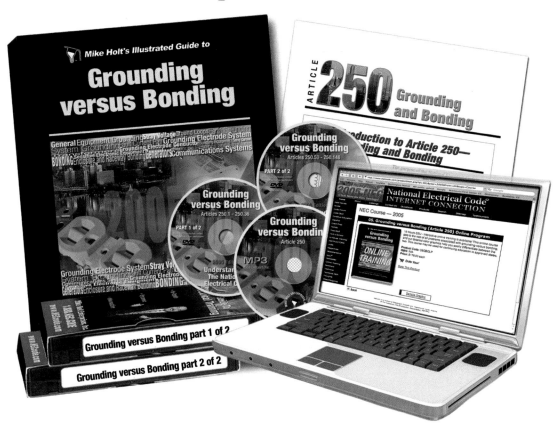

Notes

Notes

Notes

Mike Holt's 2005 Supreme Estimating Library

NAME   COMPANY   TITLE

MAILING ADDRESS   CITY   STATE   ZIP

SHIPPING ADDRESS   CITY   STATE   ZIP

PHONE   FAX   E-MAIL ADDRESS   WEB SITE

❏ CHECK   ❏ VISA   ❏ MASTER CARD   ❏ DISCOVER   ❏ AMEX   ❏ MONEY ORDER

CREDIT CARD # : _____ EXP. DATE: _____

3 or 4 digit security number on front for AmEx on back for all others: _____

❏ ESTVMP Estimating Library w/Videos and MP3	$345	25% DISCOUNT!	$258.75
❏ ESTV Estimating Library w/Videos and Cassettes	$345	25% DISCOUNT!	$258.75
❏ ESTDMP Estimating Library w/DVDs and MP3	$345	25% DISCOUNT!	$258.75
❏ ESTD Estimating Library w/DVDs and Cassettes	$345	25% DISCOUNT!	$258.75

Sales Tax FLORIDA RESIDENTS ONLY add 6% $ _____

Shipping: 4% of Total Price (or Minimum $7.50) $ _____

TOTAL DUE $ _____

No other discounts apply. Not valid on previous orders.

Coupon Code 05EXB

Mike Holt Enterprises, Inc. • 10320 NW 53rd St. Sunrise, FL 33351

FAX 1.954.720.7944 • www.NECcode.com

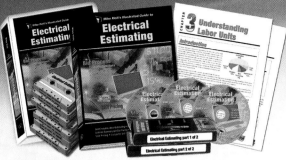

Discount 25% off

Supreme Estimating Library

Estimate like the experts. This program will show you how to take-off a job, determine material cost, accurately estimate labor cost, and how to determine your overhead, profit, and break-even point. This course also gives tips on selling and marketing your business. You'll learn how to estimate and project manage residential, commercial, and industrial projects. Learn how to make more money on every job by proper estimating and project management.

Mike Holt's 2005 *National Electrical Code®* Library

NAME   COMPANY   TITLE

MAILING ADDRESS   CITY   STATE   ZIP

SHIPPING ADDRESS   CITY   STATE   ZIP

PHONE   FAX   E-MAIL ADDRESS   WEB SITE

❏ CHECK   ❏ VISA   ❏ MASTER CARD   ❏ DISCOVER   ❏ AMEX   ❏ MONEY ORDER

CREDIT CARD # : _____ EXP. DATE: _____

3 or 4 digit security number on front for AmEx on back for all others: _____

❏ 05DECO Understanding the *National Electrical Code* Library w/Videos	$529	25% DISCOUNT!	$396.75
❏ 05DECODVD Understanding the *National Electrical Code* Library w/DVDs	$529	25% DISCOUNT!	$396.75

Sales Tax FLORIDA RESIDENTS ONLY add 6% $ _____

Shipping: 4% of Total Price (or Minimum $7.50) $ _____

TOTAL DUE $ _____

No other discounts apply. Not valid on previous orders. Standard shipping rates apply

Coupon Code 05EXB

Mike Holt Enterprises, Inc. • FAX 1.954.720.7944 • www.NECcode.com

Discount 25% off

National Electrical Code Library

If you want to really understand the *NEC*, this series is for you. Mike explains, in great detail, the history of the rule, the reason for the rule, and how to apply the *Code* for everyday use. This program explains the 2005 *Code*, how to use the *NEC*, general installation requirements, branch circuits, feeders, services and overcurrent protection, grounding versus bonding, conductors, cables, and more. ...

Mike Holt's 2005 Grounding versus Bonding Library

NAME   COMPANY   TITLE

MAILING ADDRESS   CITY   STATE   ZIP

SHIPPING ADDRESS   CITY   STATE   ZIP

PHONE   FAX   E-MAIL ADDRESS   WEB SITE

❏ CHECK   ❏ VISA   ❏ MASTER CARD   ❏ DISCOVER   ❏ AMEX   ❏ MONEY ORDER

CREDIT CARD # : _____ EXP. DATE: _____

3 or 4 digit security number on front for AmEx on back for all others: _____

❏ 05GBLIB Grounding versus Bonding Library w/Videos	$224	25% DISCOUNT!	$168.00
❏ 05GBDVD Grounding versus Bonding Library w/DVDs	$224	25% DISCOUNT!	$168.00

Sales Tax FLORIDA RESIDENTS ONLY add 6% $ _____

Shipping: 4% of Total Price (or Minimum $7.50) $ _____

TOTAL DUE $ _____

No other discounts apply. Not valid on previous orders.

Coupon Code 05EXB

Mike Holt Enterprises, Inc. • 10320 NW 53rd St. Sunrise, FL 33351

FAX 1.954.720.7944 • www.NECcode.com

Discount 25% off

Grounding versus Bonding Library

Grounding and bonding problems are at epidemic levels. Surveys repeatedly show that 90 percent of power quality problems are due to poor grounding and bonding. Electrical theory has been applied to this difficult to understand Article, making it easier for students to grasp the concepts of grounding versus bonding. The Grounding versus Bonding Library includes a textbook/workbook, a MP3 Audio CD a 16-Hour Online Program, and two videos, or two DVDs.